THE SHORT STORY:

Fiction in Transition

THE SHORT STORY:
Fiction in Transition

Edited by
J. CHESLEY TAYLOR
WASHINGTON STATE UNIVERSITY

Charles Scribner's Sons — New York

A—3.69[C]

PRINTED IN THE UNITED STATES OF AMERICA
Library of Congress Catalog Card Number 69-14264

ACKNOWLEDGMENTS

It is with great pleasure that I acknowledge the assistance rendered me by Professors Herbert Arntson and Richard Thompson. Their critical acumen helped me avoid many pitfalls; their patience and willingness to examine all of the materials with care demonstrated graphically that good teaching reflects a commitment reaching far beyond classroom performance. I am also grateful for the suggestions of Professor John Wasson, Mr. Richard Hawkins, and Mr. Robert Morrison.

ACKNOWLEDGMENTS

PREFACE

There are many approaches to the study of the short story: we might consider its basic characteristics as a literary type, the close relationship between character and action, or such elements as setting, atmosphere, and imagery, to name only a few. But regardless of how we begin, it is important that we view each story as a carefully unified whole, rather than as an example of a literary technique or, perhaps, as a mere vehicle for the theme. A good writer rarely writes a story merely to demonstrate character, point of view, theme, or any of the other literary concepts by which we analyze his achievement, nor should we assume that he did so when we approach his story as readers.

The stories in this collection, then, have not been narrowly categorized, in order to suggest that we should work toward an understanding of the artist's vision as a whole and to emphasize the point that the business of analysis is merely a means to an end. This is not to say that one element cannot function more significantly than another in any given work. But too often the narrow categorization of short stories implies that, in reading them, we should subordinate art to the mechanics of analysis. The generally chronological order used here is not, on the other hand, intended to suggest that the short story began as a primitive form and evolved onto a higher plane. We can hardly call Poe, Dostoevsky, and Melville "primitive" writers. Such an historical view is not likely to tell us anything of value about the short story. There are, however, two very broad observations about the short story as a literary type which need to be made, observations which have influenced the present ordering of the selections in this collection.

First, and most importantly, the short story is a dynamic form, constantly changing and thus constantly presenting new faces to the reader. It is a type, but not a stereotype. Every writer adds something new, of course, simply because he sees things through his own eyes, not through those of Hawthorne, James, or Hemingway, and artistic individuality is certainly one of the reasons this form of fiction has not lost its vitality. But some changes go beyond the expression of individuality to add significantly to the dimensions of the form. We can see these changes in the shift from de Maupassant's realism to the naturalism of Crane and Gorky, the surrealism of Kafka, the mysticism of Borges, and the photographic objectivity of Robbe-Grillet. There is Robert Creeley's effort to free the short story from the traditional concept of beginning, middle, and end. And Paul Bowles' symbolic method, coupled with the rejection of the principle of poetic justice, constitutes still another kind of departure. The point, of course, is that at any given moment in its history, the short story has been moving in new directions.

Although the fact of change cannot be denied, we must acknowledge also the fact of artistic continuity. The addition of the new does not necessarily mean the repudiation on all sides of what has come before. Realism, for example, is still very much alive, as is Poe's concept of unity of effect as the principle characteristic of the short story. Creeley may comment that the "old assumption of beginning and end—those very neat assertions—have fallen way completely," but what he seems to be substituting is a renewed emphasis upon the absolute unity of the short story that Poe analyzed so long ago. "Its shape," says Creeley, "if form can be so thought of, is a sphere, an egg of obdurate kind. The only possible reason for its existence is that it has, in itself, the fact of reality and the pressure." What we come to see is that many traditional elements are perpetuated at the same time that new things are happening; in short, there is at once continuity and change in the short story.

The order of the stories underscores these principles of continuity and change. Within each section, the chronological order of the stories has been less rigidly adhered to, so that similarities and differences of style, technique, and theme may be more readily observed, while the main sections themselves overlap slightly in the period covered by each. Nevertheless, the order is generally chronological in its movement from the earliest writers to the most recent.

There were additional considerations involved in the selection of these stories. Important among them was the recognition that the stories should provoke some kind of response in the student to the experience which each work communicates, thus encouraging an involvement which turns the reading of the stories into more than a mere exercise. At the same time, the stories balance the familiar with the unfamiliar and offer a wide variety of techniques, devices, styles, themes, and degrees of complexity. A few of the stories were chosen for their defects, in the belief that it is possible to learn from the inevitable mistakes and failures that plague the artist, as well as from his successes. Finally, these stories contain the richness of ambiguity: the sense that, as with life itself, there is always something waiting to be discovered.

CONTENTS

Contents

III   NEW DIRECTIONS

CHRONOLOGICAL LISTING
OF AUTHORS AND STORIES

The Short Story
as a Literary Type

The short story is only one of several forms of prose fiction, but it is one of the most complex of these forms. We may, for example, be familiar with Aesop's simple fable about the tortoise and the hare, and Mark Twain's yarn about the fabled jumping frog of Calaveras County is another relatively simple tale that many of us undoubtedly know well. Most of us have read a novel: Hemingway's *A Farewell to Arms,* or Hawthorne's *The Scarlet Letter,* or Salinger's *The Catcher in the Rye,* let us say. While the short story resembles these other forms in a number of ways, it is also significantly different from them. And if we are to study the short story, we should perhaps begin by taking a look at both the similarities and the differences.

The first resemblance among these forms is so obvious that we hardly need mention it: they all tell a story of some kind. That is, they string together a series of incidents concerning people (or animals who act like people), with an eye to their arrangement in time, as well as to their cause-and-effect relationship. We begin with a situation, a character, or a relationship, and then something happens to alter that factor. Precisely *what* happens is what makes the series of incidents a story.

When we look at the series of incidents by themselves, examining the *why* of their particular development, we are examining *plot.* Plot provides the story's framework. The plot of Flannery O'Connor's "A Good Man is Hard to Find" is easily summarized: a family of five set out on their vacation, take a side road in an effort to find an old plantation, wreck their car, and are then shot to death by an escaped convict and his two companions who happen upon them. But the story is much more than just the bare bones of plot. It is character, setting, dialogue, all the individual elements which work together to give us the whole narrative. It is especially important that we keep this fact in front of us in reading the short story. For, as we shall see, the short story is often so complex that concentrating upon any one element is likely to keep us from understanding the narrative in its entirety.

A second common characteristic of all these types is their use of prose rather than poetry. That is, the story is told through statements and/or dialogue whose word patterns resemble those of ordinary conversation, thought, and writing. We all think we can distinguish readily between poetry and prose, for example, but the distinction is actually a good deal more difficult to make than we realize. Too often we simply say, "Prose just doesn't *look* like poetry." That is, prose lacks line length and stanza patterns; and it is true that prose normally does not depend upon a rhythmic base to the extent that poetry does. But going by what the writing "looks like" will not help us much, and can, in fact, be misleading. Much modern poetry actually resembles prose because it ignores such traditional matters as line length, strict metrical patterns, and established stanza forms. Conversely, prose can become "poetic" in its *effect*, if not its appearance, through the use of concrete imagery, strong emotion, rhythmic patterns, alliteration, and other devices and characteristics that we normally associate with poetry.

The third characteristic which links these various prose forms to each other is that each is *fiction*. What do we mean by that term? Our usual response is to make some kind of distinction between fact on the one hand and invention on the other. Fiction, we say, is whatever is "made-up." But what, then, do we do with Hemingway's novel, *For Whom the Bell Tolls,* which draws heavily on the reality of the Spanish Civil War? Or Stephen Crane's short story, "The Open Boat," which is based on an experience which Crane himself underwent? If we examine the background of fiction carefully, we arrive at an important conclusion: fiction is not always invention. It frequently uses real events and people. The artist usually reorders those events, and he doesn't use everything he knows about his characters, but their source is still reality.

Which does not really answer our question. How do "facts" become fiction in the hands of one man, and history or biography, say, in the hands of another? The answer lies in the role which the writer assigns to those facts. In other words, it is their function within the story that is most important. If these facts are intended *primarily* to communicate to us the nature of an actual person or event, then we may safely say that we are not dealing with fiction. The facts not only correspond to something which exists independently of the written material—the War of 1812, for example, or the life of Franklin D. Roosevelt—but our main interest is in the *accuracy* of the correspondence.

The writer of fiction, on the other hand, may either draw on actual figures and events or he may create composites whose exact counterparts do not exist in life. It does not matter, really, which he does, because in fiction the facts are subordinated to the story that is being told, and that story exists for its own sake, not for the sake of the specific event or character which may have prompted its writing. When a narrative does not reflect reality in any way, we call it fantasy. But most of the fiction we are familiar with does make a consistent effort to reflect life as we know it to be. It may do so simply to provide entertainment, with no attempt to communicate anything significant about life. Such a reflection is usually superficial, however accurate it may be. Detective fiction, for example, often falls into this category. But a great deal of modern fiction tries both to entertain and to reveal something meaningful about the world and the people who inhabit it.

In either case, the artist tries to free his facts from their immediate source. He includes and excludes materials in accordance with the demands of his narrative and the nature of the experience he is trying to communicate; and he orders those materials as he sees fit. Historians and biographers, although they have some freedom in these matters, must finally conform to that *specific* reality that their facts represent. While the artist should present a carefully unified work, whose meaning is at least recognizable, he need not deal in realistic portrayal, or literal accuracy. Kafka's "In the Penal Colony" and Aichinger's "The Bound Man" are hardly believable in the usual sense. Here, symbol and metaphor permit the artist to reflect life through characters, incidents, and settings that in themselves are almost completely unbelievable.

We have seen three important ways in which the short story resembles other types of prose fiction. But it also differs from them in three essential ways: in the necessity for change, in the element of conflict, and in unity of effect.

The short story differs from other types of fiction in the role that change plays. One of the reasons that strictly *physical* action is not necessary at all times is because our interest lies in what the change *means*, not on what level it takes place. And usually we find that several changes have actually occurred. In Anderson's "Death in the Woods," there are meaningful changes not only in Jake Grimes and in his wife, but in the narrator as well. There may be instead a failure to change when the conditions of the narrative demand it, or a character's inability to see that change has already taken place. The two figures in Galsworthy's "The Japanese Quince" do not change; they are simply mystified by their experience, while the reader is clearly aware of the kind of change the situation calls for. The same situation occurs in Mansfield's "The Fly." If the element for change were not present in this story, we would probably be justified in calling it a character sketch, a form which is essentially *static.* Change in the short story involves growth, progress, reversal, decline, inten- sification, or simply the potential for change, including the failure to accept or recognize the fact of change. And our interest is in what that change reveals to us.

In one important aspect, the short story resembles the drama more than it does other forms of fiction: both are committed to the *dramatic* representation of reality through involving characters in some kind of conflict. This conflict need not be tragic or even seri- ous. In "The Unicorn in the Garden" it is quite humorous, in fact. Sometimes the resemblance between the two is emphasized in the short story by the development of action and character through a series of dramatic *scenes,* a basic principle of the theatre. Pirandel- lo's "In the Abyss" is founded on this procedure. We would be mak- ing a serious mistake to assume that all short stories utilize this method, however. Pirandello simply had a heightened sense of the essentially dramatic nature of narrative. (His short story, "The Man With the Flower in His Mouth," became one of the first plays ever produced on television.) The point is that action in the short story is dramatic, because the characters are involved in some kind of conflict: with themselves, with other characters, or with the situ- ation in which they find themselves. This conflict produces drama through tension, and it produces change out of the need to resolve that conflict.

The third difference, unity of effect, is one of the most impor- tant distinctions that we will deal with. Perhaps the best way to ap- proach it is to continue our comparison of the short story with the drama, but now we will discover that the short story *differs* from the drama in a way that should help clarify what we mean by "unity of effect."

The force of any dramatic conflict is largely the product of the degree to which the various elements work together as parts of a whole. We are aware that all these parts fit into some kind of pattern; and that pattern communicates to us a sense of completeness, of congruity or coherence. Plays, like short stories, need to unify their action in order to achieve this coherence. But they must also be carefully unified for reasons that have nothing to do with what is happening on stage. A play has, for example, a live audience watching, an audience that is unwilling to sit for eight or ten hours while the drama goes on, and on, and on. The time factor in the theatre is a very real, albeit mechanical, consideration. The dramatist is also limited spatially. He cannot bring on a cast of thousands, or construct a skyscraper onstage, except symbolically. The pattern which dramatic action takes on a stage is inevitably influenced by these physical limitations, limitations which are nonetheless crucial for being *external* to the play itself. They are a part of the reason a playwright must strive toward unity in his drama.

But a short story does not take place on a stage, which leads us to an important fact: the reasons for unity in the short story lie wholly *within* the form. There are no external reasons why it must, for example, be short. Such a statement contradicts what many of us have been told from the time of our first encounter with the short story as a form: that it must not exceed a length which takes more than about a half hour to read, or a word count that has been set at anything from 5,000 to 50,000.

To understand how this criterion was established in the first place, we have to go back to one of the earliest attempts to define the short story. In a review of Hawthorne's *Twice-Told Tales,* Edgar Allan Poe made the now-famous remark that the reading of a short story should require no more than "a half-hour to one or two hours," and that the reader should then be able to read a short story in a single sitting. Each of these statements seemed to refer simply to the *length* of the form. The result was the rise of the "single-sitting" concept that most of us are (unfortunately) so familiar with. The value of this definition was that it simplified matters for identifying the novel as well. If it took more than a single sitting of one or two hours to read a work of fiction, we had a novel on our hands.

But we can easily see that there are serious problems involved in making such a definition work. First of all, the time factor is vague. Second, and even more important, it attempts to define the short story through characteristics of the *reader,* not of the story. How long it takes to read a story depends very largely on how carefully a person reads, how fast he is capable of reading, even his reasons for doing the reading in the first place. And there are some people who cannot sit still for two hours regardless of what they are doing. The whole business of defining a short story in terms of its reading time —i.e., length—smacks of the absurd.

As a matter of fact, Poe has been quoted out of context and badly misinterpreted. He recognized that length was a *product* of the short story's principal characteristics, and when he wrote about length he clearly intended to subordinate length to more important factors. Length, said Poe, was determined by the need to achieve a "unity of effect or impression" in the short story. In addition, such unity "cannot be thoroughly preserved in productions whose perusal cannot be completed at one sitting." A novel may achieve a unified effect, certainly, but because its method is more discursive, it is not necessary to read it all at once. Poe, however, saw that the short story differed from the novel in that the immediacy of its impact depended on two things: first, the complete rejection of anything which does not contribute to the final effect which the writer intends; and second, uninterrupted reading. Thus we realize that Poe's most important observations are not related to length except as it is a by-product of more important considerations.

Far more significant are his comments that "In the whole composition there should be no word written, of which the tendency, direct or indirect, is not to the one pre-established design [or pattern]," and that "the immense force derivable from *totality*" depends upon uninterrupted reading. The short story, then, should be defined in terms of a *single effect* to which action, character, symbol, theme, all are carefully subordinated; and the reader must see this unity of design undisturbed if the story is to have, for him, that single effect for which the author strives. In other words, the continuity of our emotional and intellectual response must not be broken. Every part of the short story is so much a part of the *whole* that there are no convenient stopping points. The movies we see are based on much the same principle. We would hardly choose to see part of a movie one day and the rest of it the next, because we would lose the sense of totality on which its effect very largely depends. To this extent the short story and the movies are much alike.

The short story, then, is a complex form demanding a high level of artistry on the part of the writer. But it also makes certain demands upon the reader. More than anything else, we must be willing to look beyond the mechanical matter of length, beyond individual elements such as character, setting, and plot, to try to understand the design of the whole. Once we are able to do this, the term "short story" will begin to have some real meaning for us.

1
THE
EARLY
MASTERS

GENERALLY SPEAKING, the early writers of the short story used two basic methods: the realistic and the symbolic. We have to say "generally" because there were writers, like Poe and Melville, who foreshadowed in their works the techniques of more modern authors. In its method, Melville's "Bartleby the Scrivener: A Story of Wall Street" looks forward to the work of such writers as Svevo and Kafka, while Poe's "The Cask of Amontillado" is a precursor of the psychological bias of much modern fiction and is an early example of the complex use of point of view.

Among the writers pursuing an essentially realistic method, we find three basic criteria. The first is verisimilitude: the accurate rendering of details based on observation and documentation. Second, those details are taken from everyday life, rather than from the unusual and the exceptional, so that the reader has a sense of familiarity derived from his recognition of these details of character, setting, and action. Finally, the writer's stance is objective rather than subjective. De Maupassant's "Minuet" and Verga's "The She-Wolf" are realistic in their method.

The symbolic method, on the other hand, reflects a quite different approach. Realistic detail may be present but it is no longer an end in itself. Instead, it is subordinated to that "other meaning" at which the symbolic narrative points. The materials of the symbolist are primarily the product of the imagination rather than of documentation and observation, although we must be careful not to imply that the symbolist does not observe life around him or that he does not use what he observes. Finally, his stance is subjective and his view of life is often idealistic. Hawthorne's "The Artist of the Beautiful" is symbolic in its method.

The stories in this section have not been grouped simply along the lines of the symbolic and realistic methods, although this approach may result in some interesting observations. Hawthorne and Poe can also be examined in terms of style and structure. Poe's narrative is tightly constructed, highly compressed, rapid in its narrative pace. Hawthorne, on the other hand, tells a story that develops in a much more diffuse fashion. The Melville, Dostoevsky, and Chekhov stories are linked with one another through their central theme, while their approaches to that theme differ widely. The de Maupassant and Verga narratives offer interesting variations on the realistic method, but they may also be contrasted in terms of their use of point of view and setting.

NATHANIEL HAWTHORNE

(1804-1864)

Hawthorne is that rarity in American history, a great writer who was also a public servant. Educated at Bowdoin College, where Long-fellow was a classmate of his, Hawthorne took a position at a custom-house after his graduation. Although he left this position shortly, he continued to be associated with various customhouses from time to time. In 1853 he was appointed United States Consul at Liverpool, England, by his friend, President Franklin Pierce. Hawthorne held this post for four years, after which he went to Italy in an effort to improve his health. He returned to the United States in 1860. His experience with the customhouses provided background for some of his materials, and he was well established as a writer before his appointment as consul. Short stories and novels came rapidly from his pen during those years, including such classics as TWICE-TOLD TALES, THE SCARLET LETTER, and THE HOUSE OF THE SEVEN GABLES. His works are strongly symbolic and are often pervaded with an air of mysticism. Frequent themes are the Conrad-ian darkness of man's inner being, the nature of evil, the violation of the sacredness of self, and the nature of art and the artist.

The Artist
of the Beautiful

An elderly man, with his pretty daughter on his arm, was passing along the street, and emerged from the gloom of the cloudy evening into the light that fell across the pavement from the window of a small shop. It was a projecting window; and on the inside were sus-pended a variety of watches, pinchbeck, silver, and one or two of gold, all with their faces turned from the streets, as if churlishly disinclined to inform the wayfarers what o'clock it was. Seated within the shop, sidelong to the window, with his pale face bent earnestly over some delicate piece of mechanism on which was thrown the concentrated lustre of a shade lamp, appeared a young man.

"What can Owen Warland be about?" muttered old Peter Hovenden, himself a retired watchmaker, and the former master of this same young man whose occupation he was now wondering at. "What can the fellow be about? These six months past I have never come by his shop without seeing him just as steadily at work as now. It would be a flight beyond his usual foolery to seek for the perpetual motion; and yet I know enough of my old business to be certain that what he is now so busy with is no part of the machinery of a watch."

"Perhaps, father," said Annie, without showing much interest in the question, "Owen is inventing a new kind of timekeeper. I am sure he has ingenuity enough."

"Poh, child! He has not the sort of ingenuity to invent anything better than a Dutch toy," answered her father, who had formerly been put to much vexation by Owen Warland's irregular genius. "A plague on such ingenuity! All the effect that ever I knew of it was to spoil the accuracy of some of the best watches in my shop. He would turn the sun out of its orbit and derange the whole course of time, if, as I said before, his ingenuity could grasp anything bigger than a child's toy!"

"Hush, father! He hears you!" whispered Annie, pressing the old man's arm. "His ears are as delicate as his feelings; and you know how easily disturbed they are. Do let us move on."

So Peter Hovenden and his daughter Annie plodded on without further conversation, until in a by-street of the town they found themselves passing the open door of a blacksmith's shop. Within was seen the forge, now blazing up and illuminating the high and dusky roof, and now confining its lustre to a narrow precinct of the coal-strewn floor, according as the breath of the bellows was puffed forth or again inhaled into its vast leathern lungs. In the intervals of brightness it was easy to distinguish objects in remote corners of the shop and the horseshoes that hung upon the wall; in the momentary gloom the fire seemed to be glimmering amidst the vagueness of unenclosed space. Moving about in this red glare and alternate dusk was the figure of the blacksmith, well worthy to be viewed in so pic-

turesque an aspect of light and shade, where the bright blaze struggled with the black night, as if each would have snatched his comely
strength from the other. Anon he drew a white-hot bar of iron from
the coals, laid it on the anvil, uplifted his arm of might, and was
soon enveloped in the myriads of sparks which the strokes of his
hammer scattered into the surrounding gloom.

"Now, that is a pleasant sight," said the old watchmaker. "I
know what it is to work in gold; but give me the worker in iron after
all is said and done. He spends his labor upon a reality. What say
you, daughter Annie?"

"Pray don't speak so loud, father," whispered Annie, "Robert
Danforth will hear you."

"And what if he should hear me?" said Peter Hovenden. "I say
again, it is a good and a wholesome thing to depend upon
main strength and reality, and to earn one's bread with the bare
and brawny arm of a blacksmith. A watchmaker gets his brain puzzled by his wheels within a wheel, or loses his health or the nicety
of his eyesight, as was my case, and finds himself at middle age, or a
little after, past labor at his own trade and fit for nothing else, yet
too poor to live at his ease. So I say once again, give me main strength
for my money. And then, how it takes the nonsense out of a man!
Did you ever hear of a blacksmith being such a fool as Owen Warland yonder?"

"Well said, uncle Hovenden!" shouted Robert Danforth from
the forge, in a full, deep, merry voice, that made the roof reëcho.
"And what says Miss Annie to that doctrine? She, I suppose, will
think it a genteeler business to tinker up a lady's watch than to forge
a horseshoe or make a gridiron."

Annie drew her father onward without giving him time for reply.

But we must return to Owen Warland's shop, and spend more
meditation upon his history and character than either Peter Hovenden, or probably his daughter Annie, or Owen's old school-fellow,
Robert Danforth, would have thought due to so slight a subject.
From the time that his little fingers could grasp a penknife, Owen
had been remarkable for a delicate ingenuity, which sometimes produced pretty shapes in wood, principally figures of flowers and birds,
and sometimes seemed to aim at the hidden mysteries of mechanism.
But it was always for purposes of grace, and never with any mockery
of the useful. He did not, like the crowd of school-boy artisans, con-

structed, which the young artist had recently bespoken. Owen examined the article and pronounced it fashioned according to his wish.

"Why, yes," said Robert Danforth, his strong voice filling the shop as with the sound of a bass viol, "I consider myself equal to anything in the way of my own trade; though I should have made but a poor figure at yours with such a fist as this," added he, laughing, as he laid his vast hand beside the delicate one of Owen. "But what then? I put more main strength into one blow of my sledge hammer than all that you have expended since you were a 'prentice. Is not that the truth?"

"Very probably," answered the low and slender voice of Owen. "Strength is an earthly monster. I make no pretensions to it. My force, whatever there may be of it, is altogether spiritual."

"Well, but, Owen, what are you about?" asked his old schoolfellow, still in such a hearty volume of tone that it made the artist shrink, especially as the question related to a subject so sacred as the absorbing dream of his imagination. "Folks do say that you are trying to discover the perpetual motion."

"The perpetual motion? Nonsense!" replied Owen Warland, with a movement of disgust; for he was full of little petulances. "It can never be discovered. It is a dream that may delude men whose brains are mystified with matter, but not me. Besides, if such a discovery were possible, it would not be worth my while to make it only to have the secret turned to such purposes as are now effected by steam and water power. I am not ambitious to be honored with the paternity of a new kind of cotton machine."

"That would be droll enough!" cried the blacksmith, breaking out into such an uproar of laughter that Owen himself and the bell glasses on his workboard quivered in unison. "No, no, Owen! No child of yours will have iron joints and sinews. Well, I won't hinder you any more. Good night, Owen, and success, and if you need any assistance, so far as a downright blow of hammer upon anvil will answer the purpose, I'm your man."

And with another laugh the man of main strength left the shop.

"How strange it is," whispered Owen Warland to himself, leaning his head upon his hand, "that all my musings, my purposes, my passion for the beautiful, my consciousness of power to create it,— a finer, more ethereal power, of which this earthly giant can have no conception,—all, all, look so vain and idle whenever my path is crossed by Robert Danforth! He would drive me mad were I to meet him often. His hard, brute force darkens and confuses the spiritual element within me; but I, too, will be strong in my own way. I will not yield to him."

He took from beneath a glass a piece of minute machinery, which he set in the condensed light of his lamp, and looking intently at it through a magnifying glass, proceeded to operate with a delicate instrument of steel. In an instant, however, he fell back in his chair and clasped his hands, with a look of horror on his face that made its small features as impressive as those of a giant would have been.

"Heaven! What have I done?" exclaimed he. "The vapor, the influence of that brute force,—it has bewildered me and obscured my perception. I have made the very stroke—the fatal stroke—that I have dreaded from the first. It is all over—the toil of months, the object of my life. I am ruined!"

And there he sat, in strange despair, until his lamp flickered in the socket and left the Artist of the Beautiful in darkness.

Thus it is that ideas, which grow up within the imagination and appear so lovely to it and of a value beyond whatever men call valuable, are exposed to be shattered and annihilated by contact with the practical. It is requisite for the ideal artist to possess a force of character that seems hardly compatible with its delicacy; he must keep his faith in himself while the incredulous world assails him with its utter disbelief; he must stand up against mankind and be his own sole disciple, both as respects his genius and the objects to which it is directed.

For a time Owen Warland succumbed to this severe but inevitable test. He spent a few sluggish weeks with his head so continually resting in his hands that the towns-people had scarcely an opportunity to see his countenance. When at last it was again uplifted to the light of day, a cold, dull, nameless change was perceptible upon it. In the opinion of Peter Hovenden, however, and that order of sagacious understandings who think that life should be regulated, like clockwork, with leaden weights, the alteration was entirely for the better. Owen now, indeed, applied himself to business with dogged industry. It was marvellous to witness the obtuse gravity with which he would inspect the wheels of a great old silver watch; thereby delighting the owner, in whose fob it had been worn till he deemed it a portion of his own life, and was accordingly jealous of its treatment. In consequence of the good report thus acquired,

Owen Warland was invited by the proper authorities to regulate the clock in the church steeple. He succeeded so admirably in this matter of public interest that the merchants gruffly acknowledged his merits on 'Change; the nurse whispered his praises as she gave the potion in the sick-chamber; the lover blessed him at the hour of appointed interview; and the town in general thanked Owen for the punctuality of dinner time. In a word, the heavy weight upon his spirits kept everything in order, not merely within his own system, but wheresoever the iron accents of the church clock were audible. It was a circumstance, though minute, yet characteristic of his present state, that, when employed to engrave names or initials on silver spoons, he now wrote the requisite letters in the plainest possible style, omitting a variety of fanciful flourishes that had heretofore distinguished his work in this kind.

One day, during the era of this happy transformation, old Peter Hovenden came to visit his former apprentice.

"Well, Owen," said he, "I am glad to hear such good accounts of you from all quarters, and especially from the town clock yonder, which speaks in your commendation every hour of the twenty-four. Only get rid altogether of your nonsensical trash about the beautiful, which I nor nobody else, nor yourself to boot, could ever understand,—only free yourself of that, and your success in life is as sure as daylight. Why, if you go on in this way, I should even venture to let you doctor this precious old watch of mine; though, except my daughter Annie, I have nothing else so valuable in the world."

"I should hardly dare touch it, sir," replied Owen, in a depressed tone; for he was weighed down by his old master's presence.

"In time," said the latter,—"in time, you will be capable of it."

The old watchmaker, with the freedom naturally consequent on his former authority, went on inspecting the work which Owen had in hand at the moment, together with other matters that were in progress. The artist, meanwhile, could scarcely lift his head. There was nothing so antipodal to his nature as this man's cold, unimaginative sagacity, by contact with which everything was converted into a dream except the densest matter of the physical world. Owen groaned in spirit and prayed fervently to be delivered from him.

"But what is this?" cried Peter Hovenden abruptly, taking up a dusty bell glass, beneath which appeared a mechanical something, as delicate and minute as the system of a butterfly's anatomy. "What have we here? Owen! Owen! there is witchcraft in these little chains, and wheels, and paddles. See! with one pinch of my finger and thumb I am going to deliver you from all future peril."

"For Heaven's sake," screamed Owen Warland, springing up with wonderful energy, "as you would not drive me mad, do not touch it! The slightest pressure of your finger would ruin me forever."

"Aha, young man! And is it so?" said the old watchmaker, looking at him with just enough of penetration to torture Owen's soul with the bitterness of worldly criticism. "Well, take your own course; but I warn you again that in this small piece of mechanism lives your evil spirit. Shall I exorcise him?"

"You are my evil spirit," answered Owen, much excited,—"you and the hard, coarse world! The leaden thoughts and the despondency that you fling upon me are my clogs, else I should long ago have achieved the task that I was created for."

Peter Hovenden shook his head, with the mixture of contempt and indignation which mankind, of whom he was partly a representative, deem themselves entitled to feel towards all simpletons who seek other prizes than the dusty one along the highway. He then took his leave, with an uplifted finger and a sneer upon his face that haunted the artist's dreams for many a night afterwards. At the time of his old master's visit, Owen was probably on the point of taking up the relinquished task; but, by this sinister event, he was thrown back into the state whence he had been slowly emerging.

But the innate tendency of his soul had only been accumulating fresh vigor during its apparent sluggishness. As the summer advanced he almost totally relinquished his business, and permitted Father Time, so far as the old gentleman was represented by the clocks and watches under his control, to stray at random through human life, making infinite confusion among the train of bewildered hours. He wasted the sunshine, as people said, in wandering through the woods and fields and along the banks of streams. There, like a child, he found amusement in chasing butterflies or watching the motions of water insects. There was something truly mysterious in the intentness with which he contemplated these living playthings as they sported on the breeze or examined the structure of an imperial insect whom he had imprisoned. The chase of butterflies was an apt emblem of the ideal pursuit in which he had spent so many golden hours; but would the beautiful idea ever be yielded to his hand like the butterfly that symbolized it? Sweet, doubtless, were these

days, and congenial to the artist's soul. They were full of bright con-
ceptions, which gleamed through his intellectual world as the butterflies gleamed through the outward atmosphere, and were real to him,
for the instant, without the toil, and perplexity, and many disap-
pointments of attempting to make them visible to the sensual eye.
Alas that the artist, whether in poetry, or whatever other material,
may not content himself with the inward enjoyment of the beautiful,
but must chase the flitting mystery beyond the verge of his ethereal
domain, and crush its frail being in seizing it with a material grasp.
Owen Warland felt the impulse to give external reality to his ideas
as irresistibly as any of the poets or painters who have arrayed the
world in a dimmer and fainter beauty, imperfectly copied from the
richness of their visions.

The night was now his time for the slow progress of re-creating
the one idea to which all his intellectual activity referred itself. Always at the approach of dusk he stole into the town, locked himself
within his shop, and wrought with patient delicacy of touch for many
hours. Sometimes he was startled by the rap of the watchman, who,
when all the world should be asleep, had caught the gleam of lamplight through the crevices of Owen Warland's shutters. Daylight, to
the morbid sensibility of his mind, seemed to have an intrusiveness
that interfered with his pursuits. On cloudy and inclement days,
therefore, he sat with his head upon his hands, muffling, as it were, his
sensitive brain in a mist of indefinite musings; for it was a relief to
escape from the sharp distinctness with which he was compelled
to shape out his thoughts during his nightly toil.

From one of these fits of torpor he was aroused by the entrance
of Annie Hovenden, who came into the shop with the freedom of a
customer, and also with something of the familiarity of a childish
friend. She had worn a hole through her silver thimble, and wanted
Owen to repair it.

"But I don't know whether you will condescend to such a task,"
said she, laughing, "now that you are so taken up with the notion of
putting spirit into machinery."

"Where did you get that idea, Annie?" said Owen, starting in
surprise.

"Oh, out of my own head," answered she, "and from something
that I heard you say, long ago, when you were but a boy and I a little
child. But come; will you mend this poor thimble of mine?"

"Anything for your sake, Annie," said Owen Warland,—"anything, even were it to work at Robert Danforth's forge."

"And that would be a pretty sight!" retorted Annie, glancing with imperceptible slightness at the artist's small and slender frame. "Well; here is the thimble."

"But that is a strange idea of yours," said Owen, "about the spiritualization of matter."

And then the thought stole into his mind that this young girl possessed the gift to comprehend him better than all the world besides. And what a help and strength would it be to him in his lonely toil if he could gain the sympathy of the only being whom he loved! To persons whose pursuits are insulated from the common business of life—who are either in advance of mankind or apart from it—there often comes a sensation of moral cold that makes the spirit shiver as if it had reached the frozen solitudes around the pole. What the prophet, the poet, the reformer, the criminal, or any other man with human yearnings, but separated from the multitude by a peculiar lot, might feel, poor Owen felt.

"Annie," cried he, growing pale as death at the thought, "how gladly would I tell you the secret of my pursuit! You, methinks, would estimate it rightly. You, I know, would hear it with a reverence that I must not expect from the harsh, material world."

"Would I not? to be sure I would!" replied Annie Hovenden, lightly laughing. "Come; explain to me quickly what is the meaning of this little whirligig, so delicately wrought that it might be a plaything for Queen Mab. See! I will put it in motion."

"Hold!" exclaimed Owen, "hold!"

Annie had but given the slightest possible touch, with the point of a needle, to the same minute portion of complicated machinery which has been more than once mentioned, when the artist seized her by the wrist with a force that made her scream aloud. She was affrighted at the convulsion of intense rage and anguish that writhed across his features. The next instant he let his head sink upon his hands.

"Go, Annie," murmured he; "I have deceived myself, and must suffer for it. I yearned for sympathy, and thought, and fancied, and dreamed that you might give it me; but you lack the talisman, Annie, that should admit you into my secrets. That touch has undone the toil of months and the thought of a lifetime! It was not your fault, Annie; but you have ruined me!"

Poor Owen Warland! He had indeed erred, yet pardonably; for if any human spirit could have sufficiently reverenced the processes so sacred in his eyes, it must have been a woman's. Even Annie Hovenden, possibly, might not have disappointed him had she been enlightened by the deep intelligence of love.

The artist spent the ensuing winter in a way that satisfied any persons who had hitherto retained a hopeful opinion of him that he was, in truth, irrevocably doomed to inutility as regarded the world, and to an evil destiny on his own part. The decease of a relative had put him in possession of a small inheritance. Thus freed from the necessity of toil, and having lost the steadfast influence of a great purpose,—great, at least, to him,—he abandoned himself to habits from which it might have been supposed the mere delicacy of his organization would have availed to secure him. But when the ethereal portion of a man of genius is obscured, the earthly part assumes an influence the more uncontrollable, because the character is now thrown off the balance to which Providence had so nicely adjusted it, and which, in coarser natures, is adjusted by some other method. Owen Warland made proof of whatever show of bliss may be found in riot. He looked at the world through the golden medium of wine, and contemplated the visions that bubble up so gayly around the brim of the glass, and that people the air with shapes of pleasant madness, which so soon grow ghostly and forlorn. Even when this dismal and inevitable change had taken place, the young man might still have continued to quaff the cup of enchantments, though its vapor did but shroud life in gloom and fill the gloom with spectres that mocked at him. There was a certain irksomeness of spirit, which, being real, and the deepest sensation of which the artist was now conscious, was more intolerable than any fantastic miseries and horrors that the abuse of wine could summon up. In the latter case he could remember, even out of the midst of his trouble, that all was but a delusion; in the former, the heavy anguish was his actual life.

From this perilous state he was redeemed by an incident which more than one person witnessed, but of which the shrewdest could not explain or conjecture the operation on Owen Warland's mind. It was very simple. On a warm afternoon of spring, as the artist sat among his riotous companions with a glass of wine before him, a splendid butterfly flew in at the open window and fluttered about his head.

"Ah," exclaimed Owen, who had drank freely, "are you alive again, child of the sun and playmate of the summer breeze, after your dismal winter's nap? Then it is time for me to be at work!"

And, leaving his unemptied glass upon the table, he departed and was never known to sip another drop of wine.

And now, again, he resumed his wanderings in the woods and fields. It might be fancied that the bright butterfly, which had come so spirit-like into the window as Owen sat with the rude revellers, was indeed a spirit commissioned to recall him to the pure, ideal life that had so etherealized him among men. It might be fancied that he went forth to seek this spirit in its sunny haunts; for still, as in the summer time gone by, he was seen to steal gently up wherever a butterfly had alighted, and lose himself in contemplation of it. When it took flight his eyes followed the winged vision, as if its airy track would show the path to heaven. But what could be the purpose of the unseasonable toil, which was again resumed, as the watchman knew by the lines of lamplight through the crevices of Owen Warland's shutters? The towns-people had one comprehensive explanation of all these singularities. Owen Warland had gone mad! How universally efficacious—how satisfactory, too, and soothing to the injured sensibility of narrowness and dulness—is this easy method of accounting for whatever lies beyond the world's most ordinary scope! From St. Paul's days down to our poor little Artist of the Beautiful, the same talisman had been applied to the elucidation of all mysteries in the words or deeds of men who spoke or acted too wisely or too well. In Owen Warland's case the judgment of his towns-people may have been correct. Perhaps he was mad. The lack of sympathy— that contrast between himself and his neighbors which took away the restraint of example—was enough to make him so. Or possibly he had caught just so much of ethereal radiance as served to bewilder him, in an earthly sense, by its intermixture with the common daylight.

One evening, when the artist had returned from a customary ramble and had just thrown the lustre of his lamp on the delicate piece of work so often interrupted, but still taken up again, as if his fate were embodied in its mechanism, he was surprised by the entrance of old Peter Hovenden. Owen never met this man without a shrinking of the heart. Of all the world he was most terrible, by reason of a keen understanding which saw so distinctly what it did see, and disbelieved so uncompromisingly in what it could not see. On this occasion the old watchmaker had merely a gracious word or two to say.

"Owen, my lad," said he, "we must see you at my house to-morrow night."

The artist began to mutter some excuse.

"Oh, but it must be so," quoth Peter Hovenden, "for the sake of the days when you were one of the household. What, my boy! don't you know that my daughter Annie is engaged to Robert Danforth? We are making an entertainment, in our humble way, to celebrate the event."

"Ah!" said Owen.

That little monosyllable was all he uttered; its tone seemed cold and unconcerned to an ear like Peter Hovenden's; and yet there was in it the stifled outcry of the poor artist's heart, which he compressed within him like a man holding down an evil spirit. One slight outbreak, however, imperceptible to the old watchmaker, he allowed himself. Raising the instrument with which he was about to begin his work, he let it fall upon the little system of machinery that had, anew, cost him months of thought and toil. It was shattered by the stroke!

Owen Warland's story would have been no tolerable representation of the troubled life of those who strive to create the beautiful, if, amid all other thwarting influences, love had not interposed to steal the cunning from his hand. Outwardly he had been no ardent or enterprising lover; the career of his passion had confined its tumults and vicissitudes so entirely within the artist's imagination that Annie herself had scarcely more than a woman's intuitive perception of it; but, in Owen's view, it covered the whole field of his life. Forgetful of the time when she had shown herself incapable of any deep response, he had persisted in connecting all his dreams of artistical success with Annie's image; she was the visible shape in which the spiritual power that he worshipped, and on whose altar he hoped to lay a not unworthy offering, was made manifest to him. Of course he had deceived himself; there were no such attributes in Annie Hovenden as his imagination had endowed her with. She, in the aspect which she wore to his inward vision, was as much a creature of his own as the mysterious piece of mechanism would be were it ever realized. Had he become convinced of his mistake through the medium of successful love,—had he won Annie to his bosom, and there beheld her fade from angel into ordinary woman,—the disappointment might have driven him back, with concentrated energy, upon his sole remaining object. On the other hand, had he found Annie what he fancied, his lot would have been so rich in beauty that out of its mere redundancy he might have wrought the beautiful into many a worthier type than he had toiled for; but the guise in which his sorrow came to him, the sense that the angel of his life had been snatched away and given to a rude man of earth and iron, who could neither need nor appreciate her ministrations,—this was the very perversity of fate that makes human existence appear too absurd and contradictory to be the scene of one other hope or one other fear. There was nothing left for Owen Warland but to sit down like a man that had been stunned.

He went through a fit of illness. After his recovery his small and slender frame assumed an obtuser garniture of flesh than it had ever before worn. His thin cheeks became round; his delicate little hand, so spiritually fashioned to achieve fairy task-work, grew plumper than the hand of a thriving infant. His aspect had a childishness such as might have induced a stranger to pat him on the head—pausing, however, in the act, to wonder what manner of child was here. It was as if the spirit had gone out of him, leaving the body to flourish in a sort of vegetable existence. Not that Owen Warland was idiotic. He could talk, and not irrationally. Somewhat of a babbler, indeed, did people begin to think him; for he was apt to discourse at wearisome length of marvels of mechanism that he had read about in books, but which he had learned to consider as absolutely fabulous. Among them he enumerated the Man of Brass, constructed by Albertus Magnus, and the Brazen Head of Friar Bacon; and, coming down to later times, the automata of a little coach and horses, which it was pretended had been manufactured for the Dauphin of France; together with an insect that buzzed about the ear like a living fly, and yet was but a contrivance of minute steel springs. There was a story, too, of a duck that waddled, and quacked, and ate; though, had any honest citizen purchased it for dinner, he would have found himself cheated with the mere mechanical apparition of a duck.

"But all these accounts," said Owen Warland, "I am now satisfied are mere impositions."

Then, in a mysterious way, he would confess that he once thought differently. In his idle and dreamy days he had considered it possible, in a certain sense, to spiritualize machinery, and to combine with the new species of life and motion thus produced a beauty

that should attain to the ideal which Nature has proposed to herself
in all her creatures, but has never taken pains to realize. He seemed,
however, to retain no very distinct perception either of the process
of achieving this object or of the design itself.

"I have thrown it all aside now," he would say. "It was a dream
such as young men are always mystifying themselves with. Now that
I have acquired a little common sense, it makes me laugh to think of
it."

Poor, poor and fallen Owen Warland! These were the symptoms
that he had ceased to be an inhabitant of the better sphere that lies
unseen around us. He had lost his faith in the invisible, and now
prided himself, as such unfortunates invariably do, in the wisdom
which rejected much that even his eye could see, and trusted confidently in nothing but what his hand could touch. This is the calam-
ity of men whose spiritual part dies out of them and leaves the
grosser understanding to assimilate them more and more to the
things of which alone it can take cognizance; but in Owen Warland
the spirit was not dead nor passed away; it only slept.

How it awoke again is not recorded. Perhaps the torpid slumber
was broken by a convulsive pain. Perhaps, as in a former instance, the
butterfly came and hovered about his head and reinspired him,—as
indeed this creature of the sunshine had always a mysterious mission
for the artist,—reinspired him with the former purpose of his life.
Whether it were pain or happiness that thrilled through his veins,
his first impulse was to thank Heaven for rendering him again the
being of thought, imagination, and keenest sensibility that he had
long ceased to be.

"Now for my task," said he. "Never did I feel such strength for
it as now."

Yet, strong as he felt himself, he was incited to toil the more
diligently by an anxiety lest death should surprise him in the midst
of his labors. This anxiety, perhaps, is common to all men who set
their hearts upon anything so high, in their own view of it, that life
becomes of importance only as conditional to its accomplishment.
So long as we love life for itself, we seldom dread the losing it.
When we desire life for the attainment of an object, we recognize the
frailty of its texture. But, side by side with this sense of insecurity,
there is a vital faith in our invulnerability to the shaft of death while
engaged in any task that seems assigned by Providence as our proper
thing to do, and which the world would have cause to mourn for

should we leave it unaccomplished. Can the philosopher, big with the inspiration of an idea that is to reform mankind, believe that he is to be beckoned from this sensible existence at the very instant when he is mustering his breath to speak the word of light? Should he perish so, the weary ages may pass away—the world's, whose life sand may fall, drop by drop—before another intellect is prepared to develop the truth that might have been uttered then. But history affords many an example where the most precious spirit, at any particular epoch manifested in human shape, has gone hence untimely, without space allowed him, so far as mortal judgment could discern, to perform his mission on the earth. The prophet dies, and the man of torpid heart and sluggish brain lives on. The poet leaves his song half sung, or finishes it, beyond the scope of mortal ears, in a celestial choir. The painter—as Allston did—leaves half his conception on the canvas to sadden us with its imperfect beauty, and goes to picture forth the whole, if it be no irreverence to say so, in the hues of heaven. But rather such incomplete designs of this life will be perfected nowhere. This so frequent abortion of man's dearest projects must be taken as a proof that the deeds of earth, however etherealized by piety or genius, are without value, except as exercises and manifestations of the spirit. In heaven, all ordinary thought is higher and more melodious than Milton's song. Then, would he add another verse to any strain that he had left unfinished here?

But to return to Owen Warland. It was his fortune, good or ill, to achieve the purpose of his life. Pass we over a long space of intense thought, yearning effort, minute toil, and wasting anxiety, succeeded by an instant of solitary triumph: let all this be imagined; and then behold the artist, on a winter evening, seeking admittance to Robert Danforth's fireside circle. There he found the man of iron, with his massive substance thoroughly warmed and attempered by domestic influences. And there was Annie, too, now transformed into a matron, with much of her husband's plain and sturdy nature, but imbued, as Owen Warland still believed, with a finer grace, that might enable her to be the interpreter between strength and beauty. It happened, likewise, that old Peter Hovenden was a guest this evening at his daughter's fireside, and it was his well-remembered expression of keen, cold criticism that first encountered the artist's glance.

"My old friend Owen!" cried Robert Danforth, starting up, and compressing the artist's delicate fingers within a hand that was ac-

customed to gripe bars of iron. "This is kind and neighborly to come
to us at last. I was afraid your perpetual motion had bewitched you
out of the remembrance of old times."

"We are glad to see you," said Annie, while a blush reddened
her matronly cheek. "It was not like a friend to stay from us so
long."

"Well, Owen," inquired the old watchmaker, as his first greeting, "how comes on the beautiful? Have you created it at last?"

The artist did not immediately reply, being startled by the apparition of a young child of strength that was tumbling about on the
carpet,—a little personage who had come mysteriously out of the infinite, but with something so sturdy and real in his composition that
he seemed moulded out of the densest substance which earth could
supply. This hopeful infant crawled towards the new-comer, and setting himself on end, as Robert Danforth expressed the posture,
stared at Owen with a look of such sagacious observation that the
mother could not help exchanging a proud glance with her husband.
But the artist was disturbed by the child's look, as imagining a resemblance between it and Peter Hovenden's habitual expression. He
could have fancied that the old watchmaker was compressed into this
baby shape, and looking out of those baby eyes, and repeating, as he
now did, the malicious question:—

"The beautiful, Owen! How comes on the beautiful? Have you
succeeded in creating the beautiful?"

"I have succeeded," replied the artist, with a momentary light
of triumph in his eyes and a smile of sunshine, yet steeped in such
depth of thought that it was almost sadness. "Yes, my friends, it is the
truth. I have succeeded."

"Indeed!" cried Annie, a look of maiden mirthfulness peeping
out of her face again. "And is it lawful, now, to inquire what the secret is?"

"Surely; it is to disclose it that I have come," answered Owen
Warland. "You shall know, and see, and touch, and possess the secret! For, Annie,—if by that name I may still address the friend of
my boyish years,—Annie, it is for your bridal gift that I have
wrought this spiritualized mechanism, this harmony of motion, this
mystery of beauty. It comes late, indeed; but it is as we go onward in
life, when objects begin to lose their freshness of hue and our souls
their delicacy of perception, that the spirit of beauty is most needed.

If,—forgive me, Annie,—if you know how to value this gift, it can never come too late."

He produced, as he spoke, what seemed a jewel box. It was carved richly out of ebony by his own hand, and inlaid with a fanciful tracery of pearl, representing a boy in pursuit of a butterfly, which, elsewhere, had become a winged spirit, and was flying heavenward; while the boy, or youth, had found such efficacy in his strong desire that he ascended from earth to cloud, and from cloud to celestial atmosphere, to win the beautiful. This case of ebony the artist opened, and bade Annie place her finger on its edge. She did so, but almost screamed as a butterfly fluttered forth, and, alighting on her finger's tip, sat waving the ample magnificence of its purple and gold-speckled wings, as if in prelude to a flight. It is impossible to express by words the glory, the splendor, the delicate gorgeousness which were softened into the beauty of this object. Nature's ideal butterfly was here realized in all its perfection; not in the pattern of such faded insects as flit among earthly flowers, but of those which hover across the meads of paradise for child-angels and the spirits of departed infants to disport themselves with. The rich down was visible upon its wings; the lustre of its eyes seemed instinct with spirit. The firelight glimmered around this wonder—the candles gleamed upon it; but it glistened apparently by its own radiance, and illuminated the finger and outstretched hand on which it rested with a white gleam like that of precious stones. In its perfect beauty, the consideration of size was entirely lost. Had its wings overreached the firmament, the mind could not have been more filled or satisfied.

"Beautiful! beautiful!" exclaimed Annie. "Is it alive? Is it alive?"

"Alive? To be sure it is," answered her husband. "Do you suppose any mortal has skill enough to make a butterfly, or would put himself to the trouble of making one, when any child may catch a score of them in a summer's afternoon? Alive? Certainly! But this pretty box is undoubtedly of our friend Owen's manufacture; and really it does him credit."

At this moment the butterfly waved its wings anew, with a motion so absolutely lifelike that Annie was startled, and even awe-stricken; for, in spite of her husband's opinion, she could not satisfy herself whether it was indeed a living creature or a piece of wondrous mechanism.

"Is it alive?" she repeated, more earnestly than before.

"Judge for yourself," said Owen Warland, who stood gazing in her face with fixed attention.

The butterfly now flung itself upon the air, fluttered round Annie's head, and soared into a distant region of the parlor, still making itself perceptible to sight by the starry gleam in which the motion of its wings enveloped it. The infant on the floor followed its course with his sagacious little eyes. After flying about the room, it returned in a spiral curve and settled again on Annie's finger.

"But is it alive?" exclaimed she again; and the finger on which the gorgeous mystery had alighted was so tremulous that the butterfly was forced to balance himself with his wings. "Tell me if it be alive, or whether you created it."

"Wherefore ask who created it, so it be beautiful?" replied Owen Warland. "Alive? Yes, Annie; it may well be said to possess life, for it has absorbed my own being into itself; and in the secret of that butterfly, and in its beauty,—which is not merely outward, but deep as its whole system,—is represented the intellect, the imagination, the sensibility, the soul of an Artist of the Beautiful! Yes; I created it. But"—and here his countenance somewhat changed—"this butterfly is not now to me what it was when I beheld it afar off in the daydreams of my youth."

"Be it what it may, it is a pretty plaything," said the blacksmith, grinning with childlike delight. "I wonder whether it would condescend to alight on such a great clumsy finger as mine? Hold it hither, Annie."

By the artist's direction, Annie touched her finger's tip to that of her husband; and, after a momentary delay, the butterfly fluttered from one to the other. It preluded a second flight by a similar, yet not precisely the same, waving of wings as in the first experiment; then, ascending from the blacksmith's stalwart finger, it rose in a gradually enlarging curve to the ceiling, made one wide sweep around the room, and returned with an undulating movement to the point whence it had started.

"Well, that does beat all nature!" cried Robert Danforth, bestowing the heartiest praise that he could find expression for; and, indeed, had he paused there, a man of finer words and nicer perception could not easily have said more. "That goes beyond me, I confess. But what then? There is more real use in one downright blow of my sledge hammer than in the whole five years' labor that our friend Owen has wasted on this butterfly."

Here the child clapped his hands and made a great babble of indistinct utterance, apparently demanding that the butterfly should be given him for a plaything.

Owen Warland, meanwhile, glanced sidelong at Annie, to discover whether she sympathized in her husband's estimate of the comparative value of the beautiful and the practical. There was, amid all her kindness towards himself, amid all the wonder and admiration with which she contemplated the marvellous work of his hands and incarnation of his idea, a secret scorn—too secret, perhaps, for her own consciousness, and perceptible only to such intuitive discernment as that of the artist. But Owen, in the latter stages of his pursuit, had risen out of the region in which such a discovery might have been torture. He knew that the world, and Annie as the representative of the world, whatever praise might be bestowed, could never say the fitting word nor feel the fitting sentiment which should be the perfect recompense of an artist who, symbolizing a lofty moral by a material trifle,—converting what was earthly to spiritual gold,—had won the beautiful into his handiwork. Not at this latest moment was he to learn that the reward of all high performance must be sought within itself, or sought in vain. There was, however, a view of the matter which Annie and her husband, and even Peter Hovenden, might fully have understood, and which would have satisfied them that the toil of years had here been worthily bestowed. Owen Warland might have told them that this butterfly, this plaything, this bridal gift of a poor watchmaker to a blacksmith's wife, was, in truth, a gem of art that a monarch would have purchased with honors and abundant wealth, and have treasured it among the jewels of his kingdom as the most unique and wondrous of them all. But the artist smiled and kept the secret to himself.

"Father," said Annie, thinking that a word of praise from the old watchmaker might gratify his former apprentice, "do come and admire this pretty butterfly."

"Let us see," said Peter Hovenden, rising from his chair, with a sneer upon his face that always made people doubt, as he himself did, in everything but a material existence. "Here is my finger for it to alight upon. I shall understand it better when once I have touched it."

But, to the increased astonishment of Annie, when the tip of her father's finger was pressed against that of her husband, on which the butterfly still rested, the insect drooped its wings and seemed on the point of falling to the floor. Even the bright spots of gold upon its wings and body, unless her eyes deceived her, grew dim, and the glowing purple took a dusky hue, and the starry lustre that gleamed around the blacksmith's hand became faint and vanished.

"It is dying! it is dying!" cried Annie, in alarm.

"It has been delicately wrought," said the artist, calmly. "As I told you, it has imbibed a spiritual essence—call it magnetism, or what you will. In an atmosphere of doubt and mockery its exquisite susceptibility suffers torture, as does the soul of him who instilled his own life into it. It has already lost its beauty; in a few moments more its mechanism would be irreparably injured."

"Take away your hand, father!" entreated Annie, turning pale. "Here is my child; let it rest on his innocent hand. There, perhaps, its life will revive and its colors grow brighter than ever."

Her father, with an acrid smile, withdrew his finger. The butterfly then appeared to recover the power of voluntary motion, while its hues assumed much of their original lustre, and the gleam of starlight, which was its most ethereal attribute, again formed a halo round about it. At first, when transferred from Robert Danforth's hand to the small finger of the child, this radiance grew so powerful that it positively threw the little fellow's shadow back against the wall. He, meanwhile, extended his plump hand as he had seen his father and mother do, and watched the waving of the insect's wings with infantine delight. Nevertheless, there was a certain odd expression of sagacity that made Owen Warland feel as if here were old Peter Hovenden, partially, and but partially, redeemed from his hard scepticism into childish faith.

"How wise the little monkey looks!" whispered Robert Danforth to his wife.

"I never saw such a look on a child's face," answered Annie, admiring her own infant, and with good reason, far more than the artistic butterfly. "The darling knows more of the mystery than we do."

As if the butterfly, like the artist, were conscious of something not entirely congenial in the child's nature, it alternately sparkled and grew dim. At length it arose from the small hand of the infant with an airy motion that seemed to bear it upward without an effort, as if the ethereal instincts with which its master's spirit had endowed it impelled this fair vision involuntarily to a higher sphere. Had there been no obstruction, it might have soared into the sky and grown immortal. But its lustre gleamed upon the ceiling; the exquisite texture of its wings brushed against that earthly medium; and a sparkle or two, as of stardust, floated downward and lay glimmering on the carpet. Then the butterfly came fluttering down, and, instead of returning to the infant, was apparently attracted towards the artist's hand.

"Not so! not so!" murmured Owen Warland, as if his handiwork could have understood him. "Thou has gone forth out of thy master's heart. There is no return for thee."

With a wavering movement, and emitting a tremulous radiance, the butterfly struggled, as it were, towards the infant, and was about to alight upon his finger; but while it still hovered in the air, the little child of strength, with his grandsire's sharp and shrewd expression in his face, made a snatch at the marvellous insect and compressed it in his hand. Annie screamed. Old Peter Hovenden burst into a cold and scornful laugh. The blacksmith, by main force, unclosed the infant's hand, and found within the palm a small heap of glittering fragments, whence the mystery of beauty had fled forever. And as for Owen Warland, he looked placidly at what seemed the ruin of his life's labor, and which was yet no ruin. He had caught a far other butterfly than this. When the artist rose high enough to achieve the beautiful, the symbol by which he made it perceptible to mortal senses became of little value in his eyes while his spirit possessed itself in the enjoyment of the reality.

QUESTIONS

1. Hawthorne's story turns on a central conflict, that between Owen Warland on the one hand and Peter Hovenden, his daughter Annie, and the blacksmith Robert Danforth, on the other. What is the nature of that conflict? What does Warland represent and what do the three other figures represent?

2. Warland is a watchmaker, as was old Peter Hovenden. Is he a good watchmaker? Find statements which reflect upon his ability in this occupation. Describe in general terms what a watchmaker does. What is

Warland's opinion of his profession? Why do you think he has this opinion?

3. A motif is a minor, repeated theme which supports the major theme and helps to pattern the work. One motif is clearly suggested by the role of watchmaker and the frequent references to watches and clocks. Identify other motifs and discuss their relationship to the central meaning of the story.

4. This story is concerned with the development of the artist as well as with the particular work of art he is creating. How is the Warland of the final scene different from the Warland of whom Annie says, in the opening scene, "His ears are as delicate as his feelings; and you know how easily disturbed they are"?

5. In comparing the attitudes toward life held by Warland and the others, is it accurate to say that Warland is totally right and the others totally wrong? Discuss balance among the four characters. This story demonstrates the character types known as the protagonist, the antagonist, and the foil. Identify each and elaborate on his function in the story.

6. Why does Hawthorne have Warland create a butterfly instead of some other object? What relationship is there between a butterfly and a work of art? How does the butterfly resemble Warland himself? One characteristic of a butterfly is that it emerges from a chrysalis stage. Does this fact tell us anything about the nature of art and the artist, of the creative imagination, or of the creative process?

7. With so many characters and objects functioning as symbols, it might be possible to view this story as an allegory. To what extent may we place Warland, Hovenden, Annie, Danforth, the butterfly, and watchmaking (among other symbolic elements) into an allegorical framework? In what ways does "The Artist of the Beautiful" transcend the limitations of straight allegory?

EDGAR ALLAN POE

(1809-1849)

Few readers will be unfamiliar with the name of Edgar Allan Poe. Born in Boston of parents who were both actors, he was orphaned while still a child and adopted by John Allan, a well-to-do Richmond, Virginia, merchant. Given a good education, Poe went on to the Military Academy at West Point for a time but left in 1831. About the same time he began publishing his poetry and short stories. From then until his death, he dedicated himself to a literary career. His creative genius has placed him in that great triumvirate of writers (including Hawthorne and Melville) which marks the high point of American literature in the mid-nineteenth century. Poe is, of course, far more than a writer of detective stories and tales of mystery and horror. In his hands, point of view is often a complex device, and his psychological analysis of character foreshadows the more self-conscious psychologizing of the post-Freudian era. His works are numerous and are available in many editions.

The Cask of Amontillado

The thousand injuries of Fortunato I had borne as I best could, but when he ventured upon insult I vowed revenge. You, who so well know the nature of my soul, will not suppose, however, that I gave utterance to a threat. *At length* I would be avenged; this was a point definitely settled—but the very definitiveness with which it was resolved precluded the idea of risk. I must not only punish but punish with impunity. A wrong is unredressed when retribution overtakes its redresser. It is equally unredressed when the avenger fails to make himself felt as such to him who has done the wrong.

It must be understood that neither by word nor deed had I given Fortunato cause to doubt my good will. I continued, as was my wont, to smile in his face, and he did not perceive that my smile *now* was at the thought of his immolation.

He had a weak point—this Fortunato—although in other regards he was a man to be respected and even feared. He prided himself on his connoisseurship in wine. Few Italians have the true virtuoso spirit. For the most part their enthusiasm is adopted to suit the time and opportunity, to practise imposture upon the British and Austrian *millionaires*. In painting and gemmary, Fortunato, like his countrymen, was a quack, but in the matter of old wines he was sincere. In this respect I did not differ from him materially;—I was skilful in the Italian vintages myself, and bought largely whenever I could.

It was about dusk, one evening during the supreme madness of the carnival season, that I encountered my friend. He accosted me with excessive warmth, for he had been drinking much. The man wore motley. He had on a tight-fitting parti-striped dress, and his head was surmounted by the conical cap and bells. I was so pleased to see him that I thought I should never have done wringing his hand.

I said to him—"My dear Fortunato, you are luckily met. How remarkably well you are looking to-day. But I have received a pipe of what passes for Amontillado, and I have my doubts."

"How?" said he. "Amontillado? A pipe? Impossible! And in the middle of the carnival!"

"I have my doubts," I replied; "and I was silly enough to pay the full Amontillado price without consulting you in the matter. You were not to be found, and I was fearful of losing a bargain."

"Amontillado!"

"I have my doubts."

"Amontillado!"

"And I must satisfy them."

"Amontillado!"

"As you are engaged, I am on my way to Luchresi. If any one has a critical turn it is he. He will tell me——"

"Luchresi cannot tell Amontillado from Sherry."

"And yet some fools will have it that his taste is a match for your own."

"Come, let us go."

"Whither?"

"To your vaults."

"My friend, no; I will not impose upon your good nature. I perceive you have an engagement. Luchresi——"

"I have no engagement;—come."

"My friend, no. It is not the engagement, but the severe cold with which I perceive you are afflicted. The vaults are insufferably damp. They are encrusted with nitre."

"Let us go, nevertheless. The cold is merely nothing. Amontillado! You have been imposed upon. And as for Luchresi, he cannot distinguish Sherry from Amontillado."

Thus speaking, Fortunato possessed himself of my arm; and putting on a mask of black silk and drawing a *roquelaire* closely about my person, I suffered him to hurry me to my palazzo.

There were no attendants at home; they had absconded to make merry in honour of the time. I had told them that I should not return until the morning, and had given them explicit orders not to stir from the house. These orders were sufficient, I well knew, to insure their immediate disappearance, one and all, as soon as my back was turned.

I took from their sconces two flambeaux, and giving one to Fortunato, bowed him through several suites of rooms to the archway that led into the vaults. I passed down a long and winding staircase, requesting him to be cautious as he followed. We came at length to the foot of the descent, and stood together upon the damp ground of the catacombs of the Montresors.

The gait of my friend was unsteady, and the bells upon his cap jingled as he strode.

"The pipe," he said.

"It is farther on," said I; "but observe the white web-work which gleams from these cavern walls."

He turned towards me, and looked into my eyes with two filmy orbs that distilled the rheum of intoxication.

"Nitre?" he asked, at length.

"Nitre," I replied. "How long have you had that cough?"

"Ugh! ugh! ugh!—ugh! ugh! ugh!—ugh! ugh! ugh!—ugh! ugh! ugh!—ugh! ugh! ugh!"

My poor friend found it impossible to reply for many minutes. "It is nothing," he said, at last.

"Come," I said, with decision, "we will go back; your health is precious. You are rich, respected, admired, beloved; you are happy, as once I was. You are a man to be missed. For me it is no matter. We will go back; you will be ill, and I cannot be responsible. Besides, there is Luchresi——"

"Enough," he said; "the cough is a mere nothing; it will not kill me. I shall not die of a cough."

"True—true," I replied; "and, indeed, I had no intention of alarming you unnecessarily—but you should use all proper caution. A draught of this Medoc will defend us from the damps."

Here I knocked off the neck of a bottle which I drew from a long row of its fellows that lay upon the mould.

"Drink," I said, presenting him the wine.

He raised it to his lips with a leer. He paused and nodded to me familiarly, while his bells jingled.

"I drink," he said, "to the buried that repose around us."

"And I to your long life."

He again took my arm, and we proceeded.

"These vaults," he said, "are extensive."

"The Montresors," I replied, "were a great and numerous family."

"I forget your arms."

"A huge human foot d'or, in a field azure; the foot crushes a serpent rampant whose fangs are imbedded in the heel."

"And the motto?"

"Nemo me impune lacessit."

"Good!" he said.

The wine sparkled in his eyes and the bells jingled. My own fancy grew warm with the Medoc. We had passed through long walls of piled skeletons, with casks and puncheons intermingling, into the inmost recesses of the catacombs. I paused again, and this time I made bold to seize Fortunato by an arm above the elbow.

"The nitre!" I said; "see, it increases. It hangs like moss upon the vaults. We are below the river's bed. The drops of moisture trickle among the bones. Come, we will go back ere it is too late. Your cough——"

"It is nothing," he said; "let us go on. But first, another draught of the Medoc."

I broke and reached him a flagon of De Grâve. He emptied it at a breath. His eyes flashed with a fierce light. He laughed and threw the bottle upwards with a gesticulation I did not understand.

I looked at him in surprise. He repeated the movement—a grotesque one.

"You do not comprehend?" he said.

"Not I," I replied.

"Then you are not of the brotherhood."

"How?"

"You are not of the masons."

"Yes, yes," I said; "yes, yes."

"You? Impossible! A mason?"

"A mason," I replied.

"A sign," he said, "a sign."

"It is this," I answered, producing from beneath the folds of my *roquelaire* a trowel.

"You jest," he exclaimed, recoiling a few paces. "But let us proceed to the Amontillado."

"Be it so," I said, replacing the tool beneath the cloak and again offering him my arm. He leaned upon it heavily. We continued our route in search of the Amontillado. We passed through a range of low arches, descended, passed on, and descending again, arrived at a deep crypt, in which the foulness of the air caused our flambeaux rather to glow than flame.

At the most remote end of the crypt there appeared another less spacious. Its walls had been lined with human remains, piled to the vault overhead, in the fashion of the great catacombs of Paris. Three sides of this interior crypt were still ornamented in this manner. From the fourth side the bones had been thrown down, and lay promiscuously upon the earth, forming at one point a mound of some size. Within the wall thus exposed by the displacing of the bones, we perceived a still interior crypt or recess, in depth about four feet, in width three, in height six or seven. It seemed to have been constructed for no especial use within itself, but formed merely the interval between two of the colossal supports of the roof of the catacombs, and was backed by one of their circumscribing walls of solid granite.

It was in vain that Fortunato, uplifting his dull torch, endeavoured to pry into the depth of the recess. Its termination the feeble light did not enable us to see.

"Proceed," I said; "herein is the Amontillado. As for Luchresi——"

"He is an ignoramus," interrupted my friend, as he stepped unsteadily forward, while I followed immediately at his heels. In an instant he had reached the extremity of the niche, and finding his progress arrested by the rock, stood stupidly bewildered. A moment more and I had fettered him to the granite. In its surface were two iron staples, distant from each other about two feet, horizontally. From one of these depended a short chain, from the other a padlock. Throwing the links about his waist, it was but the work of a few seconds to secure it. He was too much astounded to resist. Withdrawing the key I stepped back from the recess.

"Pass your hand," I said, "over the wall; you cannot help feeling the nitre. Indeed, it is *very* damp. Once more let me *implore* you to return. No? Then I must positively leave you. But I must first render you all the little attentions in my power."

"The Amontillado!" ejaculated my friend, not yet recovered from his astonishment.

"True," I replied; "the Amontillado."

As I said these words I busied myself among the pile of bones of which I have before spoken. Throwing them aside, I soon uncovered a quantity of building stone and mortar. With these materials and with the aid of my trowel, I began vigorously to wall up the entrance of the niche.

I had scarcely laid the first tier of the masonry when I discovered that the intoxication of Fortunato had in a great measure worn off. The earliest indication I had of this was a low moaning cry from the depth of the recess. It was *not* the cry of a drunken man. There was then a long and obstinate silence. I laid the second tier, and the third, and the fourth; and then I heard the furious vibrations of the chain. The noise lasted for several minutes, during which, that I might hearken to it with the more satisfaction, I ceased my labours and sat down upon the bones. When at last the clanking subsided, I resumed the trowel, and finished without interruption the fifth, the sixth, and the seventh tier. The wall was now nearly upon a level with my breast. I again paused, and holding the flambeaux over the mason-work, threw a few feeble rays upon the figure within.

A succession of loud and shrill screams, bursting suddenly from the throat of the chained form, seemed to thrust me violently back. For a brief moment I hesitated, I trembled. Unsheathing my rapier,

I began to grope with it about the recess; but the thought of an instant reassured me. I placed my hand upon the solid fabric of the catacombs, and felt satisfied. I reapproached the wall; I replied to the yells of him who clamoured. I re-echoed, I aided, I surpassed them in volume and in strength. I did this, and the clamourer grew still.

It was now midnight, and my task was drawing to a close. I had completed the eighth, the ninth and the tenth tier. I had finished a portion of the last and the eleventh; there remained but a single stone to be fitted and plastered in. I struggled with its weight; I placed it partially in its destined position. But now there came from out the niche a low laugh that erected the hairs upon my head. It was succeeded by a sad voice, which I had difficulty in recognizing as that of the noble Fortunato. The voice said—

"Ha! ha! ha!—he! he! he!—a very good joke, indeed—an excellent jest. We will have many a rich laugh about it at the palazzo—he! he! he!—over our wine—he! he! he!"

"The Amontillado!" I said.

"He! he! he!—he! he! he!—yes, the Amontillado. But is it not getting late? Will not they be awaiting us at the palazzo, the Lady Fortunato and the rest? Let us be gone."

"Yes," I said, "let us be gone."

"For the love of God, Montresor!"

"Yes," I said, "for the love of God!"

But to these words I hearkened in vain for a reply. I grew impatient. I called aloud—

"Fortunato!"

No answer. I called again—

"Fortunato!"

No answer still. I thrust a torch through the remaining aperture and let it fall within. There came forth in return only a jingling of the bells. My heart grew sick; it was the dampness of the catacombs that made it so. I hastened to make an end of my labour. I forced the last stone into its position; I plastered it up. Against the new masonry I re-erected the old rampart of bones. For the half of a century no mortal has disturbed them. *In pace requiescat!*

HERMAN MELVILLE

(1819-1891)

Born in New York, son of a Scottish merchant, Melville went to sea in 1839. The next half-dozen years provided him with experiences ranging from life with cannibals (in the Marquesas Islands) to mutiny. Out of these experiences came the novels for which he is best known: TYPEE, OMOO, WHITE-JACKET, BILLY BUDD, and the great MOBY DICK, OR THE WHITE WHALE. His finest short stories appear in THE PIAZZA TALES. At its best, his fiction is richly ambiguous. Frequent themes are illusion and reality, and the nature of good and evil.

BARTLEBY
THE SCRIVENER

A STORY OF WALL STREET

I am a rather elderly man. The nature of my avocations, for the last thirty years, has brought me into more than ordinary contact with what would seem an interesting and somewhat singular set of men, of whom, as yet, nothing, that I know of, has ever been written—I mean, the law-copyists, or scriveners. I have known very many of them, professionally and privately, and, if I pleased, could relate divers histories, at which good-natured gentlemen might smile, and sentimental souls might weep. But I waive the biographies of all other

"Bartleby the Scrivener: A Story of Wall Street" Reprinted from *Piazza Tales,* ed. E. S. Oliver, by permission of Hendricks House, Inc.

scriveners, for a few passages in the life of Bartleby, who was a scrivener, the strangest I ever saw, or heard of. While, of other law-copyists, I might write the complete life, of Bartleby nothing of that sort can be done. I believe that no materials exist, for a full and satisfactory biography of this man. It is an irreparable loss to literature. Bartleby was one of those beings of whom nothing is ascertainable, except from the original sources, and, in his case, those are very small. What my own astonished eyes saw of Bartleby, *that* is all I know of him, except, indeed, one vague report, which will appear in the sequel.

Ere introducing the scrivener, as he first appeared to me, it is fit I make some mention of myself, my *employés,* my business, my chambers, and general surroundings; because some such description is indispensable to an adequate understanding of the chief character about to be presented. Imprimis: I am a man who, from his youth upwards, has been filled with a profound conviction that the easiest way of life is the best. Hence, though I belong to a profession proverbially energetic and nervous, even to turbulence, at times, yet nothing of that sort have I ever suffered to invade my peace. I am one of those unambitious lawyers who never addresses a jury, or in any way draws down public applause; but, in the cool tranquillity of a snug retreat, do a snug business among rich men's bonds, and mortgages, and title-deeds. All who know me, consider me an eminently *safe* man. The late John Jacob Astor, a personage little given to poetic enthusiasm, had no hesitation in pronouncing my first grand point to be prudence; my next, method. I do not speak it in vanity, but simply record the fact, that I was not unemployed in my profession by the late John Jacob Astor; a name which, I admit, I love to repeat; for it hath a rounded and orbicular sound to it, and rings like unto bullion. I will freely add, that I was not insensible to the late John Jacob Astor's good opinion.

Some time prior to the period at which this little history begins, my avocations had been largely increased. The good old office, now extinct in the State of New York, of a Master in Chancery, had been conferred upon me. It was not a very arduous office, but very pleasantly remunerative. I seldom lose my temper; much more seldom indulge in dangerous indignation at wrongs and outrages; but, I must be permitted to be rash here, and declare, that I consider the sudden and violent abrogation of the office of Master in Chancery, by the new Constitution, as a —— premature act; inasmuch as I had counted upon a life-lease of the profits, whereas I only received those of a few short years. But this is by the way.

My chambers were up stairs, at No. — Wall Street. At one end, they looked upon the white wall of the interior of a spacious sky-light shaft, penetrating the building from top to bottom.

This view might have been considered rather tame than other-wise, deficient in what landscape painters call "life". But, if so, the view from the other end of my chambers offered, at least, a contrast, if nothing more. In that direction, my windows commanded an un-obstructed view of a lofty brick wall, black by age and everlasting shade; which wall required no spy-glass to bring out its lurking beauties, but, for the benefit of all near-sighted spectators, was pushed up to within ten feet of my window panes. Owing to the great height of the surrounding buildings, and my chambers being on the second floor, the interval between this wall and mine not a little re-sembled a huge square cistern.

At the period just preceding the advent of Bartleby, I had two persons as copyists in my employment, and a promising lad as an office-boy. First, Turkey; second, Nippers; third, Ginger Nut. These may seem names, the like of which are not usually found in the Di-rectory. In truth, they were nicknames, mutually conferred upon each other by my three clerks, and were deemed expressive of their respective persons or characters. Turkey was a short, pursy English-man, of about my own age—that is, somewhere not far from sixty. In the morning, one might say, his face was of a fine florid hue, but after twelve o'clock, meridian—his dinner hour—it blazed like a grate full of Christmas coals; and continued blazing—but, as it were, with a gradual wane—till six o'clock, P.M., or thereabouts; after which, I saw no more of the proprietor of the face, which, gaining its meridian with the sun, seemed to set with it, to rise, culminate, and decline the following day, with the like regularity and undi-minished glory. There are many singular coincidences I have known in the course of my life, not the least among which was the fact, that, exactly when Turkey displayed his fullest beams from his red and radiant countenance, just then, too, at that critical moment, began the daily period when I considered his business capacities as seriously disturbed for the remainder of the twenty-four hours. Not that he was absolutely idle, or averse to business, then; far from it. The diffi-culty was, he was apt to be altogether too energetic. There was a strange, inflamed, flurried, flighty recklessness of activity about him.

He would be incautious in dipping his pen into his inkstand. All his blots upon my documents were dropped there after twelve o'clock, meridian. Indeed, not only would he be reckless, and sadly given to making blots in the afternoon, but, some days, he went further, and was rather noisy. At such times, too, his face flamed with augmented blazonry, as if cannel coal had been heaped on anthracite. He made an unpleasant racket with his chair; spilled his sand-box; in mending his pens, impatiently split them all to pieces, and threw them on the floor in a sudden passion; stood up, and leaned over his table, boxing his papers about in a most indecorous manner, very sad to behold in an elderly man like him. Nevertheless, as he was in many ways a most valuable person to me, and all the time before twelve o'clock, meridian, was the quickest, steadiest creature, too, accomplishing a great deal of work in a style not easily to be matched—for these reasons, I was willing to overlook his eccentricities, though, indeed, occasionally, I remonstrated with him. I did this very gently, however, because, though the civilest, nay, the blandest and most reverential of men in the morning, yet, in the afternoon, he was disposed, upon provocation, to be slightly rash with his tongue—in fact, insolent. Now, valuing his morning services as I did, and resolved not to lose them—yet, at the same time, made uncomfortable by his inflamed ways after twelve o'clock—and being a man of peace, unwilling by my admonitions to call forth unseemly retorts from him, I took upon me, one Saturday noon (he was always worse on Saturdays) to hint to him, very kindly, that, perhaps, now that he was growing old, it might be well to abridge his labors; in short, he need not come to my chambers after twelve o'clock, but, dinner over, had best go home to his lodgings, and rest himself till tea-time. But no; he insisted upon his afternoon devotions. His countenance became intolerably fervid, as he oratorically assured me—gesticulating with a long ruler at the other end of the room—that if his services in the morning were useful, how indispensable, then, in the afternoon?

"With submission, sir," said Turkey, on this occasion, "I consider myself your right-hand man. In the morning I but marshal and deploy my columns; but in the afternoon I put myself at their head, and gallantly charge the foe, thus"—and he made a violent thrust with the ruler.

"But the blots, Turkey," intimated I.

"True; but, with submission, sir, behold these hairs! I am getting old. Surely, sir, a blot or two of a warm afternoon is not to be

severely urged against gray hairs. Old age—even if it blot the page—
is honorable. With submission, sir, we *both* are getting old."

This appeal to my fellow-feeling was hardly to be resisted. At
all events, I saw that go he would not. So, I made up my mind to let
him stay, resolving, nevertheless, to see to it that, during the afternoon, he had to do with my less important papers.

Nippers, the second on my list, was a whiskered, sallow, and,
upon the whole, rather piratical-looking young man, of about five
and twenty. I always deemed him the victim of two evil powers—
ambition and indigestion. The ambition was evinced by a certain
impatience of the duties of a mere copyist, an unwarrantable usurpa-
tion of strictly professional affairs, such as the original drawing up of
legal documents. The indigestion seemed betokened in an occasional
nervous testiness and grinning irritability, causing the teeth to au-
dibly grind together over mistakes committed in copying; unnecessary maledictions, hissed, rather than spoken, in the heat of
business; and especially by a continual discontent with the height of
the table where he worked. Though of a very ingenious mechanical
turn, Nippers could never get this table to suit him. He put chips
under it, blocks of various sorts, bits of pasteboard, and at last went so
far as to attempt an exquisite adjustment, by final pieces of folded
blotting-paper. But no invention would answer. If, for the sake of
easing his back, he brought the table lid at a sharp angle well up towards his chin, and wrote there like a man using the steep roof of a
Dutch house for his desk, then he declared that it stopped the circula-
tion in his arms. If now he lowered the table to his waistbands, and
stooped over it in writing, then there was a sore aching in his back.
In short, the truth of the matter was, Nippers knew not what he
wanted. Or, if he wanted anything, it was to be rid of a scrivener's
table altogether. Among the manifestations of his diseased ambition
was a fondness he had for receiving visits from certain ambiguous-
looking fellows in seedy coats, whom he called his clients. Indeed, I
was aware that not only was he, at times, considerable of a ward-
politician, but he occasionally did a little business at the Justices'
courts, and was not unknown on the steps of the Tombs. I have good
reason to believe, however, that one individual who called upon him
at my chambers, and who, with a grand air, he insisted was his client,
was no other than a dun, and the alleged title-deed, a bill. But, with
all his failings, and the annoyances he caused me, Nippers, like his
compatriot Turkey, was a very useful man to me; wrote a neat, swift

hand; and, when he chose, was not deficient in a gentlemanly sort of deportment. Added to this, he always dressed in a gentlemanly sort of way; and so, incidentally, reflected credit upon my chambers. Whereas, with respect to Turkey, I had much ado to keep him from being a reproach to me. His clothes were apt to look oily, and smell of eating-houses. He wore his pantaloons very loose and baggy in summer. His coats were execrable; his hat not to be handled. But while the hat was a thing of indifference to me, inasmuch as his natural civility and deference, as a dependent Englishman, always led him to doff it the moment he entered the room, yet his coat was another matter. Concerning his coats, I reasoned with him; but with no effect. The truth was, I suppose, that a man with so small an income could not afford to sport such a lustrous face and a lustrous coat at one and the same time. As Nippers once observed, Turkey's money went chiefly for red ink. One winter day, I presented Turkey with a highly respectable-looking coat of my own—a padded gray coat, of a most comfortable warmth, and which buttoned straight up from the knee to the neck. I thought Turkey would appreciate the favor, and abate his rashness and obstreperousness of afternoons. But no; I verily believe that buttoning himself up in so downy and blanket-like a coat had a pernicious effect upon him—upon the same principle that too much oats are bad for horses. In fact, precisely as a rash, restive horse is said to feel his oats, so Turkey felt his coat. It made him insolent. He was a man whom prosperity harmed.

Though, concerning the self-indulgent habits of Turkey, I had my own private surmises, yet, touching Nippers, I was well persuaded that, whatever might be his faults in other respects, he was, at least, a temperate young man. But, indeed, nature herself seemed to have been his vintner, and, at his birth, charged him so thoroughly with an irritable, brandy-like disposition, that all subsequent potations were needless. When I consider how, amid the stillness of my chambers, Nippers would sometimes impatiently rise from his seat, and stooping over his table, spread his arms wide apart, seize the whole desk, and move it, and jerk it, with a grim, grinding motion on the floor, as if the table were a perverse voluntary agent, intent on thwarting and vexing him, I plainly perceive that, for Nippers, brandy-and-water were altogether superfluous.

It was fortunate for me that, owing to its peculiar cause—indigestion—the irritability and consequent nervousness of Nippers were mainly observable in the morning, while in the afternoon he was comparatively mild. So that, Turkey's paroxysms only coming on about twelve o'clock, I never had to do with their eccentricities at one time. Their fits relieved each other, like guards. When Nippers's was on, Turkey's was off; and *vice versa*. This was a good natural arrangement, under the circumstances.

Ginger Nut, the third on my list, was a lad, some twelve years old. His father was a car-man, ambitious of seeing his son on the bench instead of a cart, before he died. So he sent him to my office, as student at law, errand-boy, cleaner and sweeper, at the rate of one dollar a week. He had a little desk to himself, but he did not use it much. Upon inspection, the drawer exhibited a great array of the shells of various sorts of nuts. Indeed, to this quick-witted youth, the whole noble science of the law was contained in a nutshell. Not the least among the employments of Ginger Nut, as well as one which he discharged with the most alacrity, was his duty as cake and apple purveyor for Turkey and Nippers. Copying law-papers being proverbially a dry, husky sort of business, my two scriveners were fain to moisten their mouths very often with Spitzenbergs, to be had at the numerous stalls nigh the Custom House and Post Office. Also, they sent Ginger Nut very frequently for that peculiar cake—small, flat, round, and very spicy—after which he had been named by them. Of a cold morning, when business was but dull, Turkey would gobble up scores of these cakes, as if they were mere wafers—indeed, they sell them at the rate of six or eight for a penny—the scrape of his pen blending with the crunching of the crisp particles in his mouth. Of all the fiery afternoon blunders and flurried rashnesses of Turkey, was his once moistening a ginger-cake between his lips, and clapping it on to a mortgage, for a seal. I came within an ace of dismissing him then. But he mollified me by making an oriental bow, and saying—

"With submission, sir, it was generous of me to find you in stationery on my own account."

Now my original business—that of a conveyancer and title hunter, and drawer-up of recondite documents of all sorts—was considerably increased by receiving the master's office. There was now great work for scriveners. Not only must I push the clerks already with me, but I must have additional help.

In answer to my advertisement, a motionless young man one morning stood upon my office threshold, the door being open, for it was summer. I can see that figure now—pallidly neat, pitiably respectable, incurably forlorn! It was Bartleby.

After a few words touching his qualifications, I engaged him, glad to have among my corps of copyists a man of so singularly sedate an aspect, which I thought might operate beneficially upon the flighty temper of Turkey, and the fiery one of Nippers.

I should have stated before that ground glass folding-doors divided my premises into two parts, one of which was occupied by my scriveners, the other by myself. According to my humor, I threw open these doors, or closed them. I resolved to assign Bartleby a corner by the folding-doors, but on my side of them, so as to have this quiet man within easy call, in case any trifling thing was to be done. I placed his desk close up to a small side-window in that part of the room, a window which originally had afforded a lateral view of certain grimy back-yards and bricks, but which, owing to subsequent erections, commanded at present no view at all, though it gave some light. Within three feet of the panes was a wall, and the light came down from far above, between two lofty buildings, as from a very small opening in a dome. Still further to a satisfactory arrangement, I procured a high green folding screen, which might entirely isolate Bartleby from my sight, though not remove him from my voice. And thus, in a manner, privacy and society were conjoined.

At first, Bartleby did an extraordinary quantity of writing. As if long famishing for something to copy, he seemed to gorge himself on my documents. There was no pause for digestion. He ran a day and night line, copying by sun-light and by candle-light. I should have been quite delighted with his application, had he been cheerfully industrious. But he wrote on silently, palely, mechanically.

It is, of course, an indispensable part of a scrivener's business to verify the accuracy of his copy, word by word. Where there are two or more scriveners in an office, they assist each other in this examination, one reading from the copy, the other holding the original. It is a very dull, wearisome, and lethargic affair. I can readily imagine that, to some sanguine temperaments, it would be altogether intolerable. For example, I cannot credit that the mettlesome poet, Byron, would have contentedly sat down with Bartleby to examine a law document of, say five hundred pages, closely written in a crimpy hand.

Now and then, in the haste of business, it had been my habit to assist in comparing some brief document myself, calling Turkey or Nippers for this purpose. One object I had, in placing Bartleby so handy to me behind the screen, was, to avail myself of his services on such trivial occasions. It was on the third day, I think, of his being with me, and before any necessity had arisen for having his own writing examined, that, being much hurried to complete a small affair I had in hand, I abruptly called to Bartleby. In my haste and natural expectancy of instant compliance, I sat with my head bent over the original on my desk, and my right hand sideways, and somewhat nervously extended with the copy, so that, immediately upon emerging from his retreat, Bartleby might snatch it and proceed to business without the least delay.

In this very attitude did I sit when I called to him, rapidly stating what it was I wanted him to do—namely, to examine a small paper with me. Imagine my surprise, nay, my consternation, when, without moving from his privacy, Bartleby, in a singularly mild, firm voice, replied, "I would prefer not to."

I sat awhile in perfect silence, rallying my stunned faculties. Immediately it occurred to me that my ears had deceived me, or Bartleby had entirely misunderstood my meaning. I repeated my request in the clearest tone I could assume; but in quite as clear a one came the previous reply, "I would prefer not to."

"Prefer not to," echoed I, rising in high excitement, and crossing the room with a stride. "What do you mean? Are you moonstruck? I want you to help me compare this sheet here—take it," and I thrust it towards him.

"I would prefer not to," said he.

I looked at him steadfastly. His face was leanly composed; his gray eye dimly calm. Not a wrinkle of agitation rippled him. Had there been the least uneasiness, anger, impatience or impertinence in his manner; in other words, had there been any thing ordinarily human about him, doubtless I should have violently dismissed him from the premises. But as it was, I should have as soon thought of turning my pale plaster-of-paris bust of Cicero out of doors. I stood gazing at him awhile, as he went on with his own writing, and then reseated myself at my desk. This is very strange, thought I. What had one best do? But my business hurried me. I concluded to forget the matter for the present, reserving it for my future leisure. So calling Nippers from the other room, the paper was speedily examined.

A few days after this, Bartleby concluded four lengthy documents, being quadruplicates of a week's testimony taken before me in my High Court of Chancery. It became necessary to examine them. It was an important suit, and great accuracy was imperative. Having all things arranged, I called Turkey, Nippers, and Ginger Nut, from the next room, meaning to place the four copies in the hands of my four clerks, while I should read from the original. Accordingly, Turkey, Nippers, and Ginger Nut had taken their seats in a row, each with his document in his hand, when I called to Bartleby to join this interesting group.

"Bartleby! quick, I am waiting."

I heard a slow scrape of his chair legs on the uncarpeted floor, and soon he appeared standing at the entrance of his hermitage.

"What is wanted?" said he, mildly.

"The copies, the copies," said I, hurriedly. "We are going to examine them. There"—and I held towards him the fourth quadruplicate.

"I would prefer not to," he said, and gently disappeared behind the screen.

For a few moments I was turned into a pillar of salt, standing at the head of my seated column of clerks. Recovering myself, I advanced towards the screen, and demanded the reason for such extraordinary conduct.

"*Why* do you refuse?"

"I would prefer not to."

With any other man I should have flown outright into a dreadful passion, scorned all further words, and thrust him ignominiously from my presence. But there was something about Bartleby that not only strangely disarmed me, but, in a wonderful manner, touched and disconcerted me. I began to reason with him.

"These are your own copies we are about to examine. It is labor saving to you, because one examination will answer for your four papers. It is common usage. Every copyist is bound to help examine his copy. Is it not so? Will you not speak? Answer!"

"I prefer not to," he replied in a flutelike tone. It seemed to me that, while I had been addressing him, he carefully revolved every statement that I made; fully comprehended the meaning; could not gainsay the irresistible conclusion; but, at the same time, some paramount consideration prevailed with him to reply as he did.

"You are decided, then, not to comply with my request—a request made according to common usage and common sense?"

He briefly gave me to understand, that on that point my judgment was sound. Yes: his decision was irreversible.

It is not seldom the case that, when a man is browbeaten in some unprecedented and violently unreasonable way; he begins to stagger in his own plainest faith. He begins, as it were, vaguely to surmise that, wonderful as it may be, all the justice and all the reason is on the other side. Accordingly, if any disinterested persons are present, he turns to them for some reinforcement of his own faltering mind.

"Turkey," said I, "what do you think of this? Am I not right?"

"With submission, sir," said Turkey, in his blandest tone, "I think that you are."

"Nippers," said I, "what do *you* think of it?"

"I think I should kick him out of the office."

(The reader, of nice perceptions, will here perceive that, it being morning, Turkey's answer is couched in polite and tranquil terms, but Nippers replies in ill-tempered ones. Or, to repeat a previous sentence, Nippers's ugly mood was on duty, and Turkey's off.)

"Ginger Nut," said I, willing to enlist the smallest suffrage in my behalf, "what do *you* think of it?"

"I think, sir, he's a little *luny*," replied Ginger Nut, with a grin.

"You hear what they say," said I, turning towards the screen, "come forth and do your duty."

But he vouchsafed no reply. I pondered a moment in sore perplexity. But once more business hurried me. I determined again to postpone the consideration of this dilemma to my future leisure. With a little trouble we made out to examine the papers without Bartleby, though at every page or two Turkey deferentially dropped his opinion, that this proceeding was quite out of the common; while Nippers, twitching in his chair with a dyspeptic nervousness, ground out, between his set teeth, occasional hissing maledictions against the stubborn oaf behind the screen. And for his (Nippers's) part, this was the first and the last time he would do another man's business without pay.

Meanwhile Bartleby sat in his hermitage, oblivious to everything but his own peculiar business there.

Some days passed, the scrivener being employed upon another lengthy work. His late remarkable conduct led me to regard his ways narrowly. I observed that he never went to dinner; indeed, that he never went anywhere. As yet I had never, of my personal knowledge, known him to be outside of my office. He was a perpetual sentry in the corner. At about eleven o'clock though, in the morning, I noticed that Ginger Nut would advance toward the opening in Bartleby's screen, as if silently beckoned thither by a gesture invisible to me where I sat. The boy would then leave the office, jingling a few pence, and reappear with a handful of ginger-nuts, which he delivered in the hermitage, receiving two of the cakes for his trouble.

He lives, then, on ginger-nuts, thought I; never eats a dinner, properly speaking; he must be a vegetarian, then; but no; he never eats even vegetables, he eats nothing but ginger-nuts. My mind then ran on in reveries concerning the probable effects upon the human constitution of living entirely on ginger-nuts. Ginger-nuts are so called, because they contain ginger as one of their peculiar constituents, and the final flavoring one. Now, what was ginger? A hot, spicy thing. Was Bartleby hot and spicy? Not at all. Ginger, then, had no effect upon Bartleby. Probably he preferred it should have none.

Nothing so aggravates an earnest person as a passive resistance. If the individual so resisted be of a not inhumane temper, and the resisting one perfectly harmless in his passivity, then, in the better moods of the former, he will endeavor charitably to construe to his imagination what proves impossible to be solved by his judgment. Even so, for the most part, I regarded Bartleby and his ways. Poor fellow! thought I, he means no mischief; it is plain he intends no insolence; his aspect sufficiently evinces that his eccentricities are involuntary. He is useful to me. I can get along with him. If I turn him away, the chances are he will fall in with some less-indulgent employer, and then he will be rudely treated, and perhaps driven forth miserably to starve. Yes. Here I can cheaply purchase a delicious self-approval. To befriend Bartleby; to humor him in his strange willfulness, will cost me little or nothing, while I lay up in my soul what will eventually prove a sweet morsel for my conscience. But this mood was not invariable with me. The passiveness of Bartleby sometimes irritated me. I felt strangely goaded on to encounter him in new opposition—to elicit some angry spark from him answerable to my own. But, indeed, I might as well have essayed to strike fire with my knuckles against a bit of Windsor soap. But one afternoon the evil impulse in me mastered me, and the following little scene ensued:

"Bartleby," said I, "when those papers are all copied, I will compare them with you."

"I would prefer not to."

"How? Surely you do not mean to persist in that mulish vagary?" No answer.

I threw open the folding-doors near by, and, turning upon Turkey and Nippers, exclaimed:

"Bartleby a second time says, he won't examine his papers. What do you think of it, Turkey?"

It was afternoon, be it remembered. Turkey sat glowing like a brass boiler; his bald head steaming; his hands reeling among his blotted papers.

"Think of it?" roared Turkey; "I think I'll just step behind his screen, and black his eyes for him!"

So saying, Turkey rose to his feet and threw his arms into a pugilistic position. He was hurrying away to make good his promise, when I detained him, alarmed at the effect of incautiously rousing Turkey's combativeness after dinner.

"Sit down, Turkey," said I, "and hear what Nippers has to say. What do you think of it, Nippers? Would I not be justified in immediately dismissing Bartleby?"

"Excuse me, that is for you to decide, sir. I think his conduct quite unusual, and, indeed, unjust, as regards Turkey and myself. But it may only be a passing whim."

"Ah," exclaimed I, "you have strangely changed your mind, then—you speak very gently of him now."

"All beer," cried Turkey; "gentleness is effects of beer—Nippers and I dined together to-day. You see how gentle *I* am, sir. Shall I go and black his eyes?"

"You refer to Bartleby, I suppose. No, not to-day, Turkey," I replied; "pray, put up your fists."

I closed the doors, and again advanced towards Bartleby. I felt additional incentives tempting me to my fate. I burned to be rebelled against again. I remembered that Bartleby never left the office.

"Bartleby," said I, "Ginger Nut is away; just step around to the Post Office, won't you? (it was but a three minutes' walk), and see if there is anything for me."

"I would prefer not to."

"You *will* not?"

"I *prefer* not."

I staggered to my desk, and sat there in a deep study. My blind inveteracy returned. Was there any other thing in which I could procure myself to be ignominiously repulsed by this lean, penniless wight?—my hired clerk? What added thing is there, perfectly reasonable, that he will be sure to refuse to do?

"Bartleby!"

No answer.

"Bartleby," in a louder tone.

No answer.

"Bartleby," I roared.

Like a very ghost, agreeably to the laws of magical invocation, at the third summons, he appeared at the entrance of his hermitage.

"Go to the next room, and tell Nippers to come to me."

"I prefer not to," he respectfully and slowly said, and mildly disappeared.

"Very good, Bartleby," said I, in a quiet sort of serenely-severe self-possessed tone, intimating the unalterable purpose of some terrible retribution very close at hand. At the moment I half intended something of the kind. But upon the whole, as it was drawing towards my dinner-hour, I thought it best to put on my hat and walk home for the day, suffering much from perplexity and distress of mind.

Shall I acknowledge it? The conclusion of this whole business was, that it soon became a fixed fact of my chambers, that a pale young scrivener, by the name of Bartleby, had a desk there; that he copied for me at the usual rate of four cents a folio (one hundred words); but he was permanently exempt from examining the work done by him, that duty being transferred to Turkey and Nippers, out of compliment, doubtless, to their superior acuteness; moreover, said Bartleby was never, on any account, to be dispatched on the most trivial errand of any sort; and that even if entreated to take upon him such a matter, it was generally understood that he would "prefer not to"—in other words, that he would refuse point-blank.

As days passed on, I became considerably reconciled to Bartleby. His steadiness, his freedom from all dissipation, his incessant industry (except when he chose to throw himself into a standing revery behind his screen), his great stillness, his unalterableness of demeanor under all circumstances, made him a valuable acquisition. One prime thing was this—*he was always there*—first in the morn-

ing, continually through the day, and the last at night. I had a singular confidence in his honesty. I felt my most precious papers perfectly safe in his hands. Sometimes, to be sure, I could not, for the
very soul of me, avoid falling into sudden spasmodic passions with
him. For it was exceeding difficult to bear in mind all the time those
strange peculiarities, privileges, and unheard of exemptions, forming the tacit stipulations on Bartleby's part under which he remained in my office. Now and then, in the eagerness of dispatching
pressing business, I would inadvertently summon Bartleby, in a
short, rapid tone, to put his finger, say, on the incipient tie of a bit of
red tape with which I was about compressing some papers. Of course,
from behind the screen the usual answer, "I prefer not to," was sure
to come; and then, how could a human creature, with the common
infirmities of our nature, refrain from bitterly exclaiming upon such
perverseness—such unreasonableness. However, every added repulse
of this sort which I received only tended to lessen the probability of
my repeating the inadvertence.

Here it must be said, that according to the custom of most legal
gentlemen occupying chambers in densely-populated law buildings,
there were several keys to my door. One was kept by a woman resid-
ing in the attic, which person weekly scrubbed and daily swept and
dusted my apartments. Another was kept by Turkey for convenience
sake. The third I sometimes carried in my own pocket. The fourth
I knew not who had.

Now, one Sunday morning I happened to go to Trinity Church,
to hear a celebrated preacher, and finding myself rather early on the
ground I thought I would walk around to my chambers for a while.
Luckily I had my key with me; but upon applying it to the lock, I
found it resisted by something inserted from the inside. Quite surprised, I called out; when to my consternation a key was turned from
within; and thrusting his lean visage at me, and holding the door
ajar, the apparition of Bartleby appeared, in his shirt sleeves, and
otherwise in a strangely tattered deshabille, saying quietly that he
was sorry, but he was deeply engaged just then, and—preferred not
admitting me at present. In a brief word or two, he moreover added,
that perhaps I had better walk around the block two or three times,
and by that time he would probably have concluded his affairs.

Now, the utterly unsurmised appearance of Bartleby, tenanting
my law-chambers of a Sunday morning, with his cadaverously gentle-

manly *nonchalance,* yet withal firm and self-possessed, had such a strange effect upon me, that incontinently I slunk away from my own door, and did as desired. But not without sundry twinges of impotent rebellion against the mild effrontery of this unaccountable scrivener. Indeed, it was his wonderful mildness chiefly, which not only disarmed me, but unmanned me as it were. For I consider that one, for the time, is a sort of unmanned when he tranquilly permits his hired clerk to dictate to him, and order him away from his own premises. Furthermore, I was full of uneasiness as to what Bartleby could possibly be doing in my office in his shirt sleeves, and in an otherwise dismantled condition of a Sunday morning. Was anything amiss going on? Nay, that was out of the question. It was not to be thought of for a moment that Bartleby was an immoral person. But what could he be doing there?—copying? Nay again, whatever might be his eccentricities, Bartleby was an eminently decorous person. He would be the last man to sit down to his desk in any state approaching to nudity. Besides, it was Sunday; and there was something about Bartleby that forbade the supposition that he would by any secular occupation violate the proprieties of the day.

Nevertheless, my mind was not pacified; and full of a restless curiosity, at last I returned to the door. Without hindrance I inserted my key, opened it, and entered. Bartleby was not to be seen. I looked round anxiously, peeped behind his screen; but it was very plain that he was gone. Upon more closely examining the place, I surmised that for an indefinite period Bartleby must have ate, dressed, and slept in my office, and that, too without plate, mirror, or bed. The cushioned seat of a ricketty old sofa in one corner bore the faint impress of a lean, reclining form. Rolled away under his desk, I found a blanket; under the empty grate, a blacking box and brush; on a chair, a tin basin, with soap and a ragged towel; in a newspaper a few crumbs of ginger-nuts and a morsel of cheese. Yes, thought I, it is evident enough that Bartleby has been making his home here, keeping bachelor's hall all by himself. Immediately then the thought came sweeping across me, what miserable friendlessness and loneliness are here revealed! His poverty is great; but his solitude, how horrible! Think of it. Of a Sunday, Wall Street is deserted as Petra; and every night of every day it is an emptiness. This building, too, which of week-days hums with industry and life, at nightfall echoes with sheer vacancy, and all through Sunday is forlorn. And here

Bartleby makes his home; sole spectator of a solitude which he has seen all populous—a sort of innocent and transformed Marius brooding among the ruins of Carthage!

For the first time in my life a feeling of over-powering stinging melancholy seized me. Before, I had never experienced aught but a not unpleasing sadness. The bond of a common humanity now drew me irresistibly to gloom. A fraternal melancholy! For both I and Bartleby were sons of Adam. I remembered the bright silks and sparkling faces I had seen that day, in gala trim, swan-like sailing down the Mississippi of Broadway; and I contrasted them with the pallid copyist, and thought to myself, Ah, happiness courts the light, so we deem the world is gay; but misery hides aloof, so we deem that misery there is none. These sad fancyings—chimeras, doubtless, of a sick and silly brain—led on to other and more special thoughts, concerning the eccentricities of Bartleby. Presentiments of strange discoveries hovered round me. The scrivener's pale form appeared to me laid out, among uncaring strangers, in its shivering winding sheet.

Suddenly I was attracted by Bartleby's closed desk, the key in open sight left in the lock.

I mean no mischief, seek the gratification of no heartless curiosity, thought I; besides, the desk is mine, and its contents, too, so I will make bold to look within. Everything was methodically arranged, the papers smoothly placed. The pigeon holes were deep, and removing the files of documents, I groped into their recesses. Presently I felt something there, and dragged it out. It was an old bandanna handkerchief, heavy and knotted. I opened it, and saw it was a savings' bank.

I now recalled all the quiet mysteries which I had noted in the man. I remembered that he never spoke but to answer; that, though at intervals he had considerable time to himself, yet I had never seen him reading—no, not even a newspaper; that for long periods he would stand looking out, at his pale window behind the screen, upon the dead brick wall; I was quite sure he never visited any refectory or eating house; while his pale face clearly indicated that he never drank beer like Turkey, or tea and coffee even, like other men; that he never went anywhere in particular that I could learn; never went out for a walk, unless, indeed, that was the case at present; that he had declined telling who he was, or whence he came, or whether he had any relatives in the world; that though so thin and pale, he never complained of ill health. And more than all, I remembered a certain unconscious air of pallid—how shall I call it?—of pallid haughtiness, say, or rather an austere reserve about him, which had positively awed me into my tame compliance with his eccentricities, when I had feared to ask him to do the slightest incidental thing for me, even though I might know, from his long-continued motionlessness, that behind his screen he must be standing in one of those dead-wall reveries of his.

Revolving all these things, and coupling them with the recently discovered fact, that he made my office his constant abiding place and home, and not forgetful of his morbid moodiness; revolving all these things, a prudential feeling began to steal over me. My first emotions had been those of pure melancholy and sincerest pity; but just in proportion as the forlornness of Bartleby grew and grew to my imagination, did that same melancholy merge into fear, that pity into repulsion. So true it is, and so terrible, too, that up to a certain point the thought or sight of misery enlists our best affections; but, in certain special cases, beyond that point it does not. They err who would assert that invariably this is owing to the inherent selfishness of the human heart. It rather proceeds from a certain hopelessness of remedying excessive and organic ill. To a sensitive being, pity is not seldom pain. And when at last it is perceived that such pity cannot lead to effectual succor, common sense bids the soul be rid of it. What I saw that morning persuaded me that the scrivener was the victim of innate and incurable disorder. I might give alms to his body; but his body did not pain him; it was his soul that suffered, and his soul I could not reach.

I did not accomplish the purpose of going to Trinity Church that morning. Somehow, the things I had seen disqualified me for the time from church-going. I walked homeward, thinking what I would do with Bartleby. Finally, I resolved upon this—I would put certain calm questions to him the next morning, touching his history, etc., and if he declined to answer them openly and unreservedly (and I supposed he would prefer not), then to give him a twenty dollar bill over and above whatever I might owe him, and tell him his services were no longer required; but that if in any other way I could assist him, I would be happy to do so, especially if he desired to return to his native place, wherever that might be, I would willingly help to defray the expenses. Moreover, if, after reaching home, he found himself at any time in want of aid, a letter from him would be sure of a reply.

The next morning came.

"Bartleby," said I, gently calling to him behind his screen.

No reply.

"Bartleby," said I, in a still gentler tone, "come here; I am not going to ask you to do anything you would prefer not to do—I simply wish to speak to you."

Upon this he noiselessly slid into view.

"Will you tell me, Bartleby, where you were born?"

"I would prefer not to."

"Will you tell me *anything* about yourself?"

"I would prefer not to."

"But what reasonable objection can you have to speak to me? I feel friendly towards you."

He did not look at me while I spoke, but kept his glance fixed upon my bust of Cicero, which, as I then sat, was directly behind me, some six inches above my head.

"What is your answer, Bartleby," said I, after waiting a considerable time for a reply, during which his countenance remained immovable, only there was the faintest conceivable tremor of the white attenuated mouth.

"At present I prefer to give no answer," he said, and retired into his hermitage.

It was rather weak in me I confess, but his manner, on this occasion, nettled me. Not only did there seem to lurk in it a certain calm disdain, but his perverseness seemed ungrateful, considering the undeniable good usage and indulgence he had received from me.

Again I sat ruminating what I should do. Mortified as I was at his behavior, and resolved as I had been to dismiss him when I entered my office, nevertheless I strangely felt something superstitious knocking at my heart, and forbidding me to carry out my purpose, and denouncing me for a villain if I dared to breathe one bitter word against this forlornest of mankind. At last, familiarly drawing my chair behind his screen, I sat down and said: "Bartleby, never mind, then, about revealing your history; but let me entreat you, as a friend, to comply as far as may be with the usages of this office. Say now, you will help to examine papers to-morrow or next day: in short, say now, that in a day or two you will begin to be a little reasonable:—say so, Bartleby."

"At present I would prefer not to be a little reasonable," was his mildly cadaverous reply.

Just then the folding-doors opened, and Nippers approached. He seemed suffering from an unusually bad night's rest, induced by severer indigestion than common. He overheard those final words of Bartleby.

"*Prefer not*, eh?" gritted Nippers—"I'd *prefer* him, if I were you, sir," addressing me—"I'd *prefer* him; I'd give him preferences, the stubborn mule! What is it, sir, pray, that he *prefers* not to do now?"

Bartleby moved not a limb.

"Mr. Nippers," said I, "I'd prefer that you would withdraw for the present."

Somehow, of late, I had got into the way of involuntarily using this word "prefer" upon all sorts of not exactly suitable occasions. And I trembled to think that my contact with the scrivener had already and seriously affected me in a mental way. And what further and deeper aberration might it not yet produce? This apprehension had not been without efficacy in determining me to summary measures.

As Nippers, looking very sour and sulky, was departing, Turkey blandly and deferentially approached.

"With submission, sir," said he, "yesterday I was thinking about Bartleby here, and I think that if he would but prefer to take a quart of good ale every day, it would do much towards mending him, and enabling him to assist in examining his papers."

"So you have got the word, too," said I, slightly excited.

"With submission, what word, sir," asked Turkey, respectfully crowding himself into the contracted space behind the screen, and by so doing, making me jostle the scrivener. "What word, sir?"

"I would prefer to be left alone here," said Bartleby, as if offended at being mobbed in his privacy.

"*That's* the word, Turkey," said I—"*that's* it."

"Oh, *prefer?* oh yes—queer word. I never use it myself. But, sir, as I was saying, if he would but prefer—"

"Turkey," interrupted I, "you will please withdraw."

"Oh, certainly, sir, if you prefer that I should."

As he opened the folding-door to retire, Nippers at his desk caught a glimpse of me, and asked whether I would prefer to have a certain paper copied on blue paper or white. He did not in the least roguishly accent the word prefer. It was plain that it involuntarily rolled from his tongue. I thought to myself, surely I must get rid of a demented man, who already has in some degree turned the tongues, if not the heads of myself and clerks. But I thought it prudent not to break the dismission at once.

The next day I noticed that Bartleby did nothing but stand at his window in his dead-wall revery. Upon asking him why he did not write, he said that he had decided upon doing no more writing.

"Why, how now? what next?" exclaimed I, "do no more writing?"

"No more."

"And what is the reason?"

"Do you not see the reason for yourself," he indifferently replied.

I looked steadfastly at him, and perceived that his eyes looked dull and glazed. Instantly it occurred to me, that his unexampled diligence in copying by his dim window for the first few weeks of his stay with me might have temporarily impaired his vision.

I was touched. I said something in condolence with him. I hinted that of course he did wisely in abstaining from writing for a while; and urged him to embrace that opportunity of taking wholesome exercise in the open air. This, however, he did not do. A few days after this, my other clerks being absent, and being in a great hurry to dispatch certain letters by the mail, I thought that, having nothing else earthly to do, Bartleby would surely be less inflexible than usual, and carry these letters to the post-office. But he blankly declined. So, much to my inconvenience, I went myself.

Still added days went by. Whether Bartleby's eyes improved or not, I could not say. To all appearance, I thought they did. But when I asked him if they did, he vouchsafed no answer. At all events, he would do no copying. At last, in reply to my urgings, he informed me that he had permanently given up copying.

"What!" exclaimed I; "suppose your eyes should get entirely well—better than ever before—would you not copy then?"

"I have given up copying," he answered, and slid aside.

He remained as ever, a fixture in my chamber. Nay—if that were possible—he became still more of a fixture than before. What was to be done? He would do nothing in the office; why should he stay there? In plain fact, he had now become a millstone to me, not only useless as a necklace, but afflictive to bear. Yet I was sorry for him. I speak less than truth when I say that, on his own account, he occasioned me uneasiness. If he would but have named a single relative or friend, I would instantly have written, and urged their taking the poor fellow away to some convenient retreat. But he seemed alone, absolutely alone in the universe. A bit of wreck in the mid Atlantic. At length, necessities connected with my business tyrannized over all other considerations. Decently as I could, I told Bartleby that in six days time he must unconditionally leave the office. I warned him to take measures, in the interval, for procuring some other abode. I offered to assist him in this endeavor, if he himself would but take the first step towards a removal. "And when you finally quit me, Bartleby," added I, "I shall see that you go not away entirely unprovided. Six days from this hour, remember."

At the expiration of that period, I peeped behind the screen, and lo! Bartleby was there.

I buttoned up my coat, balanced myself; advanced slowly towards him, touched his shoulder, and said, "The time has come; you must quit this place; I am sorry for you; here is money; but you must go."

"I would prefer not," he replied, with his back still towards me.

"You *must*."

He remained silent.

Now I had an unbounded confidence in this man's common honesty. He had frequently restored to me sixpences and shillings carelessly dropped upon the floor, for I am apt to be very reckless in such shirt-button affairs. The proceeding, then, which followed will not be deemed extraordinary.

"Bartleby," said I, "I owe you twelve dollars on account; here are thirty-two; the odd twenty are yours— Will you take it?" and I handed the bills towards him.

But he made no motion.

"I will leave them here, then," putting them under a weight on the table. Then taking my hat and cane and going to the door, I tranquilly turned and added—"After you have removed your things from these offices, Bartleby, you will of course lock the door—since every one is now gone for the day but you—and if you please, slip your key underneath the mat, so that I may have it in the morning.

I shall not see you again; so good-by to you. If, hereafter, in your new place of abode, I can be of any service to you, do not fail to advise me by letter. Good-by, Bartleby, and fare you well."

But he answered not a word; like the last column of some ruined temple, he remained standing mute and solitary in the middle of the otherwise deserted room.

As I walked home in a pensive mood, my vanity got the better of my pity. I could not but highly plume myself on my masterly management in getting rid of Bartleby. Masterly I call it, and such it must appear to any dispassionate thinker. The beauty of my procedure seemed to consist in its perfect quietness. There was no vulgar bullying, no bravado of any sort, no choleric hectoring, and striding to and fro across the apartment, jerking out vehement commands for Bartleby to bundle himself off with his beggarly traps. Nothing of the kind. Without loudly bidding Bartleby depart—as an inferior genius might have done—I *assumed* the ground that depart he must; and upon that assumption built all I had to say. The more I thought over my procedure, the more I was charmed with it. Nevertheless, next morning, upon awakening, I had my doubts—I had somehow slept off the fumes of vanity. One of the coolest and wisest hours a man has, is just after he awakes in the morning. My procedure seemed as sagacious as ever—but only in theory. How it would prove in practice—there was the rub. It was truly a beautiful thought to have assumed Bartleby's departure; but, after all, that assumption was simply my own, and none of Bartleby's. The great point was, not whether I had assumed that he would quit me, but whether he would prefer so to do. He was more a man of preferences than assumptions.

After breakfast, I walked down town, arguing the probabilities *pro* and *con*. One moment I thought it would prove a miserable failure, and Bartleby would be found all alive at my office as usual; the next moment it seemed certain that I should find his chair empty. And so I kept veering about. At the corner of Broadway and Canal Street, I saw quite an excited group of people standing in earnest conversation.

"I'll take odds he doesn't," said a voice as I passed.

"Doesn't go?—done!" said I, "put up your money."

I was instinctively putting my hand in my pocket to produce my own, when I remembered that this was an election day. The words

I had overheard bore no reference to Bartleby, but to the success or non-success of some candidate for the mayoralty. In my intent frame of mind, I had, as it were, imagined that all Broadway shared in my excitement, and were debating the same question with me. I passed on, very thankful that the uproar of the street screened my momentary absent-mindedness.

As I had intended, I was earlier than usual at my office door. I stood listening for a moment. All was still. He must be gone. I tried the knob. The door was locked. Yes, my procedure had worked to a charm; he indeed must be vanished. Yet a certain melancholy mixed with this: I was almost sorry for my brilliant success. I was fumbling under the door mat for the key, which Bartleby was to have left there for me, when accidentally my knee knocked against a panel, producing a summoning sound, and in response a voice came to me from within—"Not yet; I am occupied."

It was Bartleby.

I was thunderstruck. For an instant I stood like the man who, pipe in mouth, was killed one cloudless afternoon long ago in Virginia, by summer lightning; at his own warm open window he was killed, and remained leaning out there upon the dreamy afternoon, till some one touched him, when he fell.

"Not gone!" I murmured at last. But again obeying that wondrous ascendancy which the inscrutable scrivener had over me, and from which ascendancy, for all my chafing, I could not completely escape, I slowly went down stairs and out into the street, and while walking round the block, considered what I should next do in this unheard-of perplexity. Turn the man out by an actual thrusting I could not; to drive him away by calling him hard names would not do; calling in the police was an unpleasant idea; and yet, permit him to enjoy his cadaverous triumph over me—this, too, I could not think of. What was to be done? or, if nothing could be done, was there anything further that I could *assume* in the matter? Yes, as before I had prospectively assumed that Bartleby would depart, so now I might retrospectively assume that departed he was. In the legitimate carrying out of this assumption, I might enter my office in a great hurry, and pretending not to see Bartleby at all, walk straight against him as if he were air. Such a proceeding would in a singular degree have the appearance of a home-thrust. It was hardly possible that Bartleby could withstand such an application of the doc-

trine of assumptions. But upon second thoughts the success of the
plan seemed rather dubious. I resolved to argue the matter over with
him again.

"Bartleby," said I, entering the office, with a quietly severe expression, "I am seriously displeased. I am pained, Bartleby. I had
thought better of you. I had imagined you of such a gentlemanly
organization, that in any delicate dilemma a slight hint would
suffice—in short, an assumption. But it appears I am deceived. Why,"
I added, unaffectedly starting, "you have not even touched that
money yet," pointing to it, just where I had left it the evening previous.

He answered nothing.

"Will you, or will you not, quit me?" I now demanded in a sudden passion, advancing close to him.

"I would prefer *not* to quit you," he replied, gently emphasizing the *not*.

"What earthly right have you to stay here? Do you pay any
rent? Do you pay my taxes? Or is this property yours?"

He answered nothing.

"Are you ready to go on and write now? Are your eyes recovered?
Could you copy a small paper for me this morning? or help examine
a few lines? or step round to the post-office? In a word, will you do
anything at all, to give a coloring to your refusal to depart the
premises?"

He silently retired into his hermitage.

I was now in such a state of nervous resentment that I thought
it but prudent to check myself at present from further demonstra-
tions. Bartleby and I were alone. I remembered the tragedy of the
unfortunate Adams and the still more unfortunate Colt in the solitary
office of the latter; and how poor Colt, being dreadfully incensed by
Adams, and imprudently permitting himself to get wildy excited,
was at unawares hurried into his fatal act—an act which certainly no
man could possibly deplore more than the actor himself. Often it
had occurred to me in my ponderings upon the subject, that had that
altercation taken place in the public street, or at a private residence,
it would not have terminated as it did. It was the circumstance of
being alone in a solitary office, up stairs, of a building entirely unhal-
lowed by humanizing domestic associations—an uncarpeted office,
doubtless, of a dusty, haggard sort of appearance—this it must have

been, which greatly helped to enhance the irritable desperation of the hapless Colt.

But when this old Adam of resentment rose in me and tempted me concerning Bartleby, I grappled him and threw him. How? Why, simply by recalling the divine injunction: "A new commandment give I unto you, that ye love one another." Yes, this it was that saved me. Aside from higher considerations, charity often operates as a vastly wise and prudent principle—a great safeguard to its possessor. Men have committed murder for jealousy's sake, and anger's sake, and hatred's sake, and selfishness' sake, and spiritual pride's sake; but no man, that ever I heard of, ever committed a diabolical murder for sweet charity's sake. Mere self-interest, then, if no better motive can be enlisted, should, especially with high-tempered men, prompt all beings to charity and philanthropy. At any rate, upon the occasion in question, I strove to drown my exasperated feelings towards the scrivener by benevolently construing his conduct. Poor fellow, poor fellow! thought I, he don't mean anything; and besides, he has seen hard times, and ought to be indulged.

I endeavored, also, immediately to occupy myself, and at the same time to comfort my despondency. I tried to fancy, that in the course of the morning, at such time as might prove agreeable to him, Bartleby, of his own free accord, would emerge from his hermitage and take up some decided line of march in the direction of the door. But no. Half-past twelve o'clock came; Turkey began to glow in the face, overturn his inkstand, and become generally obstreperous; Nippers abated down into quietude and courtesy; Ginger Nut munched his noon apple; and Bartleby remained standing at his window in one of his profoundest dead-wall reveries. Will it be credited? Ought I to acknowledge it? That afternoon I left the office without saying one further word to him.

Some days now passed, during which, at leisure intervals I looked a little into "Edwards on the Will," and "Priestly on Necessity." Under the circumstances, those books induced a salutary feeling. Gradually I slid into the persuasion that these troubles of mine, touching the scrivener, had been all predestinated from eternity, and Bartleby was billeted upon me for some mysterious purpose of an allwise Providence, which it was not for a mere mortal like me to fathom. Yes, Bartleby, stay there behind your screen, thought I; I shall persecute you no more; you are harmless and noiseless as any of these old chairs; in short, I never feel so private as when I know you are here. At last I see it, I feel it; I penetrate to the predestinated purpose of my life. I am content. Others may have loftier parts to enact; but my mission in this world, Bartleby, is to furnish you with office-room for such period as you may see fit to remain.

I believe that this wise and blessed frame of mind would have continued with me, had it not been for the unsolicited and uncharitable remarks obtruded upon me by my professional friends who visited the rooms. But thus it often is, that the constant friction of illiberal minds wears out at last the best resolves of the more generous. Though to be sure, when I reflected upon it, it was not strange that people entering my office should be struck by the peculiar aspect of the unaccountable Bartleby, and so be tempted to throw out some sinister observations concerning him. Sometimes an attorney, having business with me, and calling at my office, and finding no one but the scrivener there, would undertake to obtain some sort of precise information from him touching my whereabouts; but without heeding his idle talk, Bartleby would remain standing immovable in the middle of the room. So after contemplating him in that position for a time, the attorney would depart, no wiser than he came.

Also, when a reference was going on, and the room full of lawyers and witnesses, and business driving fast, some deeply-occupied legal gentleman present, seeing Bartleby wholly unemployed, would request him to run round to his (the legal gentleman's) office and fetch some papers for him. Thereupon, Bartleby would tranquilly decline, and yet remain idle as before. Then the lawyer would give a great stare, and turn to me. And what could I say? At last I was made aware that all through the circle of my professional acquaintance, a whisper of wonder was running round, having reference to the strange creature I kept at my office. This worried me very much. And as the idea came upon me of his possibly turning out a long-lived man, and keep occupying my chambers, and denying my authority; and perplexing my visitors; and scandalizing my professional reputation; and casting a general gloom over the premises; keeping soul and body together to the last upon his savings (for doubtless he spent but half a dime a day), and in the end perhaps outlive me, and claim possession of my office by right of his perpetual occupancy: as all these dark anticipations crowded upon me more and more, and my friends continually intruded their relentless remarks upon the apparition in my room; a great change was wrought in me.

I resolved to gather all my faculties together, and forever rid me of this intolerable incubus.

Ere revolving any complicated project, however, adapted to this end, I first simply suggested to Bartleby the propriety of his permanent departure. In a calm and serious tone, I commended the idea to his careful and mature consideration. But, having taken three days to meditate upon it, he apprised me, that his original determination remained the same; in short, that he still preferred to abide with me.

What shall I do? I now said to myself, buttoning up my coat to the last button. What shall I do? what ought I to do? what does conscience say I *should* do with this man, or, rather, ghost. Rid myself of him, I must; go, he shall. But how? You will not thrust him, the poor, pale, passive mortal—you will not thrust such a helpless creature out of your door? you will not dishonor yourself by such cruelty? No, I will not, I cannot do that. Rather would I let him live and die here, and then mason up his remains in the wall. What, then, will you do? For all your coaxing, he will not budge. Bribes he leaves under your own paper-weight on your table; in short, it is quite plain that he prefers to cling to you.

Then something severe, something unusual must be done. What! surely you will not have him collared by a constable, and commit his innocent pallor to the common jail? And upon what ground could you procure such a thing to be done?—a vagrant, is he? What! he a vagrant, a wanderer, who refuses to budge? It is because he will *not* be a vagrant, then, that you seek to count him *as* a vagrant. That is too absurd. No visible means of support: there I have him. Wrong again: for indubitably he *does* support himself, and that is the only unanswerable proof that any man can show of his possessing the means so to do. No more, then. Since he will not quit me, I must quit him. I will change my offices; I will move elsewhere, and give him fair notice, that if I find him on my new premises I will then proceed against him as a common trespasser.

Acting accordingly, next day I thus addressed him: "I find these chambers too far from the City Hall; the air is unwholesome. In a word, I propose to remove my offices next week, and shall no longer require your services. I tell you this now, in order that you may seek another place."

He made no reply, and nothing more was said.

On the appointed day I engaged carts and men, proceeded to my chambers, and, having but little furniture, everything was re-

moved in a few hours. Throughout, the scrivener remained standing behind the screen, which I directed to be removed the last thing.
It was withdrawn; and, being folded up like a huge folio, left him the
motionless occupant of a naked room. I stood in the entry watching
him a moment, while something from within me upbraided me.

I re-entered, with my hand in my pocket—and—and my heart
in my mouth.

"Good-by, Bartleby; I am going—good-by, and God some way
bless you; and take that," slipping something in his hand. But it
dropped upon the floor, and then—strange to say—I tore myself
from him whom I had so longed to be rid of.

Established in my new quarters, for a day or two I kept the door
locked, and started at every footfall in the passages. When I returned
to my rooms, after any little absence, I would pause at the threshold
for an instant, and attentively listen, ere applying my key. But these
fears were needless. Bartleby never came nigh me.

I thought all was going well, when a perturbed-looking stranger
visited me, inquiring whether I was the person who had recently occupied rooms at No. — Wall Street.

Full of forebodings, I replied that I was.

"Then, sir," said the stranger, who proved a lawyer, "you are
responsible for the man you left there. He refuses to do any copying;
he refuses to do anything; he says he prefers not to; and he refuses
to quit the premises."

"I am very sorry, sir," said I, with assumed tranquillity, but an
inward tremor, "but, really, the man you allude to is nothing to me
—he is no relation or apprentice of mine, that you should hold me
responsible for him."

"In mercy's name, who is he?"

"I certainly cannot inform you. I know nothing about him. Formerly I employed him as a copyist; but he has done nothing for me
now for some time past."

"I shall settle him, then—good morning, sir."

Several days passed, and I heard nothing more; and, though I
often felt a charitable prompting to call at the place and see poor
Bartleby, yet a certain squeamishness, of I know not what, withheld
me.

All is over with him, by this time, thought I, at last,
when, through another week, no further intelligence reached me.

But, coming to my room the day after, I found several persons waiting at my door in a high state of nervous excitement.

"That's the man—here he comes," cried the foremost one, whom I recognized as the lawyer who had previously called upon me alone.

"You must take him away, sir, at once," cried a portly person among them, advancing upon me, and whom I knew to be the landlord of No. — Wall Street. "These gentlemen, my tenants, cannot stand it any longer; Mr. B——," pointing to the lawyer, "has turned him out of his room, and he now persists in haunting the building generally, sitting upon the banisters of the stairs by day, and sleeping in the entry by night. Everybody is concerned; clients are leaving the offices; some fears are entertained of a mob; something you must do, and that without delay."

Aghast at this torrent, I fell back before it, and would fain have locked myself in my new quarters. In vain I persisted that Bartleby was nothing to me—no more than to any one else. In vain—I was the last person known to have anything to do with him, and they held me to the terrible account. Fearful, then, of being exposed in the papers (as one person present obscurely threatened), I considered the matter, and, at length, said, that if the lawyer would give me a confidential interview with the scrivener, in his (the lawyer's) own room, I would, that afternoon, strive my best to rid them of the nuisance they complained of.

Going up stairs to my old haunt, there was Bartleby silently sitting upon the banister at the landing.

"What are you doing here, Bartleby?" said I.

"Sitting upon the banister," he mildly replied.

I motioned him into the lawyer's room, who then left us.

"Bartleby," said I, "are you aware that you are the cause of great tribulation to me, by persisting in occupying the entry after being dismissed from the office?"

No answer.

"Now one of two things must take place. Either you must do something, or something must be done to you. Now what sort of business would you like to engage in? Would you like to re-engage in copying for some one?"

"No; I would prefer not to make any change."

"Would you like a clerkship in a dry-goods store?"

"There is too much confinement about that. No, I would not like a clerkship; but I am not particular."

"Too much confinement," I cried, "why you keep yourself confined all the time!"

"I would prefer not to take a clerkship," he rejoined, as if to settle that little item at once.

"How would a bar-tender's business suit you? There is no trying of the eye-sight in that."

"I would not like it at all; though, as I said before, I am not particular."

His unwonted wordiness inspirited me. I returned to the charge.

"Well, then, would you like to travel through the country collecting bills for the merchants? That would improve your health."

"No, I would prefer to be doing something else."

"How, then, would going as a companion to Europe, to entertain some young gentleman with your conversation—how would that suit you?"

"Not at all. It does not strike me that there is anything definite about that. I like to be stationary. But I am not particular."

"Stationary you shall be, then," I cried, now losing all patience, and, for the first time in all my exasperating connection with him, fairly flying into a passion. "If you do not go away from these premises before night, I shall feel bound—indeed, I *am* bound—to—to—to quit the premises myself!" I rather absurdly concluded, knowing not with what possible threat to try to frighten his immobility into compliance. Despairing of all further efforts, I was precipitately leaving him, when a final thought occurred to me—one which had not been wholly unindulged before.

"Bartleby," said I, in the kindest tone I could assume under such exciting circumstances, "will you go home with me now—not to my office, but my dwelling—and remain there till we can conclude upon some convenient arrangement for you at our leisure? Come, let us start now, right away."

"No: at present I would prefer not to make any change at all."

I answered nothing; but, effectually dodging every one by the suddenness and rapidity of my flight, rushed from the building, ran up Wall Street towards Broadway, and, jumping into the first omnibus, was soon removed from pursuit. As soon as tranquillity returned, I distinctly perceived that I had now done all that I possibly could, both in respect to the demands of the landlord and his ten-

ants, and with regard to my own desire and sense of duty, to benefit
Bartleby, and shield him from rude persecution. I now strove to be
entirely care-free and quiescent; and my conscience justified me in
the attempt; though, indeed, it was not so successful as I could have
wished. So fearful was I of being again hunted out by the incensed
landlord and his exasperated tenants, that, surrendering my business
to Nippers, for a few days, I drove about the upper part of the town
and through the suburbs, in my rockaway; crossed over to Jersey City
and Hoboken, and paid fugitive visits to Manhattanville and Astoria.
In fact, I almost lived in my rockaway for the time.

When again I entered my office, lo, a note from the landlord lay
upon the desk. I opened it with trembling hands. It informed me
that the writer had sent to the police, and had Bartleby removed to
the Tombs as a vagrant. Moreover, since I knew more about him
than any one else, he wished me to appear at that place, and make a
suitable statement of the facts. These tidings had a conflicting effect
upon me. At first I was indignant; but, at last, almost approved. The
landlord's energetic, summary disposition, had led him to adopt a
procedure which I do not think I would have decided upon myself;
and yet, as a last resort, under such peculiar circumstances, it seemed
the only plan.

As I afterwards learned, the poor scrivener, when told that he
must be conducted to the Tombs, offered not the slightest obstacle,
but, in his pale, unmoving way, silently acquiesced.

Some of the compassionate and curious bystanders joined the
party; and headed by one of the constables arm in arm with Bartleby,
the silent procession filed its way through all the noise, and heat, and
joy of the roaring thoroughfares at noon.

The same day I received the note, I went to the Tombs, or, to
speak more properly, the Halls of Justice. Seeking the right officer,
I stated the purpose of my call, and was informed that the individual
I described was, indeed, within. I then assured the functionary that
Bartleby was a perfectly honest man, and greatly to be compassion-
ated, however unaccountably eccentric. I narrated all I knew, and
closed by suggesting the idea of letting him remain in as indulgent
confinement as possible, till something less harsh might be done—
though, indeed, I hardly knew what. At all events, if nothing else
could be decided upon, the alms-house must receive him. I then
begged to have an interview.

Being under no disgraceful charge, and quite serene and harm-

less in all his ways, they had permitted him freely to wander about
the prison, and, especially, in the inclosed grass-platted yards thereof.
And so I found him there, standing all alone in the quietest of the
yards, his face towards a high wall, while all around, from the narrow slits of the jail windows, I thought I saw peering out upon
him the eyes of murderers and thieves.

"Bartleby!"

"I know you," he said, without looking round—"and I want
nothing to say to you."

"It was not I that brought you here, Bartleby," said I, keenly
pained at his implied suspicion. "And to you, this should not be so
vile a place. Nothing reproachful attaches to you by being here.
And see, it is not so sad a place as one might think. Look, there is the
sky, and here is the grass."

"I know where I am," he replied, but would say nothing more,
and so I left him.

As I entered the corridor again, a broad meat-like man, in an
apron, accosted me, and, jerking his thumb over his shoulder, said—
"Is that your friend?"

"Yes."

"Does he want to starve? If he does, let him live on the prison
fare, that's all."

"Who are you?" asked I, not knowing what to make of such an
unofficially speaking person in such a place.

"I am the grub-man. Such gentlemen as have friends here, hire
me to provide them with something good to eat."

"Is this so?" said I, turning to the turnkey.

He said it was.

"Well, then," said I, slipping some silver into the grub-man's
hands (for so they called him), "I want you to give particular attention to my friend there; let him have the best dinner you can get.
And you must be as polite to him as possible."

"Introduce me, will you?" said the grub-man, looking at me
with an expression which seemed to say he was all impatience for
an opportunity to give a specimen of his breeding.

Thinking it would prove of benefit to the scrivener, I
acquiesced; and, asking the grub-man his name, went up with him
to Bartleby.

"Bartleby, this is a friend; you will find him very useful to you."

"Your sarvant, sir, your sarvant," said the grub-man, making a low salutation behind his apron. "Hope you find it pleasant here, sir; nice grounds—cool apartments—hope you'll stay with us some-time—try to make it agreeable. What will you have for dinner to-day?"

"I prefer not to dine to-day," said Bartleby, turning away. "It would disagree with me; I am unused to dinners." So saying, he slowly moved to the other side of the inclosure, and took up a position fronting the dead-wall.

"How's this?" said the grub-man, addressing me with a stare of astonishment. "He's odd, ain't he?"

"I think he is a little deranged," said I, sadly.

"Deranged? deranged is it? Well, now, upon my word, I thought that friend of yourn was a gentleman forger; they are always pale and genteel-like, them forgers. I can't help pity 'em—can't help it, sir. Did you know Monroe Edwards?" he added, touchingly, and paused. Then, laying his hand piteously on my shoulder, sighed, "he died of consumption at Sing-Sing. So you weren't acquainted with Monroe?"

"No, I was never socially acquainted with any forgers. But I cannot stop longer. Look to my friend yonder. You will not lose by it. I will see you again."

Some few days after this, I again obtained admission to the Tombs, and went through the corridors in quest of Bartleby; but without finding him.

"I saw him coming from his cell not long ago," said a turnkey, "may be he's gone to loiter in the yards."

So I went in that direction.

"Are you looking for the silent man?" said another turnkey, passing me. "Yonder he lies—sleeping in the yard there. 'Tis not twenty minutes since I saw him lie down."

The yard was entirely quiet. It was not accessible to the common prisoners. The surrounding walls, of amazing thickness, kept off all sounds behind them. The Egyptian character of the masonry weighed upon me with its gloom. But a soft imprisoned turf grew under foot. The heart of the eternal pyramids, it seemed, wherein, by some strange magic, through the clefts, grass-seed, dropped by birds, had sprung.

Strangely huddled at the base of the wall, his knees drawn up, and lying on his side, his head touching the cold stones, I saw the wasted Bartleby. But nothing stirred. I paused; then went close up

to him; stooped over, and saw that his dim eyes were open; otherwise he seemed profoundly sleeping. Something prompted me to
touch him. I felt his hand, when a tingling shiver ran up my arm
and down my spine to my feet.

The round face of the grub-man peered upon me now. "His
dinner is ready. Won't he dine to-day, either? Or does he live without dining?"

"Lives without dining," said I, and closed the eyes.

"Eh!—He's asleep, ain't he?"

"With kings and counselors," murmured I.

*   *   *   *   *   *   *   *

There would seem little need for proceeding further in this history. Imagination will readily supply the meagre recital of poor
Bartleby's interment. But, ere parting with the reader, let me say,
that if this little narrative has sufficiently interested him, to awaken
curiosity as to who Bartleby was, and what manner of life he led
prior to the present narrator's making his acquaintance, I can only
reply, that in such curiosity I fully share, but am wholly unable to
gratify it. Yet here I hardly know whether I should divulge one little
item of rumor, which came to my ear a few months after the scrivener's decease. Upon what basis it rested, I could never ascertain; and
hence, how true it is I cannot now tell. But, inasmuch as this vague
report has not been without a certain suggestive interest to me, however sad, it may prove the same with some others; and so I will briefly
mention it. The report was this: that Bartleby had been a subordinate clerk in the Dead Letter Office at Washington, from which he
had been suddenly removed by a change in the administration. When
I think over this rumor, hardly can I express the emotions which
seize me. Dead letters! does it not sound like dead men? Conceive
a man by nature and misfortune prone to a pallid hopelessness, can
any business seem more fitted to heighten it than that of continually
handling these dead letters, and assorting them for the flames? For
by the cart-load they are annually burned. Sometimes from out
the folded paper the pale clerk takes a ring—the finger it was meant
for, perhaps, moulders in the grave; a bank-note sent in swiftest
charity—he whom it would relieve, nor eats nor hungers any more;
pardon for those who died despairing; hope for those who died un-
hoping; good tidings for those who died stifled by unrelieved ca-
lamities. On errands of life, these letters speed to death.

Ah, Bartleby! Ah, humanity!

QUESTIONS

1. Although the subject of this story is Bartleby, a scrivener in a law office, the lawyer-narrator does not immediately introduce us to him. Instead, he tells us at length about himself, his work, his office, and his assistants. What is the purpose of this lengthy introductory section? Suggest some reasons why it is important for us to know a good deal about the narrator as well as about Bartleby.

2. Examine carefully the physical lay-out of the law office. What relationship do you see between the location of the windows and the story's subtitle, "A Story of Wall Street"? One of these windows, of course, plays a major role in the drama of Bartleby. Does this fact suggest that the subtitle has a thematic significance beyond its literal meaning (i.e., that the setting of the story is in the financial district of New York)?

3. Examine the other characters closely, especially Turkey and Nippers. What are they like? Two matters, among others, deserve close attention: the fact that Turkey and Nippers occupy the same room, and that they are perfect complements. As one grows calm and efficient, the other becomes explosive and undependable; as one desires fervently to be a good scrivener, the other wishes heartily to be rid of the position altogether. Why does Melville insist upon this balance between the two men? When Bartleby is hired, he is placed in a corner in his employer's section of the office, rather than in the outer room with Turkey and Nippers. What does this arrangement suggest? Analyze the narrator's feelings toward Bartleby, as well as the relationship which develops between the two.

4. Bartleby's progress is toward increasing isolation and withdrawal. At first he does his work behind a screen, facing a wall. Then he refuses to work at all. Trace the stages in his withdrawal, to his death by starvation in the Tombs. What is the meaning of the one piece of information relating to Bartleby which comes from an outside source?

5. Analyze the pattern which Melville has imposed upon events. How does the story's structure clarify its theme?

FYODOR DOSTOEVSKY

(1821-1881)

Dostoevsky is universally considered one of the greatest of all Russian writers. His life was as dramatic as the novels for which he is best known. Condemned to death for seditious activities, Dostoevsky was told as he stood before the Czar's firing squad that the sentence was simply a cruel joke, and that he actually was to be sent to Siberia. After his release from prison and the completion of required military duty, he succumbed to a passion for gambling, losing both his money and his health in the process. His epilepsy became severe; the terrible nature of that illness may be seen in the Christ-like hero of his novel, THE IDIOT. His works reveal his intense moral and ethical concerns and are often constructed around a profound conflict between the forces of good and evil. His character portraits are magnificent, his action dramatic, his interest in psychology morbid. The atmosphere of his works is characteristically gloomy. Dostoevsky's best known novels are CRIME AND PUNISHMENT and THE BROTHERS KARAMAZOV. "The Crocodile" shows us a little known side of Dostoevsky: the ability to see life in a satirical, absurd, and wildly comic light.

The Crocodile

AN EXTRAORDINARY INCIDENT

A true story of how a gentleman of a certain age and of respectable appearance was swallowed alive by the crocodile in the Arcade, and of the consequences that followed.

> Ohé Lambert! Où est Lambert?
> As tu vu Lambert?

I

On the thirteenth of January of this present year, 1865, at half-past twelve in the day, Elena Ivanovna, the wife of my cultured friend Ivan Matveitch, who is a colleague in the same department, and may be said to be a distant relation of mine, too, expressed the desire to see the crocodile now on view at a fixed charge in the Arcade. As Ivan Matveitch had already in his pocket his ticket for a tour abroad (not so much for the sake of his health as for the improvement of his mind), and was consequently free from his official duties and had nothing whatever to do that morning, he offered no objection to his wife's irresistible fancy, but was positively aflame with curiosity himself.

"A capital idea!" he said, with the utmost satisfaction. "We'll have a look at the crocodile! On the eve of visiting Europe it is as well to acquaint ourselves on the spot with its indigenous inhabitants." And with these words, taking his wife's arm, he set off with her at once for the Arcade. I joined them, as I usually do, being an intimate friend of the family. I have never seen Ivan Matveitch in a more agreeable frame of mind than he was on that memorable morning—how true it is that we know not beforehand the fate that awaits us! On entering the Arcade he was at once full of admiration for the splendours of the building, and when we reached the shop in

"The Crocodile" Reprinted with permission of The Macmillan Company and William Heinemann Ltd. from *An Honest Thief and Other Stories* by Fyodor Dostoevsky, translated by Constance Garnett. First published in Great Britain.

which the monster lately arrived in Petersburg was being exhibited, he volunteered to pay the quarter-rouble for me to the crocodile owner—a thing which had never happened before. Walking into a little room, we observed that besides the crocodile there were in it parrots of the species known as cockatoo, and also a group of monkeys in a special case in a recess. Near the entrance, along the left wall stood a big tin tank that looked like a bath covered with a thin iron grating, filled with water to the depth of two inches. In this shallow pool was kept a huge crocodile, which lay like a log absolutely motionless and apparently deprived of all its faculties by our damp climate, so inhospitable to foreign visitors. This monster at first aroused no special interest in any one of us.

"So this is the crocodile!" said Elena Ivanovna, with a pathetic cadence of regret. "Why, I thought it was . . . something different."

Most probably she thought it was made of diamonds. The owner of the crocodile, a German, came out and looked at us with an air of extraordinary pride.

"He has a right to be," Ivan Matveitch whispered to me, "he knows he is the only man in Russia exhibiting a crocodile."

This quite nonsensical observation I ascribe also to the extremely good-humoured mood which had overtaken Ivan Matveitch, who was on other occasions of rather envious disposition.

"I fancy your crocodile is not alive," said Elena Ivanovna, piqued by the irresponsive stolidity of the proprietor, and addressing him with a charming smile in order to soften his churlishness—a manœuvre so typically feminine.

"Oh, no, madam," the latter replied in broken Russian; and instantly moving the grating half off the tank, he poked the monster's head with a stick.

Then the treacherous monster, to show that it was alive, faintly stirred its paws and tail, raised its snout and emitted something like a prolonged snuffle.

"Come, don't be cross, Karlchen," said the German caressingly, gratified in his vanity.

"How horrid that crocodile is! I am really frightened," Elena Ivanovna twittered, still more coquettishly. "I know I shall dream of him now."

"But he won't bite you if you do dream of him," the German retorted gallantly, and was the first to laugh at his own jest, but none of us responded.

"Come, Semyon Semyonitch," said Elena Ivanovna, addressing me exclusively, "let us go and look at the monkeys. I am awfully fond of monkeys; they are such darlings . . . and the crocodile is horrid."

"Oh, don't be afraid, my dear!" Ivan Matveitch called after us, gallantly displaying his manly courage to his wife. "This drowsy denison of the realms of the Pharaohs will do us no harm." And he remained by the tank. What is more, he took his glove and began tickling the crocodile's nose with it, wishing, as he said afterwards, to induce him to snort. The proprietor showed his politeness to a lady by following Elena Ivanovna to the case of monkeys.

So everything was going well, and nothing could have been foreseen. Elena Ivanovna was quite skittish in her raptures over the monkeys, and seemed completely taken up with them. With shrieks of delight she was continually turning to me, as though determined not to notice the proprietor, and kept gushing with laughter at the resemblance she detected between these monkeys and her intimate friends and acquaintances. I, too, was amused, for the resemblance was unmistakable. The German did not know whether to laugh or not, and so at last was reduced to frowning. And it was at that moment that a terrible, I may say unnatural, scream set the room vibrating. Not knowing what to think, for the first moment I stood still, numb with horror, but noticing that Elena Ivanovna was screaming too, I quickly turned round—and what did I behold! I saw— oh, heavens!—I saw the luckless Ivan Matveitch in the terrible jaws of the crocodile, held by them round the waist, lifted horizontally in the air and desperately kicking. Then—one moment, and no trace remained of him. But I must describe it in detail, for I stood all the while motionless, and had time to watch the whole process taking place before me with an attention and interest such as I never remember to have felt before. "What," I thought at that critical moment, "what if all that had happened to me instead of to Ivan Matveitch—how unpleasant it would have been for me!"

But to return to my story. The crocodile began by turning the unhappy Ivan Matveitch in his terrible jaws so that he could swallow his legs first; then bringing up Ivan Matveitch, who kept trying to jump out and clutching at the sides of the tank, sucked him down again as far as his waist. Then bringing him up again, gulped him down, and so again and again. In this way Ivan Matveitch was visibly disappearing before our eyes. At last, with a final gulp, the crocodile swallowed my cultured friend entirely, this time leaving no trace of him. From the outside of the crocodile we could see the protuberances of Ivan Matveitch's figure as he passed down the inside of the monster. I was on the point of screaming again when destiny played another treacherous trick upon us. The crocodile made a tremendous effort, probably oppressed by the magnitude of the object he had swallowed, once more opened his terrible jaws, and with a final hiccup he suddenly let the head of Ivan Matveitch pop out for a second, with an expression of despair on his face. In that brief instant the spectacles dropped off his nose to the bottom of the tank. It seemed as though that despairing countenance had only popped out to cast one last look on the objects around it, to take its last farewell of all earthly pleasures. But it had not time to carry out its intention; the crocodile made another effort, gave a gulp and instantly it vanished again—this time for ever. This appearance and disappearance of a still living human head was so horrible, but at the same—either from its rapidity and unexpectedness or from the dropping of the spectacles—there was something so comic about it that I suddenly quite unexpectedly exploded with laughter. But pulling myself together and realising that to laugh at such a moment was not the thing for an old family friend, I turned at once to Elena Ivanovna and said with a sympathetic air:

"Now it's all over with our friend Ivan Matveitch!"

I cannot even attempt to describe how violent was the agitation of Elena Ivanovna during the whole process. After the first scream she seemed rooted to the spot, and stared at the catastrophe with apparent indifference, though her eyes looked as though they were starting out of her head; then she suddenly went off into a heart-rending wail, but I seized her hands. At this instant the proprietor, too, who had at first been also petrified by horror, suddenly clasped his hands and cried, gazing upwards:

"Oh, my crocodile! *Oh mein allerliebster Karlchen! Mutter, Mutter, Mutter!*"

A door at the rear of the room opened at this cry, and the *Mutter,* a rosy-cheeked, elderly but dishevelled woman in a cap made her appearance, and rushed with a shriek to her German.

A perfect Bedlam followed. Elena Ivanovna kept shrieking out the same phrase, as though in a frenzy, "Flay him! flay him!" apparently entreating them—probably in a moment of oblivion—to flay somebody for something. The proprietor and *Mutter* took no notice whatever of either of us; they were both bellowing like calves over the crocodile.

"He did for himself! He will burst himself at once, for he did swallow a *ganz* official!" cried the proprietor.

"*Unser Karlchen, unser allerliebster Karlchen wird sterben,*" howled his wife.

"We are bereaved and without bread!" chimed in the proprietor.

"Flay him! flay him! flay him!" clamoured Elena Ivanovna, clutching at the German's coat.

"He did tease the crocodile. For what did your man tease the crocodile?" cried the German, pulling away from her. "You will if *Karlchen wird* burst, therefore pay, *das war mein Sohn, das war mein einziger Sohn.*"

I must own I was intensely indignant at the sight of such egoism in the German and the cold-heartedness of his dishevelled *Mutter;* at the same time Elena Ivanovna's reiterated shriek of "Flay him! flay him!" troubled me even more and absorbed at last my whole attention, positively alarming me. I may as well say straight off that I entirely misunderstood this strange exclamation: it seemed to me that Elena Ivanovna had for the moment taken leave of her senses, but nevertheless wishing to avenge the loss of her beloved Ivan Matveitch, was demanding by way of compensation that the crocodile should be severely thrashed, while she was meaning something quite different. Looking round at the door, not without embarrassment, I began to entreat Elena Ivanovna to calm herself, and above all not to use the shocking word "flay." For such a reactionary desire here, in the midst of the Arcade and of the most cultured society, not two paces from the hall where at this very minute Mr. Lavrov was perhaps delivering a public lecture, was not only impossible but unthinkable, and might at any moment bring upon us the hisses of culture and the caricatures of Mr. Stepanov. To my horror I was immediately proved to be correct in my alarmed suspicions: the curtain that divided the crocodile room from the little entry where the quarter-roubles were taken suddenly parted, and in the opening there appeared a figure with moustaches and beard, carrying a cap, with the upper part of its body bent a long way forward, though the feet were scrupulously held beyond the threshold of the crocodile room in order to avoid the necessity of paying the entrance money.

"Such a reactionary desire, madam," said the stranger, trying to avoid falling over in our direction and to remain standing outside the room, "does no credit to your development, and is conditioned by lack of phosphorus in your brain. You will be promptly held up to shame in the *Chronicle of Progress* and in our satirical prints . . ."

But he could not complete his remarks; the proprietor coming to himself, and seeing with horror that a man was talking in the crocodile room without having paid entrance money, rushed furiously at the progressive stranger and turned him out with a punch from each fist. For a moment both vanished from our sight behind a curtain, and only then I grasped that the whole uproar was about nothing. Elena Ivanovna turned out quite innocent; she had, as I have mentioned already, no idea whatever of subjecting the crocodile to a degrading corporal punishment, and had simply expressed the desire that he should be opened and her husband released from his interior.

"What! You wish that my crocodile be perished!" the proprietor yelled, running in again. "No! let your husband be perished first, before my crocodile! . . . *Mein Vater* showed crocodile, *mein Grossvater* showed crocodile, *mein Sohn* will show crocodile, and I will show crocodile! All will show crocodile! I am known to *ganz Europa*, and you are not known to *ganz Europa*, and you must pay me a *strafe!*"

"*Ja, ja*," put in the vindictive German woman, "we shall not let you go. *Strafe*, since Karlchen is burst!"

"And, indeed, it's useless to flay the creature," I added calmly, anxious to get Elena Ivanovna away home as quickly as possible, "as our dear Ivan Matveitch is by now probably soaring somewhere in the empyrean."

"My dear"—we suddenly heard, to our intense amazement, the voice of Ivan Matveitch—"my dear, my advice is to apply direct to the superintendent's office, as without the assistance of the police the German will never be made to see reason."

These words, uttered with firmness and aplomb, and expressing an exceptional presence of mind, for the first minute so astounded us that we could not believe our ears. But, of course, we ran at once to the crocodile's tank, and with equal reverence and incredulity listened to the unhappy captive. His voice was muffled, thin and even squeaky, as though it came from a considerable distance. It reminded one of a jocose person who, covering his mouth with a pillow, shouts from an adjoining room, trying to mimic the sound of two peasants calling to one another in a deserted plain or across a wide ravine—a performance to which I once had the pleasure of listening in a friend's house at Christmas.

"Ivan Matveitch, my dear, and so you are alive!" faltered Elena Ivanovna.

"Alive and well," answered Ivan Matveitch, "and, thanks to the Almighty, swallowed without any damage whatever. I am only uneasy as to the view my superiors may take of the incident; for after getting a permit to go abroad I've got into a crocodile, which seems anything but clever."

"But, my dear, don't trouble your head about being clever; first of all we must somehow excavate you from where you are," Elena Ivanovna interrupted.

"Excavate!" cried the proprietor. "I will not let my crocodile be excavated. Now the *publicum* will come many more, and I will *fünfzig* kopecks ask and Karlchen will cease to burst."

"*Gott sei dank!*" put in his wife.

"They are right," Ivan Matveitch observed tranquilly; "the principles of economics before everything."

"My dear! I will fly at once to the authorities and lodge a complaint, for I feel that we cannot settle this mess by ourselves."

"I think so too," observed Ivan Matveitch; "but in our age of industrial crisis it is not easy to rip open the belly of a crocodile without economic compensation, and meanwhile the inevitable question presents itself: What will the German take for his crocodile? And with it another: How will it be paid? For, as you know, I have no means . . ."

"Perhaps out of your salary . . ." I observed timidly, but the proprietor interrupted me at once.

"I will not the crocodile sell; I will for three thousand the crocodile sell! I will for four thousand the crocodile sell! Now the *publicum* will come very many. I will for five thousand the crocodile sell!"

In fact he gave himself insufferable airs. Covetousness and a revolting greed gleamed joyfully in his eyes.

"I am going!" I cried indignantly.

"And I! I too! I shall go to Andrey Osipitch himself. I will soften him with my tears," whined Elena Ivanovna.

"Don't do that, my dear," Ivan Matveitch hastened to interpose. He had long been jealous of Andrey Osipitch on his wife's account, and he knew she would enjoy going to weep before a gentleman of refinement, for tears suited her. "And I don't advise you to do so either, my friend," he added, addressing me. "It's no good plunging headlong in that slap-dash way; there's no knowing what it may lead to. You had much better go to-day to Timofey Semyonitch, as though to pay an ordinary visit; he is an old-fashioned and by no means brilliant man, but he is trustworthy, and what matters most of all, he is straightforward. Give him my greetings and describe the circumstances of the case. And since I owe him seven roubles over our last game of cards, take the opportunity to pay him the money; that will soften the stern old man. In any case his advice may serve as a guide for us. And meanwhile take Elena Ivanovna home. . . . Calm yourself, my dear," he continued, addressing her. "I am weary of these outcries and feminine squabblings, and should like a nap. It's soft and warm in here, though I have hardly had time to look round in this unexpected haven."

"Look round! Why, is it light in there?" cried Elena Ivanovna in a tone of relief.

"I am surrounded by impenetrable night," answered the poor captive, "but I can feel and, so to speak, have a look round with my hands. . . . Good-bye; set your mind at rest and don't deny yourself recreation and diversion. Till to-morrow! And you, Semyon Semyonitch, come to me in the evening, and as you are absent-minded and may forget it, tie a knot in your handkerchief."

I confess I was glad to get away, for I was overtired and somewhat bored. Hastening to offer my arm to the disconsolate Elena Ivanovna, whose charms were only enhanced by her agitation, I hurriedly led her out of the crocodile room.

"The charge will be another quarter-rouble in the evening," the proprietor called after us.

"Oh, dear, how greedy they are!" said Elena Ivanovna, looking at herself in every mirror on the walls of the Arcade, and evidently aware that she was looking prettier than usual.

"The principles of economics," I answered with some emotion, proud that passers-by should see the lady on my arm.

"The principles of economics," she drawled in a touching little voice. "I did not in the least understand what Ivan Matveitch said about those horrid economics just now."

"I will explain to you," I answered, and began at once telling her of the beneficial effects of the introduction of foreign capital into our country, upon which I had read an article in the *Petersburg News* and the *Voice* that morning.

"How strange it is," she interrupted, after listening for some time. "But do leave off, you horrid man. What nonsense you are talking. . . . Tell me, do I look purple?"

"You look perfect, and not purple!" I observed, seizing the opportunity to pay her a compliment.

"Naughty man!" she said complacently. "Poor Ivan Matveitch," she added a minute later, putting her little head on one side coquettishly. "I am really sorry for him. Oh, dear!" she cried suddenly, "how is he going to have his dinner . . . and . . . and . . . what will he do . . . if he wants anything?"

"An unforeseen question," I answered, perplexed in my turn. To tell the truth, it had not entered my head, so much more practical are women than we men in the solution of the problems of daily life!

"Poor dear! how could he have got into such a mess . . . nothing to amuse him, and in the dark. . . . How vexing it is that I have no photograph of him. . . . And so now I am a sort of widow," she added, with a seductive smile, evidently interested in her new position. "Hm! . . . I am sorry for him, though."

It was, in short, the expression of the very natural and intelligible grief of a young and interesting wife for the loss of her husband. I took her home at last, soothed her, and after dining with her and drinking a cup of aromatic coffee, set off at six o'clock to Timofey Semyonitch, calculating that at that hour all married people of settled habits would be sitting or lying down at home.

Having written this first chapter in a style appropriate to the incident recorded, I intend to proceed in a language more natural though less elevated, and I beg to forewarn the reader of the fact.

II

The venerable Timofey Semyonitch met me rather nervously, as though somewhat embarrassed. He led me to his tiny study and shut the door carefully, "that the children may not hinder us," he added with evident uneasiness. There he made me sit down on a chair by the writing-table, sat down himself in an easy chair, wrapped round him the skirts of his old wadded dressing-gown, and assumed an official and even severe air, in readiness for anything, though he was not my chief nor Ivan Matveitch's, and had hitherto been reckoned as a colleague and even a friend.

"First of all," he said, "take note that I am not a person in authority, but just such a subordinate official as you and Ivan Matveitch. . . . I have nothing to do with it, and do not intend to mix myself up in the affair."

I was surprised to find that he apparently knew all about it already. In spite of that I told him the whole story over in detail. I spoke with positive excitement, for I was at that moment fulfilling the obligations of a true friend. He listened without special surprise, but with evident signs of suspicion.

"Only fancy," he said, "I always believed that this would be sure to happen to him."

"Why, Timofey Semyonitch? It is a very unusual incident in itself . . ."

"I admit it. But Ivan Matveitch's whole career in the service was leading up to this end. He was flighty—conceited indeed. It was always 'progress' and ideas of all sorts, and this is what progress brings people to!"

"But this is a most unusual incident and cannot possibly serve as a general rule for all progressives."

"Yes, indeed it can. You see, it's the effect of over-education, I assure you. For over-education leads people to poke their noses into all sorts of places, especially where they are not invited. Though perhaps you know best," he added, as though offended. "I am an old man and not of much education. I began as a soldier's son, and this year has been the jubilee of my service."

"Oh, no, Timofey Semyonitch, not at all. On the contrary, Ivan Matveitch is eager for your advice; he is eager for your guidance. He implores it, so to say, with tears."

"So to say, with tears! Hm! Those are crocodile's tears and one cannot quite believe in them. Tell me, what possessed him to want to go abroad? And how could he afford to go? Why, he has no private means!"

"He had saved the money from his last bonus," I answered plaintively. "He only wanted to go for three months—to Switzerland . . . to the land of William Tell."

"William Tell? Hm!"

"He wanted to meet the spring at Naples, to see the museums, the customs, the animals . . ."

"Hm! The animals! I think it was simply from pride. What animals? Animals, indeed! Haven't we animals enough? We have museums, menageries, camels. There are bears quite close to Petersburg! And here he's got inside a crocodile himself . . ."

"Oh, come, Timofey Semyonitch! The man is in trouble, the man appeals to you as to a friend, as to an older relation, craves for advice—and you reproach him. Have pity at least on the unfortunate Elena Ivanovna!"

"You are speaking of his wife? A charming little lady," said Timofey Semyonitch, visibly softening and taking a pinch of snuff with relish. "Particularly prepossessing. And so plump, and always putting her pretty little head on one side. . . . Very agreeable. Andrey Osipitch was speaking of her only the other day."

"Speaking of her?"

"Yes, and in very flattering terms. Such a bust, he said, such eyes, such hair. . . . A sugar-plum, he said, not a lady—and then he laughed. He is still a young man, of course." Timofey Semyonitch blew his nose with a loud noise. "And yet, young though he is, what a career he is making for himself."

"That's quite a different thing, Timofey Semyonitch."

"Of course, of course."

"Well, what do you say then, Timofey Semyonitch?"

"Why, what can I do?"

"Give advice, guidance, as a man of experience, a relative! What are we to do? What steps are we to take? Go to the authorities and . . ."

"To the authorities? Certainly not," Timofey Semyonitch replied hurriedly. "If you ask my advice, you had better, above all, hush the matter up and act, so to speak, as a private person. It is a suspicious incident, quite unheard of. Unheard of, above all; there is no precedent for it, and it is far from creditable. . . . And so discretion above all. . . . Let him lie there a bit. We must wait and see . . ."

"But how can we wait and see, Timofey Semyonitch? What if he is stifled there?"

"Why should he be? I think you told me that he made himself fairly comfortable there?"

I told him the whole story over again. Timofey Semyonitch pondered.

"Hm!" he said, twisting his snuff-box in his hands. "To my

mind it's really a good thing he should lie there a bit, instead of going abroad. Let him reflect at his leisure. Of course he mustn't be stifled, and so he must take measures to preserve his health, avoiding a cough, for instance, and so on. . . . And as for the German, it's my personal opinion he is within his rights, and even more so than the other side, because it was the other party who got into *his* crocodile without asking permission, and not *he* who got into Ivan Matveitch's crocodile without asking permission, though, so far as I recollect, the latter has no crocodile. And a crocodile is private property, and so it is impossible to slit him open without compensation."

"For the saving of human life, Timofey Semyonitch."

"Oh, well, that's a matter for the police. You must go to them."

"But Ivan Matveitch may be needed in the department. He may be asked for."

"Ivan Matveitch needed? Ha-ha! Besides, he is on leave, so that we may ignore him—let him inspect the countries of Europe! It will be a different matter if he doesn't turn up when his leave is over. Then we shall ask for him and make inquiries."

"Three months! Timofey Semyonitch, for pity's sake!"

"It's his own fault. Nobody thrust him there. At this rate we should have to get a nurse to look after him at government expense, and that is not allowed for in the regulations. But the chief point is that the crocodile is private property, so that the principles of economics apply in this question. And the principles of economics are paramount. Only the other evening, at Luka Andreitch's, Ignaty Prokofyitch was saying so. Do you know Ignaty Prokofyitch? A capitalist, in a big way of business, and he speaks so fluently. 'We need industrial development,' he said; 'there is very little development among us. We must create it. We must create capital, so we must create a middle-class, the so-called bourgeoisie. And as we haven't capital we must attract it from abroad. We must, in the first place, give facilities to foreign companies to buy up lands in Russia as is done now abroad. The communal holding of land is poison, is ruin.' And, you know, he spoke with such heat; well, that's all right for him—a wealthy man, and not in the service. 'With the communal system,' he said, 'there will be no improvement in industrial development or agriculture. Foreign companies,' he said, 'must as far as possible buy up the whole of our land in big lots, and then split it up, split it up, split it up, in the smallest parts possible'—and do you know he pronounced the words 'split it up' with such determination

—'and then sell it as private property. Or rather, not sell it, but simply let it. When,' he said, 'all the land is in the hands of foreign companies they can fix any rent they like. And so the peasant will work three times as much for his daily bread and he can be turned out at pleasure. So that he will feel it, will be submissive and industrious, and will work three times as much for the same wages. But as it is, with the commune, what does he care? He knows he won't die of hunger, so he is lazy and drunken. And meanwhile money will be attracted into Russia, capital will be created and the bourgeoisie will spring up. The English political and literary paper, *The Times,* in an article the other day on our finances stated that the reason our financial position was so unsatisfactory was that we had no middle-class, no big fortunes, no accommodating proletariat.' Ignaty Prokofyitch speaks well. He is an orator. He wants to lay a report on the subject before the authorities, and then to get it published in the *News.* That's something very different from verses like Ivan Matveitch's . . ."

"But how about Ivan Matveitch?" I put in, after letting the old man babble on.

Timofey Semyonitch was sometimes fond of talking and showing that he was not behind the times, but knew all about things.

"How about Ivan Matveitch? Why, I am coming to that. Here we are, anxious to bring foreign capital into the country—and only consider: as soon as the capital of a foreigner, who has been attracted to Petersburg, has been doubled through Ivan Matveitch, instead of protecting the foreign capitalist, we are proposing to rip open the belly of his original capital—the crocodile. Is it consistent? To my mind, Ivan Matveitch, as the true son of his fatherland, ought to rejoice and to be proud that through him the value of a foreign crocodile has been doubled and possibly even trebled. That's just what is wanted to attract capital. If one man succeeds, mind you, another will come with a crocodile, and a third will bring two or three of them at once, and capital will grow up about them—there you have a bourgeoisie. It must be encouraged."

"Upon my word, Timofey Semyonitch!" I cried, "you are demanding almost supernatural self-sacrifice from poor Ivan Matveitch."

"I demand nothing and I beg you, before everything—as I have said already—to remember that I am not a person in authority and so cannot demand anything of any one. I am speaking as a son of the fatherland, that is, not as the *Son of the Fatherland,* but as a son of the fatherland. Again, what possessed him to get into the crocodile? A respectable man, a man of good grade in the service, lawfully married—and then to behave like that! Is it consistent?"

"But it was an accident."

"Who knows? And where is the money to compensate the owner to come from?"

"Perhaps out of his salary, Timofey Semyonitch?"

"Would that be enough?"

"No, it wouldn't, Timofey Semyonitch," I answered sadly. "The proprietor was at first alarmed that the crocodile would burst, but as soon as he was sure that it was all right, he began to bluster and was delighted to think that he could double the charge for entry."

"Treble and quadruple perhaps! The public will simply stampede the place now, and crocodile owners are smart people. Besides, it's not Lent yet, and people are keen on diversions, and so I say again, the great thing is that Ivan Matveitch should preserve his incognito, don't let him be in a hurry. Let everybody know, perhaps, that he is in the crocodile, but don't let them be officially informed of it. Ivan Matveitch is in particularly favourable circumstances for that, for he is reckoned to be abroad. It will be said he is in the crocodile, and we will refuse to believe it. That is how it can be managed. The great thing is that he should wait; and why should he be in a hurry?"

"Well, but if . . ."

"Don't worry, he has a good constitution . . ."

"Well, and afterwards, when he has waited?"

"Well, I won't conceal from you that the case is exceptional in the highest degree. One doesn't know what to think of it, and the worst of it is there is no precedent. If we had a precedent we might have something to go by. But as it is, what is one to say? It will certainly take time to settle it."

A happy thought flashed upon my mind.

"Cannot we arrange," I said, "that if he is destined to remain in the entrails of the monster and it is the will of Providence that he should remain alive, that he should send in a petition to be reckoned as still serving?"

"Hm! . . . Possibly as on leave and without salary . . ."

"But couldn't it be with salary?"

"On what grounds?"

"As sent on a special commission."

"What commission and where?"

"Why, into the entrails, the entrails of the crocodile. . . . So to speak, for exploration, for investigation of the facts on the spot. It would, of course, be a novelty, but that is progressive and would at the same time show zeal for enlightenment."

Timofey Semyonitch thought a little.

"To send a special official," he said at last, "to the inside of a crocodile to conduct a special inquiry is, in my personal opinion, an absurdity. It is not in the regulations. And what sort of special inquiry could there be there?"

"The scientific study of nature on the spot, in the living subject. The natural sciences are all the fashion nowadays, botany. . . . He could live there and report his observations. . . . For instance, concerning digestion or simply habits. For the sake of accumulating facts."

"You mean as statistics. Well, I am no great authority on that subject, indeed I am no philosopher at all. You say 'facts'—we are overwhelmed with facts as it is, and don't know what to do with them. Besides, statistics are a danger."

"In what way?"

"They are a danger. Moreover, you will admit he will report facts, so to speak, lying like a log. And, can one do one's official duties lying like a log? That would be another novelty and a dangerous one; and again, there is no precedent for it. If we had any sort of precedent for it, then, to my thinking, he might have been given the job."

"But no live crocodiles have been brought over hitherto, Timofey Semyonitch."

"Hm . . . yes," he reflected again. "Your objection is a just one, if you like, and might indeed serve as a ground for carrying the matter further; but consider again, that if with the arrival of living crocodiles government clerks begin to disappear, and then on the ground that they are warm and comfortable there, expect to receive the official sanction for their position, and then take their ease there . . . you must admit it would be a bad example. We should have every one trying to go the same way to get a salary for nothing."

"Do your best for him, Timofey Semyonitch. By the way, Ivan Matveitch asked me to give you seven roubles he had lost to you at cards."

"Ah, he lost that the other day at Nikifor Nikiforitch's. I remember. And how gay and amusing he was—and now!"

The old man was genuinely touched.

"Intercede for him, Timofey Semyonitch!"

"I will do my best. I will speak in my own name, as a private person, as though I were asking for information. And meanwhile, you find out indirectly, unofficially, how much would the proprietor consent to take for his crocodile?"

Timofey Semyonitch was visibly more friendly.

"Certainly," I answered. "And I will come back to you at once to report."

"And his wife . . . is she alone now? Is she depressed?"

"You should call on her, Timofey Semyonitch."

"I will. I thought of doing so before; it's a good opportunity. . . . And what on earth possessed him to go and look at the crocodile. Though, indeed, I should like to see it myself."

"Go and see the poor fellow, Timofey Semyonitch."

"I will. Of course, I don't want to raise his hopes by doing so. I shall go as a private person. . . . Well, good-bye, I am going to Nikifor Nikiforitch's again; shall you be there?"

"No, I am going to see the poor prisoner."

"Yes, now he is a prisoner! . . . Ah, that's what comes of thoughtlessness!"

I said good-bye to the old man. Ideas of all kinds were straying through my mind. A good-natured and most honest man, Timofey Semyonitch, yet, as I left him, I felt pleased at the thought that he had celebrated his fiftieth year of service, and that Timofey Semyonitchs are now a rarity among us. I flew at once, of course, to the Arcade to tell poor Ivan Matveitch all the news. And, indeed, I was moved by curiosity to know how he was getting on in the crocodile and how it was possible to live in a crocodile. And, indeed, was it possible to live in a crocodile at all? At times it really seemed to me as though it were all an outlandish, monstrous dream, especially as an outlandish monster was the chief figure in it.

III

And yet it was not a dream, but actual, indubitable fact. Should I be telling the story if it were not? But to continue.

It was late, about nine o'clock, before I reached the Arcade, and I had to go into the crocodile room by the back entrance, for the German had closed the shop earlier than usual that evening. Now in the seclusion of domesticity he was walking about in a greasy old frock-coat, but he seemed three times as pleased as he had been in the morning. It was evidently that he had no apprehensions now, and that the public had been coming "many more." The *Mutter* came out later, evidently to keep an eye on me. The German and the *Mutter* frequently whispered together. Although the shop was closed he charged me a quarter-rouble. What unnecessary exactitude!

"You will every time pay; the public will one rouble, and you one quarter pay; for you are the good friend of your good friend; and I a friend respect . . ."

"Are you alive, are you alive, my cultured friend?" I cried, as I approached the crocodile, expecting my words to reach Ivan Matveitch from a distance and to flatter his vanity.

"Alive and well," he answered, as though from a long way off or from under the bed, though I was standing close beside him. "Alive and well; but of that later. . . . How are things going?"

As though purposely not hearing the question, I was just beginning with sympathetic haste to question him how he was, what it was like in the crocodile, and what, in fact, there was inside a crocodile. Both friendship and common civility demanded this. But with capricious annoyance he interrupted me.

"How are things going?" he shouted, in a shrill and on this occasion particularly revolting voice, addressing me peremptorily as usual.

I described to him my whole conversation with Timofey Semyonitch down to the smallest detail. As I told my story I tried to show my resentment in my voice.

"The old man is right," Ivan Matveitch pronounced as abruptly as usual in his conversation with me. "I like practical people, and can't endure sentimental milk-sops. I am ready to admit, however, that your idea about a special commission is not altogether absurd. I certainly have a great deal to report, both from a scientific and from an ethical point of view. But now all this has taken a new and unexpected aspect, and it is not worth while to trouble about mere salary. Listen attentively. Are you sitting down?"

"No, I am standing up."

"Sit down on the floor if there is nothing else, and listen attentively."

Resentfully I took a chair and put it down on the floor with a bang, in my anger.

"Listen," he began dictatorially. "The public came to-day in masses. There was no room left in the evening, and the police came in to keep order. At eight o'clock, that is, earlier than usual, the proprietor thought it necessary to close the shop and end the exhibition to count the money he had taken and prepare for to-morrow more conveniently. So I know there will be a regular fair to-morrow. So we may assume that all the most cultivated people in the capital, the ladies of the best society, the foreign ambassadors, the leading lawyers and so on, will all be present. What's more, people will be flowing here from the remotest provinces of our vast and interesting empire. The upshot of it is that I am the cynosure of all eyes, and though hidden to sight, I am eminent. I shall teach the idle crowd. Taught by experience, I shall be an example of greatness and resignation to fate! I shall be, so to say, a pulpit from which to instruct mankind. The mere biological details I can furnish about the monster I am inhabiting are of priceless value. And so, far from repining at what has happened, I confidently hope for the most brilliant of careers."

"You won't find it wearisome?" I asked sarcastically.

What irritated me more than anything was the extreme pomposity of his language. Nevertheless, it all rather disconcerted me. "What on earth, what, can this frivolous blockhead find to be so cocky about?" I muttered to myself. "He ought to be crying instead of being cocky."

"No!" he answered my observation sharply, "for I am full of great ideas, only now can I at leisure ponder over the amelioration of the lot of humanity. Truth and light will come forth now from the crocodile. I shall certainly develop a new economic theory of my own and I shall be proud of it—which I have hitherto been prevented from doing by my official duties and by trivial distractions. I shall refute everything and be a new Fourier. By the way, did you give Timofey Semyonitch the seven roubles?"

"Yes, out of my own pocket," I answered, trying to emphasise that fact in my voice.

"We will settle it," he answered superciliously. "I confidently expect my salary to be raised, for who should get a rise if not I? I am of the utmost service now. But to business. My wife?"

"You are, I suppose, inquiring after Elena Ivanovna?"

"My wife?" he shouted, this time in a positive squeal.

There was no help for it! Meekly, though gnashing my teeth, I told him how I had left Elena Ivanovna. He did not even hear me out.

"I have special plans in regard to her," he began impatiently. "If I am celebrated *here*, I wish her to be celebrated *there*. Savants, poets, philosophers, foreign mineralogists, statesmen, after conversing in the morning with me, will visit her *salon* in the evening. From next week onwards she must have an 'At Home' every evening. With my salary doubled, we shall have the means for entertaining, and as the entertainment must not go beyond tea and hired footmen—that's settled. Both here and there they will talk of me. I have long thirsted for an opportunity for being talked about, but could not attain it, fettered by my humble position and low grade in the service. And now all this has been attained by a simple gulp on the part of the crocodile. Every word of mine will be listened to, every utterance will be thought over, repeated, printed. And I'll teach them what I am worth! They shall understand at last what abilities they have allowed to vanish in the entrails of a monster. 'This man might have been Foreign Minister or might have ruled a kingdom,' some will say. 'And that man did not rule a kingdom,' others will say. In what way am I inferior to a Garnier-Pagesishky or whatever they are called? My wife must be a worthy second—I have brains, she has beauty and charm. 'She is beautiful, and that is why she is his wife,' some will say. 'She is beautiful *because* she is his wife,' others will amend. To be ready for anything let Elena Ivanovna buy to-morrow the Encyclopædia edited by Andrey Kraevsky, that she may be able to converse on any topic. Above all, let her be sure to read the political leader in the *Petersburg News,* comparing it every day with the *Voice.* I imagine that the proprietor will consent to take me sometimes with the crocodile to my wife's brilliant *salon.* I will be in a tank in the middle of the magnificent drawing-room, and I will scintillate with witticisms which I will prepare in the morning. To the statesman I will impart my projects; to the poet I will speak in rhyme; with the ladies I can be amusing and charming without impropriety, since I shall be no danger to their husbands' peace of mind. To all the rest I shall serve as a pattern of resignation to fate and the will of Providence. I shall make my wife a brilliant literary lady; I shall bring her forward and explain her to the public; as my wife she must be full of the most striking virtues; and if they

are right in calling Andrey Alexandrovitch our Russian Alfred de
Musset, they will be still more right in calling her our Russian Yevgenia Tour."

I must confess that although this wild nonsense was rather in
Ivan Matveitch's habitual style, it did occur to me that he was in a
fever and delirious. It was the same, everyday Ivan Matveitch, but
magnified twenty times.

"My friend," I asked him, "are you hoping for a long life? Tell
me, in fact, are you well? How do you eat, how do you sleep, how do
you breathe? I am your friend, and you must admit that the incident
is most unnatural, and consequently my curiosity is most natural."

"Idle curiosity and nothing else," he pronounced sententiously,
"but you shall be satisfied. You ask how I am managing in the entrails of the monster? To begin with, the crocodile, to my amusement, turns out to be perfectly empty. His inside consists of a sort
of huge empty sack made of gutta-percha, like the elastic goods sold
in the Gorohovy Street, in the Morskaya, and, if I am not mistaken,
in the Voznesensky Prospect. Otherwise, if you think of it, how could
I find room?"

"Is it possible?" I cried, in a surprise that may well be understood. "Can the crocodile be perfectly empty?"

"Perfectly," Ivan Matveitch maintained sternly and impressively. "And in all probability, it is so constructed by the laws of
Nature. The crocodile possesses nothing but jaws furnished with
sharp teeth, and besides the jaws, a tail of considerable length—that
is all, properly speaking. The middle part between these two ex-
tremities is an empty space enclosed by something of the nature of
gutta-percha, probably really gutta-percha."

"But the ribs, the stomach, the intestines, the liver, the heart?"
I interrupted quite angrily.

"There is nothing, absolutely nothing of all that, and probably there never has been. All that is the idle fancy of frivolous
travellers. As one inflates an air-cushion, I am now with my person
inflating the crocodile. He is incredibly elastic. Indeed, you might,
as the friend of the family, get in with me if you were generous and
self-sacrificing enough—and even with you here there would be
room to spare. I even think that in the last resort I might send for
Elena Ivanovna. However, this void, hollow formation of the crocodile is quite in keeping with the teachings of natural science. If, for
instance, one had to construct a new crocodile, the question would

naturally present itself. What is the fundamental characteristic of the crocodile? The answer is clear: to swallow human beings. How is one, in constructing the crocodile, to secure that he should swallow people? The answer is clearer still: construct him hollow. It was settled by physics long ago that Nature abhors a vacuum. Hence the inside of the crocodile must be hollow so that it may abhor the vacuum, and consequently swallow and so fill itself with anything it can come across. And that is the sole rational cause why every crocodile swallows men. It is not the same in the constitution of man: the emptier a man's head is, for instance, the less he feels the thirst to fill it, and that is the one exception to the general rule. It is all as clear as day to me now. I have deduced it by my own observation and experience, being, so to say, in the very bowels of Nature, in its retort, listening to the throbbing of its pulse. Even etymology supports me, for the very word crocodile means voracity. Crocodile—*crocodillo*— is evidently an Italian word, dating perhaps from the Egyptian Pharaohs, and evidently derived from the French verb *croquer,* which means to eat, to devour, in general to absorb nourishment. All these remarks I intend to deliver as my first lecture in Elena Ivanovna's *salon* when they take me there in the tank."

"My friend, oughtn't you at least to take some purgative?" I cried involuntarily.

"He is in a fever, a fever, he is feverish!" I repeated to myself in alarm.

"Nonsense!" he answered contemptuously. "Besides, in my present position it would be most inconvenient. I knew, though, you would be sure to talk of taking medicine."

"But, my friend, how . . . how do you take food now? Have you dined to-day?"

"No, but I am not hungry, and most likely I shall never take food again. And that, too, is quite natural; filling the whole interior of the crocodile I make him feel always full. Now he need not be fed for some years. On the other hand, nourished by me, he will naturally impart to me all the vital juices of his body; it is the same as with some accomplished coquettes who embed themselves and their whole persons for the night in raw steak, and then, after their morning bath, are fresh, supple, buxom and fascinating. In that way nourishing the crocodile, I myself obtain nourishment from him, consequently we mutually nourish one another. But as it is difficult even for a crocodile to digest a man like me, he must, no doubt, be conscious of a certain weight in his stomach—an organ which he does not, however, possess—and that is why, to avoid causing the creature suffering, I do not often turn over, and although I could turn over I do not do so from humanitarian motives. This is the one drawback of my present position, and in an allegorical sense Timofey Semyonitch was right in saying I was lying like a log. But I will prove that even lying like a log—nay, that only lying like a log—one can revolutionise the lot of mankind. All the great ideas and movements of our newspapers and magazines have evidently been the work of men who were lying like logs; that is why they call them divorced from the realities of life—but what does it matter, their saying that! I am constructing now a complete system of my own, and you wouldn't believe how easy it is! You have only to creep into a secluded corner or into a crocodile, to shut your eyes, and you immediately devise a perfect millennium for mankind. When you went away this afternoon I set to work at once and have already invented three systems, now I am preparing the fourth. It is true that at first one must refute everything that has gone before, but from the crocodile it is so easy to refute it; besides, it all becomes clearer, seen from the inside of the crocodile. . . . There are some drawbacks, though small ones, in my position, however; it is somewhat damp here and covered with a sort of slime; moreover, there is rather a smell of india-rubber exactly like the smell of my old galoshes. That is all, there are no other drawbacks."

"Ivan Matveitch," I interrupted, "all this is a miracle in which I can scarcely believe. And can you, can you intend never to dine again?"

"What trivial nonsense you are troubling about, you thoughtless, frivolous creature! I talk to you about great ideas, and you . . . Understand that I am sufficiently nourished by the great ideas which light up the darkness in which I am enveloped. The good-natured proprietor has, however, after consulting the kindly *Mutter*, decided with her that they will every morning insert into the monster's jaws a bent metal tube, something like a whistle pipe, by means of which I can absorb coffee or broth with bread soaked in it. The pipe has already been bespoken in the neighbourhood, but I think this is superfluous luxury. I hope to live at least a thousand years, if it is true that crocodiles live so long, which, by the way—good thing I thought of it—you had better look up in some natural history to-morrow and tell me, for I may have been mistaken and have mixed it up with some excavated monster. There is only one reflection rather troubles me: as I am dressed in cloth and have boots on, the crocodile can obviously not digest me. Besides, I am alive, and so am opposing the process of digestion with my whole will power; for you can understand that I do not wish to be turned into what all nourishment turns into, for that would be too humiliating for me. But there is one thing I am afraid of: in a thousand years the cloth of my coat, unfortunately of Russian make, may decay, and then, left without clothing, I might perhaps, in spite of my indignation, begin to be digested; and though by day nothing would induce me to allow it, at night, in my sleep, when a man's will deserts him, I may be overtaken by the humiliating destiny of a potato, a pancake, or veal. Such an idea reduces me to fury. This alone is an argument for the revision of the tariff and the encouragement of the importation of English cloth, which is stronger and so will withstand Nature longer when one is swallowed by a crocodile. At the first opportunity I will impart this idea to some statesman and at the same time to the political writers on our Petersburg dailies. Let them publish it abroad. I trust this will not be the only idea they will borrow from me. I foresee that every morning a regular crowd of them, provided with quarter-roubles from the editorial office, will be flocking round me to seize my ideas on the telegrams of the previous day. In brief, the future presents itself to me in the rosiest light."

"Fever, fever!" I whispered to myself.

"My friend, and freedom?" I asked, wishing to learn his views thoroughly. "You are, so to speak, in prison, while every man has a right to the enjoyment of freedom."

"You are a fool," he answered. "Savages love independence, wise men love order; and if there is no order . . ."

"Ivan Matveitch, spare me, please!"

"Hold your tongue and listen!" he squealed, vexed at my interrupting him. "Never has my spirit soared as now. In my narrow refuge there is only one thing that I dread—the literary criticisms of the monthlies and the hiss of our satirical papers. I am afraid that thoughtless visitors, stupid and envious people and nihilists in general, may turn me into ridicule. But I will take measures. I am impatiently awaiting the response of the public to-morrow, and especially the opinion of the newspapers. You must tell me about the papers to-morrow."

"Very good; to-morrow I will bring a perfect pile of papers with me."

"To-morrow it is too soon to expect reports in the newspapers, for it will take four days for it to be advertised. But from today come to me every evening by the back way through the yard. I am intending to employ you as my secretary. You shall read the newspapers and magazines to me, and I will dictate to you my ideas and give you commissions. Be particularly careful not to forget the foreign telegrams. Let all the European telegrams be here every day. But enough; most likely you are sleepy by now. Go home, and do not think of what I said just now about criticisms: I am not afraid of it, for the critics themselves are in a critical position. One has only to be wise and virtuous and one will certainly get on to a pedestal. If not Socrates, then Diogenes, or perhaps both of them together—that is my future rôle among mankind."

So frivolously and boastfully did Ivan Matveitch hasten to express himself before me, like feverish weak-willed women who, as we are told by the proverb, cannot keep a secret. All that he told me about the crocodile struck me as most suspicious. How was it possible that the crocodile was absolutely hollow? I don't mind betting that he was bragging from vanity and partly to humiliate me. It is true that he was an invalid and one must make allowances for invalids; but I must frankly confess, I never could endure Ivan Matveitch. I have been trying all my life, from a child up, to escape from his tutelage and have not been able to! A thousand times over I have been tempted to break with him altogether, and every time I have been drawn to him again, as though I were still hoping to prove something to him or to revenge myself on him. A strange thing, this friendship! I can positively assert that nine-tenths of my friendship for him was made up of malice. On this occasion, however, we parted with genuine feeling.

"Your friend a very clever man!" the German said to me in an undertone as he moved to see me out; he had been listening all the time attentively to our conversation.

"*A propos*," I said, "while I think of it: how much would you ask for your crocodile in case any one wanted to buy it?"

Ivan Matveitch, who heard the question, was waiting with curiosity for the answer; it was evident that he did not want the German to ask too little; anyway, he cleared his throat in a peculiar way on hearing my question.

At first the German would not listen—was positively angry.

"No one will dare my own crocodile to buy!" he cried furiously, and turned as red as a boiled lobster. "Me not want to sell the crocodile! I would not for the crocodile a million thalers take. I took a hundred and thirty thalers from the public to-day, and I shall to-morrow ten thousand take, and then a hundred thousand every day I shall take. I will not him sell."

Ivan Matveitch positively chuckled with satisfaction. Controlling myself—for I felt it was a duty to my friend—I hinted coolly and reasonably to the crazy German that his calculations were not quite correct, that if he makes a hundred thousand every day, all Petersburg will have visited him in four days, and then there will be no one left to bring him roubles, that life and death are in God's hands, that the crocodile may burst or Ivan Matveitch may fall ill and die, and so on and so on.

The German grew pensive.

"I will him drops from the chemist's get," he said, after pondering, "and will save your friend that he die not."

"Drops are all very well," I answered, "but consider, too, that the thing may get into the law courts. Ivan Matveitch's wife may demand the restitution of her lawful spouse. You are intending to get rich, but do you intend to give Elena Ivanovna a pension?"

"No, me not intend," said the German in stern decision.

"No, we not intend," said the *Mutter,* with positive malignancy.

"And so would it not be better for you to accept something now, at once, a secure and solid though moderate sum, than to leave things to chance? I ought to tell you that I am inquiring simply from curiosity."

The German drew the *Mutter* aside to consult with her in a corner where there stood a case with the largest and ugliest monkey of his collection.

"Well, you will see!" said Ivan Matveitch.

As for me, I was at that moment burning with the desire, first, to give the German a thrashing, next, to give the *Mutter* an even sounder one, and, thirdly, to give Ivan Matveitch the soundest thrashing of all for his boundless vanity. But all this paled beside the answer of the rapacious German.

After consultation with the *Mutter* he demanded for his crocodile fifty thousand roubles in bonds of the last Russian loan with lottery voucher attached, a brick house in Gorohovy Street with a chemist's shop attached, and in addition the rank of Russian colonel.

"You see!" Ivan Matveitch cried triumphantly. "I told you so! Apart from this last senseless desire for the rank of a colonel, he is perfectly right, for he fully understands the present value of the monster he is exhibiting. The economic principle before everything!"

"Upon my word!" I cried furiously to the German. "But what should you be made a colonel for? What exploit have you performed? What service have you done? In what way have you gained military glory? You are really crazy!"

"Crazy!" cried the German, offended. "No, a person very sensible, but you very stupid! I have a colonel deserved for that I have a crocodile shown and in him a live *hofrath* sitting! And a Russian can a crocodile not show and a live *hofrath* in him sitting! Me extremely clever man and much wish colonel to be!"

"Well, good-bye, then, Ivan Matveitch!" I cried, shaking with fury, and I went out of the crocodile room almost at a run.

I felt that in another minute I could not have answered for myself. The unnatural expectations of these two blockheads were insupportable. The cold air refreshed me and somewhat moderated my indignation. At last, after spitting vigorously fifteen times on each side, I took a cab, got home, undressed and flung myself into bed. What vexed me more than anything was my having become his secretary. Now I was to die of boredom there every evening, doing the duty of a true friend! I was ready to beat myself for it, and I did, in fact, after putting out the candle and pulling up the bedclothes, punch myself several times on the head and various parts of my body. That somewhat relieved me, and at last I fell asleep fairly soundly, in fact, for I was very tired. All night long I could dream of nothing but monkeys, but towards morning I dreamt of Elena Ivanovna.

IV

The monkeys I dreamed about, I surmise, because they were shut up in the case at the German's; but Elena Ivanovna was a different story.

I may as well say at once, I loved the lady, but I make haste—post-haste—to make a qualification. I loved her as a father, neither more nor less. I judge that because I often felt an irresistible desire to kiss her little head or her rosy cheek. And though I never carried out this inclination, I would not have refused even to kiss her lips. And not merely her lips, but her teeth, which always gleamed so charmingly like two rows of pretty, well-matched pearls when she laughed. She laughed extraordinarily often. Ivan Matveitch in demonstrative moments used to call her his "darling absurdity"—a name extremely happy and appropriate. She was a perfect sugar-plum, and that was all one could say of her. Therefore I am utterly at a loss to understand what possessed Ivan Matveitch to imagine his wife as a Russian Yevgenia Tour? Anyway, my dream, with the exception of the monkeys, left a most pleasant impression upon me, and going over all the incidents of the previous day as I drank my morning cup of tea, I resolved to go and see Elena Ivanovna at once on my way to the office—which, indeed, I was bound to do as the friend of the family.

In a tiny little room out of the bedroom—the so-called little drawing-room, though their big drawing-room was little too—Elena Ivanovna was sitting, in some half-transparent morning wrapper, on a smart little sofa before a little tea-table, drinking coffee out of a little cup in which she was dipping a minute biscuit. She was ravishingly pretty, but struck me as being at the same time rather pensive.

"Ah, that's you, naughty man!" she said, greeting me with an absent-minded smile. "Sit down, feather-head, have some coffee. Well, what were you doing yesterday? Were you at the masquerade?"

"Why, were you? I don't go, you know. Besides, yesterday I was visiting our captive. . . ." I sighed and assumed a pious expression as I took the coffee.

"Whom? . . . What captive? . . . Oh, yes! Poor fellow! Well, how is he—bored? Do you know . . . I wanted to ask you . . . I suppose I can ask for a divorce now?"

"A divorce!" I cried in indignation and almost spilled the coffee. "It's that swarthy fellow," I thought to myself bitterly.

There was a certain swarthy gentleman with little moustaches who was something in the architectural line, and who came far too often to see them, and was extremely skilful in amusing Elena Ivanovna. I must confess I hated him and there was no doubt that he had succeeded in seeing Elena Ivanovna yesterday either at the masquerade or even here, and putting all sorts of nonsense into her head.

"Why," Elena Ivanovna rattled off hurriedly, as though it were a lesson she had learnt, "if he is going to stay on in the crocodile, perhaps not come back all his life, while I sit waiting for him here! A husband ought to live at home, and not in a crocodile. . . ."

"But this was an unforeseen occurrence," I was beginning, in very comprehensible agitation.

"Oh, no, don't talk to me, I won't listen, I won't listen," she cried, suddenly getting quite cross. "You are always against me, you wretch! There's no doing anything with you, you will never give me any advice! Other people tell me that I can get a divorce because Ivan Matveitch will not get his salary now."

"Elena Ivanovna! is it you I hear!" I exclaimed pathetically. "What villain could have put such an idea into your head? And divorce on such a trivial ground as a salary is quite impossible. And poor Ivan Matveitch, poor Ivan Matveitch is, so to speak, burning with love for you even in the bowels of the monster. What's more, he is melting away with love like a lump of sugar. Yesterday while you were enjoying yourself at the masquerade, he was saying that he might in the last resort send for you as his lawful spouse to join him in the entrails of the monster, especially as it appears the crocodile is exceedingly roomy, not only able to accommodate two but even three persons. . . ."

And then I told her all that interesting part of my conversation the night before with Ivan Matveitch.

"What, what!" she cried, in surprise. "You want me to get into the monster too, to be with Ivan Matveitch? What an idea! And how am I to get in there, in my hat and crinoline? Heavens, what foolishness! And what should I look like while I was getting into it, and very likely there would be some one there to see me! It's absurd! And what should I have to eat there? And . . . and . . . and what should I do there when . . . Oh, my goodness, what will they think of next? . . . And what should I have to amuse me there? . . . You say there's a smell of gutta-percha? And what should I do if we quarreled—should we have to go on staying there side by side? Foo, how horrid!"

"I agree, I agree with all those arguments, my sweet Elena Ivanovna," I interrupted, striving to express myself with that natural enthusiasm which always overtakes a man when he feels the truth is on his side. "But one thing you have not appreciated in all this, you have not realised that he cannot live without you if he is inviting

you there; that is a proof of love, passionate, faithful, ardent love.
. . . You have thought too little of his love, dear Elena Ivanovna!"

"I won't, I won't, I won't hear anything about it!" waving me
off with her pretty little hand with glistening pink nails that had
just been washed and polished. "Horrid man! You will reduce me
to tears! Get into it yourself, if you like the prospect. You are his
friend, get in and keep him company, and spend your life discussing
some tedious science. . . ."

"You are wrong to laugh at this suggestion"—I checked the
frivolous woman with dignity—"Ivan Matveitch has invited me as
it is. You, of course, are summoned there by duty; for me, it would
be an act of generosity. But when Ivan Matveitch described to me
last night the elasticity of the crocodile, he hinted very plainly that
there would be room not only for you two, but for me also as a friend
of the family, especially if I wished to join you, and therefore . . ."

"How so, the three of us?" cried Elena Ivanovna, looking at
me in surprise. "Why, how should we . . . are we going to be all
three there together? Ha-ha-ha! How silly you both are! Ha-ha-ha!
I shall certainly pinch you all the time, you wretch! Ha-ha-ha! Ha-ha-
ha!"

And falling back on the sofa, she laughed till she cried. All this
—the tears and the laughter—were so fascinating that I could not
resist rushing eagerly to kiss her hand, which she did not oppose,
though she did pinch my ears lightly as a sign of reconciliation.

Then we both grew very cheerful, and I described to her in detail all Ivan Matveitch's plans. The thought of her evening receptions
and her *salon* pleased her very much.

"Only I should need a great many new dresses," she observed,
"and so Ivan Matveitch must send me as much of his salary as possible
and as soon as possible. Only . . . only I don't know about that," she
added thoughtfully. "How can he be brought here in the tank? That's
very absurd. I don't want my husband to be carried about in a tank.
I should feel quite ashamed for my visitors to see it. . . . I don't
want that, no, I don't."

"By the way, while I think of it, was Timofey Semyonitch here
yesterday?"

"Oh, yes, he was; he came to comfort me, and do you know, we
played cards all the time. He played for sweetmeats, and if I lost he
was to kiss my hands. What a wretch he is! And only fancy, he almost
came to the masquerade with me, really!"

"He was carried away by his feelings!" I observed. "And who would not be with you, you charmer?"

"Oh, get along with your compliments! Stay, I'll give you a pinch as a parting present. I've learnt to pinch awfully well lately. Well, what do you say to that? By the way, you say Ivan Matveitch spoke several times of me yesterday?"

"N-no, not exactly. . . . I must say he is thinking more now of the fate of humanity, and wants . . ."

"Oh, let him! You needn't go on! I am sure it's fearfully boring. I'll go and see him some time. I shall certainly go tomorrow. Only not to-day; I've got a headache, and besides, there will be such a lot of people there to-day. . . . They'll say, 'That's his wife,' and I shall feel ashamed. . . . Good-bye. You will be . . . there this evening, won't you?"

"To see him, yes. He asked me to go and take him the papers."

"That's capital. Go and read to him. But don't come and see me to-day. I am not well, and perhaps I may go and see some one. Good-bye, you naughty man."

"It's that swarthy fellow is going to see her this evening," I thought.

At the office, of course, I gave no sign of being consumed by these cares and anxieties. But soon I noticed some of the most progressive papers seemed to be passing particularly rapidly from hand to hand among my colleagues, and were being read with an extremely serious expression of face. The first one that reached me was the *News-sheet,* a paper of no particular party but humanitarian in general, for which it was regarded with contempt among us, though it was read. Not without surprise I read in it the following paragraph:

"Yesterday strange rumours were circulating among the spacious ways and sumptuous buildings of our vast metropolis. A certain well-known *bon-vivant* of the highest society, probably weary of the *cuisine* at Borel's and at the X. Club, went into the Arcade, into the place where an immense crocodile recently brought to the metropolis is being exhibited, and insisted on its being prepared for his dinner. After bargaining with the proprietor he at once set to work to devour him (that is, not the proprietor, a very meek and punctilious German, but his crocodile), cutting juicy morsels with his penknife from the living animal, and swallowing them with extraordinary rapidity. By degrees the whole crocodile disappeared into the vast recesses of his stomach, so that he was even on the point of attacking an ichneumon, a constant companion of the crocodile, probably imagining that the latter would be as savoury. We are by no means opposed to that new article of diet with which foreign *gourmands* have long been familiar. We have, indeed, predicted that it would come. English lords and travellers make up regular parties for catching crocodiles in Egypt, and consume the back of the monster cooked like beefsteak, with mustard, onions and potatoes. The French who followed in the train of Lesseps prefer the paws baked in hot ashes, which they do, however, in opposition to the English, who laugh at them. Probably both ways would be appreciated among us. For our part, we are delighted at a new branch of industry, of which our great and varied fatherland stands pre-eminently in need. Probably before a year is out crocodiles would be brought in hundreds to replace this first one, lost in the stomach of a Petersburg *gourmand*. And why should not the crocodile be acclimatised among us in Russia? If the water of the Neva is too cold for these interesting strangers, there are ponds in the capital and rivers and lakes outside it. Why not breed crocodiles at Pargolovo, for instance, or at Pavlovsk, in the Presnensky Ponds and in Samoteka in Moscow? While providing agreeable, wholesome nourishment for our fastidious *gourmands,* they might at the same time entertain the ladies who walk about these ponds and instruct the children in natural history. The crocodile skin might be used for making jewel-cases, boxes, cigar-cases, pocket-books, and possibly more than one thousand saved up in the greasy notes that are peculiarly beloved of merchants might be laid by in crocodile skin. We hope to return more than once to this interesting topic."

Though I had foreseen something of the sort, yet the reckless inaccuracy of the paragraph overwhelmed me. Finding no one with whom to share my impression, I turned to Prohor Savvitch who was sitting opposite to me, and noticed that the latter had been watching me for some time, while in his hand he held the *Voice* as though he were on the point of passing it to me. Without a word he took the *News-sheet* from me, and as he handed me the *Voice* he drew a line with his nail against an article to which he probably wished to call my attention. This Prohor Savvitch was a very queer man: a taciturn old bachelor, he was not on intimate terms with any of us, scarcely spoke to any one in the office, always had an opinion of his own about everything, but could not bear to impart it to any one. He lived alone. Hardly any one among us had ever been in his lodging.

This was what I read in the *Voice*.

"Every one knows that we are progressive and humanitarian and want to be on a level with Europe in this respect. But in spite of all our exertions and the efforts of our paper we are still far from maturity, as may be judged from the shocking incident which took place yesterday in the Arcade and which we predicted long ago. A foreigner arrives in the capital bringing with him a crocodile which he begins exhibiting in the Arcade. We immediately hasten to welcome a new branch of useful industry such as our powerful and varied fatherland stands in great need of. Suddenly yesterday at four o'clock in the afternoon a gentleman of exceptional stoutness enters the foreigner's shop in an intoxicated condition, pays his entrance money, and immediately without any warning leaps into the jaws of the crocodile, who was forced, of course, to swallow him, if only from an instinct of self-preservation, to avoid being crushed. Tumbling into the inside of the crocodile, the stranger at once dropped asleep. Neither the shouts of the foreign proprietor, nor the lamentations of his terrified family, nor threats to send for the police made the slightest impression. Within the crocodile was heard nothing but laughter and a promise to flay him (*sic*), though the poor mammal, compelled to swallow such a mass, was vainly shedding tears. An uninvited guest is worse than a Tartar. But in spite of the proverb the insolent visitor would not leave. We do not know how to explain such barbarous incidents which prove our lack of culture and disgrace us in the eyes of foreigners. The recklessness of the Russian temperament has found a fresh outlet. It may be asked what was the object of the uninvited visitor? A warm and comfortable abode? But there are many excellent houses in the capital with very cheap and comfortable lodgings, with the Neva water laid on, and a staircase lighted by gas, frequently with a hall-porter maintained by the proprietor. We would call our readers' attention to the barbarous treatment of domestic animals: it is difficult, of course, for the crocodile to digest such a mass all at once, and now he lies swollen out to the size of a mountain, awaiting death in insufferable agonies. In Europe persons guilty of inhumanity towards domestic

animals have long been punished by law. But in spite of our
European enlightenment, in spite of our European pavements, in
spite of the European architecture of our houses, we are still far from
shaking off our time-honoured traditions.

"Though the houses are new, the conventions are old."

And, indeed, the houses are not new, at least the staircases in
them are not. We have more than once in our paper alluded to the
fact that in the Petersburg Side in the house of the merchant
Lukyanov the steps of the wooden staircase have decayed, fallen
away, and have long been a danger for Afimya Skapidarov, a soldier's
wife who works in the house, and is often obliged to go up the stairs
with water or armfuls of wood. At last our predictions have come
true: yesterday evening at half-past eight Afimya Skapidarov fell
down with a basin of soup and broke her leg. We do not know
whether Lukyanov will mend his staircase now, Russians are often
wise after the event, but the victim of Russian carelessness has by
now been taken to the hospital. In the same way we shall never cease
to maintain that the houseporters who clear away the mud from the
wooden pavement in the Viborgsky Side ought not to spatter the
legs of passers-by, but should throw the mud up into heaps as is done
in Europe," and so on, and so on.

"What's this?" I asked in some perplexity, looking at Prohor
Savvitch. "What's the meaning of it?"

"How do you mean?"

"Why, upon my word! Instead of pitying Ivan Matveitch, they
pity the crocodile!"

"What of it? They have pity even for a beast, a *mammal*. We
must be up to Europe, mustn't we? They have a very warm feeling for
crocodiles there too. He-he-he!"

Saying this, queer old Prohor Savvitch dived into his papers and
would not utter another word.

I stuffed the *Voice* and the *News-sheet* into my pocket and
collected as many old copies of the newspapers as I could find for
Ivan Matveitch's diversion in the evening, and though the evening
was far off, yet on this occasion I slipped away from the office early to
go to the Arcade and look, if only from a distance, at what was going
on there, and to listen to the various remarks and currents of opinion.

I foresaw that there would be a regular crush there, and turned up the collar of my coat to meet it. I somehow felt rather shy—so unaccustomed are we to publicity. But I feel that I have no right to report my own prosaic feelings when faced with this remarkable and original incident.

ANTON CHEKHOV

(1860-1904)

Born into a family barely a step above serfdom, Chekhov early was forced to work to help support them. Both financially and physically, life was a struggle. Entering medical school at the University of Moscow, he contracted tuberculosis. Nevertheless, he managed to graduate in 1884, but not before he realized that literature meant more to him than medicine. His first stories were published in 1886; by the end of his life, he had written over a thousand. Equally well known as a dramatist, he wrote plays which are still produced; among the best known are UNCLE VANYA, THE THREE SISTERS, and THE CHERRY ORCHARD. His fiction deals with common people and uses common language. The incidents tend to be ordinary. The reader ends by feeling a kinship with these figures, a response aided by the fact that Chekhov's treatment of them is compassionate as well as realistic. He does, however, cry out against the wretched conditions under which they exist, and he is a master at pointing out the psychological and spiritual havoc wreaked by such an environment.

On Official Business

The deputy examining magistrate and the county physician were on their way to an autopsy in the village of Syrnya. En route they were caught in a blizzard; they wasted a great deal of time traveling in circles and arrived at their destination not at midday, as they had intended, but in the evening when it was already dark. They put up for the night at the village headquarters.[1] It was here that the dead body happened to be lying, the corpse of the Zemstvo insurance agent Lesnitzky, who had come to Syrnya three days previously and, after settling in the village headquarters and ordering the samovar, had shot himself, to the complete surprise of everyone; and the fact that he had ended his life under such strange circumstances, with the samovar before him and the food he had brought along laid out on the table, led many to suspect murder; an inquest was in order.

In the entry the doctor and the examining magistrate stamped their feet to shake off the snow, and near by stood an old man who belonged to the lowest order of rural police: Ilya Loshadin; he was holding a little tin lamp in his hands to give them light. There was a strong smell of kerosene.

"Who are you?" asked the doctor.

"The p'liceman," answered Loshadin.

He used to spell it "pleaceman" when he signed the receipts at the post office.

"And where are the inquest witnesses?"

"They must have gone to have tea, your honor."

To the right was the best room, the travelers' or gentry's room; to the left a room for the lower orders with a big stove and a sleeping platform. The doctor and the examining magistrate, followed by the policeman, holding the lamp high above his head, went into the best room. Here, motionless on the floor, close to the table legs, lay a long body, covered with a white sheet. In the dim light of the lamp, in addition to the white cover, a pair of new rubbers could be clearly seen, and everything about the place was weird and sinister: the dark walls, and the silence, and the rubbers, and the immobility of the dead body. On the table stood a samovar, long since cold; and round it packages, probably containing food.

"To shoot oneself in the village headquarters, how tactless!" said the doctor. "If you do want to put a bullet through your brain, you ought to do it at home, in some shed."

He sank onto a bench, just as he was, in his cap, his fur coat, and his felt boots; his companion, the magistrate, sat down opposite him.

"These hysterical and neurasthenic people are great egoists," the doctor went on bitterly. "If a neurasthenic sleeps in the same

[1] A cottage in which community meetings and sessions of the village elders were held and which was sometimes used as a hostelry.

room with you, he rustles his newspaper; when he dines with you, he has a row with his wife unrestrained by your presence; and when he feels like shooting himself, he shoots himself in village headquarters, so as to give everybody the greatest amount of trouble. Under all circumstances these gentlemen think only of themselves! That's why elderly people so dislike our 'nervous age.' "

"Elderly people dislike so many things," said the magistrate, yawning. "You ought to point out to the old fellows the difference between the suicides of the past and the suicides of the present. Formerly the so-called gentleman shot himself because he had embezzled Government funds, but nowadays it's because he's fed up with life, depressed. Which is better?"

"Fed up with life, depressed; but you must admit that he might have shot himself somewhere else than at the village headquarters."

"Such aggravation!" said the policeman, "such aggravation! It's a regular punishment. Folks are all upset, your honor; they've not slept these three nights. The children are crying. The cows ought to be milked but the women won't go to the barn—they're scared—that they may see the dead gentleman in the dark. Sure they're foolish women, but some of the men is scared, too. As soon as it's dark they won't pass the place alone, but only in a drove. And the witnesses too—"

Dr. Starchenko, a middle-aged, dark-bearded man in spectacles, and the magistrate Lyzhin, a fair-haired man, still young, who had taken his degree only two years before and looked more like a student than an official, sat in silence, musing. They were annoyed at having been delayed. Now, although it was not yet six o'clock, they had to wait till morning, spending the night here; and they pictured a long evening, a long, dark night, boredom, wretched beds, cockroaches, morning chill; and listening to the storm that howled in the chimney and in the garret, they both thought how unlike all this was the life they would have wished for themselves and of which they had once dreamed, and how far away they both were from their contemporaries, who at that moment were walking about the lighted streets in town without noticing the weather, or getting ready for the theater, or sitting in their studies over a book. Oh, how much they would have given now only to stroll along the Nevsky or along Petrovka in Moscow, to listen to decent singing, to spend an hour or so in a restaurant!

Hoo-oo-oo! sang the storm in the garret, and something outside banged viciously, probably the signboard on the cottage. Hoo-oo-oo!

"You can do as you like, but I don't want to stay here," said Starchenko, getting up. "It's not six yet; it's too early to go to bed; I'll drive somewhere. Von Taunitz lives not far from here, only a couple of miles from Syrnya. I'll drive there and spend the evening with him. Officer, go and tell my coachman not to take the horses out. And what will you do?" he asked Lyzhin.

"I don't know; I'll probably go to sleep."

The doctor wrapped his fur coat round him and went out. He could be heard talking to the coachman and there was the sound of bells shaking on the frozen horses. He drove off.

"It's not right for you, sir, to spend the night in here," said the policeman. "Go into the other room. It's not clean there, but for one night it don't matter. I'll get a samovar from a peasant and heat it directly. I'll pile up some hay for you and then you can go to sleep, and God be with you, your honor."

A little later the magistrate was sitting at a table in the other room, drinking tea, while Loshadin the policeman stood at the door, talking. He was an old man of about sixty, short and very lean, hunched and white-haired, with a naive smile on his face and watery eyes; and he kept smacking his lips as though he were sucking a candy. He was wearing a short sheepskin coat and felt boots, and did not let his stick out of his hands. The magistrate's youth aroused his compassion and that was probably why he addressed him familiarly.

"Fyodor Makarych, the Elder, gave orders that he was to be informed when the police inspector or the examining magistrate came," he said, "so I reckon I must go now. It's nearly three miles to the district office, and the storm's bad, the snowdrifts are a caution—blamed if I'll get there before midnight. Listen to it howl!"

"I don't need the elder," said Lyzhin. "There's nothing for him to do here."

He looked at the old man with curiosity and asked:

"Tell me, grandfather, how many years is it you've been a policeman?"

"Why, about thirty. Five years after the Freedom[1] I got to be policeman, you can figure out for yourself. And I've been on the go every day since. People have holidays, but me, I'm always on the go. When it's Easter and the church bells are ringing and Christ has

[1] The emancipation of the serfs, proclaimed in 1861.

risen, I keep on trotting, with my bag. To the treasury, to the post office, to the police inspector's lodgings, to the district magistrate, to the tax collector, to the municipal office, to the gentry, to the peasants, to all Orthodox folk. I carry packages, notices, tax blanks, letters, all kinds of forms, reports, and you know, kind sir, your honor, they've got such forms nowadays to write numbers on—yellow, white, red—and every gentleman or priest or well-to-do peasant must write down a dozen times a year how much he has sown or harvested, how many bushels or poods he has of rye, how many of oats, and of hay, and all about the weather, you know, and insects, too, of all kinds. Of course you can write what you like, it's only a rule, but you must go and hand out the papers and then go and collect 'em again. Here, for instance, there's no call to cut open the gentleman; you know yourself it's all foolishness, you only dirty your hands, but here you've gone to the trouble, your honor, you've come because it's the rule, there's no getting round it. For thirty years I've been walking my legs off according to rule. In summer it's all right, it is warm and dry; but in winter and fall it puts you out. There were times I was drowning and times I was near froze to death; all kinds of things happened to me—wicked people in the woods took my bag away; I've got it in the neck and I've been brought to law."

"What for?"

"Fraud."

"What do you mean, fraud?"

"Why, you see, Khrisanf Grigoryev, the clerk, sold the contractor some boards as didn't belong to him—cheated him, that is. I was mixed up in it. They sent me to the tavern for vodka; well, the clerk didn't go shares with me—didn't even stand me a drink; but seeing as I'm a poor man, and so a no-account person, not to be relied on— to look at, that is—we were both brought to trial; he was sent to prison, but, praise God! I was acquitted on all counts. They read a paper, you know, in the court, about it. And they were all in uniform —in the court, I mean. I can tell you, your honor, for anyone not used to 'em, my duties are a caution, Lord keep you from them; but me, I don't mind it. Matter of fact, when I'm not on the go, my feet hurt. And at home it's worse for me. At home you have to light the stove for the clerk in the district office, to fetch water for him, to clean his boots."

"And what's your salary?" Lyzhin asked.

"Eighty-four rubles a year."

"I'll bet there are other little sums coming in. There are, aren't
there?"

"Other little sums? No, indeed! Gentlemen nowadays don't
often give tips. Gentlemen is strict nowadays, they take offense easy.
If you bring him a paper, he's offended, if you take off your cap to
him, he's offended. 'You used the wrong entrance,' he says. 'You're a
drunkard,' he says. 'You smell of onion; you're a blockhead,' he says;
'you're the son of a bitch.' There are some as is decent, of course; but
what does it get you? They only laugh at you and call you names.
Take Squire Altuhin, for instance, he's good-natured; and to look at
him, he's sober and in his right mind, but as soon as he lays eyes on
me he shouts God knows what. The name he calls me! 'You—' says
he."

The policeman pronounced some word but in such a low voice
that it was impossible to make out what he said.

"What?" asked Lyzhin. "Say it again."

" 'Administration,' " the policeman repeated aloud. "He's been
calling me that for a long time, for maybe six years. 'Hello, Administration!' But I don't mind; let him, God bless him! A lady will send
you a glass of vodka and a piece of pie sometimes, and you drink her
health. But it's mostly the peasants that give me something; peasants
are more warm-hearted, they fear God: one will give you a piece of
bread, another some cabbage soup, and there's some as stand you a
glass. The village Elders treat you to tea in the tavern. Here the inquest witnesses have gone to drink tea. 'Loshadin,' they says, 'you stay
here and keep watch for us,' and each of 'em gives me a kopeck.
They're scared, not being used to it, and yesterday they gave me fifteen kopecks and stood me a glass."

"And you, aren't you scared?"

"I am, sir; but of course it's all in the line of duty, there's no
getting round it. Last year I was taking an arrested man into town
and he laced into me and took it out of my hide! And all around us—
fields, woods—how could I get away from him? And that's how it is
here. I remember the gentleman, this Lesnitzky, when he was that
high, and I knew his father and his mama. I am from the village of
Nedoshchotova, and the Lesnitzkys, they weren't more than two
thirds of a mile from us and even less, their land bordered on ours,
and the old master, Lesnitzky, he had a sister, a God-fearing, charitable maiden lady. God rest the soul of Thy servant, Yulia, of sainted
memory! She never married, and when she was dying she divided up

all her property; she left two hundred and fifty acres to the monastery, and five hundred to our village commune for her soul's sake;
but her brother, I mean the master, he hid the paper, they say he
burnt it in the stove, and took all this land for himself. To be sure,
he thought it would be to his benefit; but no, wait, you can't get on in
the world by wrongdoing, brother. For twenty years the master
didn't go to confession. There was something as kept him from
church, you see, and he died without the sacrament. He busted. He
was as fat as they come. He busted lengthwise. Then everything was
taken away from Seryozha, the young master, I mean, to pay the
debts—every last thing. Well, he hadn't got very far with his book
learning, he couldn't do anything, and the president of the Zemstvo
Board, his uncle, he says to himself: 'I'll take him'—Seryozha, I
mean—'to be our agent; let him insure people, that's easy work.'
And the gentleman was young and proud, he wanted to live in better
style, on a grander scale, and have things his way; to be sure, it hurt
his feelings to be jolting about the county in a trashy cart and talking
to the peasants; he would walk and keep looking on the ground,
looking on the ground and saying nothing; if you called him right in
his ear, 'Sergey Sergeyich!' he would look round like this, 'Eh?' and
stare at the ground again; and now you see he's laid hands on himself. It don't fit, your honor, it's wrong, this thing, and there's no
understanding what goes on in the world, merciful Lord! Say your
father was rich and you're poor; it's eating humble pie, no denying
it, but there, you've got to put up with it. I used to live well, too, your
honor; I had two horses, three cows, I used to keep twenty head of
sheep; but that time's past, and here I am with nothing but a bag,
and even that's not mine, it's the Government's. And now in our village, if the truth be told, my house is the worst of the lot. Mokey had
four footmen to scrape and bow, Mokey is a footman himself now;
Petrak had four workmen to dig and delve, and now Petrak is a
workman himself."

"And how was it you came down in the world?" asked the magistrate.

"My sons are terrible boozers. They get so soused, so soused
there's no saying what it's like, you wouldn't believe me."

Lyzhin listened and thought how he, Lyzhin, would go back to
Moscow sooner or later, while this old man would stay here forever
and would always be on the go. And how many times in his life he
would come across such battered, unkempt, "no-account" old men,

whose souls cherished equally the fifteen kopeck piece, the glass of vodka, and the profound belief that you can't get along in this world by wrongdoing.

Then he grew tired of listening, and told the old man to bring him some hay for his bed. In the traveler's room there was an iron bedstead with a pillow and a quilt, and it could have been brought in; but the deceased had been lying beside it for nearly three days (and he may have been sitting on it just before his death), and now it would be disagreeable to sleep on it.

"It's only half past seven," thought Lyzhin, glancing at his watch. "How awful!"

He was not sleepy, but having no means of passing the time, he lay down and covered himself with a plaid. Loshadin went in and out several times, clearing away the dishes; smacking his lips and sighing, he kept stomping about the table; at last he took his little lamp and went out, and looking at his long gray hair and bent body from behind, Lyzhin reflected: "Just like a magician in an opera."

It grew dark. The moon must have been behind the clouds, as the windows and the snow on the windowframes could be seen distinctly.

"Hoo-oo-oo!" sang the storm. "Hoo-oo-oo!"

"He-e-e-lp!" shrieked a woman in the garret, or so it sounded. "He-e-e-lp!"

Thump! something outside banged against the wall. Bang!

The magistrate listened; there was no woman up there, it was the wind wailing. It was chilly, and he put his fur coat over his plaid. As he got warm, he thought how all this—the blizzard, and the cottage, and the old man, and the dead body lying in the next room—how all this was remote from the life he desired for himself, and how alien it all was to him, how petty, uninteresting. If this man had killed himself in Moscow or somewhere near the city, and he had had to hold an inquest on him there, it would have been interesting, important, and perhaps it would have seemed terrible to sleep in the room next to that in which the corpse lay. Here, hundreds of miles from Moscow, all this appeared somehow in a different light; it was not life, not human beings, but something that existed "according to rule," as Loshadin said; it would not leave the faintest trace in the memory and would be forgotten as soon as he, Lyzhin, drove away from Syrnya. The fatherland, the real Russia, was Moscow, Petersburg; but these were the provinces, the colonies. When you dream of playing a part, of becoming known, of being, for instance, examining magistrate in important cases or prosecutor in a circuit court, of being a social lion, you inevitably think of Moscow. If you are to live, then it must be in Moscow; here, nothing matters to you; you get reconciled readily to your insignificant role, and only look for one thing in life—to get away, to get away as quickly as possible. And in his mind Lyzhin hurried through the Moscow streets, called on acquaintances, met relatives, colleagues, and his heart contracted sweetly at the thought that he was only twenty-six, and that if in five or ten years he could break away from here and get to Moscow, even then it would not be too late and he would still have a whole life ahead of him. And as he began to doze off, and as his thoughts became confused, he imagined the long corridors of the Moscow court, himself delivering a speech, his sisters, the orchestra which for some reason kept droning: Hoo-oo-oo! Hoo-oo-oo!

Thump! Bang! sounded again. Thump!

And he suddenly recalled how one day, when he was talking to the bookkeeper at the Zemstvo office, a thin pale gentleman with dark eyes and black hair came up to the counter; he had a disagreeable look in his eyes such as one sees in people who have slept too long after dinner, and it marred his delicate, intelligent profile; and the high boots that he was wearing did not suit him, they looked clumsy. The bookkeeper had introduced him: "This is our Zemstvo agent."

"So that was Lesnitzky—this very man," it now occurred to Lyzhin.

He recalled Lesnitzky's low voice, called to mind his gait, and it seemed to him that someone was walking beside him now with a step like Lesnitzky's.

All at once he was terrified, his head felt cold.

"Who's there?" he asked fearfully.

"The p'liceman!"

"What do you want here?"

"I've come to ask, your honor— You said this evening as the elder wasn't needed, but I'm afraid he'll be angry. He told me to let him know. Shouldn't I go?"

"The deuce, I'm fed up with you," said Lyzhin with vexation, and covered himself up again.

"Maybe he'll be angry. I'll go, your honor. I hope you'll be all right here."

And Loshadin went out. There was coughing and whispering in the entry. The inquest witnesses must have returned.

"We'll let these poor devils get off as early as possible tomorrow—" thought the examining magistrate; "we'll do the autopsy as soon as it's light."

He began to doze off when suddenly he again became conscious of steps, not timid this time, but quick and noisy. A door slammed, voices were heard, the scratching of a match. . . .

"Are you asleep? Are you asleep?" Dr. Starchenko asked hurriedly and crossly as he lit one match after another. He was covered with snow from head to foot and he had brought cold air in with him. "Are you asleep? Get up! Let's go to von Taunitz's. He's sent his horses to fetch you. Let's go. There you will have supper, at least, and sleep decently. You see I've come for you myself. The horses are excellent, we'll get there in twenty minutes."

"What time is it now?"

"Quarter past ten."

Lyzhin, sleepy and out of sorts, put on his felt boots, his fur coat, cap and hood, and went out with the doctor. The frost had abated, but a strong, piercing wind was blowing and chasing down the street clouds of snow that seemed to flee in terror; high drifts had already piled up against fences and on door-steps. The doctor and the magistrate got into the sleigh, and the white coachman bent over them to button up the apron. They were both hot.

"Go ahead!"

They drove through the village. "Cutting a fluffy furrow there," the magistrate quoted the poet to himself, as he listlessly watched the working of the outrunner's legs. There were lights in all the cabins, as though it were the eve of a high holiday: the peasants had stayed up because they were afraid of the dead man. The coachman sullenly held his peace, he must have turned glum while he was waiting at the village headquarters, and now he too was thinking of the deceased.

"When they found out at von Taunitz's," said Starchenko, "that you were spending the night in the village, they all attacked me for not having brought you along with me."

At the turning, as they left the village behind them, the coachman suddenly shouted at the top of his voice: "Get off the road!"

A man flashed by: he was standing in the snow up to his knees, having moved off the road, and was staring at the troika. The magistrate caught sight of a hooked staff, a beard, and a bag slung sideways, and it seemed to him that it was Loshadin, and he even fancied that the man was smiling. He flashed by and vanished.

The road at first skirted the forest, then, broadening, cut through it; old pines and a young birch grove shot past, as well as tall, gnarled young oaks standing singly in the clearings where the wood had recently been cut; but soon everything was lost in clouds of snow; the coachman said that he could see the forest, but the magistrate could see nothing but the outrunner. The wind blew at their backs.

Suddenly the horses stopped.

"Well, what now?" asked Starchenko crossly.

Without a word the coachman climbed down from the box and began to run around the sleigh on his heels; he made larger and larger circles, getting further and further away from the sleigh, and it looked as though he were dancing; finally he returned and began turning off to the right.

"You've lost your way, eh?" asked Starchenko.

"No ma-a-atter—"

They came to a hamlet with not a light in it. Then again, forest and fields. And again they lost their way, and the coachman climbed down from the box and performed his dance. The troika flew along a dark road under overarching trees, flew swiftly, and the hooves of the fiery outrunner knocked against the dashboard. Here the trees roared fearfully and resonantly, and it was pitch dark, so that those in the sleigh felt as though they were rushing into an abyss. Suddenly bright light from an entrance and windows flashed upon their eyes, and they heard the friendly, steady barking of dogs and the sound of voices. They had arrived.

While they were taking off their fur coats and felt boots downstairs in the entry, *"Un petit verre de Clicquot"* was being played on the piano upstairs, and the stamping of children's feet was heard. Immediately they were enveloped in the genial warmth and the smell peculiar to an old mansion where, whatever the weather, it is warm and clean and comfortable.

"That's splendid!" said von Taunitz, a fat man with an incredibly broad neck and sidewhiskers, pressing the magistrate's hand. "That's splendid! Glad to see you here, delighted to make your acquaintance. We're by way of being colleagues, you know. At one time I served as assistant prosecutor, but not for long, only two years. I came here to see to the estate, and I have grown old here—in a word, I'm an old fogey. Glad to see you here," he continued, obviously controlling his voice so as not to speak loudly; he and his guests were on their way upstairs. "I have no wife. She died. But here are my daughters, let me introduce you," and turning round, he shouted downstairs in a stentorian voice, "Tell Ignat to have the sleigh ready by eight o'clock tomorrow!"

In the drawing room were his four daughters, young, pretty girls, all in gray dresses and with their hair done in the same style, and their cousin, also young and attractive, with her children. Starchenko, who was already acquainted with them, at once began begging them to sing something, and two of the young ladies kept on declaring that they could not sing and had no music; then the cousin sat down at the piano and with quavering voices they sang a duet from "The Queen of Spades." Again *Un petit verre de Clicquot"* was played, and the children danced about, stamping their feet in time. And Starchenko pranced about, too. Everybody laughed.

Then the children said good night and went off to bed. The magistrate laughed, danced a quadrille, paid court to the ladies, and kept wondering whether it were not all a dream. The wretched room at the village headquarters, the pile of hay in the corner, the rustle of the cockroaches, the disgusting, poverty-stricken setting, the voices of the inquest witnesses, the wind, the blizzard, the danger of getting lost; and suddenly these magnificent, bright rooms, the sound of the piano, the beautiful girls, the curly-headed children, the gay, happy laughter—such a transformation seemed to him like what happens in a fairy tale, and it seemed incredible that such transformations were possible within a distance of two miles in the course of a single hour. And dismal thoughts prevented him from enjoying himself, and he kept thinking that all about him was not life but scraps of life, fragments, that everything here was accidental, that one could draw no conclusion from it; and he even felt sorry for these girls, who were living and would die here in the wilds, in the provinces, far away from civilization where nothing is accidental, but everything is rational and governed by law, and where, for example, every suicide is intelligible, and it is possible to explain its why and wherefore and its significance in the general scheme of things. It occurred to him that since the life about him here in the wilds was unintelligible to him, and since he did not see it, it meant that it was non-existent.

At supper the talk was of Lesnitzky.

"He left a wife and child," said Starchenko. "I would forbid marriage to neurasthenics and people with a deranged nervous system, I would deprive them of the right and the capacity to have offspring. To bring neurasthenic children into the world is a crime."

"The unfortunate young man," said von Taunitz, sighing gently and shaking his head. "How much thinking you must do, how much suffering you must go through before you decide to take your own life—a young life! A misfortune like that can happen in any family, and that's terrible. It's hard to bear it, intolerable."

All the girls listened silently, with grave faces, looking at their father. On his part, Lyzhin felt that he ought to say something, but he couldn't think of anything, and merely observed:

"Yes, suicide is an undesirable phenomenon."

He slept in a warm room, in a soft bed, covered with a blanket, under which was a fine clean sheet, but for some reason did not feel comfortable; perhaps it was because the doctor and von Taunitz were talking for a long time in the next room, and overhead, in the attic and in the chimney, the wind was roaring just as it did at the village headquarters and howling as plaintively: Hoo-oo-oo-oo!

Von Taunitz's wife had died two years previously, and he had not yet reconciled himself to the fact, and no matter what he talked about, he always referred to his wife; and there was nothing about him to suggest the public prosecutor any more.

"Is it possible that I may get into such a state some day?" thought Lyzhin, as he was falling asleep and as he listened through the wall to his host's subdued and, as it were, orphaned voice.

The magistrate's sleep was restless. He was hot and uncomfortable, and he dreamed that he was not at von Taunitz's, not in the soft clean bed, but still at the village headquarters, lying on the hay, and hearing the low voices of the witnesses; he imagined that Lesnitzky was near by, fifteen paces away. In his dream he recalled how the insurance agent, black-haired, pale, wearing high, dusty boots, had approached the bookkeeper's counter. "This is our insurance agent—" Then he dreamed that Lesnitzky and Loshadin the policeman were walking through the open country in the snow, side by side, supporting each other; the blizzard was eddying above them, and the wind was blowing at their backs, but they walked on, chanting, "We go on, go on, go on. . . ."

The old man looked like a magician in an opera, and indeed both of them looked as though they were performing in a theater:

"We go on, go on, go on! You are where it is warm and bright and cozy, but we go on in the cold, in the storm, through deep snow. We know nothing of rest, we know nothing of joy. We carry the whole burden of this life, of ours and yours. Hoo-oo-oo! We go on, go on, go on . . ."

Lyzhin woke and sat up in bed. What a muddled, bad dream! And why did he couple the policeman and the agent in his dream? What nonsense! And now, as Lyzhin sat up in bed, clasping his head in his hands, his heart beating wildly, it seemed that indeed the lives of the policeman and the insurance agent had something in common. Didn't they go through life side by side, holding on to one another? Some tie, invisible yet significant and essential, existed between the two of them, even between them and von Taunitz, and among all, all; in this life, even in these wilds, nothing is accidental, everything is filled with one common idea, everything has one soul, one aim, and to understand it, it is not enough to think, to reason, perhaps one must also have the gift of insight into life, a gift which evidently is not vouchsafed to all. And the unhappy "neurasthenic"—as the doctor called him—who had broken down and killed himself, as well as the old peasant who spent his whole life trotting from one man to another every day, were accidents, fragments of life, only for him who thought of his own life as accidental, but were parts of one marvelous and rational organism for one who regarded his own life as part of that common whole, and had a penetrating insight into that fact. So Lyzhin thought, and it was a thought that he had long secretly harbored and that only now unfolded fully and distinctly in his consciousness.

He lay down and began to drop off; and suddenly they were again walking along together and chanting: "We go on, go on, go on. . . . We take from life all that it holds of what is most bitter and burdensome, and we leave to you what is easy and joyous; and sitting at supper, you can discuss coldly and reasonably why we suffer and perish, and why we are not as healthy and contented as you."

What they were chanting had occurred to him before, but this thought crouched somewhere in the background behind other thoughts and flickered timidly like a distant light in misty weather. And he felt that this suicide and the peasant's misery lay on his conscience, too; to be reconciled to the fact that these people, submitting to their fate, shouldered all that was darkest and most burdensome in life—how terrible that was! To be reconciled to this, and to wish for oneself a bright and active life among happy, contented people, and constantly to dream of such a life, that meant dreaming of new suicides of men crushed by toil and care, or of weak, forgotten men of whom people only talk sometimes at supper with vexation or sneers, but to whom no help is offered. And again:

"We go on, go on, go on. . . ."

As though someone were knocking with a little hammer on his temples.

He woke early in the morning with a headache, roused by a noise; in the next room von Taunitz was saying to the doctor in a loud voice:

"You can't leave now. Look at what's doing outdoors. Don't argue, but just ask the coachman: he won't drive you in such weather if you pay him a million."

"But it's only two miles," the doctor was saying in an imploring voice.

"But even if it were a quarter of a mile. If you can't, you can't. As soon as you drive out of the gates, it will be just hell, you will lose your way in a minute. I won't let you go, no matter what you say."

"By evening it's bound to quiet down," said the peasant who was lighting the stove.

In the next room the doctor began talking of the severe climate that influences the Russian character, of the long winters that, restricting freedom of movement, interfere with the intellectual growth of the people; and Lyzhin heard these pronouncements with vexation, looked out of the window at the drifts that had piled up against the fence, stared at the white dust that filled all visible space, at the trees that bent despairing now to the right, now to the left, listened to the howling and the banging, and thought gloomily:

"Well, what moral can you draw from all this? It's a blizzard, and that's all there is to it . . ."

They lunched at noon, then wandered aimlessly about the house; they stood at the windows.

"And Lesnitzky is lying there," thought Lyzhin, as he watched the snow eddies furiously circling above the drifts. "Lesnitzky is lying there, and the inquest witnesses are waiting—"

They spoke of the weather, remarking that the snowstorm usually lasted two days and two nights, rarely longer. At six they dined, then they played cards, sang, danced; finally they had supper. The day was over, they went to bed.

In the small hours of the morning everything quieted down. When they got up and looked out of the windows, the naked willows with their weakly drooping branches were standing quite motionless; the sky was overcast and the air was still, as though nature were now ashamed of its orgy, its mad nights, and the free rein it had given its passions. The horses, harnessed tandem, had been waiting at the steps since five o'clock in the morning. When it was fully light the doctor and the magistrate put on their fur coats and felt boots, and taking leave of their host, went out.

At the steps beside the coachman stood our policeman, Ilya Loshadin, hatless, with his old leather bag slung over his shoulder, covered with snow all over; his face was red and wet with perspiration. The footman who had gone out to help the guests into the sleigh and cover their legs, looked at him severely and said:

"What are you standing here for, you old devil? Go chase yourself!"

"Your honor, folks are uneasy," said Loshadin, a naive smile spreading over his face, and evidently glad to see at last the men he had been waiting for so long. "Folks are very uneasy, the children are crying. They thought, your honor, as you had gone back to the town again. Show us the mercy of heaven, kind gentlemen!"

The doctor and the magistrate said nothing, got into the sleigh, and drove off to Syrnya.

QUESTIONS

Chekhov's story is an example of a narrative built up by the careful integration of many elements: character, setting, theme, plot, symbol, imagery, action, point of view, and still others. In your analysis of this narrative, keep in mind the dependence of each part upon the other parts, as Chekhov undoubtedly did in composing the story. In answering each of the questions below, try to place your answer in the larger context of the story's total meaning.

1. What contrasts are established among the various characters? Do some of these characters function as symbols as well as real people? What

do they symbolize? Discuss the role of symbolism generally in the story.

2. One of the most significant characters, Lesnitzky, has died before the story begins. How does Chekhov make his presence dramatically felt throughout the narrative?

3. Chekhov has imposed a rather simple, but very effective, structural pattern upon the events of the narrative. Describe that pattern.

4. State what you think is the theme of the story. Discuss the relationship between the theme and the fact that Lesnitzky killed himself in the village headquarters after setting out food and ordering a samovar. What does the title of the story have to do with its theme? How does the meaning of the title change?

GUY DE MAUPASSANT

(1850-1893)

De Maupassant, a French novelist and short story writer, was profoundly influenced by his older compatriot, Gustave Flaubert. From him he learned the value of conciseness, precision, compression, and concrete detail, central characteristics of both his work and Flaubert's. These qualities were admirably suited to de Maupassant's brief but dramatic portrayals of character and to the emotion-packed scene around which his short stories are frequently built. The atmosphere of these stories is usually sombre, the approach analytical. He is a realist whose view of reality is narrow, an artist whose interest is as much in his art as in his subjects and themes.

Minuet

Great catastrophes barely sadden me, said Jean Bridelle, a bachelor who was looked upon as a skeptic. I have seen war at close range. Without feelings of compassion I stepped over bodies. The harsh brutalities of nature or men can make us utter cries of horror or indignation, but do not give us that wrenching of the heart, that shudder which crosses your back when you observe certain small distressing scenes.

Certainly, the most violent grief that can be felt is, for a mother, the loss of her child, and, for a man, the loss of his mother. That is violent and terrible. It overwhelms and rends a man. But you recover from those catastrophes as from wide bleeding wounds. Now, certain meetings, certain things half perceived, or guessed, certain

secret sorrows, certain treacheries of fate which stir up in us an entire world of painful thoughts, which abruptly open up before us the
mysterious portal of complex incurable moral sufferings, all the more
profound because they seem benign, all the more burning because
they seem intangible, all the more tenacious because they seem artificial, leave in our soul an aftermath of sadness, a bitter taste, the
sensation of disenchantment from which it takes a long time to be
free.

Before my eyes there are still two or three things which others
would certainly not have noticed, which have entered into me like
long thin incurable stings.

You would perhaps not understand the emotion which has remained in me from those rapid impressions. I will tell you only one.
It is very old, but alive as of yesterday. It is possible that my imagination alone is responsible for my emotion.

I am fifty. I was young then and was studying law. A bit sad,
something of a dreamer, imbued with a melancholy philosophy, I
had very little taste for noisy cafés, brawling friends or stupid girls.
I used to rise early, and one of my most cherished pleasures was to
walk alone, about eight in the morning, in the plant nursery of the
Luxembourg.

Perhaps you never knew that nursery. It was like a forgotten
garden of another century, a garden as pretty as the sweet smile of
an old lady. Bushy hedges separated the narrow regular lanes, quiet
lanes between two walls of foliage systematically trimmed. The large
shears of the gardener constantly kept in alignment those walls of
branches. Here and there, you came upon flower beds, borders
of small trees drawn up in rows like schoolboys out for a walk, companies of magnificent rosebushes or regiments of fruit trees.

An entire corner of that delightful grove was inhabited by bees.
Their straw houses, skillfully spaced on planks, opened to the sun
their doors as large as the opening of a thimble. Along the paths you
met buzzing golden honey bees, the real mistresses of that peaceful
place, the real promenaders of those criss-crossing lanes.

I came there almost every morning. I sat down on a bench and
read. At times I would let my book fall on my knees in order to

dream and listen to Paris living all about me and enjoy the infinite peacefulness of those old-fashioned groves.

But I soon realized that I was not the only one to frequent that place as soon as the gates were opened; and on occasion I met face to face, at the corner of a clump of bushes, a strange little old man.

He wore shoes with silver buckles, old-fashioned full-fall trousers, a snuff-colored frock coat, a ruff for a necktie, and—believe it or not—a gray hat with a large brim and long nap which made you think of Noah and his ark.

He was thin, very thin, angular, smirking and smiling. His bright eyes snapped and were restless beneath continually moving eyelids. He always held in his hand a magnificent gold-headed cane which must have been for him a splendid remembrance.

At first this fellow surprised me and then interested me beyond measure. I used to watch for him through the walls of leaves and would follow him at a distance, stopping at the corner of the groves in order not to be seen.

And then, one morning, when he thought he was quite alone, he began to make strange movements: a few small leaps first, then a bow. Then with his slim legs he performed a still sprightly *entrechat,* and began to whirl gallantly, jumping, flapping in a comic way, smiling as if in front of an audience, preening himself, rounding his arms, twisting his poor, puppet-like body, directing into the void slight touching ridiculous bows. He was dancing!

I remained petrified with amazement, wondering which of us was insane, he or I.

But he stopped suddenly, moved forward as actors do on the stage, then bowed and stepped back with the gracious smiles and kisses of an actress which he threw with his trembling hand to the two rows of trimmed trees.

And gravely he resumed his walk.

From that day on, I did not lose sight of him. Each morning he began his improbable exercise all over again.

I had a mad desire to speak to him. I ran the risk, and bowing to him, said:

"The weather is fine today, sir."

He bowed.

"Yes, sir, it is like the days of old."

A week later, we were friends and I knew his story. He had been dancing master at the Opéra, at the time of Louis XV. His beautiful cane was a gift from the Count of Claremont. And when you spoke about dancing, he could never stop talking.

Then, one day he confided in me:

"I married La Castris, monsieur. I will introduce you if you wish, but she only comes here in the afternoon. You see, this garden is our pleasure and our life. It is all that we have from other days. We have the feeling that we would no longer be able to exist if we did not have it. It is old and distinguished, isn't it? I think the air I breathe here has not changed since my youth. My wife and I spend all our afternoons here. But I come in the morning, because I rise early."

As soon as I had finished lunch, I returned to the Luxembourg, and soon I saw my friend who ceremoniously gave his arm to a small very old lady dressed in black, and to whom I was introduced. She was La Castris, the great dancer loved by princes and by the king and by the entire gallant century which seems to have left in the world an odor of love.

We sat down on a bench. It was the month of May. Perfume from the flowers floated in the neat lanes. A strong sun glided between the leaves and scattered over us large drops of light. The black dress of La Castris seemed all moist with light.

The garden was empty. You heard in the distance the wheels of cabs.

"Now explain to me," I said to the old dancer, "what the minuet was."

He shuddered.

"The minuet, monsieur, is the queen of dances, and the dance of queens. Do you understand? Since there are no more kings, there is no more minuet."

And he began, in a pompous style, a long dithyrambic eulogy which I did not understand. I tried to have the steps, all the movements and the positions described to me. He became confused, exasperated with his inability to explain, nervous and disconsolate.

Suddenly he turned toward his ancient companion, who had been silent and serious.

"Elise, are you willing, are you willing,—it would be good

of you—are you willing that we show this gentleman what it was?"

She looked anxiously in every direction, then got up without saying a word and took her place opposite him.

Then I saw something unforgettable.

They went back and forth with childish affectation, smiled at one another, swayed, bowed, hopped like two old dolls made to dance by an old mechanism, a bit broken, built long ago by a very skillful workman according to the fashion of the times.

And I watched them, my heart troubled by extraordinary sensations, my soul moved by indescribable melancholy. It seemed to me I was looking at a mournful and comic apparition, the out-of-fashion ghosts of an epoch. I wanted to laugh and felt like crying.

Suddenly they stopped. They had ended the movements of the dance. For a few seconds they remained standing, each facing the other, smirking in a surprising way. Then, sobbing, they embraced.

Three days afterward I left for the country. I did not see them again. When I came back to Paris, two years later, the plant nursery had been demolished. What became of them without the beloved garden of the past, and its maze of paths, its smell of other years, and the graceful curves of the groves?

Are they dead? Do they wander through modern streets like exiles without hope? Like quaint ghosts, do they dance a fantastic minuet among the cypresses of a cemetery, along paths bordered with tombs, in the moonlight?

My memory of them haunts and obsesses me, tortures me and remains in me like a wound. Why? I do not know.

Doubtless you will find all this ridiculous.

GIOVANNI VERGA

(1840-1922)

Of Sicilian birth, Verga was the son of wealthy, landed parents of the upper middle class. Although born in the Sicilian city of Catania, he spent many years in Florence and Milan, and in his young manhood he saw Italy become a unified nation for the first time in its ancient history. His writings fall into two phases. In the first phase, he wrote romances much like those of Alexandre Dumas, novels of duels, of intrigues, of passion, of "elegance and adultery," written in the Tuscan language of the cultured Florentines. Beginning in 1880, however, his works reveal a distinct shift in both style and subject matter. "The She-Wolf" derives from this second period. The language is spare, direct, concrete; the characters are peasants; the passion is at once more intense and less romantic. The realistic nature of his narratives allies him with the Italian verismo school. In this new approach, Verga saw individuals caught up in a world blind to their desires; these figures struggle against their destinies, but they do not triumph over them.

The She-Wolf

She was tall, thin; she had the firm and vigorous breasts of the olive-skinned—and yet she was no longer young; she was pale, as if always plagued by malaria, and in that pallor, two enormous eyes, and fresh red lips which devoured you.

In the village they called her the She-wolf, because she never had enough—of anything. The women made the sign of the cross

"The She-Wolf" by Giovanni Verga, from *The She-Wolf and Other Stories*. Reprinted with the permission of the University of California Press.

when they saw her pass, alone as a wild bitch, prowling about suspiciously like a famished wolf; with her red lips she sucked the blood of their sons and husbands in a flash, and pulled them behind her skirt with a single glance of those devilish eyes, even if they were before the altar of Saint Agrippina. Fortunately, the She-wolf never went to church, not at Easter, not at Christmas, not to hear Mass, not for confession.—Father Angiolino of Saint Mary of Jesus, a true servant of God, had lost his soul on account of her.

Maricchia, a good girl, poor thing, cried in secret because she was the She-wolf's daughter, and no one would marry her, though, like every other girl in the village, she had her fine linen in a chest and her good land under the sun.

One day the She-wolf fell in love with a handsome young man who had just returned from the service and was mowing hay with her in the fields of the notary; and she fell in love in the strongest sense of the word, feeling the flesh afire beneath her clothes; and staring him in the eyes, she suffered the thirst one has in the hot hours of June, deep in the plain. But he went on mowing undisturbed, his nose bent over the swaths.

"What's wrong, Pina?" he would ask.

In the immense fields, where you heard only the crackling flight of the grasshoppers, as the sun hammered down overhead, the She-wolf gathered bundle after bundle, and sheaf after sheaf, never tiring, never straightening up for an instant, never raising the flask to her lips, just to remain at the heels of Nanni, who mowed and mowed and asked from time to time:

"What is it you want, Pina?"

One evening she told him, while the men were dozing on the threshing floor, tired after the long day, and the dogs were howling in the vast, dark countryside.

"It's you I want. You who're beautiful as the sun and sweet as honey. I want you!"

"And I want your daughter, instead, who's a maid," answered Nanni laughing.

The She-wolf thrust her hands into her hair, scratching her temples, without saying a word, and walked away. And she did not appear at the threshing floor any more. But she saw Nanni again in October, when they were making olive oil, for he was working near her house, and the creaking of the press kept her awake all night.

"Get the sack of olives," she said to her daughter, "and come with me."

Nanni was pushing olives under the millstone with a shovel, shouting "Ohee" to the mule, to keep it from stopping.

"You want my daughter Maricchia?" Pina asked him.

"What'll you give your daughter Maricchia?" answered Nanni.

"She has all her father's things, and I'll give her my house too; as for me, all I need is a little corner in the kitchen, enough for a straw mattress."

"If that's the way it is, we can talk about it at Christmas," said Nanni.

Nanni was all greasy and filthy, spattered with oil and fermented olives, and Maricchia didn't want him at any price. But her mother grabbed her by the hair before the fireplace, muttering between her teeth:

"If you don't take him, I'll kill you!"

The She-wolf was almost sick, and the people were saying that when the devil gets old he becomes a hermit. She no longer roamed here and there, no longer lingered at the doorway, with those bewitched eyes. Whenever she fixed them on his face, those eyes of hers, her son-in-law began to laugh and pulled out the scapular or the Virgin to cross himself. Maricchia stayed at home nursing the babies, and her mother went into the fields to work with the men, and just like a man too, weeding, hoeing, feeding the animals, pruning the vines, despite the northeast and levantine winds of January or the August sirocco, when the mules' heads drooped and the men slept face down along the wall, on the north side. "In those hours between nones and vespers when no good woman goes roving around," [1] Pina was the only living soul to be seen wandering in the countryside, over the burning stones of the paths, through the scorched stubble of the immense fields that became lost in the suffocating heat, far, far away toward the foggy Etna, where the sky was heavy on the horizon.

"Wake up!" said the She-wolf to Nanni, who was sleeping in the

[1] An old Sicilian proverb, which refers to the hours of the early afternoon, when the Sicilian countryside lies motionless under a scorching sun and no person would dare walk on the roads. Those hours are traditionally believed to be under the spell of malignant spirits.

ditch, along the dusty hedge, his head on his arms. "Wake up. I've brought you some wine to cool your throat."

Nanni opened his drowsy eyes wide, still half asleep, and finding her standing before him, pale, with her arrogant breasts and her coal-black eyes, he stretched out his hands gropingly.

"No! no good woman goes roving around in the hours between nones and vespers!" sobbed Nanni, throwing his face back into the dry grass of the ditch, deep, deep, his nails in his scalp. "Go away! go away! don't come to the threshing floor again!"

The She-wolf was going away, in fact, retying her superb tresses, her gaze bent fixedly before her as she moved through the hot stubble, her eyes as black as coal.

But she came to the threshing floor again, and more than once, and Nanni did not complain. On the contrary, when she was late, in the hours between nones and vespers, he would go and wait for her at the top of the white, deserted path, with his forehead bathed in sweat; and he would thrust his hands into his hair, and repeat every time:

"Go away! go away! don't come to the threshing floor again!"

Maricchia cried night and day, and glared at her mother, her eyes burning with tears and jealousy, like a young she-wolf herself, every time she saw her come, mute and pale, from the fields.

"Vile, vile mother!" she said to her. "Vile mother!"

"Shut up!"

"Thief! Thief!"

"Shut up!"

"I'll go to the Sergeant, I will!"

"Go ahead!"

And she really did go, with her babies in her arms, fearing nothing, and without shedding a tear, like a madwoman, because now she too loved that husband who had been forced on her, greasy and filthy, spattered with oil and fermented olives.

The Sergeant sent for Nanni; he threatened him even with jail and the gallows. Nanni began to sob and tear his hair; he didn't deny anything, he didn't try to clear himself.

"It's the temptation!" he said. "It's the temptation of hell!"

He threw himself at the Sergeant's feet begging to be sent to jail.

"For God's sake, Sergeant, take me out of this hell! Have me killed, put me in jail; don't let me see her again, never! never!"

"No!" answered the She-wolf instead, to the Sergeant. "I kept a little corner in the kitchen to sleep in, when I gave him my house as dowry. It's my house. I don't intend to leave it."

Shortly afterward, Nanni was kicked in the chest by a mule and was at the point of death, but the priest refused to bring him the Sacrament if the She-wolf did not go out of the house. The She-wolf left, and then her son-in-law could also prepare to leave like a good Christian; he confessed and received communion with such signs of repentance and contrition that all the neighbors and the curious wept before the dying man's bed.—And it would have been better for him to die that day, before the devil came back to tempt him again and creep into his body and soul, when he got well.

"Leave me alone!" he told the She-wolf. "For God's sake, leave me in peace! I've seen death with my own eyes! Poor Maricchia is desperate. Now the whole town knows about it! If I don't see you it's better for both of us . . ."

And he would have liked to gouge his eyes out not to see those of the She-wolf, for whenever they peered into his, they made him lose his body and soul. He did not know what to do to free himself from the spell. He paid for Masses for the souls in purgatory and asked the priest and the Sergeant for help. At Easter he went to confession, and in penance he publicly licked more than four feet of pavement, crawling on the pebbles in front of the church—and then, as the She-wolf came to tempt him again:

"Listen!" he said to her. "Don't come to the threshing floor again; if you do, I swear to God, I'll kill you!"

"Kill me," answered the She-wolf, "I don't care; I can't stand it without you."

As he saw her from the distance, in the green wheat fields, Nanni stopped hoeing the vineyard, and went to pull the ax from the elm. The She-wolf saw him come, pale and wild-eyed, with the ax glistening in the sun, but she did not fall back a single step, did not lower her eyes; she continued toward him, her hands laden with red poppies, her black eyes devouring him.

"Ah! damn your soul!" stammered Nanni.

2

THE
MODERN
TEMPER

THE MODERN SHORT STORY is far too complex to permit a discussion of all its characteristic techniques, devices, themes, and methods. But there are aspects of modern fiction that we can discuss profitably. One of these is the development of psychological realism as a dominant mode. Psychological realism focuses upon human psychology, analyzing in detail the emotions and motivations of the characters. Henry James was one of the earliest practitioners of psychological realism, turning the study of manners into a plot framework within which he skillfully traced the personalities of his figures. Psychological realism has, if anything, gained in importance as a characteristic of modern fiction, reflecting such forces in human experience as Freudian psychology and the relationship between personality and social environment.

This emphasis upon human personality is paralleled by the rise of a technique which made such study both more realistic and more intriguing: stream of consciousness, which attempted to render in the very mind of the individual the thoughts, emotions, and sensations registered there. At much the same time the device known as interior monologue became an established convention in both the short story and the novel. Surrealism combined some of the characteristics of both psychological realism and stream of consciousness to produce a dream-like and apparently fragmented narrative which adapted well to the symbolic method and which was peculiarly successful in rendering certain modern themes, in particular man's existential sense of isolation and alienation. Another significant modern literary movement was naturalism, which selected realistic detail to exemplify a deterministic view of the human condition.

Henry James also contributed much of value to our theory of modern fiction; especially valuable are his ideas concerning point of view as a device. James did not invent point of view; that should be obvious from reading Poe and Melville, among others. Rather, he made other writers aware of it as a complex and enormously effective means of controlling the reader's angle of vision. It remains today an important instrument through which the writer retains command over his materials.

Completely new thematic materials, on the other hand, are less easy to single out. Fitzgerald's emphasis upon man's materialism, for example, is Hawthorne's concern, as well. But we can see certain themes increasing in importance. Dostoevsky's existentialism has become a major concern of modern writers, partly as a result of the impact on society of scientific thought and the technological revolution, partly from the consequent weakening in influence of man's spiritual heritage, partly—and here the irony is profound—as a result of the very ease with which modern man is able to communicate his thoughts and alter his physical location. Truly meaningful communication is as difficult as ever, and herein lies the frustration. The air of futility certainly belongs as much to Melville's Bartleby as it does to Dennis Lynds' John Cashmore, but we find it also in Kafka's "In the Penal Colony," Svevo's "Generous Wine," and Pirandello's "In the Abyss," so that the existential ambiance has become a predominantly modern phenomenon, at least where the short story is concerned.

These are matters which can be pursued with some profit in the stories grouped under the title, "The Modern Temper." The James, Conrad, and Powers stories might well be approached in terms of their use of point of view and their psychological realism, as might the Pirandello and Mansfield stories. Crane's naturalistic "The Blue Hotel" allows interesting comparisons and contrasts with the social realism of Gorky's "Twenty-Six Men and a Girl." Although the themes of the Joyce, Svevo, and Lynds narratives are similar, their techniques are widely divergent. Theme also links the Galsworthy, Kafka, and Fitzgerald works, but here again the techniques differ greatly. Character and atmosphere dominate Anderson's "Death in the Woods" and Faulkner's "A Rose for Emily," while the Hemingway, Rooney, and O'Connor stories stress the relationship between character and action and the element of violence. Thurber's "The Unicorn in the Garden" and Jackson's "The Witch" are both satiric in method, but the tone of each is different. Finally, Carson McCullers and Philip Roth return us to the close analysis of human psychology, but on a comic rather than tragic note.

HENRY JAMES

(1843-1916)

Henry James came from a wealthy, cultured New York family, the son of a theologian, Henry James, Sr. His brother, William James, became a famous philosopher and psychologist and the originator of the phrase, "stream of consciousness." The younger Henry James rapidly became a man of the world, touring Europe and spending long years in England, where he became a British citizen shortly before his death. James's early works chronicled the conflict between the energetic, sometimes wealthy, but always naive American on the one hand and the cultured, jaded, intriguing European on the other (see PORTRAIT OF A LADY). Later works dealt with primarily European settings and characters, but his last works returned to the conflict between the New World and the Old, most notably in THE AMBASSADORS. James also wrote plays, but these efforts met total failure on the stage. His real greatness lies in his novels and short stories, which contain some of the subtlest examinations of character and human relationships in all of modern literature. In more recent times his reputation has been founded in part upon his stature as a literary critic. His statements concerning the theory of literature have been collected in THE ART OF THE NOVEL and THE ART OF FICTION. James's complete works are readily available, and a new collected edition is now under way.

The Middle Years

The April day was soft and bright, and poor Dencombe, happy in the conceit of reasserted strength, stood in the garden of the hotel, comparing, with a deliberation in which however there was still something of languor, the attractions of easy strolls. He liked the feeling of the south so far as you could have it in the north, he liked the sandy cliffs and the clustered pines, he liked even the colourless sea. "Bournemouth as a health-resort" had sounded like a mere advertisement, but he was thankful now for the commonest conveniences. The sociable country postman, passing through the garden, had just given him a small parcel which he took out with him, leaving the hotel to the right and creeping to a bench he had already haunted, a safe recess in the cliff. It looked to the south, to the tinted walls of the Island, and was protected behind by the sloping shoulder of the down. He was tired enough when he reached it, and for a moment was disappointed; he was better of course, but better, after all, than what? He should never again, as at one or two great moments of the past, be better than himself. The infinite of life was gone, and what remained of the dose a small glass scored like a thermometer by the apothecary. He sat and stared at the sea, which appeared all surface and twinkle, far shallower than the spirit of man. It was the abyss of human illusion that was the real, the tideless deep. He held his packet, which had come by book-post, unopened on his knee, liking, in the lapse of so many joys—his illness had made him feel his age—to know it was there, but taking for granted there could be no complete renewal of the pleasure, dear to young experience, of seeing one's self "just out." Dencombe, who had a reputation, had come out too often and knew too well in advance how he should look.

His postponement associated itself vaguely, after a little, with a group of three persons, two ladies and a young man, whom, beneath him, straggling and seemingly silent, he could see move slowly together along the sands. The gentleman had his head bent over a book and was occasionally brought to a stop by the charm of this volume, which, as Dencombe could perceive even at a distance, had a cover alluringly red. Then his companions, going a little further, waited for him to come up, poking their parasols into the beach, looking around them at the sea and sky and clearly sensible of the beauty of the day. To these things the young man with the book was still more clearly indifferent; lingering, credulous, absorbed, he was an object of envy to an observer from whose connexion with literature all such artlessness had faded. One of the ladies was large and mature; the other had the spareness of comparative youth and of a social situation possibly inferior. The large lady carried back Dencombe's imagination to the age of crinoline; she wore a hat of the shape of a mushroom, decorated with a blue veil, and had the air, in her aggressive amplitude, of clinging to a vanished fashion or even a lost cause. Presently her companion produced from under the folds of a mantle a limp portable chair which she stiffened out and of which the large lady took possession. This act, and something in the movement of either party, at once characterised the performers— they performed for Dencombe's recreation—as opulent matron and humble dependent. Where moreover was the virtue of an approved novelist if one couldn't establish a relation between such figures? the clever theory for instance that the young man was the son of the opulent matron and that the humble dependent, the daughter of a clergyman or an officer, nourished a secret passion for him. Was that not visible from the way she stole behind her protectress to look back at him?—back to where he had let himself come to a full stop when his mother sat down to rest. His book was a novel, it had the catchpenny binding; so that while the romance of life stood neglected at his side he lost himself in that of the circulating library. He moved mechanically to where the sand was softer and ended by plumping down in it to finish his chapter at his ease. The humble dependent, discouraged by his remoteness, wandered with a martyred droop of the head in another direction, and the exorbitant lady, watching the waves, offered a confused resemblance to a flying-machine that had broken down.

When his drama began to fail Dencombe remembered that he had after all another pastime. Though such promptitude on the part of the publisher was rare he was already able to draw from its wrapper his "latest," perhaps his last. The cover of "The Middle Years" was duly meretricious, the smell of the fresh pages the very odour of sanctity; but for the moment he went no further—he had become conscious of a strange alienation. He had forgotten what his book was about. Had the assault of his old ailment, which he had so fallaciously come to Bournemouth to ward off, interposed utter blankness as to what had preceded it? He had finished the revision of proof before quitting London, but his subsequent fortnight in bed had passed the sponge over colour. He couldn't have chanted to himself a single sentence, couldn't have turned with curiosity or confidence to any particular page. His subject had already gone from him, leaving scarce a superstition behind. He uttered a low moan as he breathed the chill of this dark void, so desperately it seemed to represent the completion of a sinister process. The tears filled his mild eyes; something precious had passed away. This was the pang that had been sharpest during the last few years—the sense of ebbing time, of shrinking opportunity; and now he felt not so much that his last chance was going as that it was gone indeed. He had done all he should ever do, and yet hadn't done what he wanted. This was the laceration—that practically his career was over: it was as violent as a grip at his throat. He rose from his seat nervously—a creature hunted by a dread; then he fell back in his weakness and nervously opened his book. It was a single volume; he preferred single volumes and aimed at a rare compression. He began to read and, little by little, in this occupation, was pacified and reassured. Everything came back to him, but came back with a wonder, came back above all with a high and magnificent beauty. He read his own prose, he turned his own leaves, and had as he sat there with the spring sunshine on the page an emotion peculiar and intense. His career was over, no doubt, but it was over, when all was said, with *that*.

He had forgotten during his illness the work of the previous year; but what he had chiefly forgotten was that it was extraordinarily good. He dived once more into his story and was drawn down, as by a siren's hand, to where, in the dim underworld of fiction, the great glazed tank of art, strange silent subjects float. He recognised his motive and surrendered to his talent. Never probably had that talent, such as it was, been so fine. His difficulties were still there, but what was also there, to his perception, though probably, alas! to nobody's else, was the art that in most cases had surmounted them. In his surprised enjoyment of this ability he had a glimpse of a possible reprieve. Surely its force wasn't spent—there was life and service in it yet. It hadn't come to him easily, it had been backward and roundabout. It was the child of time, the nursling of delay; he had struggled and suffered for it, making sacrifices not to be counted, and now that it was really mature was it to cease to yield, to confess itself brutally beaten? There was an infinite charm for Dencombe in feeling as he had never felt before that diligence *vincit omnia*. The result produced in his little book was somehow a result beyond his conscious intention: it was as if he had planted his genius, had trusted his method, and they had grown up and flowered with this sweetness. If the achievement had been real, however, the process had been painful enough. What he saw so intensely to-day, what he felt as a nail driven in, was that only now, at the very last, had he come into possession. His development had been abnormally slow, almost grotesquely gradual. He had been hindered and retarded by experience, he had for long periods only groped his way. It had taken too much of his life to produce too little of his art. The art had come, but it had come after everything else. At such a rate a first existence was too short—long enough only to collect material; so that to fructify, to use the material, one should have a second age, an extension. This extension was what poor Dencombe sighed for. As he turned the last leaves of his volume he murmured "Ah for another go, ah for a better chance!"

The three persons drawing his attention to the sands had vanished and then reappeared; they had now wandered up a path, an artificial and easy ascent, which led to the top of the cliff. Dencombe's bench was halfway down, on a sheltered ledge, and the large lady, a massive heterogeneous person with bold black eyes and kind red cheeks, now took a few moments to rest. She wore dirty gauntlets and immense diamond ear-rings; at first she looked vulgar, but she contradicted this announcement in an agreeable off-hand tone. While her companions stood waiting for her she spread her skirts on the end of Dencombe's seat. The young man had gold spectacles, through which, with his finger still in his red-covered book, he glanced at the volume, bound in the same shade of the same colour, lying on the lap of the original occupant of the bench. After an instant Dencombe felt him struck with a resemblance; he had recognised the gilt stamp on the crimson cloth, was reading "The Middle Years" and now noted that somebody else had kept pace with him. The stranger was startled, possibly even a little ruffled, to find himself not the only person favoured with an early copy. The eyes of the two proprietors met a moment, and Dencombe borrowed amusement from the expression of those of his competitor, those, it might even be inferred, of his admirer. They confessed to some resentment—they seemed to say: "Hang it, has he got it *already*? Of course he's a brute of a reviewer!" Dencombe shuffled his copy out of sight while the opulent matron, rising from her repose, broke out: "I feel already the good of this air!"

"I can't say I do," said the angular lady. "I find myself quite let down."

"I find myself horribly hungry. At what time did you order luncheon?" her protectress pursued.

The young person put the question by. "Doctor Hugh always orders it."

"I ordered nothing to-day—I'm going to make you diet," said their comrade.

"Then I shall go home and sleep. *Qui dort dîne!*"

"Can I trust you to Miss Vernham?" asked Doctor Hugh of his elder companion.

"Don't I trust *you?*" she archly enquired.

"Not too much!" Miss Vernham, with her eyes on the ground, permitted herself to declare. "You must come with us at least to the house," she went on while the personage on whom they appeared to be in attendance began to mount higher. She had got a little out of ear-shot; nevertheless Miss Vernham became, so far as Dencombe was concerned, less distinctly audible to murmur to the young man: "I don't think you realise all you owe the Countess!"

Absently, a moment, Doctor Hugh caused his gold-rimmed spectacles to shine at her. "Is that the way I strike you? I see—I see!"

"She's awfully good to us," continued Miss Vernham, compelled by the lapse of the other's motion to stand there in spite of his discussion of private matters. Of what use would it have been that Dencombe should be sensitive to shades hadn't he detected in that arrest a strange influence from the quiet old convalescent in the great tweed cape? Miss Vernham appeared suddenly to become aware of some such connexion, for she added in a moment: "If you want to sun yourself here you can come back after you've seen us home."

Doctor Hugh, at this, hesitated, and Dencombe, in spite of a desire to pass for unconscious, risked a covert glance at him. What his eyes met this time, as happened, was, on the part of the young lady, a queer stare, naturally vitreous, which made her remind him of some figure—he couldn't name it—in a play or a novel, some sinister governess or tragic old maid. She seemed to scan him, to challenge him, to say out of general spite: "What have you got to do with us?" At the same instant the rich humour of the Countess reached them from above: "Come, come, my little lambs; you should follow your old *bergère!*" Miss Vernham turned away for it, pursuing the ascent, and Doctor Hugh, after another mute appeal to Dencombe and a minute's evident demur, deposited his book on the bench as if to keep his place, or even as a gage of earnest return, and bounded without difficulty up the rougher part of the cliff.

Equally innocent and infinite are the pleasures of observation and the resources engendered by the trick of analysing life. It amused poor Dencombe, as he dawdled in his tepid air-bath, to believe himself awaiting a revelation of something at the back of a fine young mind. He looked hard at the book on the end of the bench, but wouldn't have touched it for the world. It served his purpose to have a theory that shouldn't be exposed to refutation. He already felt better of his melancholy; he had, according to his old formula, put his head at the window. A passing Countess could draw off the fancy when, like the elder of the ladies who had just retreated, she was as obvious as the giantess of a caravan. It was indeed general views that were terrible; short ones, contrary to an opinion sometimes expressed, were the refuge, were the remedy. Doctor Hugh couldn't possibly be anything but a reviewer who had understandings for early copies with publishers or with newspapers. He reappeared in a quarter of an hour with visible relief at finding Dencombe on the spot and the gleam of white teeth in an embarrassed but generous smile. He was perceptibly disappointed at the eclipse of the other copy of the book; it made a pretext the less for speaking to the quiet gentleman. But he spoke notwithstanding; he held up his own copy and broke out pleadingly: "*Do* say, if you have occasion to speak of it, that it's the best thing he has done yet!"

Dencombe responded with a laugh: "Done yet" was so amusing to him, made such a grand avenue of the future. Better still, the young man took *him* for a reviewer. He pulled out "The Middle Years" from under his cape, but instinctively concealed any telltale look of fatherhood. This was partly because a person was always a fool for insisting to others on his work. "Is that what you're going to say yourself?" he put to his visitor.

"I'm not quite sure I shall write anything. I don't, as a regular thing—I enjoy in peace. But it's awfully fine."

Dencombe just debated. If the young man had begun to abuse him he would have confessed on the spot to his identity, but there was no harm in drawing out any impulse to praise. He drew it out with such success that in a few moments his new acquaintance, seated by his side, was confessing candidly that the works of the author of the volumes before them were the only ones he could read a second time. He had come the day before from London, where a friend of his, a journalist, had lent him his copy of the last, the copy sent to the office of the journal and already the subject of a "notice" which, as was pretended there—but one had to allow for "swagger" —it had taken a full quarter of an hour to prepare. He intimated that he was ashamed for his friend, and in the case of a work demanding and repaying study, of such inferior manners; and, with his fresh appreciation and his so irregular wish to express it, he speedily became for poor Dencombe a remarkable, a delightful apparition. Chance had brought the weary man of letters face to face with the greatest admirer in the new generation of whom it was supposable he might boast. The admirer in truth was mystifying, so rare a case was it to find a bristling young doctor—he looked like a German physiologist—enamoured of literary form. It was an accident, but happier than most accidents, so that Dencombe, exhilarated as well as confounded, spent half an hour in making his visitor talk while he kept himself quiet. He explained his premature possession of "The Middle Years" by an allusion to the friendship of the publisher, who, knowing he was at Bournemouth for his health, had paid him this graceful attention. He allowed he had been ill, for Doctor Hugh would infallibly have guessed it; he even went so far as to wonder if he mightn't look for some hygienic "tip" from a personage combining so bright an enthusiasm with a presumable knowledge of the remedies now in vogue. It would shake his faith a little perhaps to have to take a doctor seriously who could take *him* so seriously, but he enjoyed this gushing modern youth and felt with an acute pang that there would still be work to do in a world in which such odd combinations were presented. It wasn't true, what he had tried for renunciation's sake to believe, that all the combinations were exhausted. They weren't by any means—they were infinite: the exhaustion was in the miserable artist.

Doctor Hugh, an ardent physiologist, was saturated with the spirit of the age—in other words he had just taken his degree; but he was independent and various, he talked like a man who would have preferred to love literature best. He would fain have made fine phrases, but nature had denied him the trick. Some of the finest in "The Middle Years" had struck him inordinately, and he took the liberty of reading them to Dencombe in support of his plea. He grew vivid, in the balmy air, to his companion, for whose deep refreshment he seemed to have been sent; and was particularly ingenuous in describing how recently he had become acquainted, and how instantly infatuated, with the only man who had put flesh between the ribs of an art that was starving on superstitions. He hadn't yet written to him—he was deterred by a strain of respect. Dencombe at this moment rejoiced more inwardly than ever that he had never answered the photographers. His visitor's attitude promised him a luxury of intercourse, though he was sure a due freedom for Doctor Hugh would depend not a little on the Countess. He learned without delay what type of Countess was involved, mastering as well the nature of the tie that united the curious trio. The large lady, an Englishwoman by birth and the daughter of a celebrated baritone, whose taste *minus* his talent she had inherited, was the widow of a French nobleman and mistress of all that remained of the handsome fortune, the fruit of her father's earnings, that had constituted her dower. Miss Vernham, an odd creature but an accomplished pianist, was attached to her person at a salary. The Countess was generous, independent, eccentric; she travelled with her minstrel and her medical man. Ignorant and passionate she had nevertheless moments in which she was almost irresistible. Dencombe saw her sit for her portrait in Doctor Hugh's free sketch, and felt the picture of his young friend's relation to her frame itself in his mind. This young friend, for a representative of the new psychology, was himself easily hypnotised, and if he became abnormally communicative it was only a sign of his real subjection. Dencombe did accordingly what he wanted with him, even without being known as Dencombe.

Taken ill on a journey in Switzerland the Countess had picked him up at an hotel, and the accident of his happening to please her had made her offer him, with her imperious liberality, terms that couldn't fail to dazzle a practitioner without patients and whose resources had been drained dry by his studies. It wasn't the way he would have proposed to spend his time, but it was time that would pass quickly, and meanwhile she was wonderfully kind. She exacted perpetual attention, but it was impossible not to like her. He gave details about his queer patient, a "type" if there ever was one, who had in connexion with her flushed obesity, and in addition to the morbid strain of a violent and aimless will, a grave organic disorder; but he came back to his loved novelist, whom he was so good as to pronounce more essentially a poet than many of those who went in for verse, with a zeal excited, as all his indiscretion had been excited, by the happy chance of Dencombe's sympathy

and the coincidence of their occupation. Dencombe had confessed
to a slight personal acquaintance with the author of "The Middle
Years," but had not felt himself as ready as he could have wished
when his companion, who had never yet encountered a being so
privileged, began to be eager for particulars. He even divined in
Doctor Hugh's eye at that moment a glimmer of suspicion. But the
young man was too inflamed to be shrewd and repeatedly caught up
the book to exclaim: "Did you notice this?" or "Weren't you im-
mensely struck with that?" "There's a beautiful passage toward the
end," he broke out; and again he laid his hand on the volume. As
he turned the pages he came upon something else, while Dencombe
saw him suddenly change colour. He had taken up as it lay on the
bench Dencombe's copy instead of his own, and his neighbour at
once guessed the reason of his start. Doctor Hugh looked grave an
instant; then he said: "I see you've been altering the text!" Dencombe was a passionate corrector, a fingerer of style; the last thing
he ever arrived at was a form final for himself. His ideal would have
been to publish secretly, and then, on the published text, treat
himself to the terrified revise, sacrificing always a first edition and
beginning for posterity and even for the collectors, poor dears, with
a second. This morning, in "The Middle Years," his pencil had
pricked a dozen lights. He was amused at the effect of the young man's
reproach; for an instant it made him change colour. He stammered
at any rate ambiguously, then through a blur of ebbing consciousness
saw Doctor Hugh's mystified eyes. He only had time to feel he was
about to be ill again—that emotion, excitement, fatigue, the heat
of the sun, the solicitation of the air, had combined to play him a
trick, before, stretching out a hand to his visitor with a plaintive
cry, he lost his senses altogether.

Later he knew he had fainted and that Doctor Hugh had got
him home in a Bath-chair, the conductor of which, prowling within
hail for custom, had happened to remember seeing him in the garden of the hotel. He had recovered his perception on the way, and
had, in bed that afternoon, a vague recollection of Doctor Hugh's
young face, as they went together, bent over him in a comforting
laugh and expressive of something more than a suspicion of his identity. That identity was ineffaceable now, and all the more that he
was rueful and sore. He had been rash, been stupid, had gone out
too soon, stayed out too long. He oughtn't to have exposed himself

to strangers, he ought to have taken his servant. He felt as if he had fallen into a hole too deep to descry any little patch of heaven. He was confused about the time that had passed—he pieced the fragments together. He had seen his doctor, the real one, the one who had treated him from the first and who had again been very kind. His servant was in and out on tiptoe, looking very wise after the fact. He said more than once something about the sharp young gentleman. The rest was vagueness in so far as it wasn't despair. The vagueness, however, justified itself by dreams, dozing anxieties from which he finally emerged to the consciousness of a dark room and a shaded candle.

"You'll be all right again—I know all about you now," said a voice near him that he felt to be young. Then his meeting with Doctor Hugh came back. He was too discouraged to joke about it yet, but made out after a little that the interest was intense for his visitor. "Of course I can't attend you professionally—you've got your own man, with whom I've talked and who's excellent," Doctor Hugh went on. "But you must let me come to see you as a good friend. I've just looked in before going to bed. You're doing beautifully, but it's a good job I was with you on the cliff. I shall come in early to-morrow. I want to do something for you. I want to do everything. You've done a tremendous lot for me." The young man held his hand, hanging over him, and poor Dencombe, weakly aware of this living pressure, simply lay there and accepted his devotion. He couldn't do anything less—he needed help too much.

The idea of the help he needed was very present to him that night, which he spent in a lucid stillness, an intensity of thought that constituted a reaction from his hours of stupor. He was lost, he was lost—he was lost if he couldn't be saved. He wasn't afraid of suffering, of death, wasn't even in love with life; but he had had a deep demonstration of desire. It came over him in the long quiet hours that only with "The Middle Years" had he taken his flight; only on that day, visited by soundless processions, had he recognized his kingdom. He had had a revelation of his range. What he dreaded was the idea that his reputation should stand on the unfinished. It wasn't with his past but with his future that it should properly be concerned. Illness and age rose before him like spectres with pitiless eyes: how was he to bribe such fates to give him the second chance? He had had the one chance that all men have—he had had the chance of life. He went to sleep again very late, and when he awoke Doctor Hugh was sitting at hand. There was already by this time something beautifully familiar in him.

"Don't think I've turned out your physician," he said; "I'm acting with his consent. He has been here and seen you. Somehow he seems to trust me. I told him how we happened to come together yesterday, and he recognises that I've a peculiar right."

Dencombe felt his own face pressing. "How have you squared the Countess?"

The young man blushed a little, but turned it off. "Oh never mind the Countess!"

"You told me she was very exacting."

Doctor Hugh had a wait. "So she is."

"And Miss Vernham's an *intrigante*."

"How do you know that?"

"I know everything. One *has* to, to write decently!"

"I think she's mad," said limpid Doctor Hugh.

"Well, don't quarrel with the Countess—she's a present help to you."

"I don't quarrel," Doctor Hugh returned. "But I don't get on with silly women." Presently he added: "You seem very much alone."

"That often happens at my age. I've outlived, I've lost by the way."

Doctor Hugh faltered; then surmounting a soft scruple: "Whom have you lost?"

"Every one."

"Ah no," the young man breathed, laying a hand on his arm.

"I once had a wife—I once had a son. My wife died when my child was born, and my boy, at school, was carried off by typhoid."

"I wish I'd been there!" cried Doctor Hugh.

"Well—if you're here!" Dencombe answered with a smile that, in spite of dimness, showed how he valued being sure of his companion's whereabouts.

"You talk strangely of your age. You're not old."

"Hypocrite—so early!"

"I speak physiologically."

"That's the way I've been speaking for the last five years, and it's exactly what I've been saying to myself. It isn't till we *are* old that we begin to tell ourselves we're not."

"Yet I know I myself am young," Doctor Hugh returned.

"Not so well as I!" laughed his patient, whose visitor indeed would have established the truth in question by the honesty with which he changed the point of view, remarking that it must be one of the charms of age—at any rate in the case of high distinction—to feel that one has laboured and achieved. Doctor Hugh employed the common phrase about earning one's rest, and it made poor Dencombe for an instant almost angry. He recovered himself, however, to explain, lucidly enough, that if, ungraciously, he knew nothing of such a balm, it was doubtless because he had wasted inestimable years. He had followed literature from the first, but he had taken a lifetime to get abreast of her. Only to-day at last had he begun to *see*, so that all he had hitherto shown was a movement without a direction. He had ripened too late and was so clumsily constituted that he had had to teach himself by mistakes.

"I prefer your flowers then to other people's fruit, and your mistakes to other people's successes," said gallant Doctor Hugh. "It's for your mistakes I admire you."

"You're happy—you don't know," Dencombe answered.

Looking at his watch the young man had got up; he named the hour of the afternoon at which he would return. Dencombe warned him against committing himself too deeply, and expressed again all his dread of making him neglect the Countess—perhaps incur her displeasure.

"I want to be like you—I want to learn by mistakes!" Doctor Hugh laughed.

"Take care you don't make too grave a one! But do come back," Dencombe added with the glimmer of a new idea.

"You should have had more vanity!" His friend spoke as if he knew the exact amount required to make a man of letters normal.

"No, no—I only should have had more time. I want another go."

"Another go?"

"I want an extension."

"An extension?" Again Doctor Hugh repeated Dencombe's words, with which he seemed to have been struck.

"Don't you know?—I want to what they call 'live.' "

The young man, for good-bye, had taken his hand, which closed with a certain force. They looked at each other hard. "You *will* live," said Doctor Hugh.

"Don't be superficial. It's too serious!"

"You *shall* live!" Dencombe's visitor declared, turning pale.

"Ah that's better!" And as he retired the invalid, with a troubled laugh, sank gratefully back.

All that day and all the following night he wondered if it mightn't be arranged. His doctor came again, his servant was attentive, but it was to his confident young friend that he felt himself mentally appeal. His collapse on the cliff was plausibly explained and his liberation, on a better basis, promised for the morrow; meanwhile, however, the intensity of his meditations kept him tranquil and made him indifferent. The idea that occupied him was none the less absorbing because it was a morbid fancy. Here was a clever son of the age, ingenious and ardent, who happened to have set him up for connoisseurs to worship. This servant of his altar had all the new learning in science and all the old reverence in faith; wouldn't he therefore put his knowledge at the disposal of his sympathy, his craft at the disposal of his love? Couldn't he be trusted to invent a remedy for a poor artist to whose art he had paid a tribute? If he couldn't the alternative was hard: Dencombe would have to surrender to silence unvindicated and undivined. The rest of the day and all the next he toyed in secret with this sweet futility. Who would work the miracle for him but the young man who could combine such lucidity with such passion? He thought of the fairy-tales of science and charmed himself into forgetting that he looked for a magic that was not of this world. Doctor Hugh was an apparition, and that placed him above the law. He came and went while his patient, who now sat up, followed him with supplicating eyes. The interest of knowing the great author had made the young man begin "The Middle Years" afresh and would help him to find a richer sense between its covers. Dencombe had told him what he "tried for"; with all his intelligence, on a first perusal, Doctor Hugh had failed to guess it. The baffled celebrity wondered then who in the world *would* guess it: he was amused once more at the diffused massive weight that could be thrown into the missing of an intention. Yet he wouldn't rail at the general mind to-day—consoling as that ever had been: the revelation of his own slowness had seemed to make all stupidity sacred.

Doctor Hugh, after a little, was visibly worried, confessing, on enquiry, to a source of embarrassment at home. "Stick to the Countess—don't mind me," Dencombe said repeatedly; for his companion was frank enough about the large lady's attitude. She was so jealous that she had fallen ill—she resented such a breach of allegiance. She paid so much for his fidelity that she must have it all: she refused him the right to other sympathies, charged him with scheming to make her die alone, for it was needless to point out how little Miss Vernham was a resource in trouble. When Doctor Hugh mentioned that the Countess would already have left Bournemouth if he hadn't kept her in bed, poor Dencombe held his arm tighter and said with decision: "Take her straight away." They had gone out together, walking back to the sheltered nook in which, the other day, they had met. The young man, who had given his companion a personal support, declared with emphasis that his conscience was clear—he could ride two horses at once. Didn't he dream for his future of a time when he should have to ride five hundred? Longing equally for virtue, Dencombe replied that in that golden age no patient would pretend to have contracted with him for his whole attention. On the part of the Countess wasn't such an avidity lawful? Doctor Hugh denied it, said there was no contract, but only a free understanding, and that a sordid servitude was impossible to a generous spirit; he liked moreover to talk about art, and that was the subject on which, this time, as they sat together on the sunny bench, he tried most to engage the author of "The Middle Years." Dencombe, soaring again a little on the weak wings of convalescence and still haunted by that happy notion of an organised rescue, found another strain of eloquence to plead the cause of a certain splendid "last manner," the very citadel, as it would prove, of his reputation, the stronghold into which his real treasure would be gathered. While his listener gave up the morning and the great still sea ostensibly waited he had a wondrous explanatory hour. Even for himself he was inspired as he told what his treasure would consist of; the precious metals he would dig from the mine, the jewels rare, strings of pearls, he would hang between the columns of his temple. He was wondrous for himself, so thick his convictions crowded, but still more wondrous for Doctor Hugh, who assured him none the less that the very pages he had just published were already encrusted with gems. This admirer, however, panted for the combinations to come and, before the face of the beautiful day, renewed to Dencombe his guarantee that his profession would hold itself responsible for such a life. Then he suddenly clapped his hand upon his watch-pocket and asked leave to absent himself for half an hour.

Dencombe waited there for his return, but was at last recalled to the actual by the fall of a shadow across the ground. The shadow darkened into that of Miss Vernham, the young lady in attendance on the Countess; whom Dencombe, recognising her, perceived so clearly to have come to speak to him that he rose from his bench to acknowledge the civility. Miss Vernham indeed proved not particularly civil; she looked strangely agitated, and her type was now unmistakeable.

"Excuse me if I do ask," she said, "whether it's too much to hope that you may be induced to leave Doctor Hugh alone." Then before our poor friend, greatly disconcerted, could protest: "You ought to be informed that you stand in his light—that you may do him a terrible injury."

"Do you mean by causing the Countess to dispense with his services?"

"By causing her to disinherit him." Dencombe stared at this, and Miss Vernham pursued, in the gratification of seeing she could produce an impression: "It has depended on himself to come into something very handsome. He has had a grand prospect, but I think you've succeeded in spoiling it."

"Not intentionally, I assure you. Is there no hope the accident may be repaired?" Dencombe asked.

"She was ready to do anything for him. She takes great fancies, she lets herself go—it's her way. She has no relations, she's free to dispose of her money, and she's very ill," said Miss Vernham for a climax.

"I'm very sorry to hear it," Dencombe stammered.

"Wouldn't it be possible for you to leave Bournemouth? That's what I've come to see about."

He sank to his bench. "I'm very ill myself, but I'll try!"

Miss Vernham still stood there with her colourless eyes and the brutality of her good conscience. "Before it's too late, please!" she said; and with this she turned her back, in order, quickly, as if it had been a business to which she could spare but a precious moment, to pass out of his sight.

Oh yes, after this Dencombe was certainly very ill. Miss Vernham had upset him with her rough fierce news; it was the sharpest shock to him to discover what was at stake for a penniless young man of fine parts. He sat trembling on his bench, staring at the waste of waters, feeling sick with the directness of the blow. He was indeed too weak, too unsteady, too alarmed; but he would make the effort to get away, for he couldn't accept the guilt of interference and his honour was really involved. He would hobble home, at any rate, and then think what was to be done. He made his way back to the hotel and, as he went, had a characteristic vision of Miss Vernham's great motive. The Countess hated women of course—Dencombe was lucid about that; so the hungry pianist had no personal hopes and could only console herself with the bold conception of helping Doctor Hugh in order to marry him after he should get his money or else induce him to recognise her claim for compensation and buy her off. If she had befriended him at a fruitful crisis he would really, as a man of delicacy—and she knew what to think of that point—have to reckon with her.

At the hotel Dencombe's servant insisted on his going back to bed. The invalid had talked about catching a train and had begun with orders to pack; after which his racked nerves had yielded to a sense of sickness. He consented to see his physician, who immediately was sent for, but he wished it to be understood that his door was irrevocably closed to Doctor Hugh. He had his plan, which was so fine that he rejoiced in it after getting back to bed. Doctor Hugh, suddenly finding himself snubbed without mercy, would, in natural disgust and to the joy of Miss Vernham, renew his allegiance to the Countess. When his physician arrived Dencombe learned that he was feverish and that this was very wrong: he was to cultivate calmness and try, if possible, not to think. For the rest of the day he wooed stupidity; but there was an ache that kept him sentient, the probable sacrifice of his "extension," the limit of his course. His medical adviser was anything but pleased; his successive relapses were ominous. He charged this personage to put out a strong hand and take Doctor Hugh off his mind—it would contribute so much to his being quiet. The agitating name, in his room, was not mentioned again, but his security was a smothered fear, and it was not confirmed by the receipt, at ten o'clock that evening, of a telegram which his servant opened and read him and to which, with an address in London, the signature of Miss Vernham was attached. "Beseech you to use all influence to make our friend join us here in the morning. Countess much the worse for dreadful journey, but everything may still be saved." The two ladies had gathered themselves up and had been capable in the afternoon of a spiteful revolution. They had started for the capital, and if the elder one, as Miss

Vernham had announced, was very ill, she had wished to make it clear that she was proportionately reckless. Poor Dencombe, who was not reckless and who only desired that everything should indeed be "saved," sent this missive straight off to the young man's lodging and had on the morrow the pleasure of knowing that he had quitted Bournemouth by an early train.

Two days later he pressed in with a copy of a literary journal in his hand. He had returned because he was anxious and for the pleasure of flourishing the great review of "The Middle Years." Here at least was something adequate—it rose to the occasion; it was an acclamation, a reparation, a critical attempt to place the author in the niche he had fairly won. Dencombe accepted and submitted; he made neither objection nor enquiry, for old complications had returned and he had had two dismal days. He was convinced not only that he should never again leave his bed, so that his young friend might pardonably remain, but that the demand he should make on the patience of beholders would be of the most moderate. Doctor Hugh had been to town, and he tried to find in his eyes some confession that the Countess was pacified and his legacy clinched; but all he could see there was the light of his juvenile joy in two or three of the phrases of the newspaper. Dencombe couldn't read them, but when his visitor had insisted on repeating them more than once he was able to shake an unintoxicated head. "Ah no—but they would have been true of what I *could* have done!"

"What people 'could have done' is mainly what they've in fact done," Doctor Hugh contended.

"Mainly, yes; but I've been an idiot!" Dencombe said.

Doctor Hugh did remain; the end was coming fast. Two days later his patient observed to him, by way of the feeblest of jokes, that there would now be no question whatever of a second chance. At this the young man stared; then he exclaimed: "Why it has come to pass —it has come to pass! The second chance has been the public's— the chance to find the point of view, to pick up the pearl!"

"Oh the pearl!" poor Dencombe uneasily sighed. A smile as cold as a winter sunset flickered on his drawn lips as he added: "The pearl is the unwritten—the pearl is the unalloyed, the *rest,* the lost!"

From that hour he was less and less present, heedless to all appearance of what went on round him. His disease was definitely mortal, of an action as relentless, after the short arrest that had enabled him to fall in with Doctor Hugh, as a leak in a great ship. Sinking steadily, though this visitor, a man of rare resources, now cordially approved by his physician, showed endless art in guarding him from pain, poor Dencombe kept no reckoning of favour or neglect, betrayed no symptom of regret or speculation. Yet toward the last he gave a sign of having noticed how for two days Doctor Hugh hadn't been in his room, a sign that consisted of his suddenly opening his eyes to put a question. Had he spent those days with the Countess?

"The Countess is dead," said Doctor Hugh. "I knew that in a particular contingency she wouldn't resist. I went to her grave."

Dencombe's eyes opened wider. "She left you 'something handsome'?"

The young man gave a laugh almost too light for a chamber of woe. "Never a penny. She roundly cursed me."

"Cursed you?" Dencombe wailed.

"For giving her up. I gave her up for *you*. I had to choose," his companion explained.

"You chose to let a fortune go?"

"I chose to accept, whatever they might be, the consequences of my infatuation," smiled Doctor Hugh. Then as a larger pleasantry: "The fortune be hanged! It's your own fault if I can't get your things out of my head."

The immediate tribute to his humour was a long bewildered moan; after which, for many hours, many days, Dencombe lay motionless and absent. A response so absolute, such a glimpse of a definite result and such a sense of credit, worked together in his mind and, producing a strange commotion, slowly altered and transfigured his despair. The sense of cold submersion left him—he seemed to float without an effort. The incident was extraordinary as evidence, and it shed an intenser light. At the last he signed to Doctor Hugh to listen and, when he was down on his knees by the pillow, brought him very near. "You've made me think it all a delusion."

"Not your glory, my dear friend," stammered the young man.

"Not my glory—what there is of it! It *is* glory—to have been tested, to have had our little quality and cast our little spell. The thing is to have made somebody care. You happen to be crazy of course, but that doesn't affect the law."

"You're a great success!" said Doctor Hugh, putting into his young voice the ring of a marriage-bell.

Dencombe lay taking this in; then he gathered strength to speak once more. "A second chance—*that's* the delusion. There never was to be but one. We work in the dark—we do what we can—we give what we have. Our doubt is our passion and our passion is our task. The rest is the madness of art."

"If you've doubted, if you've despaired, you've always 'done' it," his visitor subtly argued.

"We've done something or other," Dencombe conceded.

"Something or other is everything. It's the feasible. It's *you!*"

"Comforter!" poor Dencombe ironically sighed.

"But it's true," insisted his friend.

"It's true. It's frustration that doesn't count."

"Frustration's only life," said Doctor Hugh.

"Yes, it's what passes." Poor Dencombe was barely audible, but he had marked with the words the virtual end of his first and only chance.

JOSEPH CONRAD

(1857-1924)

Josef Teodor Konrad Nalecz Korzeniowski was born in Poland and spoke no English until he was nineteen. Despite this fact, he became one of the greatest writers of fiction in the English language. From 1874 until 1893 he followed the sea, rising to the command of his own ships. His first novel, ALMAYER'S FOLLY, was not published until 1895, when Conrad was thirty-eight years old. Many of his finest works reflect his career at sea: "Youth," "Typhoon," "The Heart of Darkness," LORD JIM, and VICTORY. But others have quite different settings; "Il Conde" is one of these. Whether on land or at sea, however, Conrad's narratives consistently take the reader on a voyage into the dark heart of man, or reveal to him the dark and impenetrable forces against which man struggles. This struggle may bring out the heroic in man, but it is, in the end, a futile effort.

Il Conde

"Vedi Napoli e poi mori."

The first time we got into conversation was in the National Museum in Naples, in the rooms on the ground floor containing the famous collection of bronzes from Herculaneum and Pompeii: that marvellous legacy of antique art whose delicate perfection has been preserved for us by the catastrophic fury of a volcano.

He addressed me first, over the celebrated Resting Hermes which we had been looking at side by side. He said the right things

"Il Conde" From *A Set of Six* by Joseph Conrad. Reprinted with the permission of the trustees of the Joseph Conrad estate and J. M. Dent & Sons Ltd.

about the wholly admirable piece. Nothing profound. His taste was
natural rather than cultivated. He had obviously seen many fine
things in his life and appreciated them: but he had no jargon of a
dilettante or the connoisseur. A hateful tribe. He spoke like a fairly
intelligent man of the world, a perfectly unaffected gentleman.

We had known each other by sight for some few days past. Staying in the same hotel—good, but not extravagantly up to date—I
had noticed him in the vestibule going in and out. I judged he was
an old and valued client. The bow of the hotel-keeper was cordial
in its deference, and he acknowledged it with familiar courtesy.
For the servants he was *Il Conde*. There was some squabble over a
man's parasol—yellow silk with white lining sort of thing—the waiters had discovered abandoned outside the dining-room door. Our
gold-laced door-keeper recognized it and I heard him directing one
of the lift boys to run after *Il Conde* with it. Perhaps he was the
only Count staying in the hotel, or perhaps he had the distinction of
being *the* Count *par excellence,* conferred upon him because of his
tried fidelity to the house.

Having conversed at the Museo— (and by the by he had expressed his dislike of the busts and statues of Roman emperors
in the gallery of marbles: their faces were too vigorous, too pronounced for him)—having conversed already in the morning, I
did not think I was intruding when in the evening, finding the dining-room very full, I proposed to share his little table. Judging by
the quiet urbanity of his consent he did not think so either. His smile
was very attractive.

He dined in an evening waistcoat and a "smoking" (he called
it so) with a black tie. All this of very good cut, not new—just as
these things should be. He was, morning or evening, very correct in
his dress. I have no doubt that his whole existence had been correct,
well ordered and conventional, undisturbed by startling events. His
white hair, brushed upward off a lofty forehead, gave him the air of
an idealist, of an imaginative man. His white moustache, heavy but
carefully trimmed and arranged, was not unpleasantly tinted a
golden yellow in the middle. The faint scent of some very good perfume, and of good cigars (that last odour quite remarkable to come
upon in Italy) reached me across the table. It was in his eyes that
his age showed most. They were a little weary with creased eyelids.
He must have been sixty or a couple of years more. And he was com-

municative. I would not go so far as to call it garrulous—but distinctly communicative.

He had tried various climates, of Abbazia, of the Riviera, of other places, too, he told me; but the only one which suited him was the climate of the Gulf of Naples. The ancient Romans, who, he pointed out to me, were men expert in the art of living, knew very well what they were doing when they built their villas on these shores, in Baiæ, in Vico, in Capri. They came down to this seaside in search of health, bringing with them their trains of mimes and flute-players to amuse their leisure. He thought it extremely probable that the Romans of the higher classes were specially predisposed to painful rheumatic affections.

This was the only personal opinion I heard him express. It was based on no special erudition. He knew no more of the Romans than an average informed man of the world is expected to know. He argued from personal experience. He had suffered himself from a painful and dangerous rheumatic affection till he found relief in this particular spot of southern Europe.

This was three years ago, and ever since he had taken up his quarters on the shores of the gulf, either in one of the hotels in Sorrento or hiring a small villa in Capri. He had a piano, a few books: picked up transient acquaintances of a day, week, or month in the stream of travellers from all Europe. One can imagine him going out for his walks in the streets and lanes, becoming known to beggars, shopkeepers, children, country people; talking amiably over the walls to the contadini—and coming back to his rooms or his villa to sit before the piano, with his white hair brushed up and his thick orderly moustache, "to make a little music for myself." And, of course, for a change there was Naples near by—life, movement, animation, opera. A little amusement, as he said, is necessary for health. Mimes and flute-players, in fact. Only, unlike the magnates of ancient Rome, he had no affairs of the city to call him away from these moderate delights. He had no affairs at all. Probably he had never had any grave affairs to attend to in his life. It was a kindly existence, with its joys and sorrows regulated by the course of Nature—marriages, births, deaths—ruled by the prescribed usages of good society and protected by the State.

He was a widower; but in the months of July and August he ventured to cross the Alps for six weeks on a visit to his married daughter. He told me her name. It was that of a very aristocratic family. She had a castle—in Bohemia, I think. This is as near as I ever came to ascertaining his nationality. His own name, strangely enough, he never mentioned. Perhaps he thought I had seen it on the published list. Truth to say, I never looked. At any rate, he was a good European—he spoke four languages to my certain knowledge— and a man of fortune. Not of great fortune, evidently and appropriately. I imagine that to be extremely rich would have appeared to him improper, *outré*—too blatant altogether. And obviously, too, the fortune was not of his making. The making of a fortune cannot be achieved without some roughness. It is a matter of temperament. His nature was too kindly for strife. In the course of conversation he mentioned his estate quite by the way, in reference to that painful and alarming rheumatic affection. One year, staying incautiously beyond the Alps as late as the middle of September, he had been laid up for three months in that lonely country house with no one but his valet and the caretaking couple to attend to him. Because, as he expressed it, he "kept no establishment there." He had only gone for a couple of days to confer with his land agent. He promised himself never to be so imprudent in the future. The first weeks of September would find him on the shores of his beloved gulf.

Sometimes in travelling one comes upon such lonely men, whose only business is to wait for the unavoidable. Deaths and marriages have made a solitude round them, and one really cannot blame their endeavours to make the waiting as easy as possible. As he remarked to me: "At my time of life freedom from physical pain is a very important matter."

It must not be imagined that he was a wearisome hypochondriac. He was really much too well-bred to be a nuisance. He had an eye for the small weaknesses of humanity. But it was a good-natured eye. He made a restful, easy, pleasant companion for the hours between dinner and bedtime. We spent three evenings together, and then I had to leave Naples in a hurry to look after a friend who had fallen seriously ill in Taormina. Having nothing to do, *Il Conde* came to see me off at the station. I was somewhat upset, and his idleness was always ready to take a kindly form. He was by no means an indolent man.

He went along the train peering into the carriages for a good seat for me, and then remained talking cheerily from below. He declared he would miss me that evening very much, and announced his intention of going after dinner to listen to the band in the public garden, the Villa Nazionale. He would amuse himself by hearing excellent music and looking at the best society. There would be a lot of people, as usual.

I seem to see him yet—his raised face with a friendly smile under the thick moustaches, and his kind, fatigued eyes. As the train began to move, he addressed me in two languages: first in French, saying, *"Bon voyage";* then, in his very good, somewhat emphatic English, encouragingly, because he could see my concern: "All will—be—well—yet!"

My friend's illness having taken a decidedly favourable turn, I returned to Naples on the tenth day. I cannot say I had given much thought to *Il Conde* during my absence, but entering the dining-room I looked for him in his habitual place. I had an idea he might have gone back to Sorrento to his piano and his books and his fishing. He was great friends with all the boatmen, and fished a good deal with lines from a boat. But I made out his white head in a crowd of heads, and even from a distance noticed something unusual in his attitude. Instead of sitting erect, gazing all round with alert urbanity, he drooped over his plate. I stood opposite him for some time before he looked up, a little wildly, if such a strong word can be used in connection with his correct appearance.

"Ah, my dear sir! Is it you?" he greeted me. "I hope all is well."

He was very nice about my friend. Indeed, he was always nice, with the niceness of people whose hearts are genuinely humane. But this time it cost him an effort. His attempts at general conversation broke down into dulness. It occurred to me he might have been indisposed. But before I could frame the inquiry he muttered:

"You find me here very sad."

"I am sorry for that," I said. "You haven't had bad news, I hope?"

It was very kind of me to take an interest. No. It was not that. No bad news, thank God. And he became very still, as if holding his breath. Then, leaning forward a little, and in an odd tone of awed embarrassment, he took me into his confidence.

"The truth is that I have had a very—a very—how shall I say? —abominable adventure happen to me."

The energy of the epithet was sufficiently startling in that man of moderate feelings and toned-down vocabulary. The word unpleasant I should have thought would have fitted amply the worst experience likely to befall a man of his stamp. And an adventure, too. Incredible! But it is in human nature to believe the worst, and I confess I eyed him stealthily, wondering what he had been up to. In a moment, however, my unworthy suspicions vanished. There was a fundamental refinement of nature about the man which made me dismiss all idea of some more or less disreputable scrape.

"It is very serious. Very serious." He went on nervously. "I will tell you after dinner, if you will allow me."

I expressed my perfect acquiescence by a little bow, nothing more. I wished him to understand that I was not likely to hold him to that offer, if he thought better of it later on. We talked of indifferent things, but with a sense of difficulty quite unlike our former easy, gossipy intercourse. The hand raising a piece of bread to his lips, I noticed, trembled slightly. This symptom, in regard of my reading of the man, was no less than startling.

In the smoking-room he did not hang back at all. Directly we had taken our usual seats he leaned sideways over the arm of his chair and looked straight into my eyes earnestly.

"You remember," he began, "that day you went away? I told you then I would go to the Villa Nazionale to hear some music in the evening."

I remembered. His handsome old face, so fresh for his age, unmarked by any trying experience, appeared haggard for an instant. It was like the passing of a shadow. Returning his steadfast gaze, I took a sip of my black coffee. He was systematically minute in his narrative, simply in order, I think, not to let his excitement get the better of him.

After leaving the railway station, he had an ice, and read the paper in a café. Then he went back to the hotel, dressed for dinner, and dined with a good appetite. After dinner he lingered in the hall (there were chairs and tables there) smoking his cigar; talked to the little girl of the Primo Tenore of the San Carlo theatre, and exchanged a few words with that "amiable lady," the wife of the Primo Tenore. There was no performance that evening, and these people were going to the Villa also. They went out of the hotel. Very well.

At the moment of following their example—it was half-past nine already—he remembered he had a rather large sum of money in his pocket-book. He entered, therefore, the office and deposited the greater part of it with the book-keeper of the hotel. This done, he took a carozella and drove to the seashore. He got out of the cab and entered the Villa on foot from the Largo di Vittoria end.

He stared at me very hard. And I understood then how really impressionable he was. Every small fact and event of that evening stood out in his memory as if endowed with mystic significance. If he did not mention to me the colour of the pony which drew the carozella, and the aspect of the man who drove, it was a mere oversight arising from his agitation, which he repressed manfully.

He had then entered the Villa Nazionale from the Largo di Vittoria end. The Villa Nazionale is a public pleasure-ground laid out in grass plots, bushes, and flower-beds between the houses of the Riviera di Chiaja and the waters of the bay. Alleys of trees, more or less parallel, stretch its whole length—which is considerable. On the Riviera di Chiaja side the electric tramcars run close to the railings. Between the garden and the sea is the fashionable drive, a broad road bordered by a low wall, beyond which the Mediterranean splashes with gentle murmurs when the weather is fine.

As life goes on late at night in Naples, the broad drive was all astir with a brilliant swarm of carriage lamps moving in pairs, some creeping slowly, others running rapidly under the thin motionless line of electric lamps defining the shore. And a brilliant swarm of stars hung above the land humming with voices, piled up with houses, glittering with lights—and over the silent flat shadows of the sea.

The gardens themselves are not very well lit. Our friend went forward in the warm gloom, his eyes fixed upon a distant luminous region extending nearly across the whole width of the Villa, as if the air had glowed there with its own cold, bluish, and dazzling light. This magic spot, behind the black trunks of trees and masses of inky foliage, breathed out sweet sounds mingled with bursts of brassy roar, sudden clashes of metal, and grave, vibrating thuds.

As he walked on, all these noises combined together into a piece of elaborate music whose harmonious phrases came persuasively through a great disorderly murmur of voices and shuffling of feet on the gravel of that open space. An enormous crowd immersed in the electric light, as if in a bath of some radiant and tenous fluid shed upon their heads by luminous globes, drifted in its hundreds round the band. Hundreds more sat on chairs in more or less concentric circles, receiving unflinchingly the great waves of sonority that ebbed out into the darkness. The Count penetrated the throng, drifted with

it in tranquil enjoyment, listening, and looking at the faces. All
people of good society: mothers with their daughters, parents and
children, young men and young women all talking, smiling, nodding to each other. Very many pretty faces, and very many pretty
toilettes. There was, of course, a quantity of diverse types: showy old
fellows with white moustaches, fat men, thin men, officers in uniform; but what predominated, he told me, was the South Italian type
of young man, with a colourless, clear complexion, red lips, jet-
black little moustache, and liquid black eyes so wonderfully effective in leering or scowling.

Withdrawing from the throng, the Count shared a little table
in front of the café with a young man of just such a type. Our friend
had some lemonade. The young man was sitting moodily before an
empty glass. He looked up once, and then looked down again. He
also tilted his hat forward. Like this:

The Count made a gesture of a man pulling his hat down over
his brow, and went on:

"I think to myself: he is sad; something is wrong with him;
young men have their troubles. I take no notice of him, of course. I
pay for my lemonade, and go away."

Strolling about in the neighbourhood of the band, the Count
thinks he saw twice that young man wandering alone in the crowd.
Once their eyes met. It must have been the same young man, but
there were so many there of that type that he could not be certain.
Moreover, he was not very much concerned except in so far that he
had been struck by the marked, peevish discontent of that face.

Presently, tired of the feeling of confinement one experiences
in a crowd, the Count edged away from the band. An alley, very
sombre by contrast, presented itself invitingly with its promise of
solitude and coolness. He entered it, walking slowly on till the sound
of the orchestra became distinctly deadened. Then he walked back
and turned about once more. He did this several times before he noticed that there was somebody occupying one of the benches.

The spot being midway between two lamp-posts, the light was
faint.

The man lolled back in the corner of his seat, his legs stretched
out, his arms folded, and his head drooping on his breast. He never
stirred, as though he had fallen asleep there, but when the Count
passed by next time he had changed his attitude. He sat leaning for-

ward. His elbows were propped on his knees, and his hands were rolling a cigarette. He never looked up from that occupation.

The Count continued his stroll away from the band. He returned slowly, he said. I can imagine him enjoying to the full, but with his usual tranquillity, the balminess of this southern night and the sounds of music softened delightfully by the distance.

Presently he approached for the third time the man on the garden seat, still leaning forward with his elbows on his knees. It was a dejected pose. In the semi-obscurity of the alley his high shirt collar and his cuffs made small patches of vivid whiteness. The Count said that he had noticed him getting up brusquely, as if to walk away, but almost before he was aware of it the man stood before him asking in a low, gentle tone whether the signore would have the kindness to oblige him with a light.

The Count answered this request by a polite "Certainly," and dropped his hands with the intention of exploring both pockets of his trousers for the matches.

"I dropped my hands," he said, "but I never put them in my pockets. I felt a pressure there."

He put the tip of his finger on a spot close under his breastbone, the very spot of the human body where a Japanese gentleman begins the operation of the hara-kiri, which is a form of suicide following upon dishonour, upon an intolerable outrage to the delicacy of one's feelings.

"I glance down," the Count continued in an awestruck voice, "and what do I see? A knife! A long knife——"

"You don't mean to say," I exclaimed amazed, "that you have been held up like this in the Villa at half-past ten o'clock, within a stone's throw of a thousand people!"

He nodded several times, staring at me with all his might.

"The clarionet," he declared solemnly, "was finishing his solo, and I assure you I could hear every note. Then the band crashed *fortissimo*, and that creature rolled its eyes and gnashed its teeth, hissing at me with the greatest ferocity, 'Be silent! No noise or——' "

I could not get over my astonishment.

"What sort of knife was it?" I asked stupidly.

"A long blade. A stiletto—perhaps a kitchen knife. A long narrow blade. It gleamed. And his eyes gleamed. His white teeth, too.

I could see them. He was very ferocious. I thought to myself: 'If I hit him he will kill me.' How could I fight with him? He had the knife and I had nothing. I am nearly seventy, you know, and that was a young man. I seemed even to recognize him. The moody young man of the café. The young man I met in the crowd. But I could not tell. There are so many like him in this country."

The distress of that moment was reflected in his face. I should think that physically he must have been paralyzed by surprise. His thoughts, however, remained extremely active. They ranged over every alarming possibility. The idea of setting up a vigorous shouting for help occurred to him, too. But he did nothing of the kind, and the reason why he refrained gave me a good opinion of his mental self-possession. He saw in a flash that nothing prevented the other from shouting, too.

"That young man might in an instant have thrown away his knife and pretended I was the aggressor. Why not? He might have said I attacked him. Why not? It was one incredible story against another! He might have said anything—bring some dishonouring charge against me—what do I know? By his dress he was no common robber. He seemed to belong to the better classes. What could I say? He was an Italian—I am a foreigner. Of course I have my passport, and there is our consul—but to be arrested, dragged at night to the police office like a criminal!"

He shuddered. It was in his character to shrink from scandal much more than from mere death. And certainly for many people this would have always remained—considering certain peculiarities of Neapolitan manners—a deucedly queer story. The Count was no fool. His belief in the respectable placidity of life having received this rude shock, he thought that now anything might happen. But also a notion came into his head that this young man was perhaps merely an infuriated lunatic.

This was for me the first hint of his attitude toward this adventure. In his exaggerated delicacy of sentiment he felt that nobody's self-esteem need be affected by what a madman may choose to do to one. It became apparent, however, that the Count was to be denied that consolation. He enlarged upon the abominably savage way in which that young man rolled his glistening eyes and gnashed his white teeth. The band was going now through a slow movement of solemn braying by all the trombones, with deliberately repeated bangs of the big drum.

"But what did you do?" I asked, greatly excited.

"Nothing," answered the Count. "I let my hands hang down very still. I told him quietly I did not intend making a noise. He snarled like a dog, then said in an ordinary voice:

" *'Vostro porto folio.'*

"So I naturally," continued the Count—and from this point acted the whole thing in pantomime. Holding me with his eyes, he went through all the motions of reaching into his inside breast-pocket, taking out a pocket-book and handing it over. But that young man, still bearing steadily on the knife, refused to touch it.

He directed the Count to take the money out himself, received it into his left hand, motioned the pocket-book to be returned to the pocket, all this being done to the sweet thrilling of flutes and clari-onets sustained by the emotional drone of the hautboys. And the "young man," as the Count called him, said: "This seems very little."

"It was, indeed, only 340 or 360 lire," the Count pursued. "I had left my money in the hotel, as you know. I told him this was all I had on me. He shook his head impatiently and said:

" *'Vostro orologio.'* "

The Count gave me the dumb show of pulling out his watch, detaching it. But, as it happened, the valuable gold half-chronome-ter he possessed had been left at a watch-maker's for cleaning. He wore that evening (on a leather guard) the Waterbury fifty-franc thing he used to take with him on his fishing expeditions. Perceiv-ing the nature of this booty, the well-dressed robber made a contemp-tuous clicking sound with his tongue like this, "Tse-Ah!" and waved it away hastily. Then, as the Count was returning the disdained ob-ject to his pocket, he demanded with a threateningly increased pressure of the knife on the epigastrium, by way of reminder:

"Vostri anelli."

"One of the rings," went on the Count, "was given me many years ago by my wife; the other is the signet ring of my father. I said, 'No. *That* you shall not have!' "

Here the Count reproduced the gesture corresponding to that declaration by clapping one hand upon the other, and pressing both thus against his chest. It was touching in its resignation. "That you shall not have," he repeated firmly and closed his eyes, fully expecting—I don't know whether I am right in recording that such an unpleasant word had passed his lips—fully expecting to feel himself being—I really hesitate to say—being disembowelled by the push of the long, sharp blade resting murderously against the pit of his stomach—the very seat, in all human beings, of anguishing sensations.

Great waves of harmony went on flowing from the band.

Suddenly the Count felt the nightmarish pressure removed from the sensitive spot. He opened his eyes. He was alone. He had heard nothing. It is probable that the "young man" had departed, with light steps, some time before, but the sense of the horrid pressure had lingered even after the knife had gone. A feeling of weakness came over him. He had just time to stagger to the garden seat. He felt as though he had held his breath for a long time. He sat all in a heap, panting with the shock of the reaction.

The band was executing, with immense bravura, the complicated finale. It ended with a tremendous crash. He heard it unreal and remote, as if his ears had been stopped, and then the hard clapping of a thousand, more or less, pairs of hands, like a sudden hail-shower passing away. The profound silence which succeeded recalled him to himself.

A tramcar, resembling a long glass box wherein people sat with their heads strongly lighted, ran along swiftly within sixty yards of the spot where he had been robbed. Then another rustled by, and yet another going the other way. The audience about the band had broken up, and were entering the alley in small, conversing groups. The Count sat up straight and tried to think calmly of what had happened to him. The vileness of it took his breath away again. As far as I can make it out he was disgusted with himself. I do not mean to say with his behaviour. Indeed, if his pantomimic rendering of it for my information was to be trusted, it was simply perfect. No, it was not that. He was not ashamed. He was shocked at being the selected victim, not of robbery so much as of contempt. His tranquillity had been wantonly desecrated. His lifelong, kindly nicety of outlook had been defaced.

Nevertheless, at that stage, before the iron had time to sink deep, he was able to argue himself into comparative equanimity. As his agitation calmed down somewhat, he became aware that he was frightfully hungry. Yes, hungry. The sheer emotion had made him simply ravenous. He left the seat and, after walking for some time, found himself outside the gardens and before an arrested tramcar, without knowing very well how he came there. He got in as if in a dream, by a sort of instinct. Fortunately he found in his trouser pocket a copper to satisfy the conductor. Then the car stopped, and as everybody was getting out he got out, too. He recognized the Piazza San Ferdinando, but apparently it did not occur to him to take a cab and drive to the hotel. He remained in distress on the Piazza like a lost dog, thinking vaguely of the best way of getting something to eat at once.

Suddenly he remembered his twenty-franc piece. He explained to me that he had that piece of French gold for something like three years. He used to carry it about with him as a sort of reserve in case of accident. Anybody is liable to have his pocket picked—a quite different thing from a brazen and insulting robbery.

The monumental arch of the Galleria Umberto faced him at the top of a noble flight of stairs. He climbed these without loss of time, and directed his steps toward the Café Umberto. All the tables outside were occupied by a lot of people who were drinking. But as he wanted something to eat, he went into the café, which is divided into aisles by square pillars set all round with long looking-glasses. The Count sat down on a red plush bench against one of these pillars, waiting for his risotto. And his mind reverted to his abominable adventure.

He thought of the moody, well-dressed young man, with whom he had exchanged glances in the crowd around the bandstand, and who, he felt confident, was the robber. Would he recognize him again? Doubtless. But he did not want ever to see him again. The best thing was to forget this humiliating episode.

The Count looked round anxiously for the coming of his risotto, and, behold, to the left against the wall—there sat the young man. He was alone at a table, with a bottle of some sort of wine or syrup and a carafe of iced water before him. The smooth olive cheeks, the red lips, the little jet-black moustache turned up gallantly, the fine black eyes a little heavy and shaded by long eyelashes, that peculiar expression of cruel discontent to be seen only in the busts of some Roman emperors—it was he, no doubt at all. But that was a type. The Count looked away hastily. The young officer over there reading a paper was like that, too. Same type. Two young men farther away playing draughts also resembled——

The Count lowered his head with the fear in his heart of being everlastingly haunted by the vision of that young man. He began to eat his risotto. Presently he heard the young man on his left call the waiter in a bad-tempered tone.

At the call, not only his own waiter, but two other idle waiters belonging to a quite different row of tables, rushed toward him with obsequious alacrity, which is not the general characteristic of the waiters in the Café Umberto. The young man muttered something, and one of the waiters walking rapidly to the nearest door called out into the Galleria: "Pasquale! O! Pasquale!"

Everybody knows Pasquale, the shabby old fellow who, shuffling between the tables, offers for sale cigars, cigarettes, picture postcards, and matches to the clients of the café. He is in many respects an engaging scoundrel. The Count saw the gray-haired, unshaven ruffian enter the café, the glass case hanging from his neck by a leather strap, and, at a word from the waiter, make his shuffling way with a sudden spurt to the young man's table. The young man was in need of a cigar with which Pasquale served him fawningly. The old pedlar was going out, when the Count, on a sudden impulse, beckoned to him.

Pasquale approached, the smile of deferential recognition combining oddly with the cynical, searching expression of his eyes. Leaning his case on the table, he lifted the glass lid without a word. The Count took a box of cigarettes and urged by a fearful curiosity, asked as casually as he could:

"Tell me, Pasquale, who is that young signore sitting over there?"

The other bent over his box confidentially.

"That, *Signor Conde*," he said, beginning to rearrange his wares busily and without looking up, "that is a young *Cavaliere* of a very good family from Bari. He studies in the University here, and is the chief, *capo,* of an association of young men—of very nice young men."

He paused, and then, with mingled discretion and pride of knowledge, murmured the explanatory word "Camorra" and shut down the lid. "A very powerful Camorra," he breathed out. "The professors themselves respect it greatly . . . *una lira e cinquanti centesimi, Signor Conde."*

Our friend paid with the gold piece. While Pasquale was making up the change, he observed that the young man, of whom he had heard so much in a few words, was watching the transaction covertly. After the old vagabond had withdrawn with a bow, the Count settled with the waiter and sat still. A numbness, he told me, had come over him.

The young man paid, too, got up and crossed over, apparently for the purpose of looking at himself in the mirror set in the pillar nearest to the Count's seat. He was dressed all in black with a dark green bow tie. The Count looked round, and was startled by meeting a vicious glance out of the corners of the other's eyes. The young *Cavaliere* from Bari (according to Pasquale; but Pasquale is, of course, an accomplished liar) went on arranging his tie, settling his hat before the glass, and meantime he spoke just loud enough to be heard by the Count. He spoke through his teeth with the most insulting venom of contempt and gazing straight into the mirror.

"Ah! So you have some gold on you—you old liar—you old *birba*—you *furfante!* But you are not done with me yet."

The fiendishness of his expression vanished like lightning, and he lounged out of the café with a moody, impassive face.

The poor Count, after telling me this last episode, fell back trembling in his chair. His forehead broke into perspiration. There was a wanton insolence in the spirit of this outrage which appalled even me. What it was to the Count's delicacy I won't attempt to guess. I am sure that if he had not been too refined to do such a blatantly vulgar thing as dying from apoplexy in a café, he would have had a fatal stroke there and then. All irony apart, my difficulty was to keep him from seeing the full extent of my commiseration. He shrank from every excessive sentiment, and my commiseration was practically unbounded. It did not surprise me to hear that he had been in bed a week. He had got up to make his arrangements for leaving southern Italy for good and all.

And the man was convinced that he could not live through a whole year in any other climate!

No argument of mine had any effect. It was not timidity, though he did say to me once: "You do not know what a Camorra is, my dear sir. I am a marked man." He was not afraid of what could be done to him. His delicate conception of his dignity was defiled by a degrading experience. He couldn't stand that. No Japanese gentleman, outraged in his exaggerated sense of honour, could have gone about his preparations for hara-kiri with greater resolution. To go home really amounted to suicide for the poor Count.

There is a saying of Neapolitan patriotism, intended for the information of foreigners, I presume: "See Naples and then die." *Vedi Napoli e poi mori.* It is a saying of excessive vanity, and everything excessive was abhorrent to the nice moderation of the poor

Count. Yet, as I was seeing him off at the railway station, I thought he was behaving with singular fidelity to its conceited spirit. *Vedi Napoli!* . . . He had seen it. He had seen it with startling thoroughness—and now he was going to his grave. He was going to it by the *train de luxe* of the International Sleeping Car Company, *via* Trieste and Vienna. As the four long, sombre coaches pulled out of the station I raised my hat with the solemn feeling of paying the last tribute of respect to a funeral *cortège*. *Il Conde's* profile, much aged already, glided away from me in stony immobility, behind the lighted pane of glass—*Vedi Napoli e poi mori!*

J[AMES] F[ARL] POWERS

(1917-   )

Born in Jacksonville, Illinois, Powers knew the Depression years of the Thirties at first-hand. He managed to graduate from college, but the jobs he held thereafter were simply whatever he could get: department store clerk, chauffeur, door-to-door insurance salesman. "Lions, Harts, Leaping Does," written while Powers was working in a book store, catapulted him to fame in 1943. His experience with the Depression, however, has left him antagonistic toward the belief that painful struggle is a necessary part of the making of the artist. His awards have been many: in 1948, a grant from the National Institute of Arts and Letters and a Guggenheim fellowship in creative writing; a Rockefeller-Iowa University Writers' Workshop fellowship; a Rockefeller-Kenyon Review fellowship; and most recently, the National Book Award of $1,000 in 1963 for his first novel, MORTE d'URBAN. Powers is not a prolific writer; his stories are done slowly and with great care. His Catholic upbringing is manifested in his subject matter: Catholic priests and laity. But just as Philip Roth uses Jews to portray all men, so Powers does not portray a narrowly Catholic world. His priests are human, with strengths and weaknesses that we recognize regardless of our own background; his lay figures are as likely to be conniving and hypocritical as they are dedicated. Yet his purpose is not to criticize Catholics and Catholicism. Through these characters and their religion we see both the pettiness and the grandeur of the human spirit, the beauty and the tragedy of the human condition.

Lions, Harts,
Leaping Does

" 'Thirty-ninth pope. Anastasius, a Roman, appointed that while the Gospel was reading they should stand and not sit. He exempted from the ministry those that were lame, impotent, or diseased persons, and slept with his forefathers in peace, being a confessor.' "

"Anno?"

" 'Anno 404.' "

They sat there in the late afternoon, the two old men grown gray in the brown robes of the Order. Angular winter daylight forsook the small room, almost a cell in the primitive sense, and passed through the window into the outside world. The distant horizon, which it sought to join, was still bright and strong against approaching night. The old Franciscans, one priest, one brother, were left among the shadows in the room.

"Can you see to read one more, Titus?" the priest Didymus asked. "Number fourteen." He did not cease staring out the window at day becoming night on the horizon. The thirty-ninth pope said Titus might not be a priest. Did Titus, reading, understand? He could never really tell about Titus, who said nothing now. There was only silence, then a dry whispering of pages turning. "Number fourteen," Didymus said. "That's Zephyrinus. I always like the old heretic on that one, Titus."

According to one bibliographer, Bishop Bale's *Pageant of Popes Contayninge the Lyves of all the Bishops of Rome, from the Beginninge of them to the Year of Grace 1555* was a denunciation of every pope from Peter to Paul IV. However inviting to readers that might sound, it was in sober fact a lie. The first popes, persecuted and mostly martyred, wholly escaped the author's remarkable spleen and even enjoyed his crusty approbation. Father Didymus, his aged appetite for biography jaded by the orthodox lives, found the work fascinating. He usually referred to it as "Bishop Bale's funny book" and to the Bishop as a heretic.

Titus squinted at the yellowed page. He snapped a glance at the light hovering at the window. Then he closed his eyes and with great feeling recited:

" 'O how joyous and how delectable is it to see religious men devout and fervent in the love of God, well-mannered—' "

"Titus," Didymus interrupted softly.

" '—and well taught in ghostly learning.' "

"Titus, read." Didymus placed the words in their context. The First Book of *The Imitation* and Chapter, if he was not mistaken, XXV. The trick was no longer in finding the source of Titus's quotations; it was putting them in their exact context. It had become an unconfessed contest between them, and it gratified Didymus to think he had been able to place the fragment. Titus knew two books by heart, *The Imitation* and *The Little Flowers of St. Francis*. Lately, unfortunately, he had begun to learn another. He was more and more quoting from Bishop Bale. Didymus reminded himself he must not let Titus read past the point where the martyred popes left off. What Bale had to say about Peter's later successors sounded incongruous—"unmete" in the old heretic's own phrase—coming from a Franciscan brother. Two fathers had already inquired of Didymus concerning Titus. One had noted the antique style of his words and had ventured to wonder if Brother Titus, Christ preserve us, might be slightly possessed. He cited the case of the illiterate Missouri farmer who cursed the Church in a forgotten Aramaic tongue.

"Read, Titus."

Titus squinted at the page once more and read in his fine dead voice.

" 'Fourteenth pope, Zephyrinus. Zephyrinus was a Roman born, a man as writers do testify, more addicted with all endeavor to the service of God than to the cure of any worldly affairs. Whereas before his time the wine in the celebrating the communion was ministered in a cup of wood, he first did alter that, and instead thereof brought in cups or chalices of glass. And yet he did not this upon any superstition, as thinking wood to be unlawful, or glass to be more holy for that use, but because the one is more comely and seemly, as by experience it appeareth than the other. And yet some wooden dolts do dream that the wooden cups were changed by him because that part of the wine, or as they thought, the royal blood of Christ, did soak into the wood, and so it can not be in glass. Surely sooner may wine soak into any wood than any wit into those winey heads that thus both deceive themselves and slander this Godly martyr.' "

"Anno?"

Titus squinted at the page again. " 'Anno 222,' " he read.

They were quiet for a moment which ended with the clock in the tower booming once for the half hour. Didymus got up and stood so close to the window his breath became visible. Noticing it, he inhaled deeply and then, exhaling, he sent a gust of smoke churning against the freezing pane, clouding it. Some old unmelted snow in tree crotches lay dirty and white in the gathering dark.

"It's cold out today," Didymus said.

He stepped away from the window and over to Titus, whose face was relaxed in open-eyed sleep. He took Bishop Bale's funny book unnoticed from Titus's hands.

"Thank you, Titus," he said.

Titus blinked his eyes slowly once, then several times quickly. His body gave a shudder, as if coming to life.

"Yes, Father?" he was asking.

"I said thanks for reading. You are a great friend to me."

"Yes, Father."

"I know you'd rather read other authors." Didymus moved to the window, stood there gazing through the tops of trees, their limbs black and bleak against the sky. He rubbed his hands. "I'm going for a walk before vespers. Is it too cold for you, Titus?"

" 'A good religious man that is fervent in his religion taketh all things well, and doth gladly all that he is commanded to do.' "

Didymus, walking across the room, stopped and looked at Titus just in time to see him open his eyes. He was quoting again: *The Imitation* and still in Chapter XXV. Why had he said that? To himself Didymus repeated the words and decided Titus, his mind moving intelligently but so pathetically largo, was documenting the act of reading Bishop Bale when there were other books he preferred.

"I'm going out for a walk," Didymus said.

Titus rose and pulled down the full sleeves of his brown robe in anticipation of the cold.

"I think it is too cold for you, Titus," Didymus said.

Titus faced him undaunted, arms folded and hands muffled in his sleeves, eyes twinkling incredulously. He was ready to go. Didymus got the idea Titus knew himself to be the healthier of the two. Didymus was vaguely annoyed at this manifestation of the truth. *Vanitas.*

"Won't they need you in the kitchen now?" he inquired.

Immediately he regretted having said that. And the way he had said it, with some malice, as though labor *per se* were important and the intention not so. *Vanitas* in a friar, and at his age too. Confronting Titus with a distinction his simple mind could never master and which, if it could, his great soul would never recognize. Titus only knew all that was necessary, that a friar did what he was best at in the community. And no matter the nature of his toil, the variety of the means at hand, the end was the same for all friars. Or indeed for all men, if they cared to know. Titus worked in the kitchen and garden. Was Didymus wrong in teaching geometry out of personal preference and perhaps—if this was so he was—out of pride? Had the spiritual worth of his labor been vitiated because of that? He did not think so, no. No, he taught geometry because it was useful and eternally true, like his theology, and though of a lower order of truth it escaped the common fate of theology and the humanities, perverted through the ages in the mouths of dunderheads and fools. From that point of view, his work came to the same thing as Titus's. The vineyard was everywhere; they were in it, and that was essential.

Didymus, consciously humble, held open the door for Titus. Sandals scraping familiarly, they passed through dark corridors until they came to the stairway. Lights from floors above and below spangled through the carven apertures of the winding stair and fell in confusion upon the worn oaken steps.

At the outside door they were ambushed. An old friar stepped out of the shadows to intercept them. Standing with Didymus and Titus, however, made him appear younger. Or possibly it was the tenseness of him.

"Good evening, Father," he said to Didymus. "And Titus."

Didymus nodded in salutation and Titus said deliberately, as though he were the first one ever to put words in such conjunction:

"Good evening, Father Rector."

The Rector watched Didymus expectantly. Didymus studied the man's face. It told him nothing but curiosity—a luxury which could verge on vice in the cloister. Didymus frowned his incomprehension. He was about to speak. He decided against it, turning to Titus:

"Come on, Titus, we've got a walk to take before vespers."

The Rector was left standing.

They began to circle the monastery grounds. Away from the buildings it was brighter. With a sudden shudder, Didymus felt the freezing air bite into his body all over. Instinctively he drew up his cowl. That was a little better. Not much. It was too cold for him to relax, breathe deeply, and stride freely. It had not looked this cold from his window. He fell into Titus's gait. The steps were longer, but there was an illusion of warmth about moving in unison. Bit by bit he found himself duplicating every aspect of Titus in motion. Heads down, eyes just ahead of the next step, undeviating, they seemed peripatetic figures in a Gothic frieze. The stones of the walk were trampled over with frozen footsteps. Titus's feet were gray and bare in their open sandals. Pieces of ice, the thin edges of ruts, cracked off under foot, skittering sharply away. A crystal fragment lit between Titus's toes and did not melt there. He did not seem to notice it. This made Didymus lift his eyes.

A fine Franciscan! Didymus snorted, causing a flurry of vapors. He had the despicable caution of the comfortable who move mountains, if need be, to stay that way. Here he was, cowl up and heavy woolen socks on, and regretting the weather because it exceeded his anticipations. Painfully he stubbed his toe on purpose and at once accused himself of exhibitionism. Then he damned the expression for its modernity. He asked himself wherein lay the renunciation of the world, the flesh and the devil, the whole point of following after St. Francis today. Poverty, Chastity, Obedience—the three vows. There was nothing of suffering in the poverty of the friar nowadays: he was penniless, but materially rich compared to—what was the phrase he used to hear?—"one third of the nation." A beggar, a homeless mendicant by very definition, he knew nothing—except as it affected others "less fortunate"—of the miseries of begging in the streets. Verily, it was no heavy cross, this vow of Poverty, so construed and practiced, in the modern world. Begging had become unfashionable. Somewhere along the line the meaning had been lost; they had become too "fortunate." Official agencies, to whom it was a nasty but necessary business, dispensed Charity without mercy or grace. He recalled with wry amusement Frederick Barbarossa's appeal to fellow princes when opposed by the might of the medieval Church: "We have a clean conscience, and it tells us that God is with us. Ever have we striven to bring back priests and, in especial, those of the topmost rank, to the condition of the first Christian Church. In those days the clergy raised their eyes to the angels, shone through miracles, made whole the sick, raised the dead, made Kings and Princes subject to them, not with arms but with their holiness. But now they are smothered in delights. To withdraw from them the harmful riches which burden them to their own undoing is a labor of love in which all Princes should eagerly participate."

And Chastity, what of that? Well, that was all over for him—a battle he had fought and won many years ago. A sin whose temptations had prevailed undiminished through the centuries, but withal for him, an old man, a dead issue, a young man's trial. Only Obedience remained, and that, too, was no longer difficult for him. There was something—much as he disliked the term—to be said for "conditioning." He had to smile at himself: why should he bristle so at using the word? It was only contemporary slang for a theory the Church had always known. "Psychiatry," so called, and all the ghastly superstition that attended its practice, the deification of its high priests in the secular schools, made him ill. But it would pass. Just look how alchemy had flourished, and where was it today?

Clearly an abecedarian observance of the vows did not promise perfection. Stemmed in divine wisdom, they were branches meant to flower forth, but requiring of the friar the water and sunlight of sacrifice. The letter led nowhere. It was the spirit of the vows which opened the way and revealed to the soul, no matter the flux of circumstance, the means of salvation.

He had picked his way through the welter of familiar factors again—again to the same bitter conclusion. He had come to the key and core of his trouble anew. When he received the letter from Seraphin asking him to come to St. Louis, saying his years prohibited unnecessary travel and endowed his request with a certain prerogative —No, he had written back, it's simply impossible, not saying why. God help him, as a natural man, he had the desire, perhaps the inordinate desire, to see his brother again. He should not have to prove that. One of them must die soon. But as a friar, he remembered: "Unless a man be clearly delivered from the love of all creatures, he may not fully tend to his Creator." Therein, he thought, the keeping of the vows having become an easy habit for him, was his opportunity—he thought! It was plain and there was sacrifice and it would be hard. So he had not gone.

Now it was plain that he had been all wrong. Seraphin was an old man with little left to warm him in the world. Didymus asked himself—recoiling at the answer before the question was out—if his had been the only sacrifice. Rather, had he not been too intent on denying himself at the time to notice that he was denying Seraphin also? Harshly Didymus told himself he had used his brother for a hair shirt. This must be the truth, he thought; it hurts so.

The flesh just above his knees felt frozen. They were drawing near the entrance again. His face, too, felt the same way, like a slab of pasteboard, stiffest at the tip of his nose. When he wrinkled his brow and puffed out his cheeks to blow hot air up to his nose, his skin seemed to crackle like old parchment. His eyes watered from the wind. He pressed a hand, warm from his sleeve, to his exposed neck. Frozen, like his face. It would be chapped tomorrow.

Titus, white hair awry in the wind, looked just the same.

They entered the monastery door. The Rector stopped them. It was almost as before, except that Didymus was occupied with feeling his face and patting it back to life.

"Ah, Didymus! It must be cold indeed!" The Rector smiled at Titus and returned his gaze to Didymus. He made it appear that they were allied in being amused at Didymus's face. Didymus touched his nose tenderly. Assured it would stand the operation, he blew it lustily. He stuffed the handkerchief up his sleeve. The Rector, misinterpreting all this ceremony, obviously was afraid of being ignored.

"The telegram, Didymus. I'm sorry; I thought it might have been important."

"I received no telegram."

They faced each other, waiting, experiencing a hanging moment of uneasiness.

Then, having employed the deductive method, they both looked at Titus. Although he had not been listening, rather had been studying the naked toes in his sandals, he sensed their eyes questioning him.

"Yes, Father Rector?" he answered.

"The telegram for Father Didymus, Titus?" the Rector demanded. "Where is it?" Titus started momentarily out of willingness to be of service, but ended, his mind refusing to click, impassive before them. The Rector shook his head in faint exasperation and reached his hand down into the folds of Titus's cowl. He brought

forth two envelopes. One, the telegram, he gave to Didymus. The
other, a letter, he handed back to Titus.

"I gave you this letter this morning, Titus. It's for Father Anthony." Intently Titus stared unremembering at the letter. "I wish
you would see that Father Anthony gets it right away, Titus. I think
it's a bill."

Titus held the envelope tightly to his breast and said, "Father
Anthony."

Then his eyes were attracted by the sound of Didymus tearing
open the telegram. While Didymus read the telegram, Titus's expression showed he at last understood his failure to deliver it. He was
perturbed, mounting inner distress moving his lips silently.

Didymus looked up from the telegram. He saw the grief in
Titus's face and said, astonished, "How did you know, Titus?"

Titus's eyes were both fixed and lowered in sorrow. It seemed
to Didymus that Titus knew the meaning of the telegram. Didymus
was suddenly weak, as before a miracle. His eyes went to the Rector
to see how he was taking it. Then it occurred to him the Rector could
not know what had happened.

As though nothing much had, the Rector laid an absolving hand
lightly upon Titus's shoulder.

"Didymus, he can't forgive himself for not delivering the telegram now that he remembers it. That's all."

Didymus was relieved. Seeing the telegram in his hand, he
folded it quickly and stuffed it back in the envelope. He handed it to
the Rector. Calmly, in a voice quite drained of feeling, he said, "My
brother, Father Seraphin, died last night in St. Louis."

"Father Seraphin *from Rome?*"

"Yes," Didymus said, "in St. Louis. He was my brother. Appointed a confessor in Rome, a privilege for a foreigner. He was
ninety-two."

"I know that, Didymus, an honor for the Order. I had no idea
he was in this country. Ninety-two! God rest his soul!"

"I had a letter from him only recently."

"You did?"

"He wanted me to come to St. Louis. I hadn't seen him for
twenty-five years at least."

"Twenty-five years?"

"It was impossible for me to visit him."

"But if he was in this country, Didymus . . ."

The Rector waited for Didymus to explain.

Didymus opened his mouth to speak, heard the clock in the tower sound the quarter hour, and said nothing, listening, lips parted, to the last of the strokes die away.

"Why, Didymus, it could easily have been arranged," the Rector persisted.

Didymus turned abruptly to Titus, who, standing in a dream, had been inattentive since the clock struck.

"Come, Titus, we'll be late."

He hastened down the corridor with Titus. "No," he said in agitation, causing Titus to look at him in surprise. "I told him no. It was simply impossible." He was conscious of Titus's attention. "To visit him, Seraphin, who is dead." That had come naturally enough, for being the first time in his thoughts that Seraphin was dead. Was there not some merit in his dispassionate acceptance of the fact?

They entered the chapel for vespers and knelt down.

The clock struck. One, two . . . two. Two? No, there must have been one or two strokes before. He had gone to sleep. It was three. At least three, probably four. Or five. He waited. It could not be two: he remembered the brothers filing darkly into the chapel at that hour. Disturbing the shadows for matins and lauds. If it was five—he listened for faint noises in the building—it would only be a few minutes. They would come in, the earliest birds, to say their Masses. There were no noises. He looked toward the windows on the St. Joseph side of the chapel. He might be able to see a light from a room across the court. That was not certain even if it was five. It would have to come through the stained glass. Was that possible? It was still night. Was there a moon? He looked round the chapel. If there was, it might shine on a window. There was no moon. Or it was overhead. Or powerless against the glass. He yawned. It could not be five. His knees were numb from kneeling. He shifted on them. His back ached. Straightening it, he gasped for breath. He saw the sanctuary light. The only light, red. Then it came back to him. Seraphin was dead. He tried to pray. No words. Why words? Meditation in the Presence. The perfect prayer. He fell asleep . . .

. . . Spiraling brown coil on coil under the golden sun the river slithered across the blue and flower-flecked land. On an eminence they held identical hands over their eyes for visors and mistook it with pleasure for an endless murmuring serpent. They considered unafraid the prospect of its turning in its course and standing on tail to swallow them gurgling alive. They sensed it was in them to command this also by a wish. Their visor hands vanished before their eyes and became instead the symbol of brotherhood clasped between them. This they wished. Smiling the same smile back and forth they began laughing: "Jonah!" And were walking murkily up and down the brown belly of the river in mock distress. Above them, foolishly triumphant, rippling in contentment, mewed the waves. Below swam an occasional large fish, absorbed in ignoring them, and the mass of crustacea, eagerly seething, too numerous on the bottom to pretend exclusiveness. "Jonah indeed!" the brothers said, surprised to see the bubbles they birthed. They strolled then for hours this way. The novelty wearing off (without regret, else they would have wished themselves elsewhere), they began to talk and say ordinary things. Their mother had died, their father too, and how old did that make them? It was the afternoon of the funerals, which they had managed, transcending time, to have held jointly. She had seemed older and for some reason he otherwise. How, they wondered, should it be with them, *memento mori* clicking simultaneously within them, lackaday. The sound of dirt descending six feet to clatter on the coffins was memorable but unmentionable. Their own lives, well . . . only half curious (something to do) they halted to kick testingly a waterlogged rowboat resting on the bottom, the crustacea complaining and olive-green silt rising to speckle the surface with dark stars . . . well, what *had* they been doing? A crayfish pursued them, clad in sable armor, dearly desiring to do battle, brandishing hinged swords. Well, for one thing, working for the canonization of Fra Bartolomeo, had got two cardinals interested, was hot after those remaining who were at all possible, a slow business. Yes, one would judge so in the light of past canonizations, though being stationed in Rome had its advantages. Me, the same old grind, teaching, pounding away, giving Pythagoras no rest in his grave . . . They made an irresolute pass at the crayfish, who had caught up with them. More about Fra Bartolomeo, what else is there? Except, you will laugh or have me excommunicated for wanton presumption, though it's only faith in a faithless age, making a vow not to die until he's made a saint, recognized rather—he is one, convinced of it, Didymus (never can get used to calling you that), a saint sure as I'm alive, having known him, no doubt of it, something wrong with your knee? Knees then! The crayfish, he's got hold of you there, another at your back. If you like, we'll leave—only I do like it here. Well, go ahead then, you never did like St. Louis, isn't that what you used to say? Alone, in pain, he rose to the surface, parting the silt stars. The sun like molten gold squirted him in the eye. Numb now, unable to remember, and too blind to refurnish his memory by observation, he waited for this limbo to clear away. . . .

Awake now, he was face to face with a flame, blinding him. He avoided it. A dead weight bore him down, his aching back. Slowly, like ink in a blotter, his consciousness spread. The supports beneath him were kneeling limbs, his, the veined hands, bracing him, pressing flat, his own. His body, it seemed, left off there; the rest was something else, floor. He raised his head to the flame again and tried to determine what kept it suspended even with his face. He shook his head, blinking dumbly, a four-legged beast. He could see nothing, only his knees and hands, which he felt rather, and the flame floating unaccountably in the darkness. That part alone was a mystery. And then there came a pressure and pull on his shoulders, urging him up. Fingers, a hand, a rustling related to its action, then the rustling in rhythm with the folds of a brown curtain, a robe naturally, ergo a friar, holding a candle, trying to raise him up, Titus. The clock began striking.

"Put out the candle," Didymus said.

Titus closed his palm slowly around the flame, unflinching, snuffing it. The odor of burning string. Titus pinched the wick deliberately. He waited a moment, the clock falling silent, and said, "Father Rector expects you will say a Mass for the Dead at five o'clock."

"Yes, I know." He yawned deliciously. "I told him *that*." He bit his lips at the memory of the disgusting yawn. Titus had found him asleep. Shame overwhelmed him, and he searched his mind for justification. He found none.

"It is five now," Titus said.

It was maddening. "I don't see anyone else if it's five," he snapped. Immediately he was aware of a light burning in the sacristy. He blushed and grew pale. Had someone besides Titus seen him sleeping? But, listening, he heard nothing. No one else was up yet. He was no longer pale and was only blushing now. He saw it all hopefully. He was saved. Titus had gone to the sacristy to prepare for Mass. He must have come out to light the candles on the main altar. Then he had seen the bereaved keeping vigil on all fours, asleep, snoring even. What did Titus think of that? It withered him to remember, but he was comforted some that the only witness had been Titus. Had the sleeping apostles in Gethsemane been glad it was Christ?

Wrong! Hopelessly wrong! For there had come a noise after all. Someone else was in the sacristy. He stiffened and walked palely toward it. He must go there and get ready to say his Mass. A few steps he took only, his back buckling out, humping, his knees sinking to the floor, his hands last. The floor, with fingers smelling of dust and genesis, reached up and held him. The fingers were really spikes and they were dusty from holding him this way all his life. For a radiant instant, which had something of eternity about it, he saw the justice of his position. Then there was nothing.

A little snow had fallen in the night, enough to powder the dead grass and soften the impression the leafless trees etched in the sky. Grayly the sky promised more snow, but now, at the end of the day following his collapse in the chapel, it was melting. Didymus, bundled around by blankets, sat in a wheel chair at the window, unsleepy. Only the landscape wearied him. Dead and unmoving though it must be—of that he was sure—it conspired to make him see everything in it as living, moving, something to be watched, each visible tuft of grass, each cluster of snow. The influence of the snow perhaps? For the ground, ordinarily uniform in texture and drabness, had split up into individual patches. They appeared to be involved in a struggle of some kind, possibly to overlap each other, constantly shifting. But whether it was equally one against one, or one against all, he could not make out. He reminded himself he did not believe it was actually happening. It was confusing and he closed his eyes. After a time this confused and tired him in the same way. The background of darkness became a field of varicolored factions, warring, and, worse than the landscape, things like worms and comets wriggled and exploded before his closed eyes. Finally, as though to orchestrate their motions, they carried with them a bewildering noise or music which grew louder and cacophonous. The effect was cumulative, inevitably unbearable, and Didymus would have to open his eyes again. The intervals of peace became gradually rarer on the landscape. Likewise when he shut his eyes to it the restful darkness dissolved sooner than before into riot.

The door of his room opened, mercifully dispelling his illusions, and that, because there had been no knock, could only be Titus. Unable to move in his chair, Didymus listened to Titus moving about the room at his back. The tinkle of a glass once, the squeak of the bookcase indicating a book taken out or replaced—they were sounds Didymus could recognize. But that first tap-tap and the consequent click of metal on metal, irregular and scarcely audible, was disconcertingly unfamiliar. His curiosity, centering on it, raised it to a delicious mystery. He kept down the urge to shout at Titus. But he attempted to fish from memory the precise character of the corner from which the sound came with harrowing repetition. The sound stopped then, as though to thwart him on the brink of revelation. Titus's footsteps scraped across the room. The door opened and closed. For a few steps, Didymus heard Titus going down the corridor. He asked himself not to be moved by idle curiosity, a thing of the senses. He would not be tempted now.

A moment later the keystone of his good intention crumbled, and the whole edifice of his detachment with it. More shakily than quickly, Didymus moved his hands to the wheels of the chair. He would roll over to the corner and investigate the sound. . . . He would? His hands lay limply on the wheels, ready to propel him to his mind's destination, but, weak, white, powerless to grip the wheels or anything. He regarded them with contempt. He had known they would fail him; he had been foolish to give them another chance. Disdainful of his hands, he looked out the window. He could still do that, couldn't he? It was raining some now. The landscape started to move, rearing and reeling crazily, as though drunken with the rain. In horror, Didymus damned his eyes. He realized this trouble was probably going to be chronic. He turned his gaze in despair to the trees, to the branches level with his eyes and nearer than the insane ground. Hesitating warily, fearful the gentle boughs under scrutiny would turn into hideous waving tentacles, he looked. With a thrill, he knew he was seeing clearly.

Gauzily rain descended in a fine spray, hanging in fat berries from the wet black branches where leaves had been and buds would be, cold crystal drops. They fell now and then ripely of their own weight, or shaken by the intermittent wind they spilled before their time. Promptly they appeared again, pendulous.

Watching the raindrops prove gravity, he was grateful for nature's, rather than his, return to reason. Still, though he professed

faith in his faculties, he would not look away from the trees and
down at the ground, nor close his eyes. Gratefully he savored the
cosmic truth in the falling drops and the mildly trembling branches.
There was order, he thought, which in justice and science ought to
include the treacherous landscape. Risking all, he ventured a glance
at the ground. All was still there. He smiled. He was going to close
his eyes (to make it universal and conclusive), when the door opened
again.

Didymus strained to catch the meaning of Titus's movements.
Would the clicking sound begin? Titus did go to that corner of the
room again. Then it came, louder than before, but only once this
time.

Titus came behind his chair, turned it, and wheeled him over to
the corner.

On a hook which Titus had screwed into the wall hung a bird
cage covered with black cloth.

"What's all this?" Didymus asked.

Titus tapped the covered cage expectantly.

A bird chirped once.

"The bird," Titus explained in excitement, "is inside."

Didymus almost laughed. He sensed in time, however, the necessity of seeming befuddled and severe. Titus expected it.

"I don't believe it," Didymus snapped.

Titus smiled wisely and tapped the cage again.

"There!" he exclaimed when the bird chirped.

Didymus shook his head in mock anger. "You made that beastly
noise, Titus, you mountebank!"

Titus, profoundly amused by such skepticism, removed the
black cover.

The bird, a canary, flicked its head sidewise in interest, looking
them up and down. Then it turned its darting attention to the
room. It chirped once in curt acceptance of the new surroundings.
Didymus and Titus came under its black dot of an eye once more,
this time for closer analysis. The canary chirped twice, perhaps that
they were welcome, even pleasing, and stood on one leg to show
them what a gay bird it was. It then returned to the business of peck-
ing a piece of apple.

"I see you've given him something to eat," Didymus said, and
felt that Titus, though he seemed content to watch the canary,

waited for him to say something more. "I am very happy, Titus, to have this canary," he went on. "I suppose he will come in handy now that I must spend my days in this infernal chair."

Titus did not look at him while he said, "He is a good bird, Father. He is one of the Saint's own good birds."

Through the window Didymus watched the days and nights come and go. For the first time, though his life as a friar had been copiously annotated with significant references, he got a good idea of eternity. Monotony, of course, was one word for it, but like all the others, as well as the allegories worked up by imaginative retreat masters, it was empty beside the experience itself, untranslatable. He would doze and wonder if by some quirk he had been cast out of the world into eternity, but since it was neither heaven nor exactly purgatory or hell, as he understood them, he concluded it must be an uncharted isle subscribing to the mother forms only in the matter of time. And having thought this, he was faintly annoyed at his ponderous whimsy. Titus, like certain of the hours, came periodically. He would read or simply sit with him in silence. The canary was there always, but except as it showed signs of sleepiness at twilight and spirit at dawn, Didymus regarded it as a subtle device, like the days and nights and bells, to give the lie to the vulgar error that time flies. The cage was small and the canary would not sing. Time, hanging in the room like a jealous fog, possessed him and voided everything except it. It seemed impossible each time Titus came that he should be able to escape the room.

" 'After him,' " Titus read from Bishop Bale one day, " 'came Fabius, a Roman born, who (as Eusebius witnesseth) as he was returning home out of the field, and with his countrymen present to elect a new bishop, there was a pigeon seen standing on his head and suddenly he was created pastor of the Church, which he looked not for.' "

They smiled at having the same thought and both looked up at the canary. Since Didymus sat by the window most of the day now, he had asked Titus to put a hook there for the cage. He had to admit to himself he did this to let Titus know he appreciated the canary. Also, as a secondary motive, he reasoned, it enabled the canary to look out the window. What a little yellow bird could see to interest it in the frozen scene was a mystery, but that, Didymus sighed, was a two-edged sword. And he took to watching the canary more.

So far as he was able to detect the moods of the canary he participated in them. In the morning the canary, bright and clownish, flitted back and forth between the two perches in the cage, hanging from the sides and cocking its little tufted head at Didymus querulously. During these acrobatics Didymus would twitch his hands in quick imitation of the canary's stunts. He asked Titus to construct a tiny swing, such as he had seen, which the canary might learn to use, since it appeared to be an intelligent and daring sort. Titus got the swing, the canary did master it, but there seemed to be nothing Didymus could do with his hands that was like swinging. In fact, after he had been watching awhile, it was as though the canary were fixed to a pendulum, inanimate, a piece of machinery, a yellow blur —ticking, for the swing made a little sound, and Didymus went to sleep, and often when he woke the canary was still going, like a clock. Didymus had no idea how long he slept at these times, maybe a minute, maybe hours. Gradually the canary got bored with the swing and used it less and less. In the same way, Didymus suspected, he himself had wearied of looking out the window. The first meager satisfaction had worn off. The dead trees, the sleeping snow, like the swing for the canary, were sources of diversion which soon grew stale. They were captives, he and the canary, and the only thing they craved was escape. Didymus slowly considered the problem. There was nothing, obviously, for him to do. He could pray, which he did, but he was not sure the only thing wrong with him was the fact he could not walk and that to devote his prayer to that end was justifiable. Inevitably it occurred to him his plight might well be an act of God. Why this punishment, though, he asked himself, and immediately supplied the answer. He had, for one thing, gloried too much in having it in him to turn down Seraphin's request to come to St. Louis. The intention—that was all important, and he, he feared, had done the right thing for the wrong reason. He had noticed something of the faker in himself before. But it was not clear if he had erred. There was a certain consolation, at bottom dismal, in this doubt. It was true there appeared to be a nice justice in being stricken a cripple if he had been wrong in refusing to travel to see Seraphin, if human love was all he was fitted for, if he was incapable of renunciation for the right reason, if the mystic counsels were too strong for him, if he was still too pedestrian after all these years of prayer and contemplation, if . . .

The canary was swinging, the first time in several days.

The reality of his position was insupportable. There were two ways of regarding it and he could not make up his mind. Humbly he wished to get well and to be able to walk. But if this was a punishment, was not prayer to lift it declining to see the divine point? He did wish to get well; that would settle it. Otherwise his predicament could only be resolved through means more serious than he dared cope with. It would be like refusing to see Seraphin all over again. By some mistake, he protested, he had at last been placed in a position vital with meaning and precedents inescapably Christian. But was he the man for it? Unsure of himself, he was afraid to go on trial. It would be no minor trial, so construed, but one in which the greatest values were involved—a human soul and the means of its salvation or damnation. Not watered-down suburban precautions and routine pious exercises, but Faith such as saints and martyrs had, and Despair such as only they had been tempted by. No, he was not the man for it. He was unworthy. He simply desired to walk and in a few years to die a normal, uninspired death. He did not wish to see (what was apparent) the greatest significance in his affliction. He preferred to think in terms of physical betterment. He was so sure he was not a saint that he did not consider this easier road beneath him, though attracted by the higher one. That was the rub. Humbly, then, he wanted to be able to walk, but he wondered if there was not presumption in such humility.

Thus he decided to pray for health and count the divine hand not there. Decided. A clean decision—not distinction—no mean feat in the light of all the moral theology he had swallowed. The canary, all its rocking come to naught once more, slept motionless in the swing. Despite the manifest prudence of the course he had settled upon, Didymus dozed off ill at ease in his wheel chair by the window. Distastefully, the last thing he remembered was that "prudence" is a virtue more celebrated in the modern Church.

At his request in the days following a doctor visited him. The Rector came along, too. When Didymus tried to find out the nature of his illness, the doctor looked solemn and pronounced it to be one of those things. Didymus received this with a look of mystification. So the doctor went on to say there was no telling about it. Time alone would tell. Didymus asked the doctor to recommend some books dealing with cases like his. They might have one of them in the monastery library. Titus could read to him in the meantime.

For, though he disliked being troublesome, "one of those things" as a diagnosis meant very little to an unscientific beggar like him. The phrase had a philosophic ring to it, but to his knowledge neither the Early Fathers nor the Scholastics seemed to have dealt with it. The Rector smiled. The doctor, annoyed, replied drily:

"Is that a fact?"

Impatiently Didymus said, "I know how old I am, if that's it."

Nothing was lost of the communion he kept with the canary. He still watched its antics and his fingers in his lap followed them clumsily. He did not forget about himself, that he must pray for health, that it was best that way—"prudence" dictated it—but he did think more of the canary's share of their captivity. A canary in a cage, he reasoned, is like a bud which never blooms.

He asked Titus to get a book on canaries, but nothing came of it and he did not mention it again.

Some days later Titus read:

" 'Twenty-ninth pope, Marcellus, a Roman, was pastor of the Church, feeding it with wisdom and doctrine. And (as I may say with the Prophet) a man according to God's heart and full of Christian works. This man admonished Maximianus the Emperor and endeavored to remove him from persecuting the saints—' "

"Stop a moment, Titus," Didymus interrupted.

Steadily, since Titus began to read, the canary had been jumping from the swing to the bottom of the cage and back again. Now it was quietly standing on one foot in the swing. Suddenly it flew at the side of the cage nearest them and hung there, its ugly little claws, like bent wire, hooked to the slender bars. It observed them intently, first Titus and then Didymus, at whom it continued to stare. Didymus's hands were tense in his lap.

"Go ahead, read," Didymus said, relaxing his hands.

" 'But the Emperor being more hardened, commanded Marcellus to be beaten with cudgels and to be driven out of the city, wherefore he entered into the house of one Lucina, a widow, and there kept the congregation secretly, which the tyrant hearing, made a stable for cattle of the same house and committed the keeping of it to the bishop Marcellus. After that he governed the Church by writing Epistles, without any other kind of teaching, being condemned to such a vile service. And being thus daily tormented with strife and noisomeness, at length gave up the ghost. Anno 308.' "

"Very good, Titus. I wonder how we missed that one before."

The canary, still hanging on the side of the cage, had not moved, its head turned sidewise, its eye as before fixed on Didymus.

"Would you bring me a glass of water, Titus?"

Titus got up and looked in the cage. The canary hung there, as though waiting, not a feather stirring.

"The bird has water here," Titus said, pointing to the small cup fastened to the cage.

"For me, Titus, the water's for me. Don't you think I know you look after the canary? You don't forget us, though I don't see why you don't."

Titus left the room with a glass.

Didymus's hands were tense again. Eyes on the canary's eye, he got up from his wheel chair, his face strained and white with the impossible effort, and, his fingers somehow managing it, he opened the cage. The canary darted out and circled the room chirping. Before it lit, though it seemed about to make its perch triumphantly the top of the cage, Didymus fell over on his face and lay prone on the floor.

In bed that night, unsuffering and barely alive, he saw at will everything revealed in his past. Events long forgotten happened again before his eyes. Clearly, sensitively, he saw Seraphin and himself, just as they had always been—himself, never quite sure. He heard all that he had ever said and that anyone had said to him. He had talked too much, too. The past mingled with the present. In the same moment and scene he made his first Communion, was ordained, and confessed his sins for the last time.

The canary perched in the dark atop the cage, head warm under wing, already, it seemed to Didymus, without memory of its captivity, dreaming of a former freedom, an ancestral summer day with flowers and trees. Outside it was snowing.

The Rector, followed by others, came into the room and administered the last sacrament. Didymus heard them all gathered prayerfully around his bed thinking (they thought) secretly: this sacrament often strengthens the dying, tip-of-the-tongue wisdom indigenous to the priesthood, Henry the Eighth had six wives. He saw the same hackneyed smile, designed to cheer, pass bravely among them, and marveled at the crudity of it. They went away then, all except Titus, their individual footsteps sounding (for him) the character of each friar. He might have been Francis himself for what he knew then of the little brothers and the cure of souls. He heard them thinking their expectation to be called from bed before daybreak to return to his room and say the office of the dead over his body, become the body, and whispering hopefully to the contrary. Death was now an unwelcome guest in the cloister.

He wanted nothing in the world for himself at last. This may have been the first time he found his will amenable to the Divine. He had never been less himself and more the saint. Yet now, so close to sublimity, or perhaps only tempted to believe so (the Devil is most wily at the deathbed), he was beset by the grossest distractions. They were to be expected, he knew, as indelible in the order of things: the bingo game going on under the Cross for the seamless garment of the Son of Man: everywhere the sign of the contradiction, and always. When would he cease to be surprised by it? Incidents repeated themselves, twined, parted, faded away, came back clear, and would not be prayed out of mind. He watched himself mounting the pulpit of a metropolitan church, heralded by the pastor as the renowned Franciscan father sent by God in His goodness to preach this novena—like to say a little prayer to test the microphone, Father?—and later reading through the petitions to Our Blessed Mother, cynically tabulating the pleas for a Catholic boy friend, drunkenness banished, the sale of real estate and coming furiously upon one: "that I'm not pregnant." And at the same church on Good Friday carrying the crucifix along the communion rail for the people to kiss, giving them the indulgence, and afterwards in the sacristy wiping the lipstick of the faithful from the image of Christ crucified.

"Take down a book, any book, Titus, and read. Begin anywhere."

Roused by his voice, the canary fluttered, looked sharply about and buried its head once more in the warmth of its wing.

" 'By the lions,' " Titus read, " 'are understood the acrimonies and impetuosities of the irascible faculty, which faculty is as bold and daring in its acts as are the lions. By the harts and the leaping does is understood the other faculty of the soul, which is the concupiscible—that is——' "

"Skip the exegesis," Didymus broke in weakly. "I can do without that now. Read the verse."

Titus read: " 'Birds of swift wing, lions, harts, leaping does, mountains, valleys, banks, waters, breezes, heats and terrors that keep watch by night, by the pleasant lyres and by the siren's song, I conjure you, cease your wrath and touch not the wall . . .' "

"Turn off the light, Titus."

Titus went over to the switch. There was a brief period of darkness during which Didymus's eyes became accustomed to a different shade, a glow rather, which possessed the room slowly. Then he saw the full moon had let down a ladder of light through the window. He could see the snow, strangely blue, falling outside. So sensitive was his mind and eye (because his body, now faint, no longer blurred his vision?) he could count the snowflakes, all of them separately, before they drifted, winding, below the sill.

With the same wonderful clarity, he saw what he had made of his life. He saw himself tied down, caged, stunted in his apostolate, seeking the crumbs, the little pleasure, neglecting the source, always knowing death changes nothing, only immortalizes . . . and still ever lukewarm. In trivial attachments, in love of things, was death, no matter the appearance of life. In the highest attachment only, no matter the appearance of death, was life. He had always known this truth, but now he was feeling it. Unable to move his hand, only his lips, and hardly breathing, was it too late to act?

"Open the window, Titus," he whispered.

And suddenly he could pray. *Hail Mary . . . Holy Mary, Mother of God, pray for us sinners now and at the hour of our death . . .* finally the time to say, *pray for* me *now—the hour of* my *death, amen.* Lest he deceive himself at the very end that this was the answer to a lifetime of praying for a happy death, happy because painless, he tried to turn his thoughts from himself, to join them to God, thinking how at last he did—didn't he *now?*—prefer God above all else. But ashamedly not sure he did, perhaps only fearing hell, with an uneasy sense of justice he put himself foremost among the wise in their own generation, the perennials seeking after God when doctor, lawyer, and bank fails. If he wronged himself, he did so out of humility—a holy error. He ended, to make certain he had not fallen under the same old presumption disguised as the face of humility, by flooding his mind with maledictions. He suffered the piercing white voice of the Apocalypse to echo in his soul: *But because thou art lukewarm, and neither cold, nor hot, I will begin to vomit thee out of my mouth.* And St. Bernard, fiery-eyed in a white habit, thundered at him from the twelfth century: "Hell is paved with the bald pates of priests!"

There was a soft flutter, the canary flew to the window sill, paused, and tilted into the snow. Titus stepped too late to the window and stood gazing dumbly after it. He raised a trembling old hand, fingers bent in awe and sorrow, to his forehead, and turned stealthily to Didymus.

Didymus closed his eyes. He let a long moment pass before he opened them. Titus, seeing him awake then, fussed with the window latch and held a hand down to feel the draught, nodding anxiously as though it were the only evil abroad in the world, all the time straining his old eyes for a glimpse of the canary somewhere in the trees.

Didymus said nothing, letting Titus keep his secret. With his whole will he tried to lose himself in the sight of God, and failed. He was not in the least transported. Even now he could find no divine sign within himself. He knew he still had to look outside, to Titus. God still chose to manifest Himself most in sanctity.

Titus, nervous under his stare, and to account for staying at the window so long, felt for the draught again, frowned, and kept his eye hunting among the trees.

The thought of being the cause of such elaborate dissimulation in so simple a soul made Didymus want to smile—or cry, he did not know which . . . and could do neither. Titus persisted. How long would it be, Didymus wondered faintly, before Titus ungrievingly gave the canary up for lost in the snowy arms of God? The snowflakes whirled at the window, for a moment for all their bright blue beauty as though struck still by lightning, and Didymus closed his eyes, only to find them there also, but darkly falling.

STEPHEN CRANE

(1871-1900)

*In his incredibly brief life span, Crane managed not only to attend
Syracuse University, where he captained the baseball team, but managed also to establish himself as a war correspondent, to become a
friend of Joseph Conrad, and to write some of the finest novels and
short stories of his time, as well as two volumes of poetry. His most
sensitive portrait of men at war is THE RED BADGE OF COUR-
AGE. His naturalistic bent may be seen in "The Open Boat" as well
as in "The Blue Hotel." His is not, however, a simplistic approach
to naturalism. "The Open Boat" leaves the problem of naturalism
unresolved; the implications of "The Blue Hotel" go beyond naturalistic bounds. His stories are made vivid through their concrete
detail, of which Crane is a master; and his characters are much more
than mere puppets in the hands of a blind and relentless fate.*

The Blue Hotel

I

The Palace Hotel at Fort Romper was painted a light blue, a shade
that is on the legs of a kind of heron, causing the bird to declare its
position against any background. The Palace Hotel, then, was always
screaming and howling in a way that made the dazzling winter
landscape of Nebraska seem only a gray swampish hush. It stood
alone on the prairie, and when the snow was falling the town two
hundred yards away was not visible. But when the traveller alighted
at the railway station he was obliged to pass the Palace Hotel before
he could come upon the company of low clapboard houses which
composed Fort Romper, and it was not to be thought that any travel-

ler could pass the Palace Hotel without looking at it. Pat Scully, the proprietor, had proved himself a master of strategy when he chose his paints. It is true that on clear days, when the great trans-continental expresses, long lines of swaying Pullmans, swept through Fort Romper, passengers were overcome at the sight, and the cult that knows the brown-reds and the subdivisions of the dark greens of the East expressed shame, pity, horror, in a laugh. But to the citizens of this prairie town and to the people who would naturally stop there, Pat Scully had performed a feat. With this opulence and splendor, these creeds, classes, egotisms, that streamed through Romper on the rails day after day, they had no color in common.

As if the displayed delights of such a blue hotel were not sufficiently enticing, it was Scully's habit to go every morning and evening to meet the leisurely trains that stopped at Romper and work his seductions upon any man that he might see wavering, gripsack in hand.

One morning, when a snow-crusted engine dragged its long string of freight cars and its one passenger coach to the station, Scully performed the marvel of catching three men. One was a shaky and quick-eyed Swede, with a great shining cheap valise; one was a tall bronzed cowboy, who was on his way to a ranch near the Dakota line; one was a little silent man from the East, who didn't look it, and didn't announce it. Scully practically made them prisoners. He was so nimble and merry and kindly that each probably felt it would be the height of brutality to try to escape. They trudged off over the creaking board sidewalks in the wake of the eager little Irishman. He wore a heavy fur cap squeezed tightly down on his head. It caused his two red ears to stick out stiffly, as if they were made of tin.

At last, Scully, elaborately, with boisterous hospitality, conducted them through the portals of the blue hotel. The room which they entered was small. It seemed to be merely a proper temple for an enormous stove, which, in the centre, was humming with godlike violence. At various points on its surface the iron had become luminous and glowed yellow from the heat. Beside the stove Scully's son Johnnie was playing High-Five with an old farmer who had whiskers both gray and sandy. They were quarrelling. Frequently the old farmer turned his face towards a box of sawdust—colored brown from tobacco juice—that was behind the stove, and spat with an air of great impatience and irritation. With a loud flourish of words Scully destroyed the game of cards, and bustled his son up-

stairs with part of the baggage of the new guests. He himself conducted them to three basins of the coldest water in the world. The
cowboy and the Easterner burnished themselves fiery-red with this
water, until it seemed to be some kind of a metal polish. The Swede,
however, merely dipped his fingers gingerly and with trepidation.
It was notable that throughout this series of small ceremonies the
three travellers were made to feel that Scully was very benevolent.
He was conferring great favors upon them. He handed the towel
from one to the other with an air of philanthropic impulse.

Afterwards they went to the first room, and, sitting about the
stove, listened to Scully's officious clamor at his daughters, who were
preparing the mid-day meal. They reflected in the silence of experienced men who tread carefully amid new people. Nevertheless,
the old farmer, stationary, invincible in his chair near the warmest
part of the stove, turned his face from the sawdust box frequently
and addressed a glowing commonplace to the strangers. Usually he
was answered in short but adequate sentences by either the cowboy
or the Easterner. The Swede said nothing. He seemed to be occupied in making furtive estimates of each man in the room. One might
have thought that he had the sense of silly suspicion which comes
to guilt. He resembled a badly frightened man.

Later, at dinner, he spoke a little, addressing his conversation
entirely to Scully. He volunteered that he had come from New
York, where for ten years he had worked as a tailor. These facts
seemed to strike Scully as fascinating, and afterwards he volunteered that he had lived at Romper for fourteen years. The Swede
asked about the crops and the price of labor. He seemed barely to listen to Scully's extended replies. His eyes continued to rove from man
to man.

Finally, with a laugh and a wink, he said that some of these
Western communities were very dangerous; and after his statement
he straightened his legs under the table, tilted his head, and
laughed again, loudly. It was plain that the demonstration had no
meaning to the others. They looked at him wondering and in silence.

II

As the men trooped heavily back into the front-room, the two
little windows presented views of a turmoiling sea of snow. The huge
arms of the wind were making attempts—mighty, circular, futile—

to embrace the flakes as they sped. A gate-post like a still man with a blanched face stood aghast amid this profligate fury. In a hearty voice Scully announced the presence of a blizzard. The guests of the blue hotel, lighting their pipes, assented with grunts of lazy masculine contentment. No island of the sea could be exempt in the degree of this little room with its humming stove. Johnnie, son of Scully, in a tone which defined his opinion of his ability as a card-player, challenged the old farmer of both gray and sandy whiskers to a game of High-Five. The farmer agreed with a contemptuous and bitter scoff. They sat close to the stove, and squared their knees under a wide board. The cowboy and the Easterner watched the game with interest. The Swede remained near the window, aloof, but with a countenance that showed signs of an inexplicable excitement.

The play of Johnnie and the gray-beard was suddenly ended by another quarrel. The old man arose while casting a look of heated scorn at his adversary. He slowly buttoned his coat, and then stalked with fabulous dignity from the room. In the discreet silence of all other men the Swede laughed. His laughter rang somehow childish. Men by this time had begun to look at him askance, as if they wished to inquire what ailed him.

A new game was formed jocosely. The cowboy volunteered to become the partner of Johnnie, and they all then turned to ask the Swede to throw in his lot with the little Easterner. He asked some questions about the game, and, learning that it wore many names, and that he had played it when it was under an alias, he accepted the invitation. He strode towards the men nervously, as if he expected to be assaulted. Finally, seated, he gazed from face to face and laughed shrilly. This laugh was so strange that the Easterner looked up quickly, the cowboy sat intent and with his mouth open, and Johnnie paused, holding the cards with still fingers.

Afterwards there was a short silence. Then Johnnie said, "Well, let's get at it. Come on now!" They pulled their chairs forward until their knees were bunched under the board. They began to play, and their interest in the game caused the others to forget the manner of the Swede.

The cowboy was a board-whacker. Each time that he held superior cards he whanged them, one by one, with exceeding force, down upon the improvised table, and took the tricks with a glowing air of prowess and pride that sent thrills of indignation into the hearts of his opponents. A game with a board-whacker in it is sure to become intense. The countenances of the Easterner and the Swede were miserable whenever the cowboy thundered down his aces and kings, while Johnnie, his eyes gleaming with joy, chuckled and chuckled.

Because of the absorbing play none considered the strange ways of the Swede. They paid strict heed to the game. Finally, during a lull caused by a new deal, the Swede suddenly addressed Johnnie: "I suppose there have been a good many men killed in this room." The jaws of the others dropped and they looked at him.

"What in hell are you talking about?" said Johnnie.

The Swede laughed again his blatant laugh, full of a kind of false courage and defiance. "Oh, you know what I mean all right," he answered.

"I'm a liar if I do!" Johnnie protested. The card was halted, and the men stared at the Swede. Johnnie evidently felt that as the son of the proprietor he should make a direct inquiry. "Now, what might you be drivin' at, mister?" he asked. The Swede winked at him. It was a wink full of cunning. His fingers shook on the edge of the board. "Oh, maybe you think I have been to nowheres. Maybe you think I'm a tenderfoot?"

"I don't know nothin' about you," answered Johnnie, "and I don't give a damn where you've been. All I got to say is that I don't know what you're driving at. There hain't never been nobody killed in this room."

The cowboy, who had been steadily gazing at the Swede, then spoke: "What's wrong with you, mister?"

Apparently it seemed to the Swede that he was formidably menaced. He shivered and turned white near the corners of his mouth. He sent an appealing glance in the direction of the little Easterner. During these moments he did not forget to wear his air of advanced pot-valor. "They say they don't know what I mean," he remarked mockingly to the Easterner.

The latter answered after prolonged and cautious reflection. "I don't understand you," he said, impassively.

The Swede made a movement then which announced that he thought he had encountered treachery from the only quarter where he had expected sympathy, if not help. "Oh, I see you are all against me. I see—"

The cowboy was in a state of deep stupefaction. "Say," he

cried, as he tumbled the deck violently down upon the board, "—say, what are you gittin' at, hey?"

The Swede sprang up with the celerity of a man escaping from a snake on the floor. "I don't want to fight!" he shouted. "I don't want to fight!"

The cowboy stretched his long legs indolently and deliberately. His hands were in his pockets. He spat into the sawdust box. "Well, who the hell thought you did?" he inquired.

The Swede backed rapidly towards a corner of the room. His hands were out protectingly in front of his chest, but he was making an obvious struggle to control his fright. "Gentlemen," he quavered, "I suppose I am going to be killed before I can leave this house! I suppose I am going to be killed before I can leave this house!" In his eyes was the dying-swan look. Through the windows could be seen the snow turning blue in the shadow of dusk. The wind tore at the house and some loose thing beat regularly against the clap-boards like a spirit tapping.

A door opened, and Scully himself entered. He paused in surprise as he noted the tragic attitude of the Swede. Then he said, "What's the matter here?"

The Swede answered him swiftly and eagerly: "These men are going to kill me."

"Kill you!" ejaculated Scully. "Kill you! What are you talkin'?"

The Swede made the gesture of a martyr.

Scully wheeled sternly upon his son. "What is this, Johnnie?"

The lad had grown sullen. "Damned if I know," he answered. "I can't make no sense to it." He began to shuffle the cards, fluttering them together with an angry snap. "He says a good many men have been killed in this room, or something like that. And he says he's goin' to be killed here too. I don't know what ails him. He's crazy, I shouldn't wonder."

Scully then looked for explanation to the cowboy, but the cowboy simply shrugged his shoulders.

"Kill you?" said Scully again to the Swede. "Kill you? Man, you're off your nut."

"Oh, I know," burst out the Swede. "I know what will happen. Yes, I'm crazy—yes. Yes, of course, I'm crazy—yes. But I know one thing—" There was a sort of sweat of misery and terror upon his face. "I know I won't get out of here alive."

The cowboy drew a deep breath, as if his mind was passing into the last stages of dissolution. "Well, I'm dog-goned," he whispered to himself.

Scully wheeled suddenly and faced his son. "You've been troublin' this man!"

Johnnie's voice was loud with its burden of grievance. "Why, good Gawd, I ain't done nothin' to 'im."

The Swede broke in. "Gentlemen, do not disturb yourselves. I will leave this house. I will go away because"—he accused them dramatically with his glance—"because I do not want to be killed."

Scully was furious with his son. "Will you tell me what is the matter, you young divil? What's the matter, anyhow? Speak out!"

"Blame it!" cried Johnnie in despair, "don't I tell you I don't know. He—he says we want to kill him, and that's all I know. I can't tell what ails him."

The Swede continued to repeat: "Never mind, Mr. Scully; never mind. I will leave this house. I will go away, because I do not wish to be killed. Yes, of course, I am crazy—yes. But I know one thing! I will go away. I will leave this house. Never mind, Mr. Scully; never mind. I will go away."

"You will not go 'way," said Scully. "You will not go 'way until I hear the reason of this business. If anybody has troubled you I will take care of him. This is my house. You are under my roof, and I will not allow any peaceable man to be troubled here." He cast a terrible eye upon Johnnie, the cowboy, and the Easterner.

"Never mind, Mr. Scully; never mind. I will go away. I do not wish to be killed." The Swede moved towards the door, which opened upon the stairs. It was evidently his intention to go at once for his baggage.

"No, no," shouted Scully peremptorily; but the white-faced man slid by him and disappeared. "Now," said Scully severely, "what does this mane?"

Johnnie and the cowboy cried together: "Why, we didn't do nothin' to 'im!"

Scully's eyes were cold. "No," he said, "you didn't?"

Johnnie swore a deep oath. "Why, this is the wildest loon I ever see. We didn't do nothin' at all. We were jest sittin' here playin' cards, and he—"

The father suddenly spoke to the Easterner. "Mr. Blanc," he asked, "what has these boys been doin'?"

The Easterner reflected again. "I didn't see anything wrong at all," he said at last, slowly.

Scully began to howl. "But what does it mane?" He stared ferociously at his son. "I have a mind to lather you for this, me boy."

Johnnie was frantic. "Well, what have I done?" he bawled at his father.

III

"I think you are tongue-tied," said Scully finally to his son, the cowboy, and the Easterner; and at the end of this scornful sentence he left the room.

Up-stairs the Swede was swiftly fastening the straps of his great valise. Once his back happened to be half turned towards the door, and, hearing a noise there, he wheeled and sprang up, uttering a loud cry. Scully's wrinkled visage showed grimly in the light of the small lamp he carried. This yellow effulgence, streaming upward, colored only his prominent features, and left his eyes, for instance, in mysterious shadow. He resembled a murderer.

"Man! man!" he exclaimed, "have you gone daffy?"

"Oh, no! Oh, no!" rejoined the other. "There are people in this world who know pretty nearly as much as you do—understand?"

For a moment they stood gazing at each other. Upon the Swede's deathly pale cheeks were two spots brightly crimson and sharply edged, as if they had been carefully painted. Scully placed the light on the table and sat himself on the edge of the bed. He spoke ruminatively. "By cracky, I never heard of such a thing in my life. It's a complete muddle. I can't, for the soul of me, think how you ever got this idea into your head." Presently he lifted his eyes and asked: "And did you sure think they were going to kill you?"

The Swede scanned the old man as if he wished to see into his mind. "I did," he said at last. He obviously suspected that this answer might precipitate an outbreak. As he pulled on a strap his whole arm shook, the elbow wavering like a bit of paper.

Scully banged his hand impressively on the foot-board of the bed. "Why, man, we're goin' to have a line of ilictric street-cars in this town next spring."

" 'A line of electric street-cars,' " repeated the Swede, stupidly.

"And," said Scully, "there's a new railroad goin' to be built down from Broken Arm to here. Not to mintion the four churches and the smashin' big brick school-house. Then there's the big factory, too. Why, in two years Romper 'll be a met-tro-*pol*-is."

Having finished the preparation of his baggage, the Swede straightened himself. "Mr. Scully," he said, with sudden hardihood, "how much do I owe you?"

"You don't owe me anythin'," said the old man, angrily.

"Yes, I do," retorted the Swede. He took seventy-five cents from his pocket and tendered it to Scully; but the latter snapped his fingers in disdainful refusal. However, it happened that they both stood gazing in a strange fashion at three silver pieces on the Swede's open palm.

"I'll not take your money," said Scully at last. "Not after what's been goin' on here." Then a plan seemed to strike him. "Here," he cried, picking up his lamp and moving towards the door. "Here! Come with me a minute."

"No," said the Swede, in overwhelming alarm.

"Yes," urged the old man. "Come on! I want you to come and see a picter—just across the hall—in my room."

The Swede must have concluded that his hour was come. His jaw dropped and his teeth showed like a dead man's. He ultimately followed Scully across the corridor, but he had the step of one hung in chains.

Scully flashed the light high on the wall of his own chamber. There was revealed a ridiculous photograph of a little girl. She was leaning against a balustrade of gorgeous decoration, and the formidable bang to her hair was prominent. The figure was as graceful as an upright sled-stake, and, withal, it was of the hue of lead. "There," said Scully, tenderly, "that's the picter of my little girl that died. Her name was Carrie. She had the purtiest hair you ever saw! I was that fond of her, she—"

Turning then, he saw that the Swede was not contemplating the picture at all, but, instead, was keeping keen watch on the gloom in the rear.

"Look, man!" cried Scully, heartily. "That's the picter of my little gal that died. Her name was Carrie. And then here's the picter of my oldest boy, Michael. He's a lawyer in Lincoln, an' doin' well. I gave that boy a grand eddycation, and I'm glad for it now. He's a fine boy. Look at 'im now. Ain't he bold as blazes, him there in Lincoln, an honored an' respicted gintleman. An honored an' respicted gintleman," concluded Scully with a flourish. And, so saying, he smote the Swede jovially on the back.

The Swede faintly smiled.

"Now," said the old man, "there's only one more thing." He dropped suddenly to the floor and thrust his head beneath the bed. The Swede could hear his muffled voice. "I'd keep it under me piller if it wasn't for that boy Johnnie. Then there's the old woman— Where is it now? I never put it twice in the same place. Ah, now come out with you!"

Presently he backed clumsily from under the bed, dragging with him an old coat rolled into a bundle. "I've fetched him," he muttered. Kneeling on the floor, he unrolled the coat and extracted from its heart a large yellow-brown whiskey bottle.

His first manœuvre was to hold the bottle up to the light. Reassured, apparently, that nobody had been tampering with it, he thrust it with a generous movement towards the Swede.

The weak-kneed Swede was about to eagerly clutch this element of strength, but he suddenly jerked his hand away and cast a look of horror upon Scully.

"Drink," said the old man affectionately. He had risen to his feet, and now stood facing the Swede.

There was a silence. Then again Scully said: "Drink!"

The Swede laughed wildly. He grabbed the bottle, put it to his mouth, and as his lips curled absurdly around the opening and his throat worked, he kept his glance, burning with hatred, upon the old man's face.

IV

After the departure of Scully the three men, with the cardboard still upon their knees, preserved for a long time an astounded silence. Then Johnnie said: "That's the dod-dangest Swede I ever see."

"He ain't no Swede," said the cowboy, scornfully.

"Well, what is he then?" cried Johnnie. "What is he then?"

"It's my opinion," replied the cowboy deliberately, "he's some kind of a Dutchman." It was a venerable custom of the country to entitle as Swedes all light-haired men who spoke with a heavy tongue. In consequence the idea of the cowboy was not without its daring. "Yes, sir," he repeated. "It's my opinion this feller is some kind of a Dutchman."

"Well, he says he's a Swede, anyhow," muttered Johnnie, sulkily. He turned to the Easterner: "What do you think, Mr. Blanc?"

"Oh, I don't know," replied the Easterner.

"Well, what do you think makes him act that way?" asked the cowboy.

"Why, he's frightened." The Easterner knocked his pipe against a rim of the stove. "He's clear frightened out of his boots."

"What at?" cried Johnnie and the cowboy together.

The Easterner reflected over his answer.

"What at?" cried the others again.

"Oh, I don't know, but it seems to me this man has been reading dime-novels, and he thinks he's right out in the middle of it— the shootin' and stabbin' and all."

"But," said the cowboy, deeply scandalized, "this ain't Wyoming, ner none of them places. This is Nebrasker."

"Yes," added Johnnie, "an' why don't he wait till he gits *out West?*"

The travelled Easterner laughed. "It isn't different there even —not in these days. But he thinks he's right in the middle of hell."

Johnnie and the cowboy mused long.

"It's awful funny," remarked Johnnie at last.

"Yes," said the cowboy. "This is a queer game. I hope we don't git snowed in, because then we'd have to stand this here man bein' around with us all the time. That wouldn't be no good."

"I wish pop would throw him out," said Johnnie.

Presently they heard a loud stamping on the stairs, accompanied by ringing jokes in the voice of old Scully, and laughter, evidently from the Swede. The men around the stove stared vacantly at each other. "Gosh!" said the cowboy. The door flew open, and old Scully, flushed and anecdotal, came into the room. He was jabbering at the Swede, who followed him, laughing bravely. It was the entry of two roisterers from a banquet-hall.

"Come now," said Scully sharply to the three seated men, "move up and give us a chance at the stove." The cowboy and the Easterner obediently sidled their chairs to make room for the newcomers. Johnnie, however, simply arranged himself in a more indolent attitude, and then remained motionless.

"Come! Git over, there," said Scully.

"Plenty of room on the other side of the stove," said Johnnie.

"Do you think we want to sit in the draught?" roared the father.

But the Swede here interposed with a grandeur of confidence. "No, no. Let the boy sit where he likes," he cried in a bullying voice to the father.

"All right! All right!" said Scully, deferentially. The cowboy and the Easterner exchanged glances of wonder.

The five chairs were formed in a crescent about one side of the stove. The Swede began to talk; he talked arrogantly, profanely, angrily. Johnnie, the cowboy, and the Easterner maintained a morose silence, while old Scully appeared to be receptive and eager, breaking in constantly with sympathetic ejaculations.

Finally the Swede announced that he was thirsty. He moved in his chair, and said that he would go for a drink of water.

"I'll git it for you," cried Scully at once.

"No," said the Swede, contemptuously. "I'll get it for myself." He arose and stalked with the air of an owner off into the executive parts of the hotel.

As soon as the Swede was out of hearing Scully sprang to his feet and whispered intensely to the others: "Up-stairs he thought I was tryin' to poison 'im."

"Say," said Johnnie, "this makes me sick. Why don't you throw 'im out in the snow?"

"Why, he's all right now," declared Scully. "It was only that he was from the East, and he thought this was a tough place. That's all. He's all right now."

The cowboy looked with admiration upon the Easterner. "You were straight," he said. "You were on to that there Dutchman."

"Well," said Johnnie to his father, "he may be all right now, but I don't see it. Other time he was scared, but now he's too fresh."

Scully's speech was always a combination of Irish brogue and idiom, Western twang and idiom, and scraps of curiously formal diction taken from the story-books and newspapers. He now hurled a strange mass of language at the head of his son. "What do I keep? What do I keep? What do I keep?" he demanded, in a voice of thunder. He slapped his knee impressively, to indicate that he himself was going to make reply, and that all should heed. "I keep a hotel," he shouted. "A hotel, do you mind? A guest under my roof has sacred privileges. He is to be intimidated by none. Not one word shall he hear that would prijudice him in favor of goin' away.

I'll not have it. There's no place in this here town where they can say they iver took in a guest of mine because he was afraid to stay here." He wheeled suddenly upon the cowboy and the Easterner. "Am I right?"

"Yes, Mr. Scully," said the cowboy, "I think you're right."

"Yes, Mr. Scully," said the Easterner, "I think you're right."

V

At six-o'clock supper, the Swede fizzed like a fire-wheel. He sometimes seemed on the point of bursting into riotous song, and in all his madness he was encouraged by old Scully. The Easterner was encased in reserve; the cowboy sat in wide-mouthed amazement, forgetting to eat, while Johnnie wrathily demolished great plates of food. The daughters of the house, when they were obliged to replenish the biscuits, approached as warily as Indians, and, having succeeded in their purpose, fled with ill-concealed trepidation. The Swede domineered the whole feast, and he gave it the appearance of a cruel bacchanal. He seemed to have grown suddenly taller; he gazed, brutally disdainful, into every face. His voice rang through the room. Once when he jabbed out harpoon-fashion with his fork to pinion a biscuit, the weapon nearly impaled the hand of the Easterner which had been stretched quietly out for the same biscuit.

After supper, as the men filed towards the other room, the Swede smote Scully ruthlessly on the shoulder. "Well, old boy, that was a good, square meal." Johnnie looked hopefully at his father; he knew that shoulder was tender from an old fall; and, indeed, it appeared for a moment as if Scully was going to flame out over the matter, but in the end he smiled a sickly smile and remained silent. The others understood from his manner that he was admitting his responsibility for the Swede's new view-point.

Johnnie, however, addressed his parent in an aside. "Why don't you license somebody to kick you down-stairs?" Scully scowled darkly by way of reply.

When they were gathered about the stove, the Swede insisted on another game of High-Five. Scully gently deprecated the plan at first, but the Swede turned a wolfish glare upon him. The old man subsided, and the Swede canvassed the others. In his tone there was always a great threat. The cowboy and the Easterner both remarked indifferently that they would play. Scully said that he would presently have to go to meet the 6.58 train, and so the Swede turned menacingly upon Johnnie. For a moment their glances crossed like blades, and then Johnnie smiled and said, "Yes, I'll play."

They formed a square, with the little board on their knees. The Easterner and the Swede were again partners. As the play went on, it was noticeable that the cowboy was not board-whacking as usual. Meanwhile, Scully, near the lamp, had put on his spectacles and, with an appearance curiously like an old priest, was reading a newspaper. In time he went out to meet the 6.58 train, and, despite his precautions, a gust of polar wind whirled into the room as he opened the door. Besides scattering the cards, it chilled the players to the marrow. The Swede cursed frightfully. When Scully returned, his entrance disturbed a cosey and friendly scene. The Swede again cursed. But presently they were once more intent, their heads bent forward and their hands moving swiftly. The Swede had adopted the fashion of board-whacking.

Scully took up his paper and for a long time remained immersed in matters which were extraordinarily remote from him. The lamp burned badly, and once he stopped to adjust the wick. The newspaper, as he turned from page to page, rustled with a slow and comfortable sound. Then suddenly he heard three terrible words: "You are cheatin'!"

Such scenes often prove that there can be little of dramatic import in environment. Any room can present a tragic front; any room can be comic. This little den was now hideous as a torture-chamber. The new faces of the men themselves had changed it upon the instant. The Swede held a huge fist in front of Johnnie's face, while the latter looked steadily over it into the blazing orbs of his accuser. The Easterner had grown pallid; the cowboy's jaw had dropped in that expression of bovine amazement which was one of his important mannerisms. After the three words, the first sound in the room was made by Scully's paper as it floated forgotten to his feet. His spectacles had also fallen from his nose, but by a clutch he had saved them in air. His hand, grasping the spectacles, now remained poised awkwardly and near his shoulder. He stared at the card-players.

Probably the silence was while a second elapsed. Then, if the floor had been suddenly twitched out from under the men they could not have moved quicker. The five had projected themselves headlong towards a common point. It happened that Johnnie, in rising to hurl himself upon the Swede, had stumbled slightly because of his curiously instinctive care for the cards and the board. The loss of the moment allowed time for the arrival of Scully, and also allowed the cowboy time to give the Swede a great push which sent him staggering back. The men found tongue together, and hoarse shouts of rage, appeal, or fear burst from every throat. The cowboy pushed and jostled feverishly at the Swede, and the Easterner and Scully clung wildly to Johnnie; but, through the smoky air, above the swaying bodies of the peace-compellers, the eyes of the two warriors ever sought each other in glances of challenge that were at once hot and steely.

Of course the board had been overturned, and now the whole company of cards was scattered over the floor, where the boots of the men trampled the fat and painted kings and queens as the gazed with their silly eyes at the war that was waging above them.

Scully's voice was dominating the yells. "Stop now! Stop, I say! Stop, now—"

Johnnie, as he struggled to burst through the rank formed by Scully and the Easterner, was crying, "Well, he says I cheated! He says I cheated! I won't allow no man to say I cheated! If he says I cheated, he's a —— ——!"

The cowboy was telling the Swede, "Quit, now! Quit, d'ye hear—"

The screams of the Swede never ceased: "He did cheat! I saw him! I saw him—"

As for the Easterner, he was importuning in a voice that was not heeded: "Wait a moment, can't you? Oh, wait a moment. What's the good of a fight over a game of cards? Wait a moment—"

In this tumult no complete sentences were clear. "Cheat"— "Quit"—"He says"—these fragments pierced the uproar and rang out sharply. It was remarkable that, whereas Scully undoubtedly made the most noise, he was the least heard of any of the riotous band.

Then suddenly there was a great cessation. It was as if each man had paused for breath; and although the room was still lighted with the anger of men, it could be seen that there was no danger of immediate conflict, and at once Johnnie, shouldering his way forward, almost succeeded in confronting the Swede. "What did you say I cheated for? What did you say I cheated for? I don't cheat, and I won't let no man say I do!"

The Swede said, "I saw you! I saw you!"

"Well," cried Johnnie, "I'll fight any man what says I cheat!"

"No, you won't," said the cowboy. "Not here."

"Ah, be still, can't you?" said Scully, coming between them.

The quiet was sufficient to allow the Easterner's voice to be heard. He was repeating, "Oh, wait a moment, can't you? What's the good of a fight over a game of cards? Wait a moment!"

Johnnie, his red face appearing above his father's shoulder, hailed the Swede again. "Did you say I cheated?"

The Swede showed his teeth. "Yes."

"Then," said Johnnie, "we must fight."

"Yes, fight," roared the Swede. He was like a demoniac. "Yes, fight! I'll show you what kind of a man I am! I'll show you who you want to fight! Maybe you think I can't fight! Maybe you think I can't! I'll show you, you skin, you card-sharp! Yes, you cheated! You cheated! You cheated!"

"Well, let's go at it, then, mister," said Johnnie, coolly.

The cowboy's brow was beaded with sweat from his efforts in intercepting all sorts of raids. He turned in despair to Scully. "What are you goin' to do now?"

A change had come over the Celtic visage of the old man. He now seemed all eagerness; his eyes glowed.

"We'll let them fight," he answered, stalwartly. "I can't put up with it any longer. I've stood this damned Swede till I'm sick. We'll let them fight."

VI

The men prepared to go out-of-doors. The Easterner was so nervous that he had great difficulty in getting his arms into the sleeves of his new leather coat. As the cowboy drew his fur cap down over his ears his hands trembled. In fact, Johnnie and old Scully were the only ones who displayed no agitation. These preliminaries were conducted without words.

Scully threw open the door. "Well, come on," he said. Instantly a terrific wind caused the flame of the lamp to struggle at its wick, while a puff of black smoke sprang from the chimney-top. The stove was in mid-current of the blast, and its voice swelled to equal the roar of the storm. Some of the scarred and bedabbled cards were caught up from the floor and dashed helplessly against the farther wall. The men lowered their heads and plunged into the tempest as into a sea.

No snow was falling, but great whirls and clouds of flakes, swept up from the ground by the frantic winds, were streaming southward with the speed of bullets. The covered land was blue with the sheen of an unearthly satin, and there was no other hue save where, at the low, black railway station—which seemed incredibly distant—one light gleamed like a tiny jewel. As the men floundered into a thigh-deep drift, it was known that the Swede was bawling out something. Scully went to him, put a hand on his shoulder and projected an ear. "What's that you say?" he shouted.

"I say," bawled the Swede again, "I won't stand much show against this gang. I know you'll all pitch on me."

Scully smote him reproachfully on the arm. "Tut, man!" he yelled. The wind tore the words from Scully's lips and scattered them far alee.

"You are all a gang of—" boomed the Swede, but the storm also seized the remainder of this sentence.

Immediately turning their backs upon the wind, the men had swung around a corner to the sheltered side of the hotel. It was the function of the little house to preserve here, amid this great devastation of snow, an irregular V-shape of heavily incrusted grass, which crackled beneath the feet. One could imagine the great drifts piled against the windward side. When the party reached the comparative peace of this spot it was found that the Swede was still bellowing.

"Oh, I know what kind of a thing this is! I know you'll all pitch on me. I can't lick you all!"

Scully turned upon him panther fashion. "You'll not have to whip all of us. You'll have to whip my son Johnnie. An' the man what troubles you durin' that time will have me to dale with."

The arrangements were swiftly made. The two men faced each other, obedient to the harsh commands of Scully, whose face, in the subtly luminous gloom, could be seen set in the austere impersonal lines that are pictured on the countenances of the Roman veterans. The Easterner's teeth were chattering, and he was hopping up and down like a mechanical toy. The cowboy stood rock-like.

The contestants had not stripped off any clothing. Each was in his ordinary attire. Their fists were up, and they eyed each other in a calm that had the elements of leonine cruelty in it.

During this pause, the Easterner's mind, like a film, took lasting impressions of three men—the iron-nerved master of the ceremony; the Swede, pale, motionless, terrible; and Johnnie, serene yet fero-

cious, brutish yet heroic. The entire prelude had in it a tragedy
greater than the tragedy of action, and this aspect was accentuated by
the long, mellow cry of the blizzard, as it sped the tumbling and wailing flakes into the black abyss of the south.

"Now!" said Scully.

The two combatants leaped forward and crashed together like
bullocks. There was heard the cushioned sound of blows, and of a
curse squeezing out from between the tight teeth of one.

As for the spectators, the Easterner's pent-up breath exploded
from him with a pop of relief, absolute relief from the tension of the
preliminaries. The cowboy bounded into the air with a yowl. Scully
was immovable as from supreme amazement and fear at the fury of
the fight which he himself had permitted and arranged.

For a time the encounter in the darkness was such a perplexity
of flying arms that it presented no more detail than would a swiftly
revolving wheel. Occasionally a face, as if illumined by a flash of
light, would shine out, ghastly and marked with pink spots. A moment later, the men might have been known as shadows, if it were
not for the involuntary utterance of oaths that came from them in
whispers.

Suddenly a holocaust of warlike desire caught the cowboy, and
he bolted forward with the speed of a broncho. "Go it, Johnnie! go it!
Kill him! Kill him!"

Scully confronted him. "Kape back," he said; and by his glance
the cowboy could tell that this man was Johnnie's father.

To the Easterner there was a monotony of unchangeable fighting
that was an abomination. This confused mingling was eternal to his
sense, which was concentrated in a longing for the end, the priceless
end. Once the fighters lurched near him, and as he scrambled hastily
backward he heard them breathe like men on the rack.

"Kill him, Johnnie! Kill him! Kill him! Kill him!" The cowboy's face was contorted like one of those agony masks in museums.

"Keep still," said Scully, icily.

Then there was a sudden loud grunt, incomplete, cut short, and
Johnnie's body swung away from the Swede and fell with sickening
heaviness to the grass. The cowboy was barely in time to prevent the
mad Swede from flinging himself upon his prone adversary. "No,
you don't," said the cowboy, interposing an arm. "Wait a second."

Scully was at his son's side. "Johnnie! Johnnie, me boy!" His
voice had a quality of melancholy tenderness. "Johnnie! Can you go

on with it?" He looked anxiously down into the bloody, pulpy face
of his son.

There was a moment of silence, and then Johnnie answered in
his ordinary voice, "Yes, I—it—yes."

Assisted by his father he struggled to his feet. "Wait a bit now
till you git your wind," said the old man.

A few paces away the cowboy was lecturing the Swede. "No, you
don't! Wait a second!"

The Easterner was plucking at Scully's sleeve. "Oh, this is
enough," he pleaded. "This is enough! Let it go as it stands. This is
enough!"

"Bill," said Scully, "git out of the road." The cowboy stepped
aside. "Now." The combatants were actuated by a new caution as
they advanced towards collision. They glared at each other, and then
the Swede aimed a lightning blow that carried with it his entire
weight. Johnnie was evidently half stupid from weakness, but he
miraculously dodged, and his fist sent the over-balanced Swede
sprawling.

The cowboy, Scully, and the Easterner burst into a cheer that
was like a chorus of triumphant soldiery, but before its conclusion
the Swede had scuffled agilely to his feet and come in berserk
abandon at his foe. There was another perplexity of flying arms,
and Johnnie's body again swung away and fell, even as a bundle
might fall from a roof. The Swede instantly staggered to a
little wind-waved tree and leaned upon it, breathing like an engine,
while his savage and flame-lit eyes roamed from face to face as the
men bent over Johnnie. There was a splendor of isolation in his situation at this time which the Easterner felt once when, lifting his eyes
from the man on the ground, he beheld that mysterious and lonely
figure, waiting.

"Are you any good yet, Johnnie?" asked Scully in a broken voice.

The son gasped and opened his eyes languidly. After a moment
he answered, "No—I ain't—any good—any—more." Then, from
shame and bodily ill, he began to weep, the tears furrowing down
through the blood-stains on his face. "He was too—too—too heavy
for me."

Scully straightened and addressed the waiting figure. "Stranger," he said, evenly, "it's all up with our side." Then his voice
changed into that vibrant huskiness which is commonly the tone of
the most simple and deadly announcements. "Johnnie is whipped."

Without replying, the victor moved off on the route to the front door of the hotel.

The cowboy was formulating new and unspellable blasphemies. The Easterner was startled to find that they were out in a wind that seemed to come direct from the shadowed arctic floes. He heard again the wail of the snow as it was flung to its grave in the south. He knew now that all this time the cold had been sinking into him deeper and deeper, and he wondered that he had not perished. He felt indifferent to the condition of the vanquished man.

"Johnnie, can you walk?" asked Scully.

"Did I hurt—hurt him any?" asked the son.

"Can you walk, boy? Can you walk?"

Johnnie's voice was suddenly strong. There was a robust impatience in it. "I asked you whether I hurt him any!"

"Yes, yes, Johnnie," answered the cowboy, consolingly; "he's hurt a good deal."

They raised him from the ground, and as soon as he was on his feet he went tottering off, rebuffing all attempts at assistance. When the party rounded the corner they were fairly blinded by the pelting of the snow. It burned their faces like fire. The cowboy carried Johnnie through the drift to the door. As they entered some cards again rose from the floor and beat against the wall.

The Easterner rushed to the stove. He was so profoundly chilled that he almost dared to embrace the glowing iron. The Swede was not in the room. Johnnie sank into a chair, and, folding his arms on his knees, buried his face in them. Scully, warming one foot and then the other at a rim of the stove, muttered to himself with Celtic mournfulness. The cowboy had removed his fur cap, and with a dazed and rueful air he was running one hand through his tousled locks. From overhead they could hear the creaking of boards, as the Swede tramped here and there in his room.

The sad quiet was broken by the sudden flinging open of a door that led towards the kitchen. It was instantly followed by an inrush of women. They precipitated themselves upon Johnnie amid a chorus of lamentation. Before they carried their prey off to the kitchen, there to be bathed and harangued with that mixture of sympathy and abuse which is a feat of their sex, the mother straightened herself and fixed old Scully with an eye of stern reproach. "Shame be upon you, Patrick Scully!" she cried. "Your own son, too. Shame be upon you!"

"There, now! Be quiet, now!" said the old man, weakly.

"Shame be upon you, Patrick Scully!" The girls, rallying to this slogan, sniffed disdainfully in the direction of those trembling accomplices, the cowboy and the Easterner. Presently they bore Johnnie away, and left the three men to dismal reflection.

VII

"I'd like to fight this here Dutchman myself," said the cowboy, breaking a long silence.

Scully wagged his head sadly. "No, that wouldn't do. It wouldn't be right. It wouldn't be right."

"Well, why wouldn't it?" argued the cowboy. "I don't see no harm in it."

"No," answered Scully, with mournful heroism. "It wouldn't be right. It was Johnnie's fight, and now we mustn't whip the man just because he whipped Johnnie."

"Yes, that's true enough," said the cowboy; "but—he better not get fresh with me, because I couldn't stand no more of it."

"You'll not say a word to him," commanded Scully, and even then they heard the tread of the Swede on the stairs. His entrance was made theatric. He swept the door back with a bang and swaggered to the middle of the room. No one looked at him. "Well," he cried, insolently, at Scully, "I s'pose you'll tell me now how much I owe you?"

The old man remained stolid. "You don't owe me nothin'."

"Huh!" said the Swede, "huh! Don't owe 'im nothin'."

The cowboy addressed the Swede. "Stranger, I don't see how you come to be so gay around here."

Old Scully was instantly alert. "Stop!" he shouted, holding his hand forth, fingers upward. "Bill, you shut up!"

The cowboy spat carelessly into the sawdust-box. "I didn't say a word, did I?" he asked.

"Mr. Scully," called the Swede, "how much do I owe you?" It was seen that he was attired for departure, and that he had his valise in his hand.

"You don't owe me nothin'," repeated Scully in his same imperturbable way.

"Huh!" said the Swede. "I guess you're right. I guess if it was any way at all, you'd owe me somethin'. That's what I guess." He turned to the cowboy. " 'Kill him! Kill him! Kill him!' " he mimicked, and then guffawed victoriously. " 'Kill him!' " He was convulsed with ironical humor.

But he might have been jeering the dead. The three men were immovable and silent, staring with glassy eyes at the stove.

The Swede opened the door and passed into the storm, giving one derisive glance backward at the still group.

As soon as the door was closed, Scully and the cowboy leaped to their feet and began to curse. They trampled to and fro, waving their arms and smashing into the air with their fists. "Oh, but that was a hard minute!" wailed Scully. "That was a hard minute! Him there leerin' and scoffin'! One bang at his nose was worth forty dollars to me that minute! How did you stand it, Bill?"

"How did I stand it?" cried the cowboy in a quivering voice. "How did I stand it? Oh!"

The old man burst into sudden brogue. "I'd loike to take that Swade," he wailed, "and hould 'im down on a shtone flure and bate 'im to a jelly wid a shtick!"

The cowboy groaned in sympathy. "I'd like to git him by the neck and ha-ammer him"—he brought his hand down on a chair with a noise like a pistol-shot—"hammer that there Dutchman until he couldn't tell himself from a dead coyote!"

"I'd bate 'im until he—"

"I'd show *him* some things—"

And then together they raised a yearning, fanatic cry—"Oh-o-oh! if we only could—"

"Yes!"

"Yes!"

"And then I'd—"

"O-o-oh!"

VIII

The Swede, tightly gripping his valise, tacked across the face of the storm as if he carried sails. He was following a line of little naked, gasping trees, which he knew must mark the way of the road. His face, fresh from the pounding of Johnnie's fists, felt more pleasure than pain in the wind and the driving snow. A number of square shapes loomed upon him finally, and he knew them as the houses of the main body of the town. He found a street and made travel along it, leaning heavily upon the wind whenever, at a corner, a terrific blast caught him.

He might have been in a deserted village. We picture the world as thick with conquering and elate humanity, but here, with the bugles of the tempest pealing, it was hard to imagine a peopled earth. One viewed the existence of man then as a marvel, and conceded a glamour of wonder to these lice which were caused to cling to a whirling, fire-smote, ice-locked, disease-stricken, space-lost bulb. The conceit of man was explained by this storm to be the very engine of life. One was a coxcomb not to die in it. However, the Swede found a saloon.

In front of it an indomitable red light was burning, and the snow-flakes were made blood-color as they flew through the circumscribed territory of the lamp's shining. The Swede pushed open the door of the saloon and entered. A sanded expanse was before him, and at the end of it four men sat about a table drinking. Down one side of the room extended a radiant bar, and its guardian was leaning upon his elbows listening to the talk of the men at the table. The Swede dropped his valise upon the floor, and, smiling fraternally upon the barkeeper, said, "Gimme some whiskey, will you?" The man placed a bottle, a whiskey-glass, and a glass of ice-thick water upon the bar. The Swede poured himself an abnormal portion of whiskey and drank it in three gulps. "Pretty bad night," remarked the bartender, indifferently. He was making the pretension of blindness which is usually a distinction of his class; but it could have been seen that he was furtively studying the half-erased bloodstains on the face of the Swede. "Bad night," he said again.

"Oh, it's good enough for me," replied the Swede, hardily, as he poured himself some more whiskey. The barkeeper took his coin and manœuvred it through its reception by the highly nickelled cash-machine. A bell rang; a card labelled "20 cts." had appeared.

"No," continued the Swede, "this isn't too bad weather. It's good enough for me."

"So?" murmured the barkeeper, languidly.

The copious drams made the Swede's eyes swim, and he breathed a trifle heavier. "Yes, I like this weather. I like it. It suits me." It was apparently his design to impart a deep significance to these words.

"So?" murmured the bartender again. He turned to gaze

dreamily at the scroll-like birds and bird-like scrolls which had been drawn with soap upon the mirrors back of the bar.

"Well, I guess I'll take another drink," said the Swede, presently. "Have something?"

"No, thanks; I'm not drinkin'," answered the bartender. Afterwards he asked, "How did you hurt your face?"

The Swede immediately began to boast loudly. "Why, in a fight. I thumped the soul out of a man down here at Scully's hotel."

The interest of the four men at the table was at last aroused.

"Who was it?" said one.

"Johnnie Scully," blustered the Swede. "Son of the man what runs it. He will be pretty near dead for some weeks, I can tell you. I made a nice thing of him, I did. He couldn't get up. They carried him in the house. Have a drink?"

Instantly the men in some subtle way encased themselves in reserve. "No, thanks," said one. The group was of curious formation. Two were prominent local business men; one was the district-attorney; and one was a professional gambler of the kind known as "square." But a scrutiny of the group would not have enabled an observer to pick the gambler from the men of more reputable pursuits. He was, in fact, a man so delicate in manner, when among people of fair class, and so judicious in his choice of victims, that in the strictly masculine part of the town's life he had come to be explicitly trusted and admired. People called him a thoroughbred. The fear and contempt with which his craft was regarded was undoubtedly the reason that his quiet dignity shone conspicuous above the quiet dignity of men who might be merely hatters, billiard-markers, or grocery-clerks. Beyond an occasional unwary traveller, who came by rail, this gambler was supposed to prey solely upon reckless and senile farmers, who, when flush with good crops, drove into town in all the pride and confidence of an absolutely invulnerable stupidity. Hearing at times in circuitous fashion of the despoilment of such a farmer, the important men of Romper invariably laughed in contempt of the victim, and, if they thought of the wolf at all, it was with a kind of pride at the knowledge that he would never dare think of attacking their wisdom and courage. Besides, it was popular that this gambler had a real wife and two real children in a neat cottage in a suburb, where he led an exemplary home life; and when any one even suggested a discrepancy in his character, the crowd immediately vociferated descriptions of this virtuous family circle. Then men who led exemplary home lives, and men who did not lead exemplary home lives, all subsided in a bunch, remarking that there was nothing more to be said.

However, when a restriction was placed upon him—as, for instance, when a strong clique of members of the new Pollywog Club refused to permit him, even as a spectator, to appear in the rooms of the organization—the candor and gentleness with which he accepted the judgment disarmed many of his foes and made his friends more desperately partisan. He invariably distinguished between himself and a respectable Romper man so quickly and frankly that his manner actually appeared to be a continual broadcast compliment.

And one must not forget to declare the fundamental fact of his entire position in Romper. It is irrefutable that in all affairs outside of his business, in all matters that occur eternally and commonly between man and man, this thieving card-player was so generous, so just, so moral, that, in a contest, he could have put to flight the consciences of nine-tenths of the citizens of Romper.

And so it happened that he was seated in this saloon with the two prominent local merchants and the district-attorney.

The Swede continued to drink raw whiskey, meanwhile babbling at the barkeeper and trying to induce him to indulge in potations. "Come on. Have a drink. Come on. What—no? Well, have a little one, then. By gawd, I've whipped a man to-night, and I want to celebrate. I whipped him good, too. Gentlemen," the Swede cried to the men at the table, "have a drink?"

"Ssh!" said the barkeeper.

The group at the table, although furtively attentive, had been pretending to be deep in talk, but now a man lifted his eyes towards the Swede and said, shortly, "Thanks. We don't want any more."

At this reply the Swede ruffled out his chest like a rooster. "Well," he exploded, "it seems I can't get anybody to drink with me in this town. Seems so, don't it? Well!"

"Ssh!" said the barkeeper.

"Say," snarled the Swede, "don't you try to shut me up. I won't have it. I'm a gentleman, and I want people to drink with me. And I want 'em to drink with me now. *Now*—do you understand?" He rapped the bar with his knuckles.

Years of experience had calloused the bartender. He merely grew sulky. "I hear you," he answered.

"Well," cried the Swede, "listen hard then. See those men over there? Well, they're going to drink with me, and don't you forget it. Now you watch."

"Hi!" yelled the barkeeper, "this won't do!"

"Why won't it?" demanded the Swede. He stalked over to the table, and by chance laid his hand upon the shoulder of the gambler. "How about this?" he asked, wrathfully. "I asked you to drink with me."

The gambler simply twisted his head and spoke over his shoulder. "My friend, I don't know you."

"Oh, hell!" answered the Swede, "come and have a drink."

"Now, my boy," advised the gambler, kindly, "take your hand off my shoulder and go 'way and mind your own business." He was a little, slim man, and it seemed strange to hear him use this tone of heroic patronage to the burly Swede. The other men at the table said nothing.

"What! You won't drink with me, you little dude? I'll make you then! I'll make you!" The Swede had grasped the gambler frenziedly at the throat, and was dragging him from his chair. The other men sprang up. The barkeeper dashed around the corner of his bar. There was a great tumult, and then was seen a long blade in the hand of the gambler. It shot forward, and a human body, this citadel of virtue, wisdom, power, was pierced as easily as if it had been a melon. The Swede fell with a cry of supreme astonishment.

The prominent merchants and the district-attorney must have at once tumbled out of the place backward. The bartender found himself hanging limply to the arm of a chair and gazing into the eyes of a murderer.

"Henry," said the latter, as he wiped his knife on one of the towels that hung beneath the bar-rail, "you tell 'em where to find me. I'll be home, waiting for 'em." Then he vanished. A moment afterwards the barkeeper was in the street dinning through the storm for help, and, moreover, companionship.

The corpse of the Swede, alone in the saloon, had its eyes fixed upon a dreadful legend that dwelt atop of the cash-machine: "This registers the amount of your purchase."

IX

Months later, the cowboy was frying pork over the stove of a little ranch near the Dakota line, when there was a quick thud of hoofs outside, and presently the Easterner entered with the letters and the papers.

"Well," said the Easterner at once, "the chap that killed the Swede has got three years. Wasn't much, was it?"

"He has? Three years?" The cowboy poised his pan of pork, while he ruminated upon the news. "Three years. That ain't much."

"No. It was a light sentence," replied the Easterner as he unbuckled his spurs. "Seems there was a good deal of sympathy for him in Romper."

"If the bartender had been any good," observed the cowboy, thoughtfully, "he would have gone in and cracked that there Dutchman on the head with a bottle in the beginnin' of it and stopped all this here murderin'."

"Yes, a thousand things might have happened," said the Easterner, tartly.

The cowboy returned his pan of pork to the fire, but his philosophy continued. "It's funny, ain't it? If he hadn't said Johnnie was cheatin' he'd be alive this minute. He was an awful fool. Game played for fun, too. Not for money. I believe he was crazy."

"I feel sorry for that gambler," said the Easterner.

"Oh, so do I," said the cowboy. "He don't deserve none of it for killin' who he did."

"The Swede might not have been killed if everything had been square."

"Might not have been killed?" exclaimed the cowboy. "Everythin' square? Why, when he said that Johnnie was cheatin' and acted like such a jackass? And then in the saloon he fairly walked up to git hurt?" With these arguments the cowboy browbeat the Easterner and reduced him to rage.

"You're a fool!" cried the Easterner, viciously. "You're a bigger jackass than the Swede by a million majority. Now let me tell you one thing. Let me tell you something. Listen! Johnnie *was* cheating!"

"'Johnnie,'" said the cowboy, blankly. There was a minute of silence, and then he said, robustly, "Why, no. The game was only for fun."

"Fun or not," said the Easterner, "Johnnie was cheating. I saw him. I know it. I saw him. And I refused to stand up and be a man. I let the Swede fight it out alone. And you—you were simply puffing around the place and wanting to fight. And then old Scully himself! We are all in it! This poor gambler isn't even a noun. He is kind of an adverb. Every sin is the result of a collaboration. We, five of us, have collaborated in the murder of this Swede. Usually there are from a dozen to forty women really involved in every murder, but in this case it seems to be only five men—you, I, Johnnie, old Scully, and that fool of an unfortunate gambler came merely as a culmination, the apex of a human movement, and gets all the punishment."

The cowboy, injured and rebellious, cried out blindly into this fog of mysterious theory: "Well, I didn't do anythin', did I?"

QUESTIONS

Crane's "The Blue Hotel" presents a complex view of the relationship between man and the world in which he exists, a view which is largely naturalistic. His fictional technique is to communicate that view through a system of patterns: patterns of imagery, patterns of symbolism, patterns of characterization, patterns of action, and a definite structural pattern. We can arrive at some understanding of Crane's view of the nature of man, for example, by examining his pattern of characterization. We quickly see that virtually every character in the story appears in a severely critical light. Johnnie, it turns out, did cheat; the Easterner, Mr. Blanc, knew he cheated but failed to speak up; Scully acquiesces in the Code of the West, in spite of his own pronouncements about the hotel as sanctuary for any guest and in contradiction of the general consensus, as voiced by the cowboy, that "this ain't Wyoming, ner none of them places"; and the cowboy is consistently presented as slack-jawed and bovine in his stupidity. At the saloon, the gambler has the appearance of respectability in his quiet manner, careful dress, and stable family life; in actuality, he is a "wolf" who preys "solely upon reckless and senile farmers." The most that can be said for him is that, "in all affairs outside of his business," he conducts himself in an upright manner; but Crane's stricture is severe. Nor are his fellow townsmen any better. Whenever the gambler ruined someone, "the important men of Romper invariably laughed in contempt of the victim." The gambler is in the company of three of these important men: two prominent businessmen and the district attorney. Their reaction to the murder is to race out of the saloon, or, as Crane puts it, they "must have at once tumbled out of the place backward." The Swede is a far more complex figure, however, and it is he who is the key to Crane's view of human nature and human destiny. The following questions are directed toward the more significant elements in "The Blue Hotel," elements which function as parts of Crane's complex view of the cosmos.

1. The narrative focus of "The Blue Hotel" is clearly upon the Swede. In what ways does he differ from the other characters? How does he resemble them? At the hotel, the Swede undergoes a violent change in attitude toward his surroundings, from utter fear for his personal safety to an infuriating and bullying contempt for the others. What is the significance of this change?

2. Analyze the structure of the story in terms of the two locales, the Palace Hotel and the saloon. How do these two locales differ? To what extent might they be said to represent two different aspects of man's social condition? It is interesting to note that the Swede's bullying tactics lead him to triumph at the Palace Hotel, but essentially the same tactics result in his death at the saloon. What explanation is there for this reversal of fortunes?

3. There are several patterns of imagery which may be found throughout the story. Trace these patterns and suggest their symbolic significance. What shifts in imagery coincide with the Swede's movement from hotel to saloon? What is the meaning of these shifts?

4. Crane also organizes his narrative around a few definite symbols. There is one central symbol for the hotel episode, one for the saloon episode, and one symbol encompassing the story's action in its entirety. Identify these three symbols and discuss their relevance to the action.

5. At a few crucial points, the narrator intervenes to offer observations on the nature of man and on the world in which he lives. What light do these observations cast on the meaning of the narrative's events?

6. The ninth (final) section of the story has been called anti-climactic and too obviously moralizing. The action, in other words, should have ended with the dramatic announcement of the cash register, " 'This registers the amount of your purchase.' " Do you agree with this criticism?

7. After carefully examining these and other aspects of the story, try to formulate a statement of the meaning of the experience which Crane communicates, elaborating on the nature of man, the nature of the cosmos, and the relationship between the two as Crane views them.

MAXIM GORKY

(1868–1936)

The Russian Revolution of 1917 came when Gorky was almost fifty years old and well established as a writer; his was one of the few literary careers to survive that upheaval. He joined the revolutionary forces, risking his life in support of them. When he died, he was hailed by his countrymen not only as a great writer but as a great patriot as well. Characteristic of his work is a familiarity with his native country—both its geography and its peoples—which was the product of odysseys into virtually all of his land's physical and social climates. Coupled with this familiarity is a profound love of country. His experience among men taught him to see man's brutality, stupidity, and ignorance, a realistic view which he tempers with deep compassion. Man, he sees, is his own victim, and as such is to be profoundly pitied. A major theme of his works is that of freedom, implying both faith in man and hope for his eventual liberation. Gorky is, then, at once realistic and romantic in his attitude. Of his many plays, novels, short stories, and essays, the drama, THE LOWER DEPTHS, is perhaps the best known.

Twenty-Six Men and a Girl

There were six-and-twenty of us;—six-and-twenty living machines in a damp, underground cellar, where from morning till night we kneaded dough and rolled it into kringels. Opposite the under-

"Twenty-Six Men and a Girl" by Maxim Gorky, trans. Emily Jakovlev and Dora B. Montefiore. Reprinted with the permission of Gerald Duckworth & Co. Ltd.

ground window of our cellar was a bricked area, green and mouldy
with moisture. The window was protected from outside with a close
iron grating, and the light of the sun could not pierce through the
window panes, covered as they were with flour dust.

Our employer had bars placed in front of the windows, so that
we should not be able to give a bit of his bread to passing beggars,
or to any of our fellows who were out of work and hungry. Our employer called us rogues, and gave us half-rotten tripe to eat for our
mid-day meal, instead of meat. It was swelteringly close for us
cooped up in that stone underground chamber, under the low, heavy,
soot-blackened, cobwebby ceiling. Dreary and sickening was our life
between its thick, dirty, mouldy walls.

Unrefreshed, and with a feeling of not having had our sleep
out, we used to get up at five o'clock in the morning; and before six,
we were already seated, worn out and apathetic, at the table, rolling
out the dough which our mates had already prepared whilst we
slept. The whole day, from ten in the early morning until ten at
night, some of us sat round that table, working up in our hands the
yielding paste, rolling it to and fro so that it should not get stiff;
whilst the others kneaded the swelling mass of dough. And the
whole day the simmering water in the kettle, where the kringels were
being cooked, sang low and sadly; and the baker's shovel scraped
harshly over the oven floor, as he threw the slippery bits of dough
out of the kettle on to the heated bricks.

From morning till evening wood was burning in the oven, and
the red glow of the fire gleamed and flickered over the walls of the
bake-shop, as if silently mocking us. The giant oven was like the mis-
shapen head of a monster in a fairy tale; it thrust itself up out of the
floor, opened wide jaws, full of glowing fire, and blew hot breath
upon us; it seemed to be ever watching out of its black air-holes
our interminable work. Those two deep holes were like eyes—the
cold, pitiless eyes of a monster. They watched us always with the
same darkened glance, as if they were weary of seeing before them
such eternal slaves, from whom they could expect nothing human,
and therefore scorned them with the cold scorn of wisdom.

In meal dust, in the mud which we brought in from the yard on
our boots, in the hot, sticky atmosphere, day in, day out, we rolled
the dough into kringels, which we moistened with our own sweat.
And we hated our work with a glowing hatred; we never ate what

had passed through our hands, and preferred black bread to kringels. Sitting opposite each other, at a long table—nine facing nine—we moved our hands and fingers mechanically during endlessly long hours, till we were so accustomed to our monotonous work that we ceased to pay any attention to it.

We had all studied each other so constantly, that each of us knew every wrinkle of his mates' faces. It was not long also before we had exhausted almost every topic of conversation; that is why we were most of the time silent, unless we were chaffing each other; but one cannot always find something about which to chaff another man, especially when that man is one's mate. Neither were we much given to finding fault with one another; how, indeed, could one of us poor devils be in a position to find fault with another, when we were all of us half dead and, as it were, turned to stone? For the heavy drudgery seemed to crush all feeling out of us. But silence is only terrible and fearful for those who have said everything and have nothing more to say to each other; for men, on the contrary, who have never begun to communicate with one another, it is easy and simple.

Sometimes, too, we sang; and this is how it happened that we began to sing: one of us would sigh deeply in the midst of our toil, like an overdriven horse, and then we would begin one of those songs whose gentle swaying melody seems always to ease the burden on the singer's heart.

At first one sang by himself, and we others sat in silence listening to his solitary song, which, under the heavy vaulted roof of the cellar, died gradually away, and became extinguished, like a little fire in the steppes, on a wet autumn night, when the grey heaven hangs like a heavy mass over the earth. Then another would join in with the singer, and now two soft, sad voices would break into song in our narrow, dull hole of a cellar. Suddenly others would join in, and the song would roll forward like a wave, would grow louder and swell upwards, till it would seem as if the damp, foul walls of our stone prison were widening out and opening. Then, all six-and-twenty of us would be singing; our loud, harmonious song would fill the whole cellar, our voices would travel outside and beyond, striking, as it were, against the walls in moaning sobs and sighs, moving our hearts with soft, tantalizing ache, tearing open old wounds, and awakening longings.

The singers would sigh deeply and heavily; suddenly one would become silent and listen to the others singing, then let his voice flow once more in the common tide. Another would exclaim in a stifled voice, "Ah!" and would shut his eyes, whilst the deep, full sound waves would show him, as it were, a road, in front of him— a sunlit, broad road in the distance, which he himself, in thought, wandered along.

But the flame flickers once more in the huge oven, the baker scrapes incessantly with his shovel, the water simmers in the kettle, and the flicker of the fire on the wall dances as before in silent mockery. While in other men's words we sing out our dumb grief, the weary burden of live men robbed of the sunlight, the burden of slaves.

So we lived, we six-and-twenty, in the vault-like cellar of a great stone house, and we suffered each one of us, as if we had to bear on our shoulders the whole three storeys of that house.

But we had something else good, besides the singing—something we loved, that perhaps took the place of the sunshine.

In the second storey of our house there was established a gold-embroiderer's shop, and there, living amongst the other embroidery girls, was Tanya, a little maid-servant of sixteen. Every morning there peeped in through the glass door a rosy little face, with merry blue eyes; while a ringing, tender voice called out to us:

"Little prisoners! Have you any kringels, please, for me?"

At that clear sound, we knew so well, we all used to turn round, gazing with simple-hearted joy at the pure girlish face which smiled at us so sweetly. The sight of the small nose pressed against the window-pane, and of the white teeth gleaming between the half-open lips, had become for us a daily pleasure. Tumbling over each other we used to jump up to open the door, and she would step in, bright and cheerful, holding out her apron, with her head thrown on one side, and a smile on her lips. Her thick, long chestnut hair fell over her shoulder and across her breast. But we, ugly, dirty and mis-shapen as we were, looked up at her—the threshold door was four steps above the floor—looked up at her with heads thrown back, wishing her good morning, and speaking strange unaccustomed words, which we kept for her only. Our voices became softer when we spoke to her, our jests were lighter. For her—everything was different with us. The baker took from his oven a shovel of the best and the brownest kringels, and threw them deftly into Tanya's apron.

"Be off with you now, or the boss will catch you!" we warned her each time. She laughed roguishly, called out cheerfully: "Good bye, poor prisoners!" and slipped away as quick as a mouse.

That was all. But long after she had gone we talked about her to one another with pleasure. It was always the same thing as we had said yesterday and the day before, because everything about us, including ourselves and her, remained the same—as yesterday —and as always.

Painful and terrible it is when a man goes on living, while nothing changes around him; and when such an existence does not finally kill his soul, then the monotony becomes with time, even more and more painful. Generally we spoke about women in such a way, that sometimes it was loathsome to us ourselves to hear our rude, shameless talk. The women whom we knew deserved perhaps nothing better. But about Tanya we never let fall an evil word; none of us ever ventured so much as to lay a hand on her, even too free a jest she never heard from us. Maybe this was so because she never remained for long with us; she flashed on our eyes like a star falling from the sky, and vanished; and maybe because she was little and very beautiful, and everything beautiful calls forth respect, even in coarse people. And besides—though our life of penal labour had made us dull beasts, oxen, we were still men, and, like all men, could not live without worshipping something or other. Better than her we had none, and none but she took any notice of us, living in the cellar —no one, though there were dozens of people in the house. And then, too—most likely, this was the chief thing—we all regarded her as something of our own, something existing as it were only by virtue of our kringels. We took on ourselves in turns the duty of providing her with hot kringels, and this became for us like a daily sacrifice to our idol, it became almost a sacred rite, and every day it bound us more closely to her. Besides kringels, we gave Tanya a great deal of advice—to wear warmer clothes, not to run upstairs too quickly, not to carry heavy bundles of wood. She listened to all our counsels with a smile, answered them by a laugh, and never took our advice, but we were not offended at that; all we wanted was to show how much care we bestowed upon her.

Often she would apply to us with different requests, she asked us for instance to open the heavy door into the store-cellar, and to chop wood: with delight and a sort of pride, we did this for her and everything else she wanted.

But when one of us asked her to mend his solitary shirt for him, she said, with a laugh of contempt:

"What next! A likely idea!"

We made great fun of the queer fellow who could entertain such an idea, and—never asked her to do anything else. We loved her—all is said in that. Man always wants to lay his love on someone, though sometimes he crushes, sometimes he sullies, with it; he may poison another life because he loves without respecting the beloved. We were bound to love Tanya, for we had no one else to love.

At times one of us would suddenly begin to reason like this:

"And why do we make so much of the wench? What is there in her? eh? What a to-do we make about her!"

The man who dared to utter such words we promptly and coarsely cut short—we wanted something to love: we had found it and loved it, and what we twenty-six loved must be for each of us unalterable, as a holy thing, and anyone who acted against us in this was our enemy. We loved, maybe, not what was really good, but you see there were twenty-six of us, and so we always wanted to see what was precious to us held sacred by the rest.

Our love is not less burdensome than hate, and maybe that is just why some proud souls maintain that our hate is more flattering than our love. But why do they not run away from us, if it is so?

Besides our department our employer had also a bread-bakery; it was in the same house, separated from our hole only by a wall; but the bakers—there were four of them—held aloof from us, considering their work superior to ours, and therefore themselves better than us; they never used to come into our workroom, and laughed contemptuously at us when they met us in the yard. We, too, did not go to see them; this was forbidden by our employer, from fear that we should steal the fancy bread. We did not like the bakers, because we envied them; their work was lighter than ours, they were paid more, and were better fed; they had a light, spacious workroom, and they were all so clean and healthy—and that made them hateful to us. We all looked grey and yellow; three of us had syphilis, several suffered from skin diseases, one was completely crippled by rheumatism. On holidays and in their leisure time

the bakers wore pea-jackets and creaking boots, two of them had ac-
cordions, and they all used to go for strolls in the town gardens,—we
wore filthy rags and leather clogs or plaited shoes on our feet, the
police would not let us into the town gardens—could we possibly
like the bakers?

And one day we learned that their chief baker had been drunk,
the master had sacked him and had already taken on another, and
that this other was a soldier, wore a satin waistcoat and a watch and
gold chain. We were inquisitive to get a sight of such a dandy, and
in the hope of catching a glimpse of him we kept running one after
another out into the yard.

But he came of his own accord into our room. Kicking at the
door, he pushed it open, and leaving it ajar, stood in the doorway
smiling, and said to us:

"God help the work! Good morning, mates!"

The ice-cold air, which streamed in through the open door,
curled in streaks of vapour round his feet. He stood on the threshold, looked us up and down, and under his fair, twisted moustache
gleamed big yellow teeth. His waistcoat was really something quite
out of the common, blue-flowered, brilliant with shining little buttons of red stones. He also wore a watch chain.

He was a fine fellow, this soldier; tall, healthy, rosy-cheeked, and
his big, clear eyes had a friendly, cheerful glance. He wore on his
head a white starched cap, and from under his spotlessly clean apron
peeped the pointed toes of fashionable, well-blacked boots.

Our baker asked him politely to shut the door. The soldier did
so without hurrying himself, and began to question us about the
master. We explained to him, all speaking together, that our employer was a thorough-going brute, a rogue, a knave, and a slave-
driver; in a word we repeated to him all that can and must be said
about an employer, but cannot be repeated here. The soldier listened to us, twisted his moustache, and watched us with a friendly,
open-hearted look.

"But haven't you got a lot of girls here?" he asked, suddenly.

Some of us began to laugh deferentially, others put on a meaning expression, and one of us explained to the soldier that there were
nine girls here.

"You make the most of them?" asked the soldier, with a wink.

We laughed, but not so loudly, and with some embarrassment.
Many of us would have liked to have shown the soldier that we also

were tremendous fellows with the girls, but not one of us could do so; and one of our number confessed as much, when he said in a low voice:

"That sort of thing is not in our line."

"Well no, it wouldn't quite do for you," said the soldier with conviction, after having looked us over. "There is something wanting about you all. You don't look the right sort. You've no sort of appearance; and the women, you see, they like a bold appearance, they will have a well set up body. Everything has to be tip-top for them. That's why they respect strength. They want an arm like that!"

The soldier drew his right hand, with its turned-up shirt sleeve, out of his pocket, and showed us his bare arm. It was white and strong, and covered with shining yellow hairs.

"Leg and chest, all must be strong. And then a man must be dressed in the latest fashion, so as to show off his looks to advantage. Yes, all the women take to me. Whether I call to them, or whether I beckon them, they with one accord, five at a time, throw themselves at my head."

He sat down on a flour sack, and told at length all about the way women loved him, and how bold he was with them. Then he left, and after the door had creaked to behind him, we sat for a long time silent, and thought about him and his talk. Then we all suddenly broke silence together, and it became apparent that we were all equally pleased with him. He was such a nice, open-hearted fellow; he came to see us without any stand-offishness, sat down and chatted. No one else came to us like that, and no one else talked to us in that friendly sort of way. And we continued to talk of him and his coming triumph among the embroidery girls, who passed us by with contemptuous sniffs when they saw us in the yard, or who looked straight through us as if we had been air. But we admired them always when we met them outside, or when they walked past our windows; in winter, in fur jackets and toques to match; in summer, in hats trimmed with flowers, and with coloured parasols in their hands. We talked, however, about these girls in a way that would have made them mad with shame and rage, if they could have heard us.

"If only he does not get hold of little Tanya!" said the baker, suddenly, in an anxious tone of voice.

We were silent, for these words troubled us. Tanya had quite gone out of our minds, supplanted, put on one side by the strong, fine figure of the soldier.

Then began a lively discussion; some of us maintained that Tanya would never lower herself so; others thought she would not be able to resist him, and the third group proposed to give him a thrashing if he should try to annoy Tanya. And, finally, we all decided to watch the soldier and Tanya, and to warn the girl against him. This brought the discussion to an end.

Four weeks had passed by since then; during this time the soldier baked white bread, walked about with the gold-embroidery girls, visited us often, but did not talk any more about his conquests; only twisted his moustache, and licked his lips lasciviously.

Tanya called in as usual every morning for "little kringels," and was as gay and as nice and friendly with us as ever. We certainly tried once or twice to talk to her about the soldier, but she called him a "goggle-eyed calf," and made fun of him all round, and that set our minds at rest. We saw how the gold-embroidery girls carried on with the soldier, and we were proud of our girl; Tanya's behaviour reflected honour on us all; we imitated her, and began in our talks to treat the soldier with small consideration. She became dearer to us, and we greeted her with more friendliness and kindliness every morning.

One day the soldier came to see us, a bit drunk, and sat down and began to laugh. When we asked him what he was laughing about, he explained to us:

"Why two of them—that Lydka girl and Grushka—have been clawing each other on my account. You should have seen the way they went for each other! Ha! ha! One got hold of the other one by the hair, threw her down on the floor of the passage, and sat on her! Ha! ha! ha! They scratched and tore each others' faces. It was enough to make one die with laughter! Why is it women can't fight fair? Why do they always scratch one another, eh?"

He sat on the bench, healthy, fresh and jolly he sat there and went on laughing. We were silent. This time he made an unpleasant impression on us.

"Well, it's a funny thing what luck I have with the women-folk! Eh? I've laughed till I'm ill! One wink, and it's all over with them! Its the d-devil!"

He raised his white hairy hands, and slapped them down on his knees. And his eyes seem to reflect such frank astonishment, as if he were himself quite surprised at his good luck with women. His fat red face glistened with delight and self satisfaction, and he licked his lips more than ever.

Our baker scraped the shovel violently and angrily along the oven floor, and all at once he said sarcastically:

"There's no great strength needed to pull up fir saplings, but try a real pine-tree."

"Why—what do you mean by saying that to me?" asked the soldier.

"Oh, well . . ."

"What is it?"

"Nothing—it slipped out!"

"No, wait a minute! What's the point? What pine-tree?"

Our baker did not answer, working rapidly away with the shovel at the oven; flinging into it the half-cooked kringels, taking out those that were done, and noisily throwing them on the floor to the boys who were stringing them on bast. He seemed to have forgotten the soldier and his conversation with him. But the soldier had all at once dropped into a sort of uneasiness. He got up on to his feet, and went to the oven, at the risk of knocking against the handle of the shovel, which was waving spasmodically in the air.

"No, tell me, do—who is it? You've insulted me. I? There's not one could withstand me, n-no! And you say such insulting things to me?"

He really seemed genuinely hurt. He must have had nothing else to pride himself on except his gift for seducing women; maybe, except for that, there was nothing living in him, and it was only that by which he could feel himself a living man.

There are men to whom the most precious and best thing in their lives appears to be some disease of their soul or body. They spend their whole life in relation to it, and only living by it, suffering from it, they sustain themselves on it, they complain of it to others, and so draw the attention of their fellows to themselves. For that they extract sympathy from people, and apart from it they have nothing at all. Take from them that disease, cure them, and they will be miserable, because they have lost their one resource in life—they are left empty then. Sometimes a man's life is so poor, that he is driven instinctively to prize his vice and to live by it; one may say for a fact that often men are vicious from boredom.

The soldier was offended, he went up to our baker and roared: "No, tell me do—who?"

"Tell you?" the baker turned suddenly to him.

"Well?"

"You know Tanya?"

"Well?"

"Well, there then! Only try."

"I?"

"You!"

"Her? Why that's nothing to me—pooh!"

"We shall see!"

"You will see! Ha! ha!"

"She'll——"

"Give me a month!"

"What a braggart you are, soldier!"

"A fortnight! I'll prove it! Who is it? Tanya! Pooh!"

"Well, get out. You're in my way!"

"A fortnight—and it's done! Ah, you——"

"Get out, I say!"

Our baker, all at once, flew into a rage and brandished his shovel. The soldier staggered away from him in amazement, looked at us, paused, and softly, malignantly said, "Oh, all right, then!" and went away.

During the dispute we had all sat silent, absorbed in it. But when the soldier had gone, eager, loud talk and noise arose among us.

Someone shouted to the baker: "It's a bad job that you've started, Pavel!"

"Do your work!" answered the baker, savagely.

We felt that the soldier had been deeply aggrieved, and that danger threatened Tanya. We felt this, and at the same time we were all possessed by a burning curiosity, most agreeable to us. What would happen? Would Tanya hold out against the soldier? And almost all cried confidently: "Tanya? She'll hold out! You won't catch her with your bare arms!"

We longed terribly to test the strength of our idol; we forcibly proved to each other that our divinity was a strong divinity and would come victorious out of this ordeal. We began at last to fancy that we had not worked enough on the soldier, that he would forget the dispute, and that we ought to pique his vanity more keenly. From that day we began to live a different life, a life of nervous tension, such as we had never known before. We spent whole days in arguing together; we all grew, as it were, sharper; and got to talk more and better. It seemed to us that we were playing some sort of game with the devil, and the stake on our side was Tanya. And when we learnt from the bakers that the soldier had begun "running after our Tanya," we felt a sort of delighted terror, and life was so interesting that we did not even notice that our employer had taken advantage of our pre-occupation to increase our work by fourteen pounds of dough a day. We seemed, indeed, not even tired by our work. Tanya's name was on our lips all day long. And every day we looked for her with a certain special impatience. Sometimes we pictured to ourselves that she would come to us, and it would not be the same Tanya as of old, but somehow different. We said nothing to her, however, of the dispute regarding her. We asked her no questions, and behaved as well and affectionately to her as ever. But even in this a new element crept in, alien to our old feeling for Tanya— and that new element was keen curiosity, keen and cold as a steel knife.

"Mates! To-day the time's up!" our baker said to us one morning, as he set to work.

We were well aware of it without his reminder; but still we were thrilled.

"Look at her. She'll be here directly," suggested the baker.

One of us cried out in a troubled voice, "Why! as though one could notice anything!"

And again an eager, noisy discussion sprang up among us. To-day we were about to prove how pure and spotless was the vessel into which we had poured all that was best in us. This morning, for the first time, it became clear to us, that we really were playing a great game; that we might, indeed, through the exaction of this proof of purity, lose our divinity altogether.

During the whole of the intervening fortnight we had heard that Tanya was persistently followed by the soldier, but not one of us had thought of asking her how she had behaved towards him. And she came every morning to fetch her kringels, and was the same towards us as ever.

This morning, too, we heard her voice outside: "You poor prisoners! Here I am!"

We opened the door, and when she came in we all remained,

contrary to our usual custom, silent. Our eyes fixed on her, we did not know how to speak to her, what to ask her. And there we stood in front of her, a gloomy, silent crowd. She seemed to be surprised at this unusual reception; suddenly we saw her turn white, and become uneasy, then she asked, in a choking voice: "Why are you—like this?"

"And you?" the baker flung at her, grimly, never taking his eyes off her.

"What am I?"

"N—nothing."

"Well, then, give me quickly the little kringels."

Never before had she bidden us hurry.

"There's plenty of time," said the baker, not stirring, and not removing his eyes from her face.

Then, suddenly, she turned round and disappeared through the door.

The baker took his shovel and said, calmly turning away towards the oven:

"Well, that settles it! But a soldier! a common beast like that—a low cur!"

Like a flock of sheep we all pressed round the table, sat down silently, and began listlessly to work. Soon, however, one of us remarked:

"Perhaps, after all—"

"Shut up!" shouted the baker.

We were all convinced that he was a man of judgment, a man who knew more than we did about things. And at the sound of his voice we were convinced of the soldier's victory, and our spirits became sad and downcast.

At twelve o'clock—whilst we were eating our dinners—the soldier came in. He was as clean and as smart as ever, and looked at us —as usual—straight in the eyes. But we were all awkward in looking at him.

"Now then, honoured sirs, would you like me to show you a soldier's quality?" he said, chuckling proudly.

"Go out into the passage, and look through the crack—do you understand?"

We went into the passage, and stood all pushing against one another, squeezed up to the cracks of the wooden partition of the passage that looked into the yard. We had not to wait long. Very soon Tanya, with hurried footsteps and a careworn face, walked across the yard, jumping over the puddles of melting snow and mud: she disappeared into the store cellar. Then whistling, and not hurrying himself, the soldier followed in the same direction. His hands were thrust in his pockets; his moustaches were quivering.

Rain was falling, and we saw how its drops fell into the puddles, and the puddles were wrinkled by them. The day was damp and grey—a very dreary day. Snow still lay on the roofs, but on the ground dark patches of mud had begun to appear. And the snow on the roofs too was covered by a layer of brownish dirt. The rain fell slowly with a depressing sound. It was cold and disagreeable for us waiting.

The first to come out of the store cellar was the soldier; he walked slowly across the yard, his moustaches twitching, his hands in his pockets—the same as always.

Then—Tanya, too, came out. Her eyes—her eyes were radiant with joy and happiness, and her lips—were smiling. And she walked as though in a dream, staggering, with unsteady steps.

We could not bear this quietly. All of us at once rushed to the door, dashed out into the yard and—hissed at her, reviled her viciously, loudly, wildly.

She started at seeing us, and stood as though rooted in the mud under her feet. We formed a ring round her; and malignantly, without restraint, abused her with vile words, said shameful things to her.

We did this not loudly, not hurriedly, seeing that she could not get away, that she was hemmed in by us, and we could deride her to our hearts' content. I don't know why, but we did not beat her. She stood in the midst of us, and turned her head this way and that, as she heard our insults. And we—more and more violently flung at her the filth and venom of our words.

The colour had left her face. Her blue eyes, so happy a moment before, opened wide, her bosom heaved, and her lips quivered.

We in a ring round her avenged ourselves on her as though she had robbed us. She belonged to us, we had lavished on her our best, and though that best was a beggar's crumb, still we were twenty-six, she was one, and so there was no pain we could give her equal to her guilt! How we insulted her! She was still mute, still gazed at us with wild eyes, and a shiver ran all over her.

We laughed, roared, yelled. Other people ran up from somewhere and joined us. One of us pulled Tanya by the sleeve of her blouse.

Suddenly her eyes flashed; deliberately she raised her hands to her head and straightening her hair she said loudly but calmly, straight in our faces:

"Ah, you miserable prisoners!"

And she walked straight at us, walked as directly as though we had not been before her, as though we were not blocking her way.

And hence it was that no one did actually prevent her passing.

Walking out of our ring, without turning round, she said loudly and with indescribable contempt:

"Ah you scum—brutes."

And—was gone.

We were left in the middle of the yard, in the rain, under the grey sky without the sun.

Then we went mutely away to our damp stone cellar. As before—the sun never peeped in at our windows, and Tanya came no more!

JAMES JOYCE

(1882-1941)

Joyce was an Irishman who saw Dublin as a microcosmic reflection of the world. He left Ireland in 1904 for a variety of reasons, a good many of which can be found in the characters and atmosphere which he creates for his stories. The remainder of his life was spent in this self-imposed exile on the Continent, mainly in Trieste, Paris, and Zurich, plagued by failing eyesight and publishing woes. His present reputation as one of the greatest of modern writers rests primarily on three works: his collection of short stories, DUBLINERS, from which "Counterparts" is taken; the short and largely autobiographical novel, A PORTRAIT OF THE ARTIST AS A YOUNG MAN; and the complex and rewarding long novel, ULYSSES. His last major work, FINNEGAN'S WAKE, has been called both his finest achievement and his most obvious failure. These stories and novels see the richness and beauty of Ireland hidden beneath the meanness, prejudice, and sterility of its people and their way of life. Joyce helped to establish the techniques of interior monologue and stream of consciousness, and the use of mythic parallels in the development of plot. He was also responsible for directing international attention to many fine writers, among them Luigi Pirandello and Italo Svevo.

Counterparts

The bell rang furiously and, when Miss Parker went to the tube, a furious voice called out in a piercing North of Ireland accent:

"Counterparts" From *Dubliners* by James Joyce. Originally published by B. W. Huebsch, Inc. in 1916; all rights reserved. Reprinted by permission of The Viking Press, Inc. and The Society of Authors as the literary representative of the Estate of the late James Joyce.

"Send Farrington here!"

Miss Parker returned to her machine, saying to a man who was writing at a desk:

"Mr. Alleyne wants you upstairs."

The man muttered "*Blast* him!" under his breath and pushed back his chair to stand up. When he stood up he was tall and of great bulk. He had a hanging face, dark wine-coloured, with fair eyebrows and moustache: his eyes bulged forward slightly and the whites of them were dirty. He lifted up the counter and, passing by the clients, went out of the office with a heavy step.

He went heavily upstairs until he came to the second landing, where a door bore a brass plate with the inscription *Mr. Alleyne*. Here he halted, puffing with labour and vexation, and knocked. The shrill voice cried:

"Come in!"

The man entered Mr. Alleyne's room. Simultaneously Mr. Alleyne, a little man wearing gold-rimmed glasses on a clean-shaven face, shot his head up over a pile of documents. The head itself was so pink and hairless it seemed like a large egg reposing on the papers. Mr. Alleyne did not lose a moment:

"Farrington? What is the meaning of this? Why have I always to complain of you? May I ask you why you haven't made a copy of that contract between Bodley and Kirwan? I told you it must be ready by four o'clock."

"But Mr. Shelley said, sir——"

"*Mr. Shelley said, sir.* . . . Kindly attend to what I say and not to what *Mr. Shelley says, sir.* You have always some excuse or another for shirking work. Let me tell you that if the contract is not copied before this evening I'll lay the matter before Mr. Crosbie. . . . Do you hear me now?"

"Yes, sir."

"Do you hear me now? . . . Ay and another little matter! I might as well be talking to the wall as talking to you. Understand once for all that you get a half an hour for your lunch and not an hour and a half. How many courses do you want, I'd like to know. . . . Do you mind me now?"

"Yes, sir."

Mr. Alleyne bent his head again upon his pile of papers. The man stared fixedly at the polished skull which directed the affairs of Crosbie & Alleyne, gauging its fragility. A spasm of rage gripped his throat for a few moments and then passed, leaving after it a sharp sensation of thirst. The man recognised the sensation and felt that he must have a good night's drinking. The middle of the month was passed and, if he could get the copy done in time, Mr. Alleyne might give him an order on the cashier. He stood still, gazing fixedly at the head upon the pile of papers. Suddenly Mr. Alleyne began to upset all the papers, searching for something. Then, as if he had been unaware of the man's presence till that moment, he shot up his head again, saying:

"Eh? Are you going to stand there all day? Upon my word, Farrington, you take things easy!"

"I was waiting to see . . ."

"Very good, you needn't wait to see. Go downstairs and do your work."

The man walked heavily towards the door and, as he went out of the room, he heard Mr. Alleyne cry after him that if the contract was not copied by evening Mr. Crosbie would hear of the matter.

He returned to his desk in the lower office and counted the sheets which remained to be copied. He took up his pen and dipped it in the ink but he continued to stare stupidly at the last words he had written: *In no case shall the said Bernard Bodley be* . . . The evening was falling and in a few minutes they would be lighting the gas: then he could write. He felt that he must slake the thirst in his throat. He stood up from his desk and, lifting the counter as before, passed out of the office. As he was passing out the chief clerk looked at him inquiringly.

"It's all right, Mr. Shelley," said the man, pointing with his finger to indicate the objective of his journey.

The chief clerk glanced at the hat-rack, but, seeing the row complete, offered no remark. As soon as he was on the landing the man pulled a shepherd's plaid cap out of his pocket, put it on his head and ran quickly down the rickety stairs. From the street door he walked on furtively on the inner side of the path towards the corner and all at once dived into a doorway. He was now safe in the dark snug of O'Neill's shop, and filling up the little window that looked into the bar with his inflamed face, the colour of dark wine or dark meat, he called out:

"Here, Pat, give us a g.p., like a good fellow."

The curate brought him a glass of plain porter. The man drank it at a gulp and asked for a caraway seed. He put his penny on the counter and, leaving the curate to grope for it in the gloom, retreated out of the snug as furtively as he had entered it.

Darkness, accompanied by a thick fog, was gaining upon the dusk of February and the lamps in Eustace Street had been lit. The man went up by the houses until he reached the door of the office, wondering whether he could finish his copy in time. On the stairs a moist pungent odour of perfumes saluted his nose: evidently Miss Delacour had come while he was out in O'Neill's. He crammed his cap back again into his pocket and re-entered the office, assuming an air of absentmindedness.

"Mr. Alleyne has been calling for you," said the chief clerk severely. "Where were you?"

The man glanced at the two clients who were standing at the counter as if to intimate that their presence prevented him from answering. As the clients were both male the chief clerk allowed himself a laugh.

"I know that game," he said. "Five times in one day is a little bit. . . . Well, you better look sharp and get a copy of our correspondence in the Delacour case for Mr. Alleyne."

This address in the presence of the public, his run upstairs and the porter he had gulped down so hastily confused the man and, as he sat down at his desk to get what was required, he realised how hopeless was the task of finishing his copy of the contract before half past five. The dark damp night was coming and he longed to spend it in the bars, drinking with his friends amid the glare of gas and the clatter of glasses. He got out the Delacour correspondence and passed out of the office. He hoped Mr. Alleyne would not discover that the last two letters were missing.

The moist pungent perfume lay all the way up to Mr. Alleyne's room. Miss Delacour was a middle-aged woman of Jewish appearance. Mr. Alleyne was said to be sweet on her or on her money. She came to the office often and stayed a long time when she came. She was sitting beside his desk now in an aroma of perfumes, smoothing the handle of her umbrella and nodding the great black feather in her hat. Mr. Alleyne had swivelled his chair round to face her and thrown his right foot jauntily upon his left knee. The man put the correspondence on the desk and bowed respectfully but neither Mr.

Alleyne nor Miss Delacour took any notice of his bow. Mr. Alleyne tapped a finger on the correspondence and then flicked it towards him as if to say: *"That's all right: you can go."*

The man returned to the lower office and sat down again at his desk. He stared intently at the incomplete phrase: *In no case shall the said Bernard Bodley be* . . . and thought how strange it was that the last three words began with the same letter. The chief clerk began to hurry Miss Parker, saying she would never have the letters typed in time for post. The man listened to the clicking of the machine for a few minutes and then set to work to finish his copy. But his head was not clear and his mind wandered away to the glare and rattle of the public-house. It was a night for hot punches. He struggled on with his copy, but when the clock struck five he had still fourteen pages to write. Blast it! He couldn't finish it in time. He longed to execrate aloud, to bring his fist down on something violently. He was so enraged that he wrote *Bernard Bernard* instead of *Bernard Bodley* and had to begin again on a clean sheet.

He felt strong enough to clear out the whole office single-handed. His body ached to do something, to rush out and revel in violence. All the indignities of his life enraged him. . . . Could he ask the cashier privately for an advance? No, the cashier was no good, no damn good: he wouldn't give an advance. . . . He knew where he would meet the boys: Leonard and O'Halloran and Nosey Flynn. The barometer of his emotional nature was set for a spell of riot.

His imagination had so abstracted him that his name was called twice before he answered. Mr. Alleyne and Miss Delacour were standing outside the counter and all the clerks had turned round in anticipation of something. The man got up from his desk. Mr. Alleyne began a tirade of abuse, saying that two letters were missing. The man answered that he knew nothing about them, that he had made a faithful copy. The tirade continued: it was so bitter and violent that the man could hardly restrain his fist from descending upon the head of the manikin before him:

"I know nothing about any other two letters," he said stupidly.

"You—know—nothing. Of course you know nothing," said Mr. Alleyne. "Tell me," he added, glancing first for approval to the lady beside him, "do you take me for a fool? Do you think me an utter fool?"

The man glanced from the lady's face to the little egg-shaped head and back again; and, almost before he was aware of it, his tongue had found a felicitous moment:

"I don't think, sir," he said, "that that's a fair question to put to me."

There was a pause in the very breathing of the clerks. Everyone was astounded (the author of the witticism no less than his neighbours) and Miss Delacour, who was a stout amiable person, began to smile broadly. Mr. Alleyne flushed to the hue of a wild rose and his mouth twitched with a dwarf's passion. He shook his fist in the man's face till it seemed to vibrate like the knob of some electric machine:

"You impertinent ruffian! You impertinent ruffian! I'll make short work of you! Wait till you see! You'll apologise to me for your impertinence or you'll quit the office instanter! You'll quit this, I'm telling you, or you'll apologise to me!"

He stood in a doorway opposite the office watching to see if the cashier would come out alone. All the clerks passed out and finally the cashier came out with the chief clerk. It was no use trying to say a word to him when he was with the chief clerk. The man felt that his position was bad enough. He had been obliged to offer an abject apology to Mr. Alleyne for his impertinence but he knew what a hornet's nest the office would be for him. He could remember the way in which Mr. Alleyne had hounded little Peake out of the office in order to make room for his own nephew. He felt savage and thirsty and revengeful, annoyed with himself and with everyone else. Mr. Alleyne would never give him an hour's rest; his life would be a hell to him. He had made a proper fool of himself this time. Could he not keep his tongue in his cheek? But they had never pulled together from the first, he and Mr. Alleyne, ever since the day Mr. Alleyne had overheard him mimicking his North of Ireland accent to amuse Higgins and Miss Parker: that had been the beginning of it. He might have tried Higgins for the money, but sure Higgins never had anything for himself. A man with two establishments to keep up, of course he couldn't. . . .

He felt his great body again aching for the comfort of the public-house. The fog had begun to chill him and he wondered could he touch Pat in O'Neill's. He could not touch him for more than a bob —and a bob was no use. Yet he must get money somewhere or other: he had spent his last penny for the g.p. and soon it would be too late for getting money anywhere. Suddenly, as he was fingering his watch-chain, he thought of Terry Kelly's pawn-office in Fleet Street. That was the dart! Why didn't he think of it sooner?

He went through the narrow alley of Temple Bar quickly, muttering to himself that they could all go to hell because he was going to have a good night of it. The clerk in Terry Kelly's said *A crown!* but the consignor held out for six shillings; and in the end the six shillings was allowed him literally. He came out of the pawn-office joyfully, making a little cylinder of the coins between his thumb and fingers. In Westmoreland Street the footpaths were crowded with young men and women returning from business and ragged urchins ran here and there yelling out the names of the evening editions. The man passed through the crowd, looking on the spectacle generally with proud satisfaction and staring masterfully at the office-girls. His head was full of the noises of tram-gongs and swishing trolleys and his nose already sniffed the curling fumes of punch. As he walked on he preconsidered the terms in which he would narrate the incident to the boys:

"So, I just looked at him—coolly, you know, and looked at her. Then I looked back at him again—taking my time, you know. 'I don't think that that's a fair question to put to me,' says I."

Nosey Flynn was sitting up in his usual corner of Davy Byrne's and, when he heard the story, he stood Farrington a half-one, saying it was as smart a thing as ever he heard. Farrington stood a drink in his turn. After a while O'Halloran and Paddy Leonard came in and the story was repeated to them. O'Halloran stood tailors of malt, hot, all round and told the story of the retort he had made to the chief clerk when he was in Callan's of Fownes's Street; but, as the retort was after the manner of the liberal shepherds in the eclogues, he had to admit that it was not as clever as Farrington's retort. At this Farrington told the boys to polish off that and have another.

Just as they were naming their poisons who should come in but Higgins! Of course he had to join in with the others. The men asked him to give his version of it, and he did so with great vivacity for the sight of five small hot whiskies was very exhilarating. Everyone roared laughing when he showed the way in which Mr. Alleyne shook his fist in Farrington's face. Then he imitated Farrington, saying, *"And here was my nabs, as cool as you please,"* while Farrington looked at the company out of his heavy dirty eyes, smiling and at times drawing forth stray drops of liquor from his moustache with the aid of his lower lip.

When that round was over there was a pause. O'Halloran had money but neither of the other two seemed to have any; so the whole party left the shop somewhat regretfully. At the corner of Duke Street Higgins and Nosey Flynn bevelled off to the left while the other three turned back towards the city. Rain was drizzling down on the cold streets and, when they reached the Ballast Office, Farrington suggested the Scotch House. The bar was full of men and loud with the noise of tongues and glasses. The three men pushed past the whining matchsellers at the door and formed a little party at the corner of the counter. They began to exchange stories. Leonard introduced them to a young fellow named Weathers who was performing at the Tivoli as an acrobat and knockabout *artiste*. Farrington stood a drink all round. Weathers said he would take a small Irish and Apollinaris. Farrington, who had definite notions of what was what, asked the boys would they have an Apollinaris too; but the boys told Tim to make theirs hot. The talk became theatrical. O'Halloran stood a round and then Farrington stood another round, Weathers protesting that the hospitality was too Irish. He promised to get them in behind the scenes and introduce them to some nice girls. O'Halloran said that he and Leonard would go, but that Farrington wouldn't go because he was a married man; and Farrington's heavy dirty eyes leered at the company in token that he understood he was being chaffed. Weathers made them all have just one little tincture at his expense and promised to meet them later on at Mulligan's in Poolbeg Street.

When the Scotch House closed they went round to Mulligan's. They went into the parlour at the back and O'Halloran ordered small hot specials all round. They were all beginning to feel mellow. Farrington was just standing another round when Weathers came back. Much to Farrington's relief he drank a glass of bitter this time. Funds were getting low but they had enough to keep them going. Presently two young women with big hats and a young man in a check suit came in and sat at a table close by. Weathers saluted them and told the company that they were out of the Tivoli. Farrington's eyes wandered at every moment in the direction of one of the young women. There was something striking in her appearance. An immense scarf of peacock-blue muslin was wound round her hat and knotted in a great bow under her chin; and she wore bright yellow gloves, reaching to the elbow. Farrington gazed admiringly at the plump arm which she moved very often and with much grace; and when, after a little time, she answered his gaze he admired still more her large dark brown eyes. The oblique staring expression in them fascinated him. She glanced at him once or twice and, when the party was leaving the room, she brushed against his chair and said "O, pardon!" in a London accent. He watched her leave the room in the hope that she would look back at him, but he was disappointed. He cursed his want of money and cursed all the rounds he had stood, particularly all the whiskies and Apollinaris which he had stood to Weathers. If there was one thing that he hated it was a sponge. He was so angry that he lost count of the conversation of his friends.

When Paddy Leonard called him he found that they were talking about feats of strength. Weathers was showing his biceps muscle to the company and boasting so much that the other two had called on Farrington to uphold the national honour. Farrington pulled up his sleeve accordingly and showed his biceps muscle to the company. The two arms were examined and compared and finally it was agreed to have a trial of strength. The table was cleared and the two men rested their elbows on it, clasping hands. When Paddy Leonard said "Go!" each was to try to bring down the other's hand on to the table. Farrington looked very serious and determined.

The trial began. After about thirty seconds Weathers brought his opponent's hand slowly down on to the table. Farrington's dark wine-coloured face flushed darker still with anger and humiliation at having been defeated by such a stripling.

"You're not to put the weight of your body behind it. Play fair," he said.

"Who's not playing fair?" said the other.

"Come on again. The two best out of three."

The trial began again. The veins stood out on Farrington's forehead, and the pallor of Weathers' complexion changed to peony. Their hands and arms trembled under the stress. After a long struggle Weathers again brought his opponent's hand slowly on to the table. There was a murmur of applause from the spectators. The curate, who was standing beside the table, nodded his red head towards the victor and said with stupid familiarity:

"Ah! that's the knack!"

"What the hell do you know about it?" said Farrington fiercely, turning on the man. "What do you put in your gab for?"

"Sh, sh!" said O'Halloran, observing the violent expression of

Farrington's face. "Pony up, boys. We'll have just one little smahan more and then we'll be off."

A very sullen-faced man stood at the corner of O'Connell Bridge waiting for the little Sandymount tram to take him home. He was full of smouldering anger and revengefulness. He felt humiliated and discontented; he did not even feel drunk; and he had only two-pence in his pocket. He cursed everything. He had done for himself in the office, pawned his watch, spent all his money; and he had not even got drunk. He began to feel thirsty again and he longed to be back again in the hot reeking public-house. He had lost his reputa-tion as a strong man, having been defeated twice by a mere boy. His heart swelled with fury and, when he thought of the woman in the big hat who had brushed against him and said *Pardon!* his fury nearly choked him.

His tram let him down at Shelbourne Road and he steered his great body along in the shadow of the wall of the barracks. He loathed returning to his home. When he went in by the side-door he found the kitchen empty and the kitchen fire nearly out. He bawled upstairs:

"Ada! Ada!"

His wife was a little sharp-faced woman who bullied her hus-band when he was sober and was bullied by him when he was drunk. They had five children. A little boy came running down the stairs.

"Who is that?" said the man, peering through the darkness.

"Me, pa."

"Who are you? Charlie?"

"No, pa. Tom."

"Where's your mother?"

"She's out at the chapel."

"That's right. . . . Did she think of leaving any dinner for me?"

"Yes, pa. I——"

"Light the lamp. What do you mean by having the place in darkness? Are the other children in bed?"

The man sat down heavily on one of the chairs while the little boy lit the lamp. He began to mimic his son's flat accent, saying half to himself: *"At the chapel. At the chapel, if you please!"* When the lamp was lit he banged his fist on the table and shouted:

"What's for my dinner?"

"I'm going . . . to cook it, pa," said the little boy.

The man jumped up furiously and pointed to the fire.

"On that fire! You let the fire out! By God, I'll teach you to do that again!"

He took a step to the door and seized the walking-stick which was standing behind it.

"I'll teach you to let the fire out!" he said, rolling up his sleeve in order to give his arm free play.

The little boy cried *"O, pa!"* and ran whimpering round the table, but the man followed him and caught him by the coat. The little boy looked about him wildly but, seeing no way of escape, fell upon his knees.

"Now, you'll let the fire out the next time!" said the man, striking at him vigorously with the stick. "Take that, you little whelp!"

The boy uttered a squeal of pain as the stick cut his thigh. He clasped his hands together in the air and his voice shook with fright.

"O, pa!" he cried. "Don't beat me, pa! And I'll . . . I'll say a *Hail Mary* for you. . . . I'll say a *Hail Mary* for you, pa, if you don't beat me. . . . I'll say a *Hail Mary*. . . ."

ITALO SVEVO

(1861-1928)

Real name: Ettore Schmitz. Svevo was an Italian industrialist whose literary productions were totally ignored by critics and public alike until the last few years of his life. Because his business required him to make frequent trips to England, Svevo engaged a young man to tutor him in English. The young man was James Joyce. Joyce was profoundly impressed by Svevo's writings, and when Ulysses *completed Joyce's own rise to fame, he used his position of eminence to direct attention to Svevo. International acclaim followed, but the triumph was short-lived. Svevo died in an automobile accident before his next work could be completed. His fiction is realistic, verging on the naturalistic, with its intense focus on the details of ordinary life and its clinical analysis of inept protagonists. His style is direct and uncluttered, and he frequently makes use of interior monologue and stream of consciousness techniques. See also THE HOAX, THE NICE OLD MAN AND THE PRETTY GIRL AND OTHER STORIES, CONFESSIONS OF ZENO, and AS A MAN GROWS OLDER.*

Generous Wine

A niece of mine was getting married at the age when girls cease to be girls and degenerate into old maids. The poor thing had renounced the world not long before, but family pressure had induced her to return to it, giving up her desire for purity and religion; and

"Generous Wine" From *Short Sentimental Journey* by Italo Svevo. Reprinted with the permission of the University of California Press and Martin Secker & Warburg Limited.

she had consented to receive the addresses of a young man chosen by the family because he was a good match. Almost immediately there was an end of religion, an end to dreams of virtuous solitude. The date of the marriage was fixed even sooner than the relations had wished. And now they were seated at the supper for the eve of the wedding.

Being a licentious old fellow, I laughed. What had the young man done to induce her to change her mind so quickly? Probably he had taken her in his arms to make her feel the pleasure of living, and had seduced her instead of convincing her. That is why they needed so many good wishes. All people when they marry need good wishes, but this girl more than anyone. It would be disastrous if one day she had cause to regret having let herself be induced to return to the path which she had instinctively abhorred. And I even accompanied some of the glasses I drained with wishes that I managed to invent for this particular case: "May you be contented for a year or two, then you will endure the other long years more easily, thanks to your gratitude for having experienced enjoyment. One regrets past joy, and this is a pain, but a pain which numbs the fundamental one, the real pain in life."

The bride did not appear to feel the need of so many good wishes. Indeed, her face seemed to me to be positively crystallized into an expression of confident abandonment. But it was the same expression she had worn when she announced her desire to retire into a convent. Once again she was making a vow, this time a vow to be happy for her whole life. Some people are always making vows in this way. Would she keep this one better than the other?

Everyone else at that table was thoroughly natural in his merriment, as onlookers always are. There was a complete lack of naturalness in me. It was a memorable evening for me. My wife had induced Dr. Paoli to let me eat and drink like everyone else for this once. Such liberty was all the more precious from the warning that it would be revoked immediately afterwards. And I behaved just like a young man who has been given a latchkey for the first time. I ate and drank, not because I was hungry or thirsty, but from a craving for liberty. Every mouthful, every sip was to be an assertion of my independence. I opened my mouth more widely than necessary to take in each mouthful. The wine passed from the bottle to my glass to overflowing, nor did I leave it there more than a single moment. I felt a longing to move and there, glued to my seat, I had the feeling of running and jumping like a dog slipped from his chain.

My wife made matters worse by telling a neighbour about the diet which I usually had to keep to, while my daughter Emma, aged fifteen, listened to her and put on an air of importance as she supplemented her mother's information. So they would remind me of my chain even now that it had been undone, would they? All my torture was described; how they weighed the little meat I was allowed at midday, taking all taste from it, and how at night there was nothing to weigh, because supper consisted of a roll with a morsel of ham and a glass of hot milk without sugar, which nauseated me. And while they were talking I was criticizing the doctor's science and their affection. If my system was in such a bad way, how did it come about, just because they had brought off their *coup* of making someone marry who would never have done so from choice, that this evening it could suddenly endure so much harmful and indigestible stuff? And as I drank I prepared for rebellion on the morrow. They should see.

The others stuck to champagne, but, after taking a few glasses to drink the various toasts, I had gone back to ordinary wine, a dry and honest Istrian wine, which a friend of the family had sent for the occasion. I liked that wine, as one likes memories, and I felt confidence in it, nor was I surprised when, instead of bringing me gaiety and forgetfulness, it only increased the ire in my heart.

How could I help being angry? They had made part of my life a burden to me. Frightened and depressed, I had let all my generous instincts die to make room for pastilles, drops and powders. No more socialism. What could it matter to me that the land, contrary to all the most enlightened scientific ideas, was still private property? What if on that account many people did not get their daily bread and the modicum of liberty that should adorn every day of a man's life? Had I either the one or the other?

That blessed evening I tried to be quite my old self. When my nephew, Giovanni, a huge man weighing seventeen stone, began in his stentorian voice to tell stories about his own smartness and other people's gullibility in business, I felt the old altruism stir in my heart. "What will you do," I cried, "when the struggle between men is no longer one for money?"

For a moment Giovanni was dumbfounded by my charged re-mark, which arrived quite unexpectedly to upset his world. He stared fixedly at me with his eyes magnified by his spectacles. He was looking for explanations in my face to give him his bearings. Then, while everyone was looking at him, expecting to be made to laugh by the answer of this ignorant yet clever materialist, his mind a mixture of simplicity and cunning, a mind still full of surprises, though it existed even before Sancho Panza, he gained time by saying that wine alters every man's outlook on the present, but in my case it was altering the future. This was something, but then he thought he had found something better and shouted: "When everyone stops to struggle for money, I shall have it all without struggling, all of it, all!" There was a long laugh, especially at a frequent gesture of his huge arms, which he first spread out to their full extent, then drew in, clenching his fists to give the idea that he had seized all the money that would flow to him from every direction.

The discussion went on, and no one noticed that when I was not talking, I was drinking. And I drank much and said little, being wholly absorbed in studying my inner self, to see whether it would overflow with benevolence and altruism. I began to burn slightly in-side, but it was a burning that would afterwards spread in a gradual glow, in the feeling of youth that wine produces, if only for too brief a moment.

And in expectation of this I shouted to Giovanni: "If you collar the money the others refuse, they will run you in."

But Giovanni shouted back readily enough: "And I will bribe the gaolers and have the people who have not got money to bribe them run in."

"But money will not bribe anybody any more."

"Then why not let me have it?"

I grew violently angry: "We will hang you," I shouted. "You don't deserve anything else. A rope round your neck and weights on your feet."

I paused in astonishment. It seemed to me that I had failed to express my thoughts clearly. Was I really like that? No, certainly not. I reflected: How to recover my love for all living creatures, among whom must be included even Giovanni? I smiled at him at once, making a great effort to master myself and excuse and love him. But he prevented me, because he paid not the slightest atten-tion to my kindly smile, and said, as if resigning himself to acknowledging a monstrosity: "Yes, in practice all socialists end up calling in the executioner."

He had scored off me, but I hated him. He had poisoned my whole life, even those years before the intervention of the doctor, upon which I looked back with pride and regret. He had scored off me by raising the very doubt which I had felt so poignantly before he spoke.

And immediately afterwards another punishment was visited upon me. "How well he looks," my sister remarked, gazing at me approvingly. The remark was unfortunate, because as soon as my wife heard it she felt the excessive good health that beamed in my face might produce its equivalent in illness. She was as frightened as if someone had just warned her of an approaching danger and attacked me fiercely: "Stop that," she shouted. "Put that glass down." She appealed to my neighbour for help, a certain Alberi, one of the tallest men in the town, clean, dried up and healthy, but spectacled like Giovanni. "Please, take that glass out of his hand." Seeing that Alberi hesitated, she became excited and anxious: "Signor Alberi, be good enough to take away his glass."

I tried to laugh, or rather I guessed that a well-bred person ought to laugh, but I couldn't. I had planned my rebellion for the morrow, and it was not my fault if it broke out at once. These quarrels in public were truly shameful. Alberi, who did not care twopence for me or my wife or any of these people who were entertaining him, made things worse by making fun of my plight. He looked over his spectacles at the glass I was clutching, moved his hands towards it as if he were really going to snatch it from me, then ended by drawing them comically back, as if he were afraid of me, when I looked at him. Everybody laughed at me, Giovanni with a peculiarly noisy laugh which left him gasping.

My daughter Emma thought her mother needed help. In tones of exaggerated pleading, as I thought, she said: "Daddy, don't drink any more."

And it was on this innocent child that I vented my wrath. I used a hard and threatening word to her, the effect of the resentment of an old man and a father. Her eyes filled with tears, and her mother, engrossed in comforting her, paid no more attention to me.

My son Ottavio, a boy of thirteen, then ran up to his mother. He had noticed nothing, neither his sister's tears, nor the quarrel that had caused them. He wanted to be allowed to go to the pictures with some friends, who had just proposed it, on the following evening. But my wife paid no attention to him, being too busy comforting Emma.

Anxious to recover my self-respect by asserting my authority, I shouted my permission: "Yes, of course you shall go to the pictures. I give you my permission, and that is enough." Without waiting for more, Ottavio went back to his friends, saying: "Thank you, Papa." A pity he was in such a hurry. If he had stayed with us, his happiness, due to my assertion of authority, would have cheered me up.

Good humour had vanished from the table for a few minutes, and I felt that I had failed in my duty even towards the bride, with whom that good humour stood for good wishes and a good omen. And yet she was the only person who understood my feelings, or so it seemed to me. She looked at me quite maternally, ready to excuse me and be nice to me. That girl had always given an impression of confidence in her own opinions. Just as when she was longing for a cloistered life, so now she regarded herself as superior to everyone else in having renounced it. Now she was looking down upon me, upon my wife and upon my daughter. She pitied us, and her beautiful grey eyes rested serenely upon us, to see where the fault lay, for, in her opinion, there was no suffering without someone being at fault.

This increased my rancour towards my wife, whose conduct was humiliating me in this way. She was degrading me below everyone, even the meanest, at that table. Down at the end even my sister-in-law's children had stopped talking and were putting their small heads together, discussing what had happened. I seized my glass, wondering whether I should empty it or hurl it at the wall or, better, against the windows opposite. I ended by draining it at a draught. This was the surest proof of energy, being an assertion of my independence. I thought it the best wine I had tasted that evening. I prolonged the action by pouring more wine into my glass and drinking a little of it. But joy refused to come and the whole fierce, too fierce, life flooding my veins too, the form of rancour. I was seized with a strange idea. My own rebellion was not enough to put things right. Could not I suggest to the bride that she should join me in rebelling? By good luck at that very moment she smiled sweetly at the man who sat confident by her side. And I thought: "She does not know yet, and she is convinced that she knows."

I remember again that Giovanni said: "Let him drink. Wine is the milk of the old." I looked at him, wrinkling my face into the semblance of a smile, but I could not like him. I knew that all he cared about was good humour, and he wanted to soothe me like a bad-tempered child who was spoiling a gathering of grown-ups.

After that I drank little, and then only when people were looking at me, nor did I open my mouth. Everyone round me was shouting merrily and this annoyed me. I did not listen, but it was difficult not to hear. Alberi and Giovanni had begun to argue, and everyone enjoyed watching the duel between the fat man and the thin. What they were quarrelling about, I do not know, but I heard pretty aggressive words from both parties. I noticed Alberi on his feet, leaning towards Giovanni and bringing his spectacles almost over the middle of the table, quite close to his opponent. Giovanni, with his seventeen stone, stretched comfortably upon an armchair, which had been given him by way of a joke at the end of the meal, was gazing intently at him, like the good fencer he was, as if looking for an opening for his rapier thrust. But Alberi, too, cut a good figure, woefully thin, indeed, but healthy, active and serene.

And I remember also the endless good wishes and greetings at the moment of parting. The bride kissed me with a smile that still seemed maternal. I received her kiss absent-mindedly. I was wondering when I should have an opportunity of telling her something about this life of ours.

At that moment a name was mentioned by someone, that of a friend of my wife and an old friend of mine, Anna. I don't know by whom or in what connection, but I know it was the last name I heard before being left in peace by the guests. For years I had been used to seeing her often with my wife, and greeting her with the friendly indifference of people who have no reason to remark on having been born in the same town and about the same time. Now, however, I remembered that many years ago she had been my one backsliding. I had courted her almost up to the moment of marrying my wife. But no one had ever commented on my treacherous behaviour, which had been so brusque I had not even tried to mitigate it by a single word, because she had also married very soon after and had been very happy. She had not been at the supper on account of a slight attack of influenza, which had kept her in bed—nothing serious. But it was strange and serious that I now remembered my offence against love, which came to weigh upon my conscience, already sufficiently troubled. I actually felt that at that moment my former offence was being punished. From her bed, where she was probably convalescent, I heard my victim protest: "It would not be fair for you to be happy." I went to my bedroom very depressed. I was rather confused, because it did not seem fair to me that my wife should be commissioned to avenge one whom she had supplanted.

Emma came to wish me good night. She was smiling, rosy and fresh. Her short outbreak of crying had given way to a reaction of joy, as is usual with healthy and youthful systems. I had recently learnt to understand other people's characters, and my daughter was as transparent as glass. My outburst had served to give her importance in the eyes of everyone, and she enjoyed it in all innocence. I gave her a kiss, and I am sure that I thought it was lucky for me that she was so happy and contented. For her own good it would, of course, have been my duty to point out to her that she had not treated me with becoming respect. But I could not find the words and I held my tongue. She went off, and the only lingering result of my attempt to find words was a preoccupation, a confusion, an effort which did not leave me for some time. To quiet myself I thought: "I will speak to her tomorrow. I will give her my reasons." But it was useless. I had offended her and she had offended me. But it was a further offence that she had forgotten all about it, whereas I never ceased brooding over it.

Ottavio also came to bid me good night. A strange boy. He said good night to his mother and myself almost without noticing us. He had already left the room when I called after him: "Are you glad to be going to the pictures?" He stopped and made an effort to remember and before going further said dryly: "Yes." He was very sleepy.

My wife handed me the box of pills. "Are these the ones?" I asked with a mask of ice on my face.

"Yes, of course," said she gently. She looked enquiringly at me, and, not being able to guess my thoughts in any other way, asked hesitatingly: "Are you all right?"

"Perfectly all right," I answered firmly, as I took off one of my boots. And at that very moment my stomach began to burn horribly.

"This is what she wanted," I thought, with a logic about which I am only now doubtful.

I swallowed the pill with some water and felt a slight relief. I kissed my wife mechanically upon the cheek. It was a kiss such as might go with the pills. I could not have avoided it if I wanted to escape discussions and explanations. But I could not settle down to rest without clearing up my position in the struggle which was not yet over for me, and I said just as I snuggled down in bed: "I think the pills would have been more effective taken with wine."

She put out the light, and very soon the regularity of her breathing told me that she had a clear conscience—that is to say, I thought at once, a total indifference to all that concerns me. I had anxiously awaited that moment, and immediately said to myself that I was at last free to breathe noisily, as the condition of my system seemed to demand, or even to sob, as, in my depression, I should have liked to do. But the suffering, the moment I was free, became even more intense. This was no liberty. How was I to vent the anger that raged within me? All I could do was to think over what I should say to my wife and daughter next day. "You are very anxious about my health, when it comes to nagging me before other people." It was so true. Here was I raging alone in my bed while they slept in peace. What a burning! A huge tract of it had invaded my system and was trying to vent itself through my throat. There should be a bottle of water on the little table by my bedside. I reached out for it, but knocked against the empty glass, and the slight noise was enough to wake my wife. Yes, she slept with one eye open.

"Are you feeling ill?" she asked in a low voice—she was not certain she had heard correctly, and didn't want to disturb me. I guessed part of this, but had the bizarre idea that she was gloating over my illness, as being the proof that she had been right. I gave up the idea of the water, and settled down once more. At once she fell back into that light slumber of hers, which enabled her to keep watch over me.

Clearly, if I was not to get the worst of it in my quarrel with my wife, I must go to sleep. I shut my eyes and turned over on my side, but I was obliged to change my position at once. However, I was obstinate, and did not open my eyes. But every position meant the sacrifice of a part of my body. I thought: "With a body like this sleep is out of the question." I was all movement, all wakefulness. A man running cannot think of sleep. I had the breathlessness of a man running and, in my ears, the sound of my footsteps, heavily shod. I thought that, perhaps, I was turning too gently in my bed to hit upon the right position for all my limbs at once. It was no good searching for it. I must let every part of me find the place that suited it. I flung myself over as violently as possible. At once my wife whispered: "Are you feeling ill?" If she had used different words, I would have answered by asking her to help me. But I refused to answer those particular words, which referred offensively to our quarrel.

Yet to lie still should be so easy. What trouble can there be in lying, just lying, in bed? I went over all the great difficulties that beset our path in this world and found that really, compared with any of these, lying still was nothing. Any worn-out old horse can stand still. In my determination I discovered a position that was complicated, but remarkably tenacious. I dug my teeth into the top of the pillow and twisted myself in such a way that my chest also rested on the pillow, while my right leg was outside the bed and almost touching the ground, and the left was stiff on the bed, pinning me to it. Yes, I had discovered a new system. It was not I that held the bed, but the bed that held me. And this conviction of my own inertness was such that even when the oppression increased, I refused to relax. When at last I had to give way, I comforted myself with the thought that at least a part of that dreadful night was over, and I was also rewarded by feeling, once I had freed myself from the bed, as exhilarated as a wrestler who has shaken off his adversary's hold.

I don't know how long I then kept still. I was tired. To my surprise I noticed a strange brilliance in my closed eyes, a whirlwind of flames which I imagined was caused by the fire I felt inside me. They were not real flames, but colours like them. Then they diminished and shaped themselves into circular forms, or rather into drops of a viscous liquid, which soon became all blue, mild, but surrounded by a glowing red border. They fell from a point above, grew longer and, becoming detached, disappeared below. It was I who first thought that these drops could see me. Immediately, to see me better, they were transformed into so many huge eyes. As they grew elongated in falling a little circle formed in their centre, which, shedding its blue covering, displayed a real eye, evil and malevolent. I was being followed by a crowd that hated me. I rebelled in my bed, groaning and calling out: "My God!"

"Are you feeling ill?" asked my wife at once.

Some time must have gone by before I answered. But then it happened that I realized I was not lying in my bed any longer, but was clinging to it, and that it had been transformed into a slope, down which I was slipping. I called out: "I am ill, very ill."

My wife had lit a candle and was standing by me in her pink nightdress. The light reassured me, and I even had the clear conviction that I had slept and had only then woken up. The bed had straightened and I was lying on it quite comfortably. I looked at my wife in surprise, because now, realizing that I had been asleep, I was no longer certain that I had called for her help. "What do you want?" I asked her.

She looked at me, half asleep and tired. My call had been sufficient to make her jump out of bed, but not to rob her of her longing for sleep, which was so great that she did not even care whether she had been in the right or not. Not to waste time she asked: "Would you like those drops the doctor gave you to make you sleep?"

I hesitated, strong though my desire to feel better was. "If you like," I said, trying only to appear resigned. To take the drops was not by any means an admission that I was unwell.

Then there followed a moment during which I enjoyed perfect peace. It lasted while my wife in her pink nightdress, by the frail light of the candle, stood by me counting the drops. The bed was a real horizontal bed and my eyelids, when I closed them, were sufficient to shut out all light from my eyes. From time to time I opened them and that light and the pink of the nightdress gave me as much relief as complete darkness. But she did not want to go on helping me a moment longer than was needed, and I was once again plunged into the night to fight for peace alone.

I remembered that, when I was young, to send myself to sleep, I used to force myself to think of a hideous old woman who helped me to forget the lovely visions that haunted me. Now, however, I might call up beauty without danger and it would certainly help me. It was an advantage, and the only one, of old age. I thought of several beautiful women, the loves of my young days, of a time when beautiful women had abounded in extraordinary numbers, and called upon them by name. But they did not come. Not even then did they yield themselves. And I called and called them continuously until out of the night there rose up a single lovely face: Anna, yes, she, as she had been many years before, but her face, her beautiful pink-complexioned face, was wearing an expression of pain and reproof. For she meant to bring me not peace, but remorse. That was clear. And as she was there I talked to her. I had jilted her, but she had immediately married someone else, which was only fair. And she had brought into the world a daughter, now fifteen, who was like her in her delicate colouring, her golden hair and blue eyes; but then her face was spoilt by the intervention of the father who had been chosen for her. The gentle wave of the hair had been turned into a mass of tight curls, the cheeks were large, the mouth broad, the lips much too full. The mother's colouring combined with the lines of the father produced the effect of a shameless kiss, in public. What did she want of me now, after she had let me see her so often arm-in-arm with her husband?

It was the first time that evening that I could feel that I had won. Anna became more gentle, almost changing her mind. And then her company was no longer distasteful to me. She might stay. And I fell asleep, admiring her, good and beautiful and won over to my view. I soon fell asleep.

A horrible dream. I was in a complicated building, which I understood at once, as though I had been a part of it. It was a huge cave, rugged, without any of those ornaments which nature amuses herself creating in caves, and therefore certainly the work of man, and it was dark. There I sat on a three-legged stool beside a glass chest, feebly illuminated by a light which I considered must be a quality of itself, the only light there was in the vast structure, though it was strong enough to illuminate myself, a huge wall consisting of great, rough stones and below it a cemented wall. How vivid are the constructions of dreams! You will reply that this is because their architect can easily understand them, and does not remember having done so even when awake, and as he turns his thoughts back to the world which he has left, where these constructions sprung up so easily, it may surprise him that everything is understood there without the need of a single word.

I knew at once that the cave had been built by men who were using it for a cure invented by themselves, a cure that would prove fatal to one of those who were imprisoned in it—there must have been a number of people down there in the dark—but highly beneficial to all the others. Yes, a sort of religion which required a victim, and naturally I was not surprised.

It was even more easy to guess that, since they had put me so close to the glass chest in which the victim was to be asphyxiated, I had been chosen to die for the sake of all the others. And already I endured in anticipation the pain of the ugly death in store for me. I breathed with difficulty and my head ached and was heavy, so that I rested it on my hands, my elbows on my knees.

Suddenly everything I already knew was said by a number of people concealed in the darkness. My wife appeared first: "Be quick, the doctor has said that it is you who must get into the chest." I thought it painful, but perfectly natural, so I made no protest, but pretended not to hear. And I thought: "I always considered my wife's love silly." A number of other voices shouted imperiously: "Will you make up your mind to obey?" Among them I distinguished clearly that of Dr. Paoli. I could not protest, but thought: "He is doing it for money."

I raised my head to examine once again the glass chest that was waiting for me. Then I discovered seated on the top of it the bride. Even in that position she kept her perennial air of calm self-possession. I heartily despised the silly woman, but I was suddenly aware that she was very important for me. I should have found this out in real life as well from seeing her seated on the instrument that was to compass my death. And then I looked at her, wagging my tail. I felt like one of those tiny little dogs that make their way through life wagging their tails.

Then the bride spoke. Without any violence, as if it were the most natural thing in the world, she said: "Uncle, the chest is for you."

I should have to fight for my life single-handed. That also I guessed. I had the feeling of knowing how to make an enormous effort without anyone being able to realize it. Just as at first I had felt within me an organ that enabled me to win the favour of my judge without opening my mouth, so now I discovered within me another organ, though I do not know what it was, with which I could fight without moving and thus fall upon my enemies when off their guard. And the effort immediately took effect. There was Giovanni, fat Giovanni, seated in the luminous glass chest on a wooden chair like mine and in the same position. He was leaning forward, as the chest was too low, and holding his glasses in his hand to prevent them

from falling off his nose. In this attitude he looked as if he were engaged on a business problem and had taken off his glasses to be able
to think better without seeing anything. And in fact, though he was
bathed in perspiration and already very short of breath, he was not
thinking of his approaching death, but was full of mischief, as was
clear from his eyes, by which I saw that he meant to make the same
effort that I had made a little while previously. Hence I could feel
no pity for him, for I was afraid of him.

Giovanni also made the effort successfully. Soon afterwards his
place was taken by Alberi, the long, thin and healthy Alberi, in the
same position that Giovanni had been in, but he was worse off owing
to his height. He was actually bent double and would really have
awakened my compassion, if he also, in addition to his suffering, had
not displayed the same malice. He looked me up and down with an
evil smile, knowing that he could, whenever he chose, escape death
in the chest.

Once again the bride spoke from the top of the chest: "Now, of
course, it is your turn, Uncle." She pronounced each syllable with
pedantic distinctness. Her words were accompanied by another
sound, very distant, far overhead. From the prolonged noise made by
someone hurriedly moving away I learned that the cave ended in a
steep passage leading to the surface of the earth. It was only a hiss,
but a hiss of consent, and it came from Anna, who once more let me
see her hate. She had not the pluck to put it into words, because I
had really convinced her that she had been more guilty towards me
than I towards her. But this conviction means nothing when it is a
question of hate.

I was condemned by everyone. Some way from me, in another
part of the cave, my wife and the doctor were walking up and
down, waiting, and I knew by intuition that my wife's face wore a
resentful expression. She was gesticulating violently as she described
my crimes, the wine, the food and my rough treatment of herself and
my daughter.

I felt myself drawn towards the chest by the look of triumph
Alberi was turning upon me. I drew slowly towards it with my seat,
barely an inch at a time, but I knew that when I was within a yard
of it—this was the law—I should be carried right up to it at a single
bound, gasping.

But there was still a hope of escape. Giovanni, quite recovered
from the effects of his hard struggle, had appeared close to the chest,

which he could no longer fear, since he had been in it already. This also was the law there. He was standing erect in the full light, looking now at Alberi, who was gasping and threatening, now at me, as I slowly drew near the chest.

I shouted: "Giovanni, help me to keep him inside. I will pay you." The whole cave echoed to my cry, and it sounded like a mocking laugh. I understood. It was useless to implore mercy. It was not the first, nor the second who found himself inside the chest who was to die there, but the third. This also was a law of the cave, which, like all the others, was bringing about my undoing. But it was hard that I had to realize it had not been made at that moment deliberately to harm me. This also was a result of that darkness and that light. Giovanni did not even answer and shrugged his shoulders to show his regret at not being able to save me, and at not being able to sell me my safety.

And then I shouted again: "If there is no other way, take my daughter. She is asleep here close by. It will be easy." These cries were also sent back to me by a loud echo. Useless though it was, I shouted again to call my daughter: "Emma, Emma, Emma!"

And from the depths of the cave there actually came Emma's answer, the sound of her voice, still so childish: "Here I am, Daddy, here I am."

It seemed to me that she did not answer at once. Then there was a violent convulsion, which I thought was the result of my leap into the chest. Again I thought: "That girl is always so slow in obeying." This time her slowness was the cause of my undoing, and I was full of injured bitterness.

I woke up. It was a convulsion, a leap from one world into the other. My head and torso were out of the bed, and I should have fallen out if my wife had not run up to save me. She asked me: "Have you been dreaming?" And then, moved: "You were calling for your daughter. You see how you love her."

At first I was dazzled by reality, where everything seemed to me out of focus and false. And I said to my wife, who also ought to know everything: "How can we get our children to forgive us for having brought them into the world?"

But she answered, in her simplicity: "Our children are happy to be alive."

The world which I then felt to be the real one, the dream-world, was still all round me, and I wanted to proclaim it: "Because they don't know anything yet."

Then I stopped and took refuge in silence. The window by my bed was growing light, and in that light I understood at once that I must not describe my dream, because I must conceal the shame of it. But soon, as the sunlight, so soft and bluish, yet commanding, continued to flood the room, I ceased to feel the shame any more.

The dream-world was not my world, nor was I the man who wagged his tail and who was ready to sacrifice his own daughter to save himself.

However, at all costs, I must never return to that horrible cave. And that is how I became submissive and ready to obey the doctor's orders. Should it happen that, from no fault of mine, that is, not as a result of excessive potations, but owing to the last fever, I had to go back to the cave, I would jump straight into the glass chest, if it was there, so as not to tail-wag and betray.

QUESTIONS

1. The protagonist of this story is a typical Svevo figure. Through the observations he makes about himself and others, what do we learn about the narrator?

2. The narrative very clearly progresses by stages, providing a definite narrative structure. Identify and discuss those stages.

3. The high point of the story is obviously the dream. What does this dream mean, and what effect does it have on the narrator? Describe the changes which the narrator undergoes.

4. Discuss the stream of consciousness technique by which much of the story is told. At what points can we identify the method as interior monologue, and at what points does the narrator delve deep beneath the surface of conscious thought?

5. Discuss the various meanings of the title, "Generous Wine."

DENNIS LYNDS

(1924-   )

Born in St. Louis, Dennis Lynds now lives in New York City. He served with the infantry in Europe during the Second World War, receiving the Purple Heart and three battle stars. COMBAT SOLDIER derives from his military experience; he has also published a book entitled UPTOWN, DOWNTOWN. Lynds is sensitive to the frustrations of modern living; the theme of liberation is central to "A Blue Blonde in the Sky over Pennsylvania."

A Blue Blonde in the Sky over Pennsylvania

John Cashmore lay on his side in bed. He watched the moving pattern on his bedroom floor made by the early morning sunlight through the leaves of the old oak outside his window. Connecticut, he said to himself, is lousy with old oaks. If there was one thing Connecticut had it was old oaks. Very good to sit under in the early sunlight on spring mornings. Only no one sat under trees on a Thursday except bums and children. Not in Connecticut.

"You look like you slept on nails," his wife said.

Wide awake and dressed, she came into his bedroom carrying his morning cup of tea. She raised the window shade all the way and the sunlight flooded against his eyes.

He said, "Do you enjoy blinding me?"

"Drink your tea. Bad day yesterday?"

"Since I didn't come home until eleven-thirty that's a pretty stupid question. We planned Chicago. Expense accounts again." He sipped the hot tea and watched the sky outside his window. "God! I thought all that would be over once I made department head, but it goes on and on."

She sat on the foot of his bed. "Get another job. You could get a hundred jobs."

"Where?"

"Anywhere! Look."

"Another job would be just the same," he said.

She said, "I think you just need something to be angry about."

"Thanks," he said.

She said, "Let's start all over. Good morning."

He smiled to her. A tall woman who was going grey, and her body was smoothly solid. She stood and walked to the window. With her short hair and thickened body she seemed shorter than she was. If she lost fifteen pounds, he estimated, she would still look a little like the girl he had married.

"It *is* a lovely day," she said. "You know, I think that Sears boy is home again. The Army must be getting very lenient. That boy spends more time at home than he does in camp. Thank God you missed all that."

"Good thing for Mary I missed all that, might not be here at all."

"What a thing to say."

"Let's try for another right now."

"Come on, now, you'll miss your train."

"I forgot, it's not Saturday night."

She picked up his empty tea cup. "If that's all you want find a chorus girl."

"I wonder if you'd mind at all?"

"I'll start your shower," she said. "And I would mind."

"Sorry. It was last night."

In the shower the hot water washed down his body. He shut his eyes as if in a shell of thick warmth. Wrapped in warmth and carried far away into a liquid world where he felt he would never have to move or open his eyes. The shock of the cold water made him clench his teeth. But he forced himself to stay under until he had counted twenty-five. Once he had made it a rule to stay under the cold water until he had counted his age, but that was going too far now. When he was dry, he dressed and went downstairs to breakfast.

"Dad," his son Johnny said, "go to a new hotel, okay? I already got two Chicago postcards."

"You *have* two Chicago cards," his wife corrected.

"Have," his son said, "will you Dad?"

"All right," he said.

His daughter said, "You'll be back for the dance, won't you? It's Sunday, I said you'd chaperone."

"I'll be back," he said. "Who are you going with?"

"Freddie Sears, he's on furlough."

He poured a second cup of coffee. "Why don't you try to find a boy who lives, say, half a mile away? You know, give the world a chance."

His wife said, "I like Freddie Sears."

"Sorry again," he said, "don't pay any attention to me."

When he left the house the sun was above the hills to the east across the valley. The whole valley seemed different because he had decided to walk down the hill. The sensation of walking in the warm spring air was pleasant, but the bright sun hurt his eyes. The last time he had walked regularly down the hill was during the war when it had been unpatriotic to ride too often. Now it was unpatriotic to walk. Detroit didn't approve. People looked at him from the windows. He remembered all the small flags with blue stars in the windows during the war. Faces instead of blue stars now, and he stopped at the last rise above the station to give all the faces a chance to see him so they could talk about it later. *The Cashmores' car must be busted.* Beyond the red-tile roof of the station, and beyond the many-colored roofs of the town, the white houses far across the valley on the opposite hill seemed to shine in the blue morning light like the houses of an Indian hill station or the forts of Moroccan sheiks. White houses like toys through the blue morning haze of the valley. He wondered if there was a man standing on the opposite hill gazing across at all the white houses on his hill.

On the train he read his newspaper carefully all the way in to Grand Central where he caught a taxi for Pennsylvania Station and the Chicago train. Charley Addison was waiting in their compartment. A big, red-faced man, Charley was the company's best salesman. Smoking a cigar, Charley began to complain about old J.J. and his penny-pinching ways before the train left the station.

"I tell you true, Johnny, I've about had it. I'm not used to that kind of kicking around. Not one damn, you know?"

"Why don't you get another job?"

"I've been keeping my eyes open, I kid you not."

The train emerged into the desolate smoke and marshland and dumps of the Jersey Flats. Here the sun was thin and pale. Even spring was grey and cold on the desolation of the Flats.

He said, "Let's get going on the presentation."

"Already? Let's go to the club car for an eye-opener."

"Work now, play later," he said. "Start with the floor space figures, okay?"

"You're the boss," Charley said.

They were still working when the train passed through Philadelphia and turned west toward Pittsburgh.

2

The blonde was blue from the ribbon holding her long hair to the sharp points of her shoes. Pale blue eyes the color of the light Wedgwood dinner set he had brought his wife from London six years ago. A tight blue skirt and a powder blue cashmere sweater stretched by high breasts. He sat watching her. Charley was talking with her and with a young man who worked for Dupont. The sky outside the club car was a soft golden bronze of evening.

Charley was saying, ". . . that'll give us all Saturday to show you the town. How's it sound?"

"It's a straight offer," the blonde said.

Her narrow blue skirt projected like a canopy over the knee of her crossed leg. Long legs and smooth.

"The country's different out here," he said. "It's bigger. You feel it's part of a very big country. I don't feel that in Connecticut."

"Where do you live in Connecticut?" the blonde asked. "No, let me guess. An old house, very comfortable. It's painted white and there's a lawn with trees all around."

"Something like that," he said.

She had straight, almost severe features that clashed with the soft smile she gave the waiter when he brought her Scotch and water. Charley and the young man from Dupont both reached for the check. The young man won. It gave him a pleasant feeling of power to let Charley reach for the checks. The young man from Dupont left too large a tip and the smiling waiter bobbed his head up and down like the Japanese spies in the old war movies on television.

"Television is going to raise a damned confused generation," he said to the blonde. "If they watch the new movies they'll love the Japanese and Germans, and hate the Chinese and Russians. If they watch the old movies on television they'll hate the Japanese and Germans, and love the Chinese and Russians."

"Is that bad?" the blonde asked.

"I suppose not. They might be so confused they'll wonder if war isn't pretty damned stupid."

Charley said, "Stupid is right. Four lousy years."

He said, "Charley started as a lieutenant and ended as a major. Infantry, too. Isn't that right, Charley?"

"Yeh, I was a hero," Charley said.

The young man from Dupont said, "I was in Europe. Sixty-sixth Division."

He sipped at his drink while they talked of a war he had known only as a gasoline shortage and too many trips to Washington. He would probably know the next one better. His son would not be as lucky as he had been, and the next one would probably end it for everyone. No more control over it than over the pale evening sunlight that cast a geometric pattern on the club car floor like the pattern of oak leaves on his bedroom floor that morning. And outside the train window the giant slag heaps of outer Pittsburgh steamed with waves of heat. In the black factory buildings small figures seemed to be dancing around the red flames of the blast furnaces that were brighter than the evening sun. Once, he saw a stream of white-hot steel pouring into glowing red molds on a flat car.

The blonde said, "It's beautiful in a way, isn't it?"

He nodded. "When I look at a steel mill I think that there are people really working, making something, changing the world. They must have a real sense of doing something."

"I don't expect they think about it," the blonde said.

"I guess not," he said.

In the dark Pittsburgh station misty rays of sun filtered down from the high ceiling. On the platform a man in grimy overalls waved to the blonde. She smiled and waved back. The man rolled his eyes up toward the station ceiling. The blonde laughed an open laugh that reminded him of his daughter laughing at a dance where she was enjoying herself. The man on the platform shrugged in mock despair and walked away to work somewhere on the train. And he could have been the man out there. A man wearing overalls and admiring a blonde through a train window. If his father had been a different man. If his father had been an immigrant worker instead of a minor executive in a construction company. Then he would have been a different man in a different job. A laborer, perhaps, instead of Director of Design for J. J. Salisbury & Co., Architects, New York. Of course he could have been something else if he had wanted to be something else but somehow the question of wanting to be something in particular had never come up except once when he was ten years old and had wanted to be a pirate. *A pirate, his father had laughed, Well now, that's a noble ambition, Johnny. A bit bloody, but definitely noble. The market's very limited, though. How about a second choice just in case?* His father had been such a big man then. A big, laughing giant. Later his father had become so small, and the joviality changed somehow to weakness and too much whisky. The big, friendly eyes became the confused eyes of a man who could never make a decision and was Assistant Purchasing Agent in the same construction company for twenty-two years. And there had been a blonde. A blonde little girl who clapped her hands and said she was going to be first mate on his pirate ship until he told her that girls could not go on a pirate ship. Then she screamed at him, *Pirates aren't real anyhow! I'm going to marry a doctor and have a big house and a butler and a trillion million dollars!* And that was the only time the question of wanting to be something special had ever come up that he could remember now. His mother analyzing, *I think architecture would be good, John. Your father still has influence in the building field. You have a flair for drawing anyway. Yes, architecture sounds right, don't you think?* That was the summer in Maine, just before he went up to Cornell. Nearly eighteen and he had still wanted to be a pirate only he had known enough not to mention that to his mother. Late in the season and almost alone in the deserted hotel. The wind cold on the open Maine coast. A few stray people bundled in sweaters on the beaches. And a seventeen year old boy hidden high on a cold sand dune where the tall grass bent in the wind. A boy dreaming of a stormy sea and sails straining overhead and white water washing over him where he stood at the wheel of his ship.

"You're in a brown study," the blonde said.

He said, "Kids are crazy. In my day it was pirates, or Indians, or white hunters on safari. Today it's spacemen or underwater explorers."

"Children have a small world," she said.

"Or a big one," he said.

A train flashed past in the opposite direction. He realized that they had left Pittsburgh and were travelling across open countryside again. The sun was low and pale, and the faces of the people on the other train were white blurs. And all the faces on that other train were seeing him as a white blur flashing past and gone.

"Time to tie on the feed bag," Charley said. "Let's go."

"I suppose so," he said.

"Tell you what," Charley said, "how about a little pinochle after dinner? What say, George, join us?"

George was the young man from Dupont. "Thanks, I'd like to."

He said to the blonde, "Are you eating?"

"Not yet. I don't like to eat while it's still light, too much to see out there."

At dinner he let the other two talk and watched the countryside that was now the color of orange copper in the fading sunlight. The copper and blue haze of evening. The fields were copper, and the houses. The roads dark copper bordered by copper and blue trees that swayed in the evening breeze. The few people were small and black but with a copper sheen. People who seemed frozen immobile as the train passed their fields and homes. And above the houses and barns and fields and trees the body of the blonde in the club car lay soft and naked. Naked and copper and blue in the evening sky. And in the sky she moved and all her copper and blue skin seemed to shine like a rising moon.

"Now for some serious pinochle," Charley said.

He drank his coffee slowly. "You two start without me, I'll be along."

"You can't play two-handed pinochle," Charley said.

"Play canasta for a while," he said.

When he entered the club car the blonde was still sitting alone. In the chair on her right a heavy young man wearing a good grey suit watched her from the corner of his eye. The chair on her left was empty. He sat down.

"No card game?" she asked.

"Didn't feel much like it," he said. He looked for a waiter but the single attendant in the car did not seem to be able to see him. He said to the blonde, "What did you say you do?"

"Designer," she said. "Fashion and all that."

"So am I," he said, "buildings and all that."

She smiled. "We have something in common."

He felt her close beside him as if her body were covered with small fingers that reached and touched him. Perfume cascaded over him like the hot water this morning down his naked body. And he was conscious of his body as if he were in front of his bathroom mirror. He saw that her blue shoes had small blue bows on them.

"You're very beautiful," he said, "did you know?"

"Yes, I know, do you mind?"

He waved his arm toward the window. "It's all copper out there. In the sky I mean. And the houses."

He looked out the window to show her how copper it was but it was no longer copper at all. The buildings had faded into darkness. The fields were a faint blue-grey. The lights of the houses were small and remote. All the copper was gone, and the dark sky had gone with the copper. Only a dark night.

"Do you have a light?"

She was holding a cigarette. She leaned toward him, the cigarette between her fingers, and he saw on the slender fingers the faint brown stains of a heavy smoker.

"Of course," he said. "Just a moment, I . . . know . . . I think I have . . ." His fingers searched through his pockets. There were no matches. No matches in his pockets anywhere, and no matches on the small metal table in front of him. "I'm sorry, I'm afraid I never learned to smoke. Never felt the need somehow. I . . ."

The young man in the grey suit who sat on her right snapped his lighter and it blazed into flame.

He said to the blonde, "I think the young man there . . ."

She turned and bent for the light, the flame. A blue back toward the flame. Smoke billowing up about her bent head. And he heard her thank the young man. The young man said something and waved in the air and the waiter hurried forward. The blonde was smiling and talking to the young man. Outside the window in the night a small village sparkled with distant points of light. He was smiling at his face in the window. The town vanished as the train rushed on. He looked at his watch. His wife would probably be at the movies now if she had managed to send the children somewhere. In the balcony and ten rows back. Someday he would have to ask her why she liked the balcony. She had probably told him once but he could not remember. Perhaps she was a little farsighted. After a few minutes he got up and walked back to his compartment where the young man from Dupont and Charley were waiting for him.

3

It had been a successful trip, the building sold and the plans all decided, and he did not wake up until the train back from Chicago was passing through Trenton. Charley lay in his bed smoking a morning cigarette in half-awake contentment. When Charley saw that he was awake, Charley grinned and patted his bloated belly and said, "Gone to pot. Gone all the way to pot, eh Johnny?" Smoking and patting the belly that had once been flat, and there was something close to satisfaction in Charley's voice.

He said, "Did you ever notice I don't smoke?"

"You're lucky," Charley said. "The first one always tastes like the floor of a barn."

"But I wonder why I don't smoke?"

"Because you never started, that's easy."

"Why didn't I start? Everyone I know smokes. Why not me? Why didn't I ever feel the need?"

"Hell, start thinking like that and you'll go crazy," Charley said, "let's eat."

After Newark, he sat and drank his coffee and looked down at the black water of the Hackensack River and then out across the Jersey Flats where tall towers of burning gas stood high above the distant refineries. Towers like burning beacons above the salt marshes and city dumps and rows of billboards. In the distance, faint above the cliffs of the Palisades, he saw the hazy towers of New York. As if the city and the burning flames were reaching for something unseen in the sky. And just before the train went into the dark of the tunnel beneath the river he saw the flashing red neon signs of the Federal Container Corp. Signs that meant New York and home. Signs that had always meant New York and, soon, his home. And all he could think of now was that the signs would be there flashing red day and night long after he was dead.

"Here we are," Charley said as the train slowed to a stop in the dingy station. "Might as well report to J.J. and get the brawl over with."

They reported to J. J. Salisbury. And it was a brawl. And when it was over he declined an invitation to lunch from J. J. Angry, he declined lunch and sat alone in his office. The main office beyond his closed door was quiet and almost empty. He had not been in the office at lunchtime for many years. Too many years. Quiet and peaceful. And sunk in silence, his eyes closed, he tried to think of nothing at all so that his anger would calm. Thinking of nothing until his hand moved. Aware that his right hand had moved as if reaching for something on the desk in front of him. He opened his eyes and looked at his hand. He looked at the desk. His book. A long time ago. When he was a young man who worked hard and ate his lunch in the office. There had always been a book. A novel, or a book of philosophy, or even a book of poems. Always a book and he had forgotten. Not even remembering when it had stopped, when the first day had come when there was not a book on his desk. But his hand had remembered. The quiet of a lunchtime office. He put on his jacket and left the office.

In Brentano's on Fifth Avenue he walked slowly up and down the rows of books. So many books and so many years. He finally chose *The Town,* by Faulkner, because he remembered reading Faulkner. And on his way back to the office he stopped in a delicatessen to buy his lunch. He stood at the end of the line that waited to buy and read the menu on the wall. He decided on roast beef with swiss cheese on white bread, a large container of coffee, and a french cruller. A woman walked past him to the head of the line and gave her order. The counterman began to fill her order. He stared at the woman. She turned her head and grinned at the people who stood waiting. He was staring so hard that he did not notice a man in a tweed coat push past him and up to the counter until the man was giving his order. A sharp wave of anger. He pushed forward.

"Hey! Stop the shovin'!"

He was at the counter beside the man who had cheated the line.

"Roast beef and swiss cheese on white," he said.

The counterman looked at him. "I got a order, just hold it."

He said, "This pig bucked the line! I want a roast beef with swiss cheese on . . ."

"Hold your water," the man who had cheated said.

"Do you always cheat?" He faced the man. "Are you just stupid, or were your parents cheats, too? I suppose where you come from everyone is a cheating pig!"

"Go to hell," the man said.

And someone pushed him. In a fury he pushed hard in return and heard a voice behind him swear. A sharp blow struck his back. He turned with his hands raised to punch whoever had hit him and found himself facing a red-faced middle-aged woman. His heart was pounding with his rage and he held onto the counter. Then he pushed through the crowd of waiting people and out into the street. The street seemed to be shaking before his eyes. The pigs! The animal bastards! The whole street moved before him and the pigs did not deserve to be alive. Cheat and lie and push to get a sandwich two minutes sooner. The stupid goddamned bastards! The whole goddamned cheating, lying, pushing world!

Too angry to work, he sat in his office for the rest of the afternoon. Sat behind his closed door with his feet on his desk. And at five o'clock he knew he was not going to catch the 5:20 for Connecticut. He called his wife. He told her he was going to a meeting. She was not happy but she did not question him. She would never question him. It would never cross her mind that he might be telling her a lie. But why not, everyone else did.

At five-thirty Charley looked into his office. "Gonna make the 6:15?"

"Can't," he said.

"Okay slave, see you tomorrow."

After Charley had gone the silence of the empty office began to oppress him. He left his desk and walked out into the large main office. All the desks were clean and empty. One of his own rules, *Nothing is to be left on a desk at night. The desks will be clean and devoid of all encumbrances other than a pen and ink stand, a calendar, and a memo pad with the top page clean and unused.* How long? When the books had stopped being there on his desk and when he had become the man who could write rules like those. When? Three long rows of neat desks as clean and sterile as the rows of tombstones in a military cemetery. And as he stepped through the office his footsteps struck sharp and echoing on his ears. He turned back into his office and shut the door.

He had been sitting in his chair for a long time when the young man came into his office. Just sitting there with no sense of time and wondering what a free man could do in New York on a Monday night. His door opened and a young man walked in.

"Oh . . . I'm sorry, sir. Didn't know you were still here. I need MacDonald's address. You said I should go, the open house? I don't have the address."

"MacDonald? 445 Madison Avenue, tenth floor." He studied the young man. "How are things going, Sasso? Like it here?"

"Yessir, very much."

"Why?"

"What, sir?"

He said, "Why do you like it here."

Young Sasso blinked, unsure of what to say. "Well, the pay's good, the work's fine, there's a future."

Sasso said more, but he stopped listening. He knew all the words. MacDonald Bros., Contractors. The company did occasional business with them. He clicked them off in his mind. Size, medium. Reliability, fair. Fees, average. Work, good but not spectacular.

He said, "Do you think MacDonald would mind a gate crasher?"

"You, sir? They'd die happy."

He laughed, "It's good to keep in touch. And stop calling me sir. If you can't make it John, try Mr. Cashmore."

"All right, Mr. Cashmore."

"That's better. Eddie, isn't it? All right, Eddie, let's make the MacDonalds happy. Maybe you'll have dinner with me later."

4

He stood near the window that overlooked Park Avenue and the distant East River. The blue-grey buildings of Brooklyn were still visible in the setting sun. John MacDonald was talking.

". . . damned glad you could make it. I've been meaning to call you about that project of yours over in Newark, the middle-income semi-detached. Now it's a big job, I admit, we couldn't handle all of it, but I think our price for the . . ."

Birnbaum, the junior partner since old MacDonald had died, hovered on the far side of the room watching them. They were not glad to see him. Pushing for business. Nothing more. Taking advantage of an unexpected opportunity. Pushing ahead in the goddamned line to get their goddamned sandwich.

He said, "MacDonald, I came here to have a few drinks."

"Jesus, kick me! How's the drink? No more business, a man's got to relax, eh? Later maybe we'll talk. Another drink coming up."

Young Sasso was talking to Birnbaum now. Business. Young Sasso was glad he, the boss, was there. It gave Sasso a lot more importance. A young man getting ahead, and if they thought he was important enough to be with the boss it wouldn't hurt Sasso. Someone handed him a fresh drink. Outside the window it was dark now. All the lights of the great city spread out against the darkness.

"Hello," the girl said. A small, thin brunette. A round face and large breasts under a tight green blouse.

"Good evening," he said.

"I'm Ruth Wizbicki. I work here."

"John Cashmore," he said.

"I know. Do you like these parties? I don't, too crowded."

"Then why do you come?"

She laughed. "You kidding? I work here, I said. Command performance, you know how it is. You're nice, you know?"

"Thank you," he said.

"I'm starved, are you? Let's go somewhere."

"Well . . ."

"Oh it's okay, the boss said I should. We can go to the Town House and charge it to the company."

He felt a hand on his shoulder. John MacDonald stood beside him. MacDonald was grinning.

"You and Ruthie doin' all right? Why don't you two go get some dinner, party's breaking up anyway. I tell you, John, I'd take you myself but I promised the wife I'd be home. I owe Ruthie a dinner anyway, you can fill in and bill it to me." And MacDonald winked at him.

The girl said, "He's cuter than you anyway, Mr. MacDonald."

"That does it," MacDonald said. "Powder your nose and don't keep the man waiting."

Both the girl and MacDonald seemed to vanish. He knew, of course, what the girl was really offering. Or perhaps she wasn't offering that. Perhaps she was only offering a dinner and some small talk for a lonely businessman. And maybe MacDonald had not winked again before he vanished somewhere in the room where everyone was leaving now. But he would never know what the girl was offering, or whether MacDonald had winked at him again or not. He realized that when he was walking rapidly down the stairs of the building. He told himself that he should turn back and at least find out what the girl was offering. But he walked on down the ten long flights of silent stairs and out into Madison Avenue. On the Avenue he turned north toward Grand Central Station. He walked through the bright night streets and wondered how much MacDonald had planned to pay the girl. Or was a free dinner and a chance to please the boss payment enough? Maybe she was a professional on call for the purpose. Maybe she was just a lonely girl who wanted a man to talk to, perhaps to love. At least to hold if nothing more. But not like that. Not for any woman and not for him. Never like that. Love like pushing for a sandwich in a delicatessen. And he seemed to see the blonde from the train. Standing in front of him and moving just ahead of him and speaking to him. *You don't make the rules. She knows what she's doing and she wants to do it. At least she's alive.*

He reached out to touch the blonde, saying aloud, "I don't want her, I want you."

The blonde seemed to sneer at him. *You couldn't do it. It's not in you. It's too late for you and it always has been.* And the blonde laughed at him.

He said aloud, "Don't laugh! I'll learn to smoke!"

Two men stopped to stare at him, but he was watching the blonde float before his eyes. She was still laughing. *You can't even order a sandwich and get it!*

He tried to touch her again, but she floated backwards just out of reach. She seemed to be floating there forever in the night filled with the rush of passing taxis. Just out of his reach. Taunting him past people who stared at him and cursed as he bumped into them. Floating there until she suddenly turned into a tavern. He followed her into the tavern.

"What'll it be?"

The bartender was small and dark and needed a shave. He stood at the bar and blinked at the waiting bartender. The blonde was gone.

"You want something, mister?"

He looked for the blonde. The tavern was a long, bare room with a white tile floor and long rows of bottles on the shelves. Four men in the bar were watching him. But the blonde was not there.

"No," he said. "Sorry, I don't want anything."

Behind him as he walked out he heard the bartender say something and heard the other men laugh. In the street he turned north again. And walked into Grand Central Station. In the station he called his wife. He told her he would be home in an hour. On the empty train he sat near a window and looked out because he had forgotten to buy a newspaper or anything else to read. The trip seemed longer than he remembered and the stations seemed strange, unfamiliar. It had been so long since he had looked out the window on this train. Or maybe it was the whole night. All the small suburban stations were dark and deserted and somehow impermanent as if they and all the towns did not belong to the land but only sat precariously on it ready to blow away in the next wind storm. At his station his wife was waiting with the car. He kissed her and as they drove up the hill he sat and looked across the valley, but all the white houses were only pinpoints of light in windows of rooms that held nothing but all the people like himself.

"Did something go wrong at the meeting?"

"No," he said.

"Where's the newspaper?"

"I forgot it."

"You could have told me, I'd have bought one."

"I'm sorry, I forgot it."

"All right," she said, "don't tell me what's wrong."

In the house he walked to the liquor cabinet and poured a long Scotch on the rocks. He drank it and poured a second. He drank the second one slowly, waiting for the first to begin to affect him. She was hanging up her coat in silence.

"Have a drink?" he asked her.

"The children will be home soon."

"What should I do, cheer?"

She turned on the television and sat in her armchair to watch. He poured another Scotch. A quiz show. Idiots with memories answering questions. For ten thousand dollars what two men won the Most Valuable Player award three times in the National League? Stan Musial and Roy Campanella, he said to himself, pay me the ten thousand dollars. Entertainment!

He said, "In college I always walked up to the front of the lunch line and had a friend buy my lunch for me. I hate people who cheat lines."

"Then why did you do it?" But her eyes were still watching the television set.

"You really want to know?"

Her head turned sharply. "I don't know what went wrong tonight, or in Chicago, or wherever it was, but I don't have to put up with your mood! I'm trying to watch television, do you mind?"

He gulped his whisky. "I damn near quit today. Do you know that?"

She stood and walked to the television and turned it off. Then she stood looking at him. "All right, John. You haven't told me what it is, but it doesn't matter, it's always something. There's something wrong with your job, or this house, or your children, or our friends, or me. Old J.J. is a cheap bastard. Mary is too conformist. I'm not sexual enough. There's always something. Tell me, John, what was it you wanted so much? I think it's time I knew, I've had to live with it just about long enough!"

He sat down. On the edge of the couch and turning his glass of whisky in his hand as if he could learn something from the feel of the glass itself. But it was only a glass of whisky he raised and drank from.

"I wanted to be a pirate."

"I'm not joking!"

He nodded. *I never wanted to push and cheat and lie to save three minutes and get ahead. I never did, and Oh God if I only could.* "There were two kids. One of them wanted to be a vice president before he was forty. Maybe even president, own his own company. The other kid wanted to really do something. He didn't know what. Maybe he just wanted to sit in the sun and read a book all day. Neither of them could make it." And he brushed hard at his eyes with the hand that was not holding the glass. The tears poured down his face while his mouth smiled at her. She came to hold his face against her breasts. He smelled her body and her hair. Her hands were soft on his face.

"John! What is it? Please, darling, the children."

He raised his head. "Is it such a terrible thing for them to see their father cry? Maybe they should see that more often." He smiled at her. "Well, what do you suggest? Woodworking in the cellar? Amateur theatrics? Cold showers three times a day? Raise mink? Run ten miles a day?" And he rested his head against her breasts again. "I really do love you."

His face against her breasts, and he felt her arms go around him, and he did love her, but it was the face of the blue blonde in the sky over Pennsylvania he saw in his mind. He wanted the blue blonde. And he wanted to chop down all the old oaks in Connecticut, and he wanted to spit in J.J.'s pompous face, and he wanted to quit his job, and he wanted to learn to smoke. Nothing was going to change any of that. Not the love of his wife, not all the full and busy hours of the world.

JOHN GALSWORTHY

(1867-1933)

Galsworthy is one of the best guides to that conservative, restrained, well-to-do English upper middle class which two world wars and the Welfare State have done much to erase. Himself the son of a solicitor (lawyer) of established social standing, Galsworthy studied law at Oxford. Instead of practicing law, however, he went to sea, voyaging to the Far East on a succession of merchant ships. During this journey he met Joseph Conrad, who became a life-long friend. His fiction deals with the moneyed society which he knew best; he is not uncritical of that milieu, but his restraint blunts the sharpness of his attacks. His epic novel, THE FORSYTE SAGA, is a good example of the approach which he takes. Galsworthy's dramas, on the other hand, were much more pointed and forceful in their criticism of a social system which treated criminals and the poor by an entirely different standard of justice from that which applied to the rich and influential; THE SILVER BOX, STRIFE, and JUSTICE are perhaps most representative of Galsworthy's concern with the need for social reform.

The Japanese Quince

As Mr. Nilson, well known in the City, opened the window of his dressing-room on Campden Hill, he experienced a peculiar sweetish sensation in the back of his throat, and a feeling of emptiness just under his fifth rib. Hooking the window back, he noticed that a little tree in the Square Gardens had come out in blossom, and that the thermometer stood at sixty. "Perfect morning," he thought; "Spring at last!"

Resuming some meditations on the price of Tintos, he took up an ivory-backed hand-glass and scrutinised his face. His firm, well-coloured cheeks, with their neat brown moustaches, and his round, well-opened, clear grey eyes, wore a reassuring appearance of good health. Putting on his black frock coat, he went downstairs.

In the dining-room his morning paper was laid out on the side-board. Mr. Nilson had scarcely taken it in his hand when he again became aware of that queer feeling. Somewhat concerned, he went to the French window and descended the scrolled iron steps into the fresh air. A cuckoo clock struck eight.

"Half an hour to breakfast," he thought; "I'll take a turn in the Gardens."

He had them to himself, and proceeded to pace the circular path with his morning paper clasped behind him. He had scarcely made two revolutions, however, when it was borne in on him that, instead of going away in the fresh air, the feeling had increased. He drew several deep breaths, having heard deep breathing recommended by his wife's doctor; but they augmented rather than diminished the sensation—as of some sweetish liquor in course within him, together with a faint aching just above his heart. Running over what he had eaten the night before, he could recollect no unusual dish, and it occurred to him that it might possibly be some smell affecting him. But he could detect nothing except a faint sweet lemony scent, rather agreeable than otherwise, which evidently emanated from the bushes budding in the sunshine. He was on the point of resuming his promenade, when a blackbird close by burst into song, and, looking up, Mr. Nilson saw at a distance of perhaps five yards a little tree, in the heart of whose branches the bird was perched. He stood staring curiously at this tree, recognising it for that which he had noticed from his window. It was covered with young blossoms, pink and white, and little bright green leaves both round and spikey; and on all this blossom and these leaves the sunlight glistened. Mr. Nilson smiled; the little tree was so alive and pretty! And instead of passing on, he stayed there smiling at the tree.

"Morning like this!" he thought; "and here I am the only person in the Square who has the—to come out and——!" But he had no sooner conceived this thought, than he saw quite near him a man with his hands behind him, who was also staring up and smiling at the little tree. Rather taken aback, Mr. Nilson ceased to smile, and looked furtively at the stranger. It was his next-door neighbour, Mr. Tandram, well known in the City, who had occupied the adjoining house for some five years. Mr. Nilson perceived at once the awkwardness of his position, for, being married, they had not yet had occasion to speak to one another. Doubtful as to his proper conduct, he decided at last to murmur: "Fine morning!" and was passing on, when Mr. Tandram answered: "Beautiful, for the time of year!" Detecting a slight nervousness in his neighbour's voice, Mr. Nilson was emboldened to regard him openly. He was of about Mr. Nilson's own height, with firm, well-coloured cheeks, neat brown moustaches, and round, well-opened, clear grey eyes; and he was wearing a black frock coat. Mr. Nilson noticed that he had his morning paper clasped behind him as he looked up at the little tree. And, visited somehow by the feeling that he had been caught out, he said abruptly:

"Er—can you give me the name of that tree?"

Mr. Tandram answered:

"I was about to ask you that," and stepped towards it. Mr. Nilson also approached the tree.

"Sure to have its name on, I should think," he said.

Mr. Tandram was the first to see the little label, close to where the blackbird had been sitting. He read it out.

"Japanese quince!"

"Ah!" said Mr. Nilson, "thought so. Early flowerers."

"Very," assented Mr. Tandram, and added: "Quite a feelin' in the air to-day."

Mr. Nilson nodded.

"It was a blackbird singin'," he said.

"Blackbirds," answered Mr. Tandram, "I prefer them to thrushes myself; more body in the note." And he looked at Mr. Nilson in an almost friendly way.

"Quite," murmured Mr. Nilson. "These exotics, they don't bear fruit. Pretty blossom!" and he again glanced up at the blossom, thinking: "Nice fellow, this, I rather like him."

Mr. Tandram also gazed up at the blossom. And the little tree, as if appreciating their attention, quivered and glowed. From a distance, the blackbird gave a loud, clear call. Mr. Nilson dropped his eyes. It struck him suddenly that Mr. Tandram looked a little foolish; and, as if he had seen himself, he said: "I must be going in. Good morning!"

A shade passed over Mr. Tandram's face, as if he, too, had suddenly noticed something about Mr. Nilson.

"Good morning," he replied, and clasping their journals to their backs they separated.

Mr. Nilson retraced his steps towards his garden window, walking slowly so as to avoid arriving at the same time as his neighbour. Having seen Mr. Tandram mount his scrolled iron steps, he ascended his own in turn. On the top step he paused.

With the slanting Spring sunlight darting and quivering into it, the Japanese quince seemed more living than a tree. The blackbird had returned to it, and was chanting out his heart.

Mr. Nilson sighed; again he felt that queer sensation, that chokey feeling in his throat.

The sound of a cough or sigh attracted his attention. There, in the shadow of his French window, stood Mr. Tandram, also looking forth across the Gardens at the little quince tree.

Unaccountably upset, Mr. Nilson turned abruptly into the house, and opened his morning paper.

FRANZ KAFKA

(1883-1924)

Kafka was born of middle-class Jewish parents in Germany; the themes and situations which characterized his life are reflected in his fiction. He spent several years as a minor government clerk, followed by more years in sanatoriums (tuberculosis) and the failure (as a result of his personal sense of inadequacy) of his efforts to marry. His short stories and novels delineate human beings caught in the grasp of blind and impersonal forces; they are trapped in a world which has rejected its spiritual heritage; they are creatures who suffer the pain of frustration, isolation, alienation, and futility. His stories are often symbolic, and they are frequently surrealistic in their nightmare quality. At the same time, a religious sense pervades his narratives. See also "A Hunger Artist," "A Country Doctor," and the famous short novel, "Metamorphosis," for examples of his techniques and themes.

In the Penal Colony

"It's a remarkable piece of apparatus," said the officer to the explorer and surveyed with a certain air of admiration the apparatus which was after all quite familiar to him. The explorer seemed to have accepted merely out of politeness the Commandant's invitation to witness the execution of a soldier condemned to death for disobedience and insulting behavior to a superior. Nor did the colony itself betray much interest in this execution. At least, in the small sandy valley, a deep hollow surrounded on all sides by naked crags, there was no one present save the officer, the explorer, the condemned man, who was a stupid-looking wide-mouthed creature with bewildered hair and face, and the soldier who held the heavy chain controlling the small chains locked on the prisoner's ankles, wrists and neck chains which were themselves attached to each other by communicating links. In any case, the condemned man looked so like a submissive dog that one might have thought he could be left to run free on the surrounding hills and would only need to be whistled for when the execution was due to begin.

The explorer did not much care about the apparatus and walked up and down behind the prisoner with almost visible indifference while the officer made the last adjustments, now creeping beneath the structure, which was bedded deep in the earth, now climbing a ladder to inspect its upper parts. These were tasks that might well have been left to a mechanic, but the officer performed them with great zeal, whether because he was a devoted admirer of the apparatus or because of other reasons the work could be entrusted to no one else. "Ready now!" he called at last and climbed down from the ladder. He looked uncommonly limp, breathed with his mouth wide open and had tucked two fine ladies' handkerchiefs under the collar of his uniform. "These uniforms are too heavy for the tropics, surely," said the explorer, instead of making some inquiry about the apparatus, as the officer had expected. "Of course," said the officer, washing his oily and greasy hands in a bucket of water that stood ready, "but they mean home to us; we don't want to forget about home. Now just have a look at this machine," he added at once, simultaneously drying his hands on a towel and indicating the apparatus. "Up till now a few things still had to be set by hand, but from this moment it works all by itself." The explorer nodded and followed him. The officer, anxious to secure himself against all contingencies, said: "Things sometimes go wrong, of course; I hope that nothing goes wrong today, but we have to allow for the possibility. The machinery should go on working continuously for twelve hours. But if anything does go wrong it will only be some small matter that can be set right at once."

"Won't you take a seat?" he asked finally, drawing a cane chair out from among a heap of them and offering it to the explorer, who could not refuse it. He was now sitting at the edge of a pit, into which he glanced for a fleeting moment. It was not very deep.

On one side of the pit the excavated soil had been piled up in a rampart, on the other side of it stood the apparatus. "I don't know," said the officer, "if the Commandant has already explained this apparatus to you." The explorer waved one hand vaguely; the officer asked for nothing better, since now he could explain the apparatus himself. "This apparatus," he said, taking hold of a crank handle and leaning against it, "was invented by our former Commandant. I assisted at the very earliest experiments and had a share in all the work until its completion. But the credit of inventing it belongs to him alone. Have you ever heard of our former Commandant? No? Well, it isn't saying too much if I tell you that the organization of the whole penal colony is his work. We who were his friends knew even before he died that the organization of the colony was so perfect that his successor, even with a thousand new schemes in his head, would find it impossible to alter anything, at least for many years to come. And our prophecy has come true; the new Commandant has had to acknowledge its truth. A pity you never met the old Commandant!—But," the officer interrupted himself, "I am rambling on, and here stands his apparatus before us. It consists, as you see, of three parts. In the course of time each of these parts has acquired a kind of popular nickname. The lower one is called the 'Bed,' the upper one the 'Designer,' and this one here in the middle that moves up and down is called the 'Harrow.'" "The Harrow?" asked the explorer. He had not been listening very attentively, the glare of the sun in the shadeless valley was altogether too strong, it was difficult to collect one's thoughts. All the more did he admire the officer, who in spite of his tight-fitting full-dress uniform coat, amply befrogged and weighed down by epaulettes, was pursuing his subject with such enthusiasm and, besides talking, was still tightening a screw here and there with a spanner. As for the soldier, he seemed to be in much the same condition as the explorer. He had wound the prisoner's chain round both his wrists, propped himself on his rifle, let his head hang and was paying no attention to anything. That did not surprise the explorer, for the officer was speaking French, and certainly neither the soldier nor the prisoner understood a word of French. It was all the more remarkable, therefore, that the prisoner was none the less making an effort to follow the officer's explanations. With a kind of drowsy persistence he directed his gaze wherever the officer pointed a finger, and at the interruption of the explorer's question he, too, as well as the officer, looked round.

"Yes, the Harrow," said the officer, "a good name for it. The needles are set in like the teeth of a harrow and the whole thing works something like a harrow, although its action is limited to one place and contrived with much more artistic skill. Anyhow, you'll soon understand it. On the Bed here the condemned man is laid— I'm going to describe the apparatus first before I set it in motion. Then you'll be able to follow the proceedings better. Besides, one of the cog wheels in the Designer is badly worn; it creaks a lot when it's working; you can hardly hear yourself speak; spare parts, unfortunately, are difficult to get here.—Well, here is the Bed, as I told you. It is completely covered with a layer of cotton wool; you'll find out why later. On this cotton wool the condemned man is laid, face down, quite naked, of course; here are straps for the hands, here for the feet, and here for the neck, to bind him fast. Here at the head of the bed, where the man, as I said, first lays down his face, is this little gag of felt, which can be easily regulated to go straight into his mouth. It is meant to keep him from screaming and biting his tongue. Of course the man is forced to take the felt into his mouth, for otherwise his neck would be broken by the strap." "Is that cotton wool?" asked the explorer, bending forward. "Yes, certainly," said the officer, with a smile, "feel it for yourself." He took the explorer's hand and guided it over the bed. "It's specially prepared cotton wool, that's why it looks so different; I'll tell you presently what it's for." The explorer already felt a dawning interest in the apparatus; he sheltered his eyes from the sun with one hand and gazed up at the structure. It was a huge affair. The Bed and the Designer were of the same size and looked like two dark wooden chests. The Designer hung about two meters above the Bed; each of them was bound at the corners with four rods of brass that almost flashed out rays in the sunlight. Between the chests shuttled the Harrow on a ribbon of steel.

The officer had scarcely noticed the explorer's previous indifference, but he was now well aware of his dawning interest; so he stopped explaining in order to leave a space of time for quiet observation. The condemned man imitated the explorer; since he could not use a hand to shelter his eyes he gazed upwards without shade.

"Well, the man lies down," said the explorer, leaning back in his chair and crossing his legs.

"Yes," said the officer, pushing his cap back a little and passing one hand over his heated face, "now listen! Both the Bed and the

Designer have an electric battery each; the Bed needs one for itself, the Designer for the Harrow. As soon as the man is strapped down, the Bed is set in motion. It quivers in minute, very rapid vibrations, both from side to side and up and down. You will have seen similar apparatus in hospitals; but in our Bed the movements are all precisely calculated; you see, they have to correspond very exactly to the movements of the Harrow. And the Harrow is the instrument for the actual execution of the sentence."

"And how does the sentence run?" asked the explorer.

"You don't know that either?" said the officer in amazement, and bit his lips. "Forgive me if my explanations seem rather incoherent. I do beg your pardon. You see, the Commandant always used to do the explaining; but the new Commandant shirks this duty; yet that such an important visitor"—the explorer tried to deprecate the honor with both hands, the officer, however, insisted —"that such an important visitor should not even be told about the kind of sentence we pass is a new development, which—" He was just on the point of using strong language but checked himself and said only: "I was not informed, it is not my fault. In any case, I am certainly the best person to explain our procedure, since I have here" —he patted his breast pocket—"the relevant drawings made by our former Commandant."

"The Commandant's own drawings?" asked the explorer. "Did he combine everything in himself, then? Was he soldier, judge, mechanic, chemist and draughtsman?"

"Indeed he was," said the officer, nodding assent, with a remote, glassy look. Then he inspected his hands critically; they did not seem clean enough to him for touching the drawings; so he went over to the bucket and washed them again. Then he drew out a small leather wallet and said: "Our sentence does not sound severe. Whatever commandment the prisoner has disobeyed is written upon his body by the Harrow. This prisoner, for instance"—the officer indicated the man—"will have written on his body: HONOR THY SUPERIORS!"

The explorer glanced at the man; he stood, as the officer pointed him out, with bent head, apparently listening with all his ears in an effort to catch what was being said. Yet the movement of his blubber lips, closely pressed together, showed clearly that he could not understand a word. Many questions were troubling the explorer, but at the sight of the prisoner he asked only: "Does he know his sentence?" "No," said the officer, eager to go on with his exposition, but the explorer interrupted him: "He doesn't know the sentence that has been passed on him?" "No," said the officer again, pausing a moment as if to let the explorer elaborate his question, and then said: "There would be no point in telling him. He'll learn it on his body." The explorer intended to make no answer, but he felt the prisoner's gaze turned on him; it seemed to ask if he approved such ongoings. So he bent forward again, having already leaned back in his chair, and put another question: "But surely he knows that he has been sentenced?" "Nor that either," said the officer, smiling at the explorer as if expecting him to make further surprising remarks. "No," said the explorer, wiping his forehead, "then he can't know either whether his defense was effective?" "He has had no chance of putting up a defense," said the officer, turning his eyes away as if speaking to himself and so sparing the explorer the shame of hearing self-evident matters explained. "But he must have had some chance of defending himself," said the explorer, and rose from his seat.

The officer realized that he was in danger of having his exposition of the apparatus held up for a long time; so he went up to the explorer, took him by the arm, waved a hand towards the condemned man, who was standing very straight now that he had so obviously become the center of attention—the soldier had also given the chain a jerk—and said: "This is how the matter stands. I have been appointed judge in this penal colony. Despite my youth. For I was the former Commandant's assistant in all penal matters and know more about the apparatus than anyone. My guiding principle is this: Guilt is never to be doubted. Other courts cannot follow that principle, for they consist of several opinions and have higher courts to scrutinize them. That is not the case here, or at least, it was not the case in the former Commandant's time. The new man has certainly shown some inclination to interfere with my judgments, but so far I have succeeded in fending him off and will go on succeeding. You wanted to have the case explained; it is quite simple, like all of them. A captain reported to me this morning that this man, who had been assigned to him as a servant and sleeps before his door, had been asleep on duty. It is his duty, you see, to get up every time the hour strikes and salute the captain's door. Not an exacting duty, and very necessary, since he has to be a sentry as well as a servant, and must be alert in both functions. Last night the captain wanted to see if the man was doing his duty. He opened the door as the clock struck two and there was his man curled up asleep. He took his riding whip and lashed him across the face. Instead of getting up and begging pardon, the man caught hold of his master's legs, shook him and cried: 'Throw that whip away or I'll eat you alive.'—That's the evidence. The captain came to me an hour ago, I wrote down his statement and appended the sentence to it. Then I had the man put in chains. That was all quite simple. If I had first called the man before me and interrogated him, things would have got into a confused tangle. He would have told lies, and had I exposed these lies he would have backed them up with more lies, and so on and so forth. As it is, I've got him and I won't let him go.—Is that quite clear now? But we're wasting time, the execution should be beginning and I haven't finished explaining the apparatus yet." He pressed the explorer back into his chair, went up again to the apparatus and began: "As you see, the shape of the Harrow corresponds to the human form; here is the harrow for the torso, here are the harrows for the legs. For the head there is only this one small spike. Is that quite clear?" He bent amiably forward towards the explorer, eager to provide the most comprehensive explanations.

The explorer considered the Harrow with a frown. The explanation of the judicial procedure had not satisfied him. He had to remind himself that this was in any case a penal colony where extraordinary measures were needed and that military discipline must be enforced to the last. He also felt that some hope might be set on the new Commandant, who was apparently of a mind to bring in, although gradually, a new kind of procedure which the officer's narrow mind was incapable of understanding. This train of thought prompted his next question: "Will the Commandant attend the execution?" "It is not certain," said the officer, wincing at the direct question, and his friendly expression darkened. "That is just why we have to lose no time. Much as I dislike it, I shall have to cut my explanations short. But of course tomorrow, when the apparatus has been cleaned—its one drawback is that it gets so messy—I can recapitulate all the details. For the present, then, only the essentials.— When the man lies down on the Bed and it begins to vibrate, the Harrow is lowered onto his body. It regulates itself automatically so that the needles barely touch his skin; once contact is made the steel ribbon stiffens immediately into a rigid band. And then the performance begins. An ignorant onlooker would see no difference between one punishment and another. The Harrow appears to do its work with uniform regularity. As it quivers, its points pierce the skin of the body which is itself quivering from the vibration of the Bed. So that the actual progress of the sentence can be watched, the Harrow is made of glass. Getting the needles fixed in the glass was a technical problem, but after many experiments we overcame the difficulty. No trouble was too great for us to take, you see. And now anyone can look through the glass and watch the inscription taking form on the body. Wouldn't you care to come a little nearer and have a look at the needles?"

The explorer got up slowly, walked across and bent over the Harrow. "You see," said the officer, "there are two kinds of needles arranged in multiple patterns. Each long needle has a short one beside it. The long needle does the writing, and the short needle sprays a jet of water to wash away the blood and keep the inscription clear. Blood and water together are then conducted here through small runnels into this main runnel and down a waste pipe into the pit." With his finger the officer traced the exact course taken by the blood and water. To make the picture as vivid as possible he held both hands below the outlet of the waste pipe as if to catch the outflow, and when he did this the explorer drew back his head and feeling behind him with one hand sought to return to his chair. To his horror he found that the condemned man too had obeyed the officer's invitation to examine the Harrow at close quarters and had followed him. He had pulled forward the sleepy soldier with the chain and was bending over the glass. One could see that his uncertain eyes were trying to perceive what the two gentlemen had been looking at, but since he had not understood the explanation he could not make head or tail of it. He was peering this way and that way. He kept running his eyes along the glass. The explorer wanted to drive him away, since what he was doing was probably culpable. But the officer firmly restrained the explorer with one hand and with the other took a clod of earth from the rampart and threw it at the soldier. He opened his eyes with a jerk, saw what the condemned man had dared to do, let his rifle fall, dug his heels into the ground, dragged his prisoner back so that he stumbled and fell immediately, and then stood looking down at him, watching him struggling and rattling in his chains. "Set him on his feet!" yelled the officer, for he noticed that the explorer's attention was being too much distracted by the prisoner. In fact he was even leaning right across the Harrow, without taking any notice of it, intent only on finding out

what was happening to the prisoner. "Be careful with him!" cried
the officer again. He ran round the apparatus, himself caught the
condemned man under the shoulders and with the soldier's help got
him up on his feet, which kept slithering from under him.

"Now I know all about it," said the explorer as the officer came
back to him. "All except the most important thing," he answered,
seizing the explorer's arm and pointing upwards: "In the Designer are all the cogwheels that control the movements of the Harrow, and this machinery is regulated according to the inscription demanded by the sentence. I am still using the guiding plans drawn
by the former Commandant. Here they are"—he extracted some
sheets from the leather wallet—"but I'm sorry I can't let you handle
them, they are my most precious possessions. Just take a seat and
I'll hold them in front of you like this, then you'll be able to see
everything quite well." He spread out the first sheet of paper. The
explorer would have liked to say something appreciative, but all he
could see was a labyrinth of lines crossing and re-crossing each other,
which covered the paper so thickly that it was difficult to discern the
blank spaces between them. "Read it," said the officer. "I can't," said
the explorer. "Yet it's clear enough," said the officer. "It's very ingenious," said the explorer evasively, "but I can't make it out."
"Yes," said the officer with a laugh, putting the paper away again,
"it's no calligraphy for school children. It needs to be studied
closely. I'm quite sure that in the end you would understand it too.
Of course the script can't be a simple one; it's not supposed to kill a
man straight off, but only after an interval of, on an average, twelve
hours; the turning point is reckoned to come at the sixth hour. So
there have to be lots and lots of flourishes around the actual script;
the script itself runs round the body only in a narrow girdle; the
rest of the body is reserved for the embellishments. Can you appreciate now the work accomplished by the Harrow and the whole apparatus?—Just watch it!" He ran up the ladder, turned a wheel,
called down: "Look out, keep to one side!" and everything started
working. If the wheel had not creaked, it would have been marvelous. The officer, as if surprised by the noise of the wheel, shook
his fist at it, then spread out his arms in excuse to the explorer and
climbed down rapidly to peer at the working of the machine from
below. Something perceptible to no one save himself was still not in
order; he clambered up again, did something with both hands in the
interior of the Designer, then slid down one of the rods, instead of

using the ladder, so as to get down quicker, and with the full force of his lungs, to make himself heard at all in the noise, yelled in the explorer's ear: "Can you follow it? The Harrow is beginning to write; when it finishes the first draft of the inscription on the man's back, the layer of cotton wool begins to roll and slowly turns the body over, to give the Harrow fresh space for writing. Meanwhile the raw part that has been written on lies on the cotton wool, which is specially prepared to staunch the bleeding and so makes all ready for a new deepening of the script. Then these teeth at the edge of the Harrow, as the body turns further round, tear the cotton wool away from the wounds, throw it into the pit, and there is more work for the Harrow. So it keeps on writing deeper and deeper for the whole twelve hours. The first six hours the condemned man stays alive almost as before, he suffers only pain. After two hours the felt gag is taken away, for he has no longer strength to scream. Here, into this electrically heated basin at the head of the bed, some warm rice pap is poured, from which the man, if he feels like it, can take as much as his tongue can lap. Not one of them ever misses the chance. I can remember none, and my experience is extensive. Only about the sixth hour does the man lose all desire to eat. I usually kneel down here at that moment and observe what happens. The man rarely swallows his last mouthful, he only rolls it round his mouth and spits it out into the pit. I have to duck just then or he would spit it in my face. But how quiet he grows at just about the sixth hour! Enlightenment comes to the most dull-witted. It begins around the eyes. From there it radiates. A moment that might tempt one to get under the Harrow oneself. Nothing more happens than that the man begins to understand the inscription, he purses his mouth as if he were listening. You have seen how difficult it is to decipher the script with one's eyes; but our man deciphers it with his wounds. To be sure, that is a hard task; he needs six hours to accomplish it. By that time the Harrow has pierced him quite through and casts him into the pit, where he pitches down upon the blood and water and the cotton wool. Then the judgment has been fulfilled, and we, the soldier and I, bury him."

The explorer had inclined his ear to the officer and with his hands in his jacket pockets watched the machine at work. The condemned man watched it too, but uncomprehendingly. He bent forward a little and was intent on the moving needles when the soldier, at a sign from the officer, slashed through his shirt and trousers from behind with a knife, so that they fell off; he tried to catch at his falling clothes to cover his nakedness, but the soldier lifted him into the air and shook the last remnants from him. The officer stopped the machine, and in the sudden silence the condemned man was laid under the Harrow. The chains were loosened and the straps fastened on instead; in the first moment that seemed almost a relief to the prisoner. And now the Harrow was adjusted a little lower, since he was a thin man. When the needle points touched him a shudder ran over his skin; while the soldier was busy strapping his right hand, he flung out his left hand blindly; but it happened to be in the direction towards where the explorer was standing. The officer kept watching the explorer sideways, as if seeking to read from his face the impression made on him by the execution, which had been at least cursorily explained to him.

The wrist strap broke; probably the soldier had drawn it too tight. The officer had to intervene, the soldier held up the broken piece of strap to show him. So the officer went over to him and said, his face still turned towards the explorer: "This is a very complex machine, it can't be helped that things are breaking or giving way here and there; but one must not thereby allow oneself to be diverted in one's general judgment. In any case, this strap is easily made good; I shall simply use a chain; the delicacy of the vibrations for the right arm will of course be a little impaired." And while he fastened the chains, he added: "The resources for maintaining the machine are now very much reduced. Under the former Commandant I had free access to a sum of money set aside entirely for this purpose. There was a store, too, in which spare parts were kept for repairs of all kinds. I confess I have been almost prodigal with them, I mean in the past, not now as the new Commandant pretends, always looking for an excuse to attack our old way of doing things. Now he has taken charge of the machine money himself, and if I send for a new strap they ask for the broken old strap as evidence, and the new strap takes ten days to appear and then is of shoddy material and not much good. But how I am supposed to work the machine without a strap, that's something nobody bothers about."

The explorer thought to himself: It's always a ticklish matter to intervene decisively in other people's affairs. He was neither a member of the penal colony nor a citizen of the state to which it belonged. Were he to denounce this execution or actually try to stop it, they could say to him: You are a foreigner, mind your own business. He could make no answer to that, unless he were to add that he was amazed at himself in this connection, for he traveled only as an observer, with no intention at all of altering other people's methods of administering justice. Yet here he found himself strongly tempted. The injustice of the procedure and the inhumanity of the execution were undeniable. No one could suppose that he had any selfish interest in the matter, for the condemned man was a complete stranger, not a fellow countryman or even at all sympathetic to him. The explorer himself had recommendations from high quarters, had been received here with great courtesy, and the very fact that he had been invited to attend the execution seemed to suggest that his views would be welcome. And this was all the more likely since the Commandant, as he had heard only too plainly, was no upholder of the procedure and maintained an attitude almost of hostility to the officer.

At that moment the explorer heard the officer cry out in rage. He had just, with considerable difficulty, forced the felt gag into the condemned man's mouth when the man in an irresistible access of nausea shut his eyes and vomited. Hastily the officer snatched him away from the gag and tried to hold his head over the pit; but it was too late, the vomit was running all over the machine. "It's all the fault of that Commandant!" cried the officer, senselessly shaking the brass rods in front, "the machine is befouled like a pigsty." With trembling hands he indicated to the explorer what had happened. "Have I not tried for hours at a time to get the Commandant to understand that the prisoner must fast for a whole day before the execution. But our new, mild doctrine thinks otherwise. The Commandant's ladies stuff the man with sugar candy before he's led off. He has lived on stinking fish his whole life long and now he has to eat sugar candy! But it could still be possible, I should have nothing to say against it, but why won't they get me a new felt gag, which I have been begging for the last three months. How should a man not feel sick when he takes a felt gag into his mouth which more than a hundred men have already slobbered and gnawed in their dying moments?"

The condemned man had laid his head down and looked peaceful, the soldier was busy trying to clean the machine with the prisoner's shirt. The officer advanced towards the explorer, who in some vague presentiment fell back a pace, but the officer seized him by the hand, and drew him to one side. "I should like to exchange a few words with you in confidence," he said, "may I?" "Of course," said the explorer, and listened with downcast eyes.

"This procedure and method of execution, which you are now having the opportunity to admire, has at the moment no longer any open adherents in our colony. I am its sole advocate, and at the same time the sole advocate of the old Commandant's tradition. I can no longer reckon on any further extension of the method, it takes all my energy to maintain it as it is. During the old Commandant's lifetime the colony was full of his adherents; his strength of conviction I still have in some measure, but not an atom of his power; consequently the adherents have skulked out of sight, there are still many of them but none of them will admit it. If you were to go into the teahouse today, on execution day, and listen to what is being said, you would perhaps hear only ambiguous remarks. These would all be made by adherents, but under the present Commandant and his present doctrines they are of no use to me. And now I ask you: because of this Commandant and the women who influence him, is such a piece of work, the work of a lifetime"—he pointed to the machine—"to perish? Ought one to let that happen? Even if one has only come as a stranger to our island for a few days? But there's no time to lose, an attack of some kind is impending on my function as judge; conferences are already being held in the Commandant's office from which I am excluded; even your coming here today seems to me a significant move; they are cowards and use you as a screen, you, a stranger.—How different an execution was in the old days! A whole day before the ceremony the valley was packed with people; they all came only to look on; early in the morning the Commandant appeared with his ladies; fanfares roused the whole camp; I reported that everything was in readiness; the assembled company—no high official dared to absent himself—arranged itself round the machine; this pile of cane chairs is a miserable survival from that epoch. The machine was freshly cleaned and glittering, I got new spare parts for almost every execution. Before hundreds of spectators—all of them standing on tiptoe as far as the heights there—the condemned man was laid under the Harrow by the Commandant himself. What is left today for a common soldier to do was then my task, the task of the presiding judge, and was an honor for me. And then the execution began! No discordant noise spoilt the working of the machine. Many did not care to watch it but lay with closed eyes in the sand; they all knew: Now Justice is being done. In the silence one heard nothing but the condemned man's sighs, half muffled by the felt gag. Nowadays the machine can no longer wring from anyone a sigh louder than the felt gag can stifle; but in those days the writing needles let drop an acid fluid, which we're no longer permitted to use. Well, and then came the sixth hour! It was impossible to grant all the requests to be allowed to watch it from near by. The Commandant in his wisdom ordained that the children should have the preference; I, of course, because of my office had the privilege of always being at hand; often enough I would be squatting there with a small child in either arm. How we all absorbed the look of transfiguration on the face of the sufferer, how we bathed our cheeks in the radiance of that justice, achieved at last and fading so quickly! What times these were, my comrade!" The officer had obviously forgotten whom he was addressing; he had embraced the explorer and laid his head on his shoulder. The explorer was deeply embarrassed, impatiently he stared over the officer's head. The soldier had finished his cleaning job and was now pouring rice pap from a pot into the basin. As soon as the condemned man, who seemed to have recovered entirely, noticed this action he began to reach for the rice with his tongue. The soldier kept pushing him away, since the rice pap was certainly meant for a later hour, yet it was just as unfitting that the soldier himself should thrust his dirty hands into the basin and eat out of it before the other's avid face.

The officer quickly pulled himself together. "I didn't want to upset you," he said, "I know it is impossible to make those days credible now. Anyhow, the machine is still working and it is still effective in itself. It is effective in itself even though it stands alone in this valley. And the corpse still falls at the last into the pit with an incomprehensibly gentle wafting motion, even although there are no hundreds of people swarming round like flies as formerly. In those days we had to put a strong fence round the pit, it has long since been torn down."

The explorer wanted to withdraw his face from the officer and looked round him at random. The officer thought he was surveying the valley's desolation; so he seized him by the hands, turned him round to meet his eyes, and asked: "Do you realize the shame of it?"

But the explorer said nothing. The officer left him alone for a little; with legs apart, hands on hips, he stood very still, gazing at the ground. Then he smiled encouragingly at the explorer and said: "I was quite near you yesterday when the Commandant gave you the invitation. I heard him giving it. I know the Commandant. I divined at once what he was after. Although he is powerful enough to take measures against me, he doesn't dare to do it yet, but he certainly means to use your verdict against me, the verdict of an illustrious foreigner. He has calculated it carefully: this is your second day on the island, you did not know the old Commandant and his ways, you are conditioned by European ways of thought, perhaps you object on principle to capital punishment in general and to such mechanical instruments of death in particular, besides you will see that the execution has no support from the public, a shabby ceremony—carried out with a machine already somewhat old and worn—now, taking all that into consideration, would it not be likely (so thinks the Commandant) that you might disapprove of my methods? And if you disapprove, you wouldn't conceal the fact (I'm still speaking from the Commandant's point of view), for you are a man to feel confidence in your own well-tried conclusions. True, you have seen and learned to appreciate the peculiarities of many peoples, and so you would not be likely to take a strong line against our proceedings, as you might do in your own country. But the Commandant has no need of that. A casual, even an unguarded remark will be enough. It doesn't even need to represent what you really think, so long as it can be used speciously to serve his purpose. He will try to prompt you with sly questions, of that I am certain. And his ladies will sit around you and prick up their ears; you might be saying something like this: 'In our country we have a different criminal procedure,' or 'In our country the prisoner is interrogated before he is sentenced,' or 'We haven't used torture since the Middle Ages.' All these statements are as true as they seem natural to you, harmless remarks that pass no judgment on my methods. But how would the Commandant react to them? I can see him, our good Commandant, pushing his chair away immediately and rushing on to the balcony, I can see his ladies streaming out after him, I can hear his voice—the ladies call it a voice of thunder—well, and this is what he says: 'A famous Western investigator, sent out to study criminal procedure in all the countries of the world, has just said that our old tradition of administering justice is inhumane. Such a verdict from such a personality makes it impossible for me to countenance these methods any longer. Therefore from this very day I ordain . . .' and so on. You may want to interpose that you never said any such thing, that you never called my methods inhumane, on the contrary your profound experience leads you to believe they are most humane and most in consonance with human dignity, and you admire the machine greatly— but it will be too late; you won't even get onto the balcony, crowded as it will be with ladies; you may try to draw attention to yourself; you may want to scream out; but a lady's hand will close your lips— and I and the work of the old Commandant will be done for."

The explorer had to suppress a smile; so easy, then, was the task he had felt to be so difficult. He said evasively: "You overestimate my influence; the Commandant has read my letters of recommendation, he knows that I am no expert in criminal procedure. If I were to give an opinion, it would be as a private individual, an opinion no more influential than that of any ordinary person, and in any case much less influential than that of the Commandant, who, I am given to understand, has very extensive powers in this penal colony. If his attitude to your procedure is as definitely hostile as you believe, then I fear the end of your tradition is at hand, even without any humble assistance from me."

Had it dawned on the officer at last? No, he still did not understand. He shook his head emphatically, glanced briefly round at the condemned man and the soldier, who both flinched away from the rice, came close up to the explorer and without looking at his face but fixing his eye on some spot on his coat said in a lower voice than before: "You don't know the Commandant; you feel yourself—forgive the expression—a kind of outsider so far as all of us are concerned; yet, believe me, your influence cannot be rated too highly. I was simply delighted when I heard that you were to attend the execution all by yourself. The Commandant arranged it to aim a blow at me, but I shall turn it to my advantage. Without being distracted by lying whispers and contemptuous glances—which could not have been avoided had a crowd of people attended the execution—you have heard my explanations, seen the machine and are now in course of watching the execution. You have doubtless already formed your own judgment; if you still have some small uncertainties the sight of the execution will resolve them. And now I make this request to you: help me against the Commandant!"

The explorer would not let him go on. "How could I do that," he cried, "it's quite impossible. I can neither help nor hinder you."

"Yes, you can," the officer said. The explorer saw with a certain apprehension that the officer had clenched his fists. "Yes, you can," repeated the officer, still more insistently. "I have a plan that is bound to succeed. You believe your influence is insufficient. I know that it is sufficient. But even granted that you are right, is it not necessary, for the sake of preserving this tradition, to try even what might prove insufficient? Listen to my plan, then. The first thing necessary for you to carry it out is to be as reticent as possible today regarding your verdict on these proceedings. Unless you are asked a direct question you must say nothing at all; but what you do say must be brief and general; let it be remarked that you would prefer not to discuss the matter, that you are out of patience with it, that if you are to let yourself go you would use strong language. I don't ask you to tell any lies; by no means; you should only give curt answers, such as: 'Yes, I saw the execution,' or 'Yes, I had it explained to me.' Just that, nothing more. There are grounds enough for any impatience you betray, although not such as will occur to the Commandant. Of course, he will mistake your meaning and interpret it to please himself. That's what my plan depends on. Tomorrow in the Commandant's office there is to be a large conference of all the high administrative officials, the Commandant presiding. Of course the Commandant is the kind of man to have turned these conferences into public spectacles. He has had a gallery built that is always packed with spectators. I am compelled to take part in the conferences, but they make me sick with disgust. Now, whatever happens, you will certainly be invited to this conference; if you behave today as I suggest the invitation will become an urgent request. But if for some mysterious reason you're not invited, you'll have to ask for an invitation; there's no doubt of your getting it then. So tomorrow you're sitting in the Commandant's box with the ladies. He keeps looking up to make sure you're there. After various trivial and ridiculous matters, brought in merely to impress the audience—mostly harbor works, nothing but harbor works!—our judicial procedure comes up for discussion too. If the Commandant doesn't introduce it, or not soon enough, I'll see that it's mentioned. I'll stand up and report that today's execution has taken place. Quite briefly, only a statement. Such a statement is not usual, but I shall make it. The Commandant thanks me, as always, with an amiable smile, and then he can't restrain himself, he seizes the excellent opportunity. 'It has just been reported,' he will say, or words to that effect, 'that an execution has taken place. I should like merely to add that this execution was witnessed by the famous explorer who has, as you all know, honored our colony so greatly by his visit to us. His presence at today's session of our conference also contributes to the importance of this occasion. Should we not now ask the famous explorer to give us his verdict on our traditional mode of execution and the procedure that leads up to it?' Of course there is loud applause, general agreement, I am more insistent than anyone. The Commandant bows to you and says: 'Then in the name of the assembled company, I put the question to you.' And now you advance to the front of the box. Lay your hands where everyone can see them, or the ladies will catch them and press your fingers.—And then at last you can speak out. I don't know how I'm going to endure the tension of waiting for that moment. Don't put any restraint on yourself when you make your speech, publish the truth aloud, lean over the front of the box, shout, yes indeed, shout your verdict, your unshakable conviction, at the Commandant. Yet perhaps you wouldn't care to do that, it's not in keeping with your character, in your country perhaps people do these things differently, well, that's all right too, that will be quite as effective, don't even stand up, just say a few words, even in a whisper, so that only the officials beneath you will hear them, that will be quite enough, you don't even need to mention the lack of public support for the execution, the creaking wheel, the broken strap, the filthy gag of felt, no, I'll take all that upon me, and, believe me, if my indictment doesn't drive him out of the conference hall, it will force him to his knees to make the acknowledgment: Old Commandant, I humble myself before you.—That is my plan; will you help me to carry it out? But of course you are willing, what is more, you must." And the officer seized the explorer by both arms and gazed, breathing heavily, into his face. He had shouted the last sentence so loudly that even the soldier and the condemned man were startled into attending; they had not understood a word but they stopped eating and looked over at the explorer, chewing their previous mouthfuls.

From the very beginning the explorer had no doubt about what answer he must give; in his lifetime he had experienced too much to have any uncertainty here; he was fundamentally honorable and unafraid. And yet now, facing the soldier and the condemned man, he did hesitate, for as long as it took to draw one breath. At last, however, he said, as he had to: "No." The officer blinked several times but did not turn his eyes away. "Would you like me to explain?" asked the explorer. The officer nodded wordlessly. "I do not approve of your procedure," said the explorer then, "even before you took me into your confidence—of course I shall never in any circumstances betray your confidence—I was already wondering whether it would be my duty to intervene and whether my intervention would have the slightest chance of success. I realized to whom I ought to turn: to the Commandant, of course. You have made that fact even clearer, but without having strengthened my resolution, on the contrary, your sincere conviction has touched me, even though it cannot influence my judgment."

The officer remained mute, turned to the machine, caught hold of a brass rod, and then, leaning back a little, gazed at the Designer as if to assure himself that all was in order. The soldier and the condemned man seemed to have come to some understanding; the condemned man was making signs to the soldier, difficult though his movements were because of the tight straps; the soldier was bending down to him; the condemned man whispered something and the soldier nodded.

The explorer followed the officer and said: "You don't know yet what I mean to do. I shall tell the Commandant what I think of the procedure, certainly, but not at a public conference, only in private; nor shall I stay here long enough to attend any conference; I am going away early tomorrow morning, or at least embarking on my ship."

It did not look as if the officer had been listening. "So you did not find the procedure convincing," he said to himself and smiled, as an old man smiles at childish nonsense and yet pursues his own meditations behind the smile.

"Then the time has come," he said at last, and suddenly looked at the explorer with bright eyes that held some challenge, some appeal for co-operation. "The time for what?" asked the explorer uneasily, but got no answer.

"You are free," said the officer to the condemned man in the native tongue. The man did not believe it at first. "Yes, you are set free," said the officer. For the first time the condemned man's face woke to real animation. Was it true? Was it only a caprice of the officer's, that might change again? Had the foreign explorer begged him off? What was it? One could read these questions on his face. But not for long. Whatever it might be, he wanted to be really free if he might, and he began to struggle so far as the Harrow permitted him.

"You'll burst my straps," cried the officer, "lie still! We'll soon loosen them." And signing the soldier to help him, he set about doing so. The condemned man laughed wordlessly to himself, now he turned his face left towards the officer, now right towards the soldier, nor did he forget the explorer.

"Draw him out," ordered the officer. Because of the Harrow this had to be done with some care. The condemned man had already torn himself a little in the back through his impatience.

From now on, however, the officer paid hardly any attention to him. He went up to the explorer, pulled out the small leather wallet again, turned over the papers in it, found the one he wanted and showed it to the explorer. "Read it," he said. "I can't," said the explorer, "I told you before that I can't make out these scripts." "Try taking a close look at it," said the officer and came quite near to the explorer so that they might read it together. But when even that proved useless, he outlined the script with his little finger, holding it high above the paper as if the surface dared not be sullied by touch, in order to help the explorer to follow the script in that way. The explorer did make an effort, meaning to please the officer in this respect at least, but he was quite unable to follow. Now the officer began to spell it, letter by letter, and then read out the words. " 'BE JUST!' is what is written there," he said, "surely you can read it now." The explorer bent so close to the paper that the officer feared he might touch it and drew it farther away; the explorer made no remark, yet it was clear that he still could not decipher it. " 'BE JUST!' is what is written there," said the officer once more. "Maybe," said the explorer, "I am prepared to believe you." "Well, then," said the officer, at least partly satisfied, and climbed up the ladder with the paper; very carefully he laid it inside the Designer and seemed to be changing the disposition of all the cogwheels; it was a troublesome piece of work and must have involved wheels that were extremely small, for sometimes the officer's head vanished altogether from sight inside the Designer, so precisely did he have to regulate the machinery.

The explorer, down below, watched the labor uninterruptedly, his neck grew stiff and his eyes smarted from the glare of sunshine over the sky. The soldier and the condemned man were now busy together. The man's shirt and trousers, which were already lying in the pit, were fished out by the point of the soldier's bayonet. The shirt was abominably dirty and its owner washed it in the bucket of water. When he put on the shirt and trousers both he and the soldier could not help guffawing, for the garments were of course slit up behind. Perhaps the condemned man felt it incumbent on him to amuse the soldier, he turned round and round in his slashed garments before the soldier, who squatted on the ground beating his knees with mirth. All the same, they presently controlled their mirth out of respect for the gentlemen.

When the officer had at length finished his task aloft, he surveyed the machinery in all its details once more, with a smile, but this time shut the lid of the Designer, which had stayed open till now, climbed down, looked into the pit and then at the condemned man, noting with satisfaction that the clothing had been taken out, then went over to wash his hands in the water bucket, perceived too late that it was disgustingly dirty, was unhappy because he could not wash his hands, in the end thrust them into the sand—this alternative did not please him, but he had to put up with it—then stood upright and began to unbutton his uniform jacket. As he did this, the two ladies' handkerchiefs he had tucked under his collar fell into his hands. "Here are your handkerchiefs," he said, and threw them to the condemned man. And to the explorer he said in explanation: "A gift from the ladies."

In spite of the obvious haste with which he was discarding first his uniform jacket and then all his clothing, he handled each garment with loving care, he even ran his fingers caressingly over the silver lace on the jacket and shook a tassel into place. This loving care was certainly out of keeping with the fact that as soon as he had a garment off he flung it at once with a kind of unwilling jerk into the pit. The last thing left to him was his short sword with the sword belt. He drew it out of the scabbard, broke it, then gathered all together, the bits of the sword, the scabbard and the belt, and flung them so violently down that they clattered into the pit.

Now he stood naked there. The explorer bit his lips and said nothing. He knew very well what was going to happen, but he had no right to obstruct the officer in anything. If the judicial procedure which the officer cherished were really so near its end—possibly as a result of his own intervention, as to which he felt himself pledged—then the officer was doing the right thing; in his place the explorer would not have acted otherwise.

The soldier and the condemned man did not understand at first what was happening, at first they were not even looking on. The condemned man was gleeful at having got the handkerchiefs back, but he was not allowed to enjoy them for long, since the soldier snatched them with a sudden, unexpected grab. Now the condemned man in turn was trying to twitch them from under the belt where the soldier had tucked them, but the soldier was on his guard. So they were wrestling, half in jest. Only when the officer stood quite naked was their attention caught. The condemned man especially seemed struck with the notion that some great change was impending. What had happened to him was now going to happen to the officer. Perhaps even to the very end. Apparently the foreign explorer had given the order for it. So this was revenge. Although he himself had not suffered to the end, he was to be revenged to the end. A broad, silent grin now appeared on his face and stayed there all the rest of the time.

The officer, however, had turned to the machine. It had been clear enough previously that he understood the machine well, but now it was almost staggering to see how he managed it and how it obeyed him. His hand had only to approach the Harrow for it to rise and sink several times till it was adjusted to the right position for receiving him; he touched only the edge of the Bed and already it was vibrating; the felt gag came to meet his mouth, one could see that the officer was really reluctant to take it but he shrank from it only a moment, soon he submitted and received it. Everything was ready, only the straps hung down at the sides, yet they were obviously unnecessary, the officer did not need to be fastened down. Then the condemned man noticed the loose straps, in his opinion the execution was incomplete unless the straps were buckled, he gestured eagerly to the soldier and they ran together to strap the officer down. The latter had already stretched out one foot to push the lever that started the Designer; he saw the two men coming up; so he drew his foot back and let himself be buckled in. But now he could not reach the lever; neither the soldier nor the condemned man would be able to find it, and the explorer was determined not to lift a finger. It was not necessary; as soon as the straps were fastened the machine began to work; the Bed vibrated, the needles flickered above the skin, the Harrow rose and fell. The explorer had been staring at it quite a while before he remembered that a wheel in the Designer should have been creaking; but everything was quiet, not even the slightest hum could be heard.

Because it was working so silently the machine simply escaped

one's attention. The explorer observed the soldier and the condemned man. The latter was the more animated of the two, everything in the machine interested him, now he was bending down and
now stretching up on tiptoe, his forefinger was extended all the
time pointing out details to the soldier. This annoyed the explorer.
He was resolved to stay till the end, but he could not bear the sight
of these two. "Go back home," he said. The soldier would have been
willing enough, but the condemned man took the order as a punishment. With clasped hands he implored to be allowed to stay, and
when the explorer shook his head and would not relent, he even
went down on his knees. The explorer saw that it was no use merely
giving orders, he was on the point of going over and driving them
away. At that moment he heard a noise above him in the Designer.
He looked up. Was that cogwheel going to make trouble after all?
But it was something quite different. Slowly the lid of the Designer
rose up and then clicked wide open. The teeth of a cogwheel showed
themselves and rose higher, soon the whole wheel was visible, it
was as if some enormous force were squeezing the Designer so that
there was no longer room for the wheel, the wheel moved up till it
came to the very edge of the Designer, fell down, rolled along the
sand a little on its rim and then lay flat. But a second wheel was already rising after it, followed by many others, large and small and
indistinguishably minute, the same thing happened to all of them,
at every moment one imagined the Designer must now really be
empty, but another complex of numerous wheels was already rising
into sight, falling down, trundling along the sand and lying flat.
This phenomenon made the condemned man completely forget the
explorer's command, the cogwheels fascinated him, he was always
trying to catch one and at the same time urging the soldier to help,
but always drew back his hand in alarm, for another wheel always
came hopping along which, at least on its first advance, scared him
off.

The explorer, on the other hand, felt greatly troubled; the
machine was obviously going to pieces; its silent working was a delusion; he had a feeling that he must now stand by the officer, since
the officer was no longer able to look after himself. But while the
tumbling cogwheels absorbed his whole attention he had forgotten
to keep an eye on the rest of the machine; now that the last cogwheel had left the Designer, however, he bent over the Harrow
and had a new and still more unpleasant surprise. The Harrow was
not writing, it was only jabbing, and the bed was not turning the

body over but only bringing it up quivering against the needles. The explorer wanted to do something, if possible, to bring the whole machine to a standstill, for this was no exquisite torture such as the officer desired, this was plain murder. He stretched out his hands. But at that moment the Harrow rose with the body spitted on it and moved to the side, as it usually did only when the twelfth hour had come. Blood was flowing in a hundred streams, not mingled with water, the water jets too had failed to function. And now the last action failed to fulfil itself, the body did not drop off the long needles, streaming with blood it went on hanging over the pit without falling into it. The Harrow tried to move back to its old position, but as if it had itself noticed that it had not yet got rid of its burden it stuck after all where it was, over the pit. "Come and help!" cried the explorer to the other two, and himself seized the officer's feet. He wanted to push against the feet while the others seized the head from the opposite side and so the officer might be slowly eased off the needles. But the other two could not make up their minds to come; the condemned man actually turned away; the explorer had to go over to them and force them into position at the officer's head. And here, almost against his will, he had to look at the face of the corpse. It was as it had been in life; no sign was visible of the promised redemption; what the others had found in the machine the officer had not found; the lips were firmly pressed together, the eyes were open, with the same expression as in life, the look was calm and convinced, through the forehead went the point of the great iron spike.

As the explorer, with the soldier and the condemned man behind him, reached the first houses of the colony, the soldier pointed to one of them and said: "There is the teahouse."

In the ground floor of the house was a deep, low, cavernous space, its walls and ceiling blackened with smoke. It was open to the road all along its length. Although this teahouse was very little different from the other houses of the colony, which were all very dilapidated, even up to the Commandant's palatial headquarters, it made on the explorer the impression of a historic tradition of some kind, and he felt the power of past days. He went near to it, followed by his companions, right up between the empty tables which stood in the street before it, and breathed the cool, heavy air that came from the interior. "The old man's buried here," said the soldier, "the priest wouldn't let him lie in the churchyard. Nobody knew where to

bury him for a while, but in the end they buried him here. The officer never told you about that, for sure, because of course that's what
he was most ashamed of. He even tried several times to dig the old
man up by night, but he was always chased away." "Where is the
grave?" asked the explorer, who found it impossible to believe the
soldier. At once both of them, the soldier and the condemned man,
ran before him pointing with outstretched hands in the direction
where the grave should be. They led the explorer right up to the
back wall, where guests were sitting at a few tables. They were apparently dock laborers, strong men with short, glistening, full black
beards. None had a jacket, their shirts were torn, they were poor,
humble creatures. As the explorer drew near, some of them got up,
pressed close to the wall, and stared at him. "It's a foreigner," ran the
whisper around him, "he wants to see the grave." They pushed one
of the tables aside, and under it there was really a gravestone. It was
a simple stone, low enough to be covered by a table. There was an
inscription on it in very small letters, the explorer had to kneel
down to read it. This was what it said: "Here rests the old Commandant. His adherents, who now must be nameless, have dug this
grave and set up this stone. There is a prophecy that after a certain
number of years the Commandant will rise again and lead his adherents from this house to recover the colony. Have faith and wait!"
When the explorer had read this and risen to his feet he saw all the
bystanders around him smiling, as if they too had read the inscription, had found it ridiculous and were expecting him to agree with
them. The explorer ignored this, distributed a few coins among
them, waiting till the table was pushed over the grave again, quitted
the teahouse and made for the harbor.

The soldier and the condemned man had found some acquaintances in the teahouse, who detained them. But they must have soon
shaken them off, for the explorer was only halfway down the long
flight of steps leading to the boats when they came rushing after
him. Probably they wanted to force him at the last minute to take
them with him. While he was bargaining below with a ferryman to
row him to the steamer, the two of them came headlong down the
steps, in silence, for they did not dare to shout. But by the time they
reached the foot of the steps the explorer was already in the boat,
and the ferryman was just casting off from the shore. They could
have jumped into the boat, but the explorer lifted a heavy knotted
rope from the floor boards, threatened them with it and so kept
them from attempting the leap.

F. SCOTT FITZGERALD

(1896-1940)

Francis Scott Key Fitzgerald was born in Minnesota and educated in the East. The two regions seemed to him to represent contrasting values and ways of life, a conflict which was to be expressed in many of his stories, notably THE GREAT GATSBY and "Winter Dreams." The East of New York and the Ivy League held a life-long fascination for Fitzgerald, but at the same time he recognized its materialistic orientation. Leaving Princeton to join the Army in 1917, Fitzgerald served as an infantry lieutenant for three years. Thereafter his fiction limned to perfection the "jazz age" of the twenties, from his first novel, THIS SIDE OF PARADISE, through a large number of short stories and several more novels. He came to see that the American dream was wealth, and that this dream could both ennoble and destroy.

The Diamond as Big as the Ritz

John T. Unger came from a family that had been well known in Hades—a small town on the Mississippi River—for several generations. John's father had held the amateur golf championship through many a heated contest; Mrs. Unger was known "from hot-box to hot-bed," as the local phrase went, for her political addresses; and young John T. Unger, who had just turned sixteen, had danced all the latest dances from New York before he put on long trousers. And now, for a certain time, he was to be away from home. That respect for a New England education which is the bane of all provincial places, which drains them yearly of their most promising young men, had seized upon his parents. Nothing would suit them but that he should go to St. Midas' School near Boston—Hades was too small to hold their darling and gifted son.

Now in Hades—as you know if you ever have been there—the names of the more fashionable preparatory schools and colleges mean very little. The inhabitants have been so long out of the world that, though they make a show of keeping up to date in dress and manners and literature, they depend to a great extent on hearsay, and a function that in Hades would be considered elaborate would doubtless be hailed by a Chicago beef-princess as "perhaps a little tacky."

John T. Unger was on the eve of departure. Mrs. Unger, with maternal fatuity, packed his trunks full of linen suits and electric fans, and Mr. Unger presented his son with an asbestos pocket-book stuffed with money.

"Remember, you are always welcome here," he said. "You can be sure, boy, that we'll keep the home fires burning."

"I know," answered John huskily.

"Don't forget who you are and where you come from," continued his father proudly, "and you can do nothing to harm you. You are an Unger—from Hades."

So the old man and the young shook hands and John walked away with tears streaming from his eyes. Ten minutes later he had passed outside the city limits, and he stopped to glance back for the last time. Over the gates the old-fashioned Victorian motto seemed strangely attractive to him. His father had tried time and time again to have it changed to something with a little more push and verve about it, such as "Hades—Your Opportunity," or else a plain "Welcome" sign set over a hearty handshake pricked out in electric lights. The old motto was a little depressing, Mr. Unger had thought—but now. . . .

So John took his look and then set his face resolutely toward his destination. And, as he turned away, the lights of Hades against the sky seemed full of a warm and passionate beauty.

St. Midas' School is half an hour from Boston in a Rolls-Pierce motor-car. The actual distance will never be known, for no one, except John T. Unger, had ever arrived there save in a Rolls-Pierce and probably no one ever will again. St. Midas' is the most expensive and the most exclusive boys' preparatory school in the world.

John's first two years there passed pleasantly. The fathers of all the boys were money-kings and John spent his summers visiting at fashionable resorts. While he was very fond of all the boys he visited, their fathers struck him as being much of a piece, and in his boyish way he often wondered at their exceeding sameness. When he told them where his home was they would ask jovially, "Pretty hot down there?" and John would muster a faint smile and answer, "It certainly is." His response would have been heartier had they not all made this joke—at best varying it with, "Is it hot enough for you down there?" which he hated just as much.

In the middle of his second year at school, a quiet, handsome boy named Percy Washington had been put in John's form. The newcomer was pleasant in his manner and exceedingly well dressed even for St. Midas', but for some reason he kept aloof from the other boys. The only person with whom he was intimate was John T. Unger, but even to John he was entirely uncommunicative concerning his home or his family. That he was wealthy went without saying, but beyond a few such deductions John knew little of his friend, so it promised rich confectionery for his curiosity when Percy invited him to spend the summer at his home "in the West." He accepted, without hesitation.

It was only when they were in the train that Percy became, for the first time, rather communicative. One day while they were eating lunch in the dining-car and discussing the imperfect characters of several of the boys at school, Percy suddenly changed his tone and made an abrupt remark.

"My father," he said, "is by far the richest man in the world."

"Oh," said John, politely. He could think of no answer to make to this confidence. He considered "That's very nice," but it sounded hollow and was on the point of saying, "Really?" but refrained since it would seem to question Percy's statement. And such an astounding statement could scarcely be questioned.

"By far the richest," repeated Percy.

"I was reading in the *World Almanac*," began John, "that there

was one man in America with an income of over five million a year
and four men with incomes of over three million a year, and——"

"Oh, they're nothing," Percy's mouth was a half-moon of scorn.
"Catch-penny capitalists, financial small-fry, petty merchants and
money-lenders. My father could buy them out and not know he'd
done it."

"But how does he——"

"Why haven't they put down *his* income tax? Because he doesn't
pay any. At least he pays a little one—but he doesn't pay any on his
real income."

"He must be very rich," said John simply. "I'm glad. I like
very rich people.

"The richer a fella is, the better I like him." There was a look
of passionate frankness upon his dark face. "I visited the Schnlitzer-
Murphys last Easter. Vivian Schnlitzer-Murphy had rubies as big as
hen's eggs, and sapphires that were like globes with lights inside
them——"

"I love jewels," agreed Percy enthusiastically. "Of course I
wouldn't want any one at school to know about it, but I've got quite
a collection myself. I used to collect them instead of stamps."

"And diamonds," continued John eagerly. "The Schnlitzer-
Murphys had diamonds as big as walnuts——"

"That's nothing." Percy had leaned forward and dropped his
voice to a low whisper. "That's nothing at all. My father has a diamond bigger than the Ritz-Carlton Hotel."

II

The Montana sunset lay between two mountains like a gigantic
bruise from which dark arteries spread themselves over a poisoned
sky. An immense distance under the sky crouched the village of
Fish, minute, dismal, and forgotten. There were twelve men, so it
was said, in the village of Fish, twelve sombre and inexplicable souls
who sucked a lean milk from the almost literally bare rock upon
which a mysterious populatory force had begotten them. They had
become a race apart, these twelve men of Fish, like some species
developed by an early whim of nature, which on second thought had
abandoned them to struggle and extermination.

Out of the blue-black bruise in the distance crept a long line of moving lights upon the desolation of the land, and the twelve men of Fish gathered like ghosts at the shanty depot to watch the passing of the seven o'clock train, the Transcontinental Express from Chicago. Six times or so a year the Transcontinental Express, through some inconceivable jurisdiction, stopped at the village of Fish, and when this occurred a figure or so would disembark, mount into a buggy that always appeared from out of the dusk, and drive off toward the bruised sunset. The observation of this pointless and preposterous phenomenon had become a sort of cult among the men of Fish. To observe, that was all; there remained in them none of the vital quality of illusion which would make them wonder or speculate, else a religion might have grown up around these mysterious visitations. But the men of Fish were beyond all religion—the barest and most savage tenets of even Christianity could gain no foothold on that barren rock—so there was no altar, no priest, no sacrifice; only each night at seven the silent concourse by the shanty depot, a congregation who lifted up a prayer of dim, anæmic wonder.

On this June night, the Great Brakeman, whom, had they deified any one, they might well have chosen as their celestial protagonist, had ordained that the seven o'clock train should leave its human (or inhuman) deposit at Fish. At two minutes after seven Percy Washington and John T. Unger disembarked, hurried past the spellbound, the agape, the fearsome eyes of the twelve men of Fish, mounted into a buggy which had obviously appeared from nowhere, and drove away.

After half an hour, when the twilight had coagulated into dark, the silent negro who was driving the buggy hailed an opaque body somewhere ahead of them in the gloom. In response to his cry, it turned upon them a luminous disk which regarded them like a malignant eye out of the unfathomable night. As they came closer, John saw that it was the tail-light of an immense automobile, larger and more magnificent than any he had ever seen. Its body was of gleaming metal richer than nickel and lighter than silver, and the hubs of the wheels were studded with iridescent geometric figures of green and yellow—John did not dare to guess whether they were glass or jewel.

Two negroes, dressed in glittering livery such as one sees in pictures of royal processions in London, were standing at attention beside the car and as the two young men dismounted from the buggy they were greeted in some language which the guest could not understand, but which seemed to be an extreme form of the Southern negro's dialect.

"Get in," said Percy to his friend, as their trunks were tossed to the ebony roof of the limousine. "Sorry we had to bring you this far in that buggy, but of course it wouldn't do for the people on the train or those Godforsaken fellas in Fish to see this automobile."

"Gosh! What a car!" This ejaculation was provoked by its interior. John saw that the upholstery consisted of a thousand minute and exquisite tapestries of silk, woven with jewels and embroideries, and set upon a background of cloth of gold. The two armchair seats in which the boys luxuriated were covered with stuff that resembled duvetyn, but seemed woven in numberless colors of the ends of ostrich feathers.

"What a car!" cried John again, in amazement.

"This thing?" Percy laughed. "Why, it's just an old junk we use for a station wagon."

By this time they were gliding along through the darkness toward the break between the two mountains.

"We'll be there in an hour and a half," said Percy, looking at the clock. "I may as well tell you it's not going to be like anything you ever saw before."

If the car was any indication of what John would see, he was prepared to be astonished indeed. The simple piety prevalent in Hades has the earnest worship of and respect for riches as the first article of its creed—had John felt otherwise than radiantly humble before them, his parents would have turned away in horror at the blasphemy.

They had now reached and were entering the break between the two mountains and almost immediately the way became much rougher.

"If the moon shone down here, you'd see that we're in a big gulch," said Percy, trying to peer out of the window. He spoke a few words into the mouthpiece and immediately the footman turned on a searchlight and swept the hillsides with an immense beam.

"Rocky, you see. An ordinary car would be knocked to pieces in half an hour. In fact, it'd take a tank to navigate it unless you knew the way. You notice we're going uphill now."

They were obviously ascending, and within a few minutes the car was crossing a high rise, where they caught a glimpse of a pale moon newly risen in the distance. The car stopped suddenly and several figures took shape out of the dark beside it—these were negroes also. Again the two young men were saluted in the same dimly recognizable dialect; then the negroes set to work and four immense cables dangling from overhead were attached with hooks to the hubs of the great jeweled wheels. At a resounding "Hey-yah!" John felt the car being lifted slowly from the ground—up and up—clear of the tallest rocks on both sides—then higher, until he could see a wavy, moonlit valley stretched out before him in sharp contrast to the quagmire of rocks that they had just left. Only on one side was there still rock—and then suddenly there was no rock beside them or anywhere around.

It was apparent that they had surmounted some immense knife-blade of stone, projecting perpendicularly into the air. In a moment they were going down again, and finally with a soft bump they were landed upon the smooth earth.

"The worst is over," said Percy, squinting out the window. "It's only five miles from here, and our own road—tapestry brick—all the way. This belongs to us. This is where the United States ends, father says."

"Are we in Canada?"

"We are not. We're in the middle of the Montana Rockies. But you are now on the only five square miles of land in the country that's never been surveyed."

"Why hasn't it? Did they forget it?"

"No," said Percy, grinning, "they tried to do it three times. The first time my grandfather corrupted a whole department of the State survey; the second time he had the official maps of the United States tinkered with—that held them for fifteen years. The last time was harder. My father fixed it so that their compasses were in the strongest magnetic field ever artificially set up. He had a whole set of surveying instruments made with a slight defection that would allow for this territory not to appear, and he substituted them for the ones that were to be used. Then he had a river deflected and he had what looked like a village built up on its banks—so that they'd see it, and think it was a town ten miles farther up the valley. There's only one thing my father's afraid of," he concluded, "only one thing in the world that could be used to find us out."

"What's that?"

Percy sank his voice to a whisper.

"Aeroplanes," he breathed. "We've got half a dozen anti-air-craft guns and we've arranged it so far—but there've been a few deaths and a great many prisoners. Not that we mind *that,* you know, father and I, but it upsets mother and the girls, and there's always the chance that some time we won't be able to arrange it."

Shreds and tatters of chinchilla, courtesy clouds in the green moon's heaven, were passing the green moon like precious Eastern stuffs paraded for the inspection of some Tartar Khan. It seemed to John that it was day, and that he was looking at some lads sailing above him in the air, showering down tracts and patent medicine circulars, with their messages of hope for despairing, rockbound hamlets. It seemed to him that he could see them look down out of the clouds and stare—and stare at whatever there was to stare at in this place whither he was bound— What then? Were they induced to land by some insidious device there to be immured far from patent medicines and from tracts until the judgment day—or, should they fail to fall into the trap, did a quick puff of smoke and the sharp round of a splitting shell bring them drooping to earth—and "up-set" Percy's mother and sisters. John shook his head and the wraith of a hollow laugh issued silently from his parted lips. What des-perate transaction lay hidden here? What a moral expedient of a bizarre Crœsus? What terrible and golden mystery? . . .

The chinchilla clouds had drifted past now and outside the Montana night was bright as day. The tapestry brick of the road was smooth to the tread of the great tires as they rounded a still, moon-lit lake; they passed into darkness for a moment, a pine grove, pungent and cool, then they came out into a broad avenue of lawn and John's exclamation of pleasure was simultaneous with Percy's taciturn "We're home."

Full in the light of the stars, an exquisite château rose from the borders of the lake, climbed in marble radiance half the height of an adjoining mountain, then melted in grace, in perfect symmetry, in translucent feminine languor, into the massed darkness of a forest of pine. The many towers, the slender tracery of the sloping para-pets, the chiselled wonder of a thousand yellow windows with their oblongs and hectagons and triangles of golden light, the shattered softness of the intersecting planes of star-shine and blue shade, all trembled on John's spirit like a chord of music. On one of the tow-ers, the tallest, the blackest at its base, an arrangement of exterior lights at the top made a sort of floating fairyland—and as John gazed up in warm enchantment the faint acciaccatura sound of violins drifted down in a rococo harmony that was like nothing he had ever heard before. Then in a moment the car stopped before wide, high marble steps around which the night air was fragrant with a host of flowers. At the top of the steps two great doors swung silently open and amber light flooded out upon the darkness, silhouetting the figure of an exquisite lady with black, high-piled hair, who held out her arms toward them.

"Mother," Percy was saying, "this is my friend, John Unger, from Hades."

Afterward John remembered that first night as a daze of many colors, of quick sensory impressions, of music soft as a voice in love, and of the beauty of things, lights and shadows, and motions and faces. There was a white-haired man who stood drinking a many-hued cordial from a crystal thimble set on a golden stem. There was a girl with a flowery face, dressed like Titania with braided sapphires in her hair. There was a room where the solid, soft gold of the walls yielded to the pressure of his hand, and a room that was like a platonic conception of the ultimate prison—ceiling, floor, and all, it was lined with an unbroken mass of diamonds, diamonds of every size and shape, until, lit with tall violet lamps in the corners, it dazzled the eyes with a whiteness that could be compared only with itself, beyond human wish or dream.

Through a maze of these rooms the two boys wandered. Sometimes the floor under their feet would flame in brilliant patterns from lighting below, patterns of barbaric clashing colors, of pastel delicacy, of sheer whiteness, or of subtle and intricate mosaic, surely from some mosque on the Adriatic Sea. Sometimes beneath layers of thick crystal he would see blue or green water swirling, inhabited by vivid fish and growths of rainbow foliage. Then they would be treading on furs of every texture and color or along corridors of palest ivory, unbroken as though carved complete from the gigantic tusks of dinosaurs extinct before the age of man. . . .

Then a hazily remembered transition, and they were at dinner —where each plate was of two almost imperceptible layers of solid diamond between which was curiously worked a filigree of emerald design, a shaving sliced from green air. Music, plangent and unobtrusive, drifted down through far corridors—his chair, feathered and curved insidiously to his back, seemed to engulf and overpower him as he drank his first glass of port. He tried drowsily to answer a question that had been asked him, but the honeyed luxury that clasped his body added to the illusion of sleep—jewels, fabrics, wines, and metals blurred before his eyes into a sweet mist. . . .

"Yes," he replied with a polite effort, "it certainly is hot enough for me down there."

He managed to add a ghostly laugh; then, without movement, without resistance, he seemed to float off and away, leaving an iced dessert that was pink as a dream. . . . He fell asleep.

When he awoke he knew that several hours had passed. He was in a great quiet room with ebony walls and a dull illumination that was too faint, too subtle, to be called a light. His young host was standing over him.

"You fell asleep at dinner," Percy was saying. "I nearly did, too —it was such a treat to be comfortable again after this year of school. Servants undressed and bathed you while you were sleeping."

"Is this a bed or a cloud?" sighed John. "Percy, Percy—before you go, I want to apologize."

"For what?"

"For doubting you when you said you had a diamond as big as the Ritz-Carlton Hotel."

Percy smiled.

"I thought you didn't believe me. It's that mountain, you know."

"What mountain?"

"The mountain the château rests on. It's not very big, for a mountain. But except about fifty feet of sod and gravel on top it's solid diamond. *One* diamond, one cubic mile without a flaw. Aren't you listening? Say——"

But John T. Unger had again fallen asleep.

III

Morning. As he awoke he perceived drowsily that the room had at the same moment become dense with sunlight. The ebony panels of one wall had slid aside on a sort of track, leaving his chamber half open to the day. A large negro in a white uniform stood beside his bed.

"Good-evening," muttered John, summoning his brains from the wild places.

"Good-morning, sir. Are you ready for your bath, sir? Oh, don't get up—I'll put you in, if you'll just unbutton your pajamas—there. Thank you, sir."

John lay quietly as his pajamas were removed—he was amused and delighted; he expected to be lifted like a child by this black Gargantua who was tending him, but nothing of the sort happened; instead he felt the bed tilt up slowly on its side—he began to roll, startled at first, in the direction of the wall, but when he reached the wall its drapery gave way, and sliding two yards farther down a fleecy incline he plumped gently into water the same temperature as his body.

He looked about him. The runway or rollway on which he had arrived had folded gently back into place. He had been projected into another chamber and was sitting in a sunken bath with his head just above the level of the floor. All about him, lining the walls of the room and the sides and bottom of the bath itself, was a blue aquarium, and gazing through the crystal surface on which he sat, he could see fish swimming among amber lights and even gliding without curiosity past his outstretched toes, which were separated from them only by the thickness of the crystal. From overhead, sunlight came down through sea-green glass.

"I suppose, sir, that you'd like hot rosewater and soapsuds this morning, sir—and perhaps cold salt water to finish."

The negro was standing beside him.

"Yes," agreed John, smiling inanely, "as you please." Any idea of ordering this bath according to his own meagre standards of living would have been priggish and not a little wicked.

The negro pressed a button and a warm rain began to fall, apparently from overhead, but really, so John discovered after a moment, from a fountain arrangement near by. The water turned to a pale rose color and jets of liquid soap spurted into it from four miniature walrus heads at the corners of the bath. In a moment a dozen little paddle-wheels, fixed to the sides, had churned the mixture into a radiant rainbow of pink foam which enveloped him softly with its delicious lightness, and burst in shining, rosy bubbles here and there about him.

"Shall I turn on the moving-picture machine, sir?" suggested the negro deferentially. "There's a good one-reel comedy in this machine to-day, or I can put in a serious piece in a moment, if you prefer it."

"No, thanks," answered John, politely but firmly. He was en-

joying his bath too much to desire any distraction. But distraction
came. In a moment he was listening intently to the sound of flutes
from just outside, flutes dripping a melody that was like a water-
fall, cool and green as the room itself, accompanying a frothy piccolo,
in play more fragile than the lace of suds that covered and charmed
him.

After a cold salt-water bracer and a cold fresh finish, he stepped
out and into a fleecy robe, and upon a couch covered with the same
material he was rubbed with oil, alcohol, and spice. Later he sat in
a voluptuous chair while he was shaved and his hair was trimmed.

"Mr. Percy is waiting in your sitting-room," said the negro,
when these operations were finished. "My name is Gygsum, Mr.
Unger, sir. I am to see to Mr. Unger every morning."

John walked out into the brisk sunshine of his living-room,
where he found breakfast waiting for him and Percy, gorgeous in
white kid knickerbockers, smoking in an easy chair.

IV

This is a story of the Washington family as Percy sketched it
for John during breakfast.

The father of the present Mr. Washington had been a Virginian,
a direct descendant of George Washington, and Lord Baltimore. At
the close of the Civil War he was a twenty-five-year-old Colonel with
a played-out plantation and about a thousand dollars in gold.

Fitz-Norman Culpepper Washington, for that was the young
Colonel's name, decided to present the Virginia estate to his younger
brother and go West. He selected two dozen of the most faithful
blacks, who, of course, worshipped him, and bought twenty-five tick-
ets to the West, where he intended to take out land in their names
and start a sheep and cattle ranch.

When he had been in Montana for less than a month and things
were going very poorly indeed, he stumbled on his great discovery.
He had lost his way when riding in the hills, and after a day without
food he began to grow hungry. As he was without his rifle, he was
forced to pursue a squirrel, and in the course of the pursuit he noticed that it was carrying something shiny in its mouth. Just before
it vanished into its hole—for Providence did not intend that this
squirrel should alleviate his hunger—it dropped its burden. Sitting
down to consider the situation Fitz-Norman's eye was caught by a

gleam in the grass beside him. In ten seconds he had completely lost his appetite and gained one hundred thousand dollars. The squirrel, which had refused with annoying persistence to become food, had made him a present of a large and perfect diamond.

Late that night he found his way to camp and twelve hours later all the males among his darkies were back by the squirrel hole digging furiously at the side of the mountain. He told them he had discovered a rhinestone mine, and, as only one or two of them had ever seen even a small diamond before, they believed him, without question. When the magnitude of his discovery became apparent to him, he found himself in a quandary. The mountain was *a* diamond —it was literally nothing else but solid diamond. He filled four saddle bags full of glittering samples and started on horseback for St. Paul. There he managed to dispose of half a dozen small stones— when he tried a larger one a storekeeper fainted and Fitz-Norman was arrested as a public disturber. He escaped from jail and caught the train for New York, where he sold a few medium-sized diamonds and received in exchange about two hundred thousand dollars in gold. But he did not dare to produce any exceptional gems—in fact, he left New York just in time. Tremendous excitement had been created in jewelry circles, not so much by the size of his diamonds as by their appearance in the city from mysterious sources. Wild rumors became current that a diamond mine had been discovered in the Catskills, on the Jersey coast, on Long Island, beneath Washington Square. Excursion trains, packed with men carrying picks and shovels began to leave New York hourly, bound for various neighboring El Dorados. But by that time young Fitz-Norman was on his way back to Montana.

By the end of a fortnight he had estimated that the diamond in the mountain was approximately equal in quantity to all the rest of the diamonds known to exist in the world. There was no valuing it by any regular computation, however, for it was *one solid diamond* —and if it were offered for sale not only would the bottom fall out of the market, but also, if the value should vary with its size in the usual arithmetical progression, there would not be enough gold in the world to buy a tenth part of it. And what could any one do with a diamond that size?

It was an amazing predicament. He was, in one sense, the richest man that ever lived—and yet was he worth anything at all? If his secret should transpire there was no telling to what measures the

Government might resort in order to prevent a panic, in gold as well as in jewels. They might take over the claim immediately and institute a monopoly.

There was no alternative—he must market his mountain in secret. He sent South for his younger brother and put him in charge of his colored following—darkies who had never realized that slavery was abolished. To make sure of this, he read them a proclamation that he had composed, which announced that General Forrest had reorganized the shattered Southern armies and defeated the North in one pitched battle. The negroes believed him implicitly. They passed a vote declaring it a good thing and held revival services immediately.

Fitz-Norman himself set out for foreign parts with one hundred thousand dollars and two trunks filled with rough diamonds of all sizes. He sailed for Russia in a Chinese junk and six months after his departure from Montana he was in St. Petersburg. He took obscure lodgings and called immediately upon the court jeweller, announcing that he had a diamond for the Czar. He remained in St. Petersburg for two weeks, in constant danger of being murdered, living from lodging to lodging, and afraid to visit his trunks more than three or four times during the whole fortnight.

On his promise to return in a year with larger and finer stones, he was allowed to leave for India. Before he left, however, the Court Treasurers had deposited to his credit, in American banks, the sum of fifteen million dollars—under four different aliases.

He returned to America in 1868, having been gone a little over two years. He had visited the capitals of twenty-two countries and talked with five emperors, eleven kings, three princes, a shah, a khan, and a sultan. At that time Fitz-Norman estimated his own wealth at one billion dollars. One fact worked consistently against the disclosure of his secret. No one of his larger diamonds remained in the public eye for a week before being invested with a history of enough fatalities, amours, revolutions, and wars to have occupied it from the days of the first Babylonian Empire.

From 1870 until his death in 1900, the history of Fitz-Norman Washington was a long epic in gold. There were side issues, of course —he evaded the surveys, he married a Virginia lady, by whom he had a single son, and he was compelled, due to a series of unfortunate complications, to murder his brother, whose unfortunate habit of drinking himself into an indiscreet stupor had several times endangered their safety. But very few other murders stained these happy years of progress and expansion.

Just before he died he changed his policy, and with all but a few million dollars of his outside wealth bought up rare minerals in bulk, which he deposited in the safety vaults of banks all over the world, marked as bric-à-brac. His son, Braddock Tarleton Washington, followed this policy on an even more tensive scale. The minerals were converted into the rarest of all elements—radium—so that the equivalent of a billion dollars in gold could be placed in a receptacle no bigger than a cigar box.

When Fitz-Norman had been dead three years his son, Braddock, decided that the business had gone far enough. The amount of wealth that he and his father had taken out of the mountain was beyond all exact computation. He kept a note-book in cipher in which he set down the approximate quantity of radium in each of the thousand banks he patronized, and recorded the alias under which it was held. Then he did a very simple thing—he sealed up the mine.

He sealed up the mine. What had been taken out of it would support all the Washingtons yet to be born in unparalleled luxury for generations. His one care must be the protection of his secret, lest in the possible panic attendant on its discovery he should be reduced with all the property-holders in the world to utter poverty.

This was the family among whom John T. Unger was staying. This was the story he heard in his silver-walled living-room the morning after his arrival.

V

After breakfast, John found his way out the great marble entrance, and looked curiously at the scene before him. The whole valley, from the diamond mountain to the steep granite cliff five miles away, still gave off a breath of golden haze which hovered idly above the fine sweep of lawns and lakes and gardens. Here and there clusters of elms made delicate groves of shade, contrasting strangely with the tough masses of pine forest that held the hills in a grip of dark-blue green. Even as John looked he saw three fawns in single file patter out from one clump about a half mile away and disappear with awkward gayety into the black-ribbed half-light of another.

John would not have been surprised to see a goat-foot piping his way among the trees or to catch a glimpse of pink nymph-skin and flying yellow hair between the greenest of the green leaves.

In some such cool hope he descended the marble steps, disturbing faintly the sleep of two silky Russian wolfhounds at the bottom, and set off along a walk of white and blue brick that seemed to lead in no particular direction.

He was enjoying himself as much as he was able. It is youth's felicity as well as its insufficiency that it can never live in the present, but must always be measuring up the day against its own radiantly imagined future—flowers and gold, girls and stars, they are only prefigurations and prophecies of that incomparable, unattainable young dream.

John rounded a soft corner where the massed rosebushes filled the air with heavy scent, and struck off across a park toward a patch of moss under some trees. He had never lain upon moss, and he wanted to see whether it was really soft enough to justify the use of its name as an adjective. Then he saw a girl coming toward him over the grass. She was the most beautiful person he had ever seen.

She was dressed in a white little gown that came just below her knees, and a wreath of mignonettes clasped with blue slices of sapphire bound up her hair. Her pink bare feet scattered the dew before them as she came. She was younger than John—not more than sixteen.

"Hello," she cried softly, "I'm Kismine."

She was much more than that to John already. He advanced toward her, scarcely moving as he drew near lest he should tread on her bare toes.

"You haven't met me," said her soft voice. Her blue eyes added, "Oh, but you've missed a great deal!" . . . "You met my sister, Jasmine, last night. I was sick with lettuce poisoning," went on her soft voice, and her eyes continued, "and when I'm sick I'm sweet—and when I'm well."

"You have made an enormous impression on me," said John's eyes, "and I'm not so slow myself"—"How do you do?" said his voice. "I hope you're better this morning."—"You darling," added his eyes tremulously.

John observed that they had been walking along the path. On her suggestion they sat down together upon the moss, the softness of which he failed to determine.

He was critical about women. A single defect—a thick ankle, a hoarse voice, a glass eye—was enough to make him utterly indifferent. And here for the first time in his life he was beside a girl who seemed to him the incarnation of physical perfection.

"Are you from the East?" asked Kismine with charming interest.

"No," answered John simply. "I'm from Hades."

Either she had never heard of Hades, or she could think of no pleasant comment to make upon it, for she did not discuss it further.

"I'm going East to school this fall," she said. "D'you think I'll like it? I'm going to New York to Miss Bulge's. It's very strict, but you see over the weekends I'm going to live at home with the family in our New York house, because father heard that the girls had to go walking two by two."

"Your father wants you to be proud," observed John.

"We are," she answered, her eyes shining with dignity. "None of us has ever been punished. Father said we never should be. Once when my sister Jasmine was a little girl she pushed him down-stairs and he just got up and limped away.

"Mother was—well, a little startled," continued Kismine, "when she heard that you were from—from where you *are* from, you know. She said that when she was a young girl—but then, you see, she's a Spaniard and old-fashioned."

"Do you spend much time out here?" asked John, to conceal the fact that he was somewhat hurt by this remark. It seemed an unkind allusion to his provincialism.

"Percy and Jasmine and I are here every summer, but next summer Jasmine is going to Newport. She's coming out in London a year from this fall. She'll be presented at court."

"Do you know," began John hesitantly, "you're much more sophisticated than I thought you were when I first saw you?"

"Oh, no, I'm not," she exclaimed hurriedly. "Oh, I wouldn't think of being. I think that sophisticated young people are *terribly* common, don't you? I'm not at all, really. If you say I am, I'm going to cry."

She was so distressed that her lip was trembling. John was impelled to protest:

"I didn't mean that; I only said it to tease you."

"Because I wouldn't mind if I *were*," she persisted, "but I'm *not*. I'm very innocent and girlish. I never smoke, or drink, or read anything except poetry. I know scarcely any mathematics or chemistry. I dress *very* simply—in fact, I scarcely dress at all. I think sophisticated is the last thing you can say about me. I believe that girls ought to enjoy their youths in a wholesome way."

"I do too," said John heartily.

Kismine was cheerful again. She smiled at him, and a still-born tear dripped from the corner of one blue eye.

"I like you," she whispered, intimately. "Are you going to spend all your time with Percy while you're here, or will you be nice to me? Just think—I'm absolutely fresh ground. I've never had a boy in love with me in all my life. I've never been allowed even to *see* boys alone—except Percy. I came all the way out here into this grove hoping to run into you, where the family wouldn't be around."

Deeply flattered, John bowed from the hips as he had been taught at dancing school in Hades.

"We'd better go now," said Kismine sweetly. "I have to be with mother at eleven. You haven't asked me to kiss you once. I thought boys always did that nowadays."

John drew himself up proudly.

"Some of them do," he answered, "but not me. Girls don't do that sort of thing—in Hades."

Side by side they walked back toward the house.

VI

John stood facing Mr. Braddock Washington in the full sunlight. The elder man was about forty with a proud, vacuous face, intelligent eyes, and a robust figure. In the mornings he smelt of horses—the best horses. He carried a plain walking-stick of gray birch with a single large opal for a grip. He and Percy were showing John around.

"The slaves' quarters are there." His walking-stick indicated a cloister of marble on their left that ran in graceful Gothic along the side of the mountain. "In my youth I was distracted for a while from the business of life by a period of absurd idealism. During that time they lived in luxury. For instance, I equipped every one of their rooms with a tile bath."

"I suppose," ventured John, with an ingratiating laugh, "that they used the bathtubs to keep coal in. Mr. Schnlitzer-Murphy told me that once he——"

"The opinions of Mr. Schnlitzer-Murphy are of little importance, I should imagine," interrupted Braddock Washington, coldly. "My slaves did not keep coal in their bathtubs. They had orders to bathe every day, and they did. If they hadn't I might have ordered a sulphuric acid shampoo. I discontinued the baths for quite another reason. Several of them caught cold and died. Water is not good for certain races—except as a beverage."

John laughed, and then decided to nod his head in sober agreement. Braddock Washington made him uncomfortable.

"All these negroes are descendants of the ones my father brought North with him. There are about two hundred and fifty now. You notice that they've lived so long apart from the world that their original dialect has become an almost indistinguishable patois. We bring a few of them up to speak English—my secretary and two or three of the house servants.

"This is the golf course," he continued, as they strolled along the velvet winter grass. "It's all a green, you see—no fairway, no rough, no hazards."

He smiled pleasantly at John.

"Many men in the cage, father?" asked Percy suddenly.

Braddock Washington stumbled, and let forth an involuntary curse.

"One less than there should be," he ejaculated darkly—and then added after a moment, "We've had difficulties."

"Mother was telling me," exclaimed Percy, "that Italian teacher——"

"A ghastly error," said Braddock Washington angrily. "But of course there's a good chance that we may have got him. Perhaps he fell somewhere in the woods or stumbled over a cliff. And then there's always the probability that if he did get away his story wouldn't be believed. Nevertheless, I've had two dozen men looking for him in different towns around here."

"And no luck?"

"Some. Fourteen of them reported to my agent that they'd each killed a man answering to that description, but of course it was probably only the reward they were after——"

He broke off. They had come to a large cavity in the earth about the circumference of a merry-go-round and covered by a strong iron grating. Braddock Washington beckoned to John, and pointed his cane down through the grating. John stepped to the edge and gazed.

Immediately his ears were assailed by a wild clamor from below.

"Come on down to Hell!"

"Hello, kiddo, how's the air up there?"

"Hey! Throw us a rope!"

"Got an old doughnut, Buddy, or a couple of second-hand sandwiches?"

"Say, fella, if you'll push down that guy you're with, we'll show you a quick disappearance scene."

"Paste him one for me, will you?"

It was too dark to see clearly into the pit below, but John could tell from the coarse optimism and rugged vitality of the remarks and voices that they proceeded from middle-class Americans of the more spirited type. Then Mr. Washington put out his cane and touched a button in the grass, and the scene below sprang into light.

"These are some adventurous mariners who had the misfortune to discover El Dorado," he remarked.

Below them there had appeared a large hollow in the earth shaped like the interior of a bowl. The sides were steep and apparently of polished glass, and on its slightly concave surface stood about two dozen men clad in the half costume, half uniform, of aviators. Their upturned faces, lit with wrath, with malice, with despair, with cynical humor, were covered by long growths of beard, but with the exception of a few who had pined perceptibly away, they seemed to be a well-fed, healthy lot.

Braddock Washington drew a garden chair to the edge of the pit and sat down.

"Well, how are you, boys?" he inquired genially.

A chorus of execration in which all joined except a few too dispirited to cry out, rose up into the sunny air, but Braddock Washington heard it with unruffled composure. When its last echo had died away he spoke again.

"Have you thought up a way out of your difficulty?"

From here and there among them a remark floated up.

"We decided to stay here for love!"

"Bring us up there and we'll find us a way!"

Braddock Washington waited until they were again quiet. Then he said:

"I've told you the situation. I don't want you here. I wish to heaven I'd never seen you. Your own curiosity got you here, and any time that you can think of a way out which protects me and my interests I'll be glad to consider it. But so long as you confine your efforts to digging tunnels—yes. I know about the new one you've started—you won't get very far. This isn't as hard on you as you make it out, with all your howling for the loved ones at home. If you were the type who worried much about the loved ones at home, you'd never have taken up aviation."

A tall man moved apart from the others, and held up his hand to call his captor's attention to what he was about to say.

"Let me ask you a few questions!" he cried. "You pretend to be a fair-minded man."

"How absurd. How could a man of *my* position be fair-minded toward *you?* You might as well speak of a Spaniard being fair-minded toward a piece of steak."

At this harsh observation the faces of the two dozen steaks fell, but the tall man continued:

"All right!" he cried. "We've argued this out before. You're not a humanitarian and you're not fair-minded, but you're human—at least you say you are—and you ought to be able to put yourself in our place for long enough to think how—how—how——"

"How what?" demanded Washington, coldly.

"—how unnecessary——"

"Not to me."

"Well,—how cruel——"

"We've covered that. Cruelty doesn't exist where self-preservation is involved. You've been soldiers: you know that. Try another."

"Well, then, how stupid."

"There," admitted Washington, "I grant you that. But try to think of an alternative. I've offered to have all or any of you painlessly executed if you wish. I've offered to have your wives, sweethearts, children, and mothers kidnapped and brought out here. I'll enlarge your place down there and feed and clothe you the rest of your lives. If there was some method of producing permanent amnesia I'd have all of you operated on and released immediately, somewhere outside of my preserves. But that's as far as my ideas go."

"How about trusting us not to peach on you?" cried some one.

"You don't proffer that suggestion seriously," said Washington, with an expression of scorn. "I did take out one man to teach my daughter Italian. Last week he got away."

A wild yell of jubilation went up suddenly from two dozen

throats and a pandemonium of joy ensued. The prisoners clog-danced and cheered and yodled and wrestled with one another in a sudden uprush of animal spirits. They even ran up the glass sides of the bowl as far as they could, and slid back to the bottom upon the natural cushions of their bodies. The tall man started a song in which they all joined——

> *"Oh, we'll hang the kaiser*
> *On a sour apple tree——"*

Braddock Washington sat in inscrutable silence until the song was over.

"You see," he remarked, when he could gain a modicum of attention. "I bear you no ill-will. I like to see you enjoying yourselves. That's why I didn't tell you the whole story at once. The man—what was his name? Critchtichiello?—was shot by some of my agents in fourteen different places."

Not guessing that the places referred to were cities, the tumult of rejoicing subsided immediately.

"Nevertheless," cried Washington with a touch of anger, "he tried to run away. Do you expect me to take chances with any of you after an experience like that?"

Again a series of ejaculations went up.

"Sure!"

"Would your daughter like to learn Chinese?"

"Hey, I can speak Italian! My mother was a wop."

"Maybe she'd like t'learna speak N'Yawk!"

"If she's the little one with the big blue eyes I can teach her a lot of things better than Italian."

"I know some Irish songs—and I could hammer brass once't."

Mr. Washington reached forward suddenly with his cane and pushed the button in the grass so that the picture below went out instantly, and there remained only that great dark mouth covered dismally with the black teeth of the grating.

"Hey!" called a single voice from below, "you ain't goin' away without givin' us your blessing?"

But Mr. Washington, followed by the two boys, was already strolling on toward the ninth hole of the golf course, as though the pit and its contents were no more than a hazard over which his facile iron had triumphed with ease.

VII

July under the lee of the diamond mountain was a month of blanket nights and of warm, glowing days. John and Kismine were in love. He did not know that the little gold football (inscribed with the legend *Pro deo et patria et St. Mida*) which he had given her rested on a platinum chain next to her bosom. But it did. And she for her part was not aware that a large sapphire which had dropped one day from her simple coiffure was stowed away tenderly in John's jewel box.

Late one afternoon when the ruby and ermine music room was quiet, they spent an hour there together. He held her hand and she gave him such a look that he whispered her name aloud. She bent toward him—then hesitated.

"Did you say 'Kismine'?" she asked softly, "or——"

She had wanted to be sure. She thought she might have misunderstood.

Neither of them had ever kissed before, but in the course of an hour it seemed to make little difference.

The afternoon drifted away. That night when a last breath of music drifted down from the highest tower, they each lay awake, happily dreaming over the separate minutes of the day. They had decided to be married as soon as possible.

VIII

Every day Mr. Washington and the two young men went hunting or fishing in the deep forests or played golf around the somnolent course—games which John diplomatically allowed his host to win—or swam in the mountain coolness of the lake. John found Mr. Washington a somewhat exacting personality—utterly uninterested in any ideas or opinions except his own. Mrs. Washington was aloof and reserved at all times. She was apparently indifferent to her two daughters, and entirely absorbed in her son Percy, with whom she held interminable conversations in rapid Spanish at dinner.

Jasmine, the elder daughter, resembled Kismine in appearance —except that she was somewhat bow-legged, and terminated in large hands and feet—but was utterly unlike her in temperament. Her favorite books had to do with poor girls who kept house for widowed fathers. John learned from Kismine that Jasmine had never recovered from the shock and disappointment caused her by the termination of the World War, just as she was about to start for Europe as a canteen expert. She had even pined away for a time, and Braddock Washington had taken steps to promote a new war in the Balkans—but she had seen a photograph of some wounded Serbian soldiers and lost interest in the whole proceedings. But Percy and Kismine seemed to have inherited the arrogant attitude in all its harsh magnificence from their father. A chaste and consistent selfishness ran like a pattern through their every idea.

John was enchanted by the wonders of the château and the valley. Braddock Washington, so Percy told him, had caused to be kidnapped a landscape gardener, an architect, a designer of state settings, and a French decadent poet left over from the last century. He had put his entire force of negroes at their disposal, guaranteed to supply them with any materials that the world could offer, and left them to work out some ideas of their own. But one by one they had shown their uselessness. The decadent poet had at once begun bewailing his separation from the boulevards in spring—he made some vague remarks about spices, apes, and ivories, but said nothing that was of any practical value. The stage designer on his part wanted to make the whole valley a series of tricks and sensational effects—a state of things that the Washingtons would soon have grown tired of. And as for the architect and the landscape gardener, they thought only in terms of convention. They must make this like this and that like that.

But they had, at least, solved the problem of what was to be done with them—they all went mad early one morning after spending the night in a single room trying to agree upon the location of a fountain, and were now confined comfortably in an insane asylum at Westport, Connecticut.

"But," inquired John curiously, "who did plan all your wonderful reception rooms and halls, and approaches and bathrooms——?"

"Well," answered Percy, "I blush to tell you, but it was a moving-picture fella. He was the only man we found who was used to playing with an unlimited amount of money, though he did tuck his napkin in his collar and couldn't read or write."

As August drew to a close John began to regret that he must soon go back to school. He and Kismine had decided to elope the following June.

"It would be nicer to be married here," Kismine confessed, "but of course I could never get father's permission to marry you at all. Next to that I'd rather elope. It's terrible for wealthy people to be married in America at present—they always have to send out bulletins to the press saying that they're going to be married in remnants, when what they mean is just a peck of old second-hand pearls and some used lace worn once by the Empress Eugénie."

"I know," agreed John fervently. "When I was visiting the Schnlitzer-Murphys, the eldest daughter, Gwendolyn, married a man whose father owns half of West Virginia. She wrote home saying what a tough struggle she was carrying on on his salary as a bank clerk—and then she ended up by saying that 'Thank God, I have four good maids anyhow, and that helps a little.'"

"It's absurd," commented Kismine. "Think of the millions and millions of people in the world, laborers and all, who get along with only two maids."

One afternoon late in August a chance remark of Kismine's changed the face of the entire situation, and threw John into a state of terror.

They were in their favorite grove, and between kisses John was indulging in some romantic forebodings which he fancied added poignancy to their relations.

"Sometimes I think we'll never marry," he said sadly. "You're too wealthy, too magnificent. No one as rich as you are can be like other girls. I should marry the daughter of some well-to-do wholesale hardware man from Omaha or Sioux City, and be content with her half-million."

"I knew the daughter of a wholesale hardware man once," remarked Kismine. "I don't think you'd have been contented with her. She was a friend of my sister's. She visited here."

"Oh, then you've had other guests?" exclaimed John in surprise.

Kismine seemed to regret her words.

"Oh, yes," she said hurriedly, "we've had a few."

"But aren't you—wasn't your father afraid they'd talk outside?"

"Oh, to some extent, to some extent," she answered. "Let's talk about something pleasanter."

But John's curiosity was aroused.

"Something pleasanter!" he demanded. "What's unpleasant about that? Weren't they nice girls?"

To his great surprise Kismine began to weep.

"Yes—th—that's the—the whole t-trouble. I grew qu-quite attached to some of them. So did Jasmine, but she kept inv-viting them anyway. I couldn't under*stand* it."

A dark suspicion was born in John's heart.

"Do you mean that they *told,* and your father had them—removed?"

"Worse than that," she muttered brokenly. "Father took no chances—and Jasmine kept writing them to come, and they had *such* a good time!"

She was overcome by a paroxysm of grief.

Stunned with the horror of this revelation, John sat there openmouthed, feeling the nerves of his body twitter like so many sparrows perched upon his spinal column.

"Now, I've told you, and I shouldn't have," she said, calming suddenly and drying her dark blue eyes.

"Do you mean to say that your father had them *murdered* before they left?"

She nodded.

"In August usually—or early in September. It's only natural for us to get all the pleasure out of them that we can first."

"How abominable! How—why, I must be going crazy! Did you really admit that——"

"I did," interrupted Kismine, shrugging her shoulders. "We can't very well imprison them like those aviators, where they'd be a continual reproach to us every day. And it's always been made easier for Jasmine and me, because father had it done sooner than we expected. In that way we avoided any farewell scene——"

"So you murdered them! Uh!" cried John.

"It was done very nicely. They were drugged while they were asleep—and their families were always told that they died of scarlet fever in Butte."

"But—I fail to understand why you kept on inviting them!"

"I didn't," burst out Kismine. "I never invited one. Jasmine did. And they always had a very good time. She'd give them the nicest presents towards the last. I shall probably have visitors too—I'll harden up to it. We can't let such an inevitable thing as death stand in the way of enjoying life while we have it. Think how lonesome it'd be out here if we never had *any* one. Why, father and mother have sacrificed some of their best friends just as we have."

"And so," cried John accusingly, "and so you were letting me make love to you and pretending to return it, and talking about marriage, all the time knowing perfectly well that I'd never get out of here alive——"

"No," she protested passionately. "Not any more. I did at first. You were here. I couldn't help that, and I thought your last days might as well be pleasant for both of us. But then I fell in love with you, and—and I'm honestly sorry you're going to—going to be put away—though I'd rather you'd be put away than ever kiss another girl."

"Oh, you would, would you?" cried John ferociously.

"Much rather. Besides, I've always heard that a girl can have more fun with a man whom she knows she can never marry. Oh, why did I tell you? I've probably spoiled your whole good time now, and we were really enjoying things when you didn't know it. I knew it would make things sort of depressing for you."

"Oh, you did, did you?" John's voice trembled with anger. "I've heard about enough of this. If you haven't any more pride and decency than to have an affair with a fellow that you know isn't much better than a corpse, I don't want to have any more to do with you!"

"You're not a corpse!" she protested in horror. "You're not a corpse! I won't have you saying that I kissed a corpse!"

"I said nothing of the sort!"

"You did! You said I kissed a corpse!"

"I didn't!"

Their voices had risen, but upon a sudden interruption they both subsided into immediate silence. Footsteps were coming along the path in their direction, and a moment later the rose bushes were parted displaying Braddock Washington, whose intelligent eyes set in his good-looking vacuous face were peering in at them.

"Who kissed a corpse?" he demanded in obvious disapproval.

"Nobody," answered Kismine quickly. "We were just joking."

"What are you two doing here, anyhow?" he demanded gruffly. "Kismine, you ought to be—to be reading or playing golf with your sister. Go read! Go play golf! Don't let me find you here when I come back!"

Then he bowed at John and went up the path.

"See?" said Kismine crossly, when he was out of hearing.

"You've spoiled it all. We can never meet any more. He won't let me meet you. He'd have you poisoned if he thought we were in love."

"We're not, any more!" cried John fiercely, "so he can set his mind at rest upon that. Moreover, don't fool yourself that I'm going to stay around here. Inside of six hours I'll be over those mountains, if I have to gnaw a passage through them, and on my way East."

They had both got to their feet, and at this remark Kismine came close and put her arm through his.

"I'm going, too."

"You must be crazy——"

"Of course I'm going," she interrupted impatiently.

"You most certainly are not. You——"

"Very well," she said quietly, "we'll catch up with father now and talk it over with him."

Defeated, John mustered a sickly smile.

"Very well, dearest," he agreed, with pale and unconvincing affection, "we'll go together."

His love for her returned and settled placidly on his heart. She was his—she would go with him to share his dangers. He put his arms about her and kissed her fervently. After all she loved him; she had saved him, in fact.

Discussing the matter, they walked slowly back toward the château. They decided that since Braddock Washington had seen them together they had best depart the next night. Nevertheless, John's lips were unusually dry at dinner, and he nervously emptied a great spoonful of peacock soup into his left lung. He had to be carried into the turquoise and sable card-room and pounded on the back by one of the under-butlers, which Percy considered a great joke.

IX

Long after midnight John's body gave a nervous jerk, and he sat suddenly upright, staring into the veils of somnolence that draped the room. Through the squares of blue darkness that were his open windows, he had heard a faint far-away sound that died upon a bed of wind before identifying itself on his memory, clouded with uneasy dreams. But the sharp noise that had succeeded it was nearer, was just outside the room—the click of a turned knob, a footstep, a whisper, he could not tell; a hard lump gathered in the pit of his stomach, and his whole body ached in the moment that he strained agonizingly to hear. Then one of the veils seemed to dissolve, and he saw a vague figure standing by the door, a figure only faintly limned and blocked in upon the darkness, mingled so with the folds of the drapery as to seem distorted, like a reflection seen in a dirty pane of glass.

With a sudden movement of fright or resolution John pressed the button by his bedside, and the next moment he was sitting in the green sunken bath of the adjoining room, waked into alertness by the shock of the cold water which half filled it.

He sprang out, and, his wet pajamas scattering a heavy trickle of water behind him, ran for the aquamarine door which he knew led out onto the ivory landing of the second floor. The door opened noiselessly. A single crimson lamp burning in a great dome above lit the magnificent sweep of the carved stairways with a poignant beauty. For a moment John hesitated, appalled by the silent splendor massed about him, seeming to envelop in its gigantic folds and contours the solitary drenched little figure shivering upon the ivory landing. Then simultaneously two things happened. The door of his own sitting-room swung open, precipitating three naked negroes into the hall—and, as John swayed in wild terror toward the stairway, another door slid back in the wall on the other side of the corridor, and John saw Braddock Washington standing in the lighted lift, wearing a fur coat and a pair of riding boots which reached to his knees and displayed, above, the glow of his rose-colored pajamas.

On the instant the three negroes—John had never seen any of them before, and it flashed through his mind that they must be the professional executioners—paused in their movement toward John, and turned expectantly to the man in the lift, who burst out with an imperious command:

"Get in here! All three of you! Quick as hell!"

Then, within the instant, the three negroes darted into the cage, the oblong of light was blotted out as the lift door slid shut, and John was again alone in the hall. He slumped weakly down against an ivory stair.

It was apparent that something portentous had occurred, something which, for the moment at least, had postponed his own petty disaster. What was it? Had the negroes risen in revolt? Had the aviators forced aside the iron bars of the grating? Or had the men of Fish stumbled blindly through the hills and gazed with bleak, joyless eyes upon the gaudy valley? John did not know. He heard a faint whir of air as the lift whizzed up again, and then, a moment later, as it descended. It was probable that Percy was hurrying to his father's assistance, and it occurred to John that this was his opportunity to join Kismine and plan an immediate escape. He waited until the lift had been silent for several minutes; shivering a little with the night cool that whipped in through his wet pajamas, he returned to his room and dressed himself quickly. Then he mounted a long flight of stairs and turned down the corridor carpeted with Russian sable which led to Kismine's suite.

The door of her sitting-room was open and the lamps were lighted. Kismine, in an angora kimono, stood near the window of the room in a listening attitude, and as John entered noiselessly, she turned toward him.

"Oh, it's you!" she whispered, crossing the room to him. "Did you hear them?"

"I heard your father's slaves in my——"

"No," she interrupted excitedly. "Aeroplanes!"

"Aeroplanes? Perhaps that was the sound that woke me."

"There're at least a dozen. I saw one a few moments ago dead against the moon. The guard back by the cliff fired his rifle and that's what roused father. We're going to open on them right away."

"Are they here on purpose?"

"Yes—it's that Italian who got away——"

Simultaneously with her last word, a succession of sharp cracks tumbled in through the open window. Kismine uttered a little cry, took a penny with fumbling fingers from a box on her dresser, and ran to one of the electric lights. In an instant the entire château was in darkness—she had blown out the fuse.

"Come on!" she cried to him. "We'll go up to the roof garden, and watch it from there!"

Drawing a cape about her, she took his hand, and they found their way out the door. It was only a step to the tower lift, and as she pressed the button that shot them upward he put his arms around her in the darkness and kissed her mouth. Romance had come to John Unger at last. A minute later they had stepped out upon the star-white platform. Above, under the misty moon, sliding in and out of the patches of cloud that eddied below it, floated a dozen dark-winged bodies in a constant circling course. From here and there in the valley flashes of fire leaped toward them, followed by sharp detonations. Kismine clapped her hands with pleasure, which a moment later, turned to dismay as the aeroplanes at some prearranged signal, began to release their bombs and the whole of the valley became a panorama of deep reverberate sound and lurid light.

Before long the aim of the attackers became concentrated upon the points where the anti-aircraft guns were situated, and one of them was almost immediately reduced to a giant cinder to lie smouldering in a park of rose bushes.

"Kismine," begged John, "you'll be glad when I tell you that this attack came on the eve of my murder. If I hadn't heard that guard shoot off his gun back by the pass I should now be stone dead——"

"I can't hear you!" cried Kismine, intent on the scene before her. "You'll have to talk louder!"

"I simply said," shouted John, "that we'd better get out before they begin to shell the château!"

Suddenly the whole portico of the negro quarters cracked asunder, a geyser of flame shot up from under the colonnades, and great fragments of jagged marble were hurled as far as the borders of the lake.

"There go fifty thousand dollars' worth of slaves," cried Kismine, "at prewar prices. So few Americans have any respect for property."

John renewed his efforts to compel her to leave. The aim of the aeroplanes was becoming more precise minute by minute, and only two of the anti-aircraft guns were still retaliating. It was obvious that the garrison, encircled with fire, could not hold out much longer.

"Come on!" cried John, pulling Kismine's arm, "we've got to go. Do you realize that those aviators will kill you without question if they find you?"

She consented reluctantly.

"We'll have to wake Jasmine!" she said, as they hurried toward the lift. Then she added in a sort of childish delight: "We'll be poor, won't we? Like people in books. And I'll be an orphan and utterly free. Free and poor! What fun!" She stopped and raised her lips to him in a delighted kiss.

"It's impossible to be both together," said John grimly. "People have found that out. And I should choose to be free as preferable of the two. As an extra caution you'd better dump the contents of your jewel box into your pockets."

Ten minutes later the two girls met John in the dark corridor and they descended to the main floor of the château. Passing for the last time through the magnificence of the splendid halls, they stood for a moment out on the terrace, watching the burning negro quarters and the flaming embers of two planes which had fallen on the other side of the lake. A solitary gun was still keeping up a sturdy popping, and the attackers seemed timorous about descending lower, but sent their thunderous fireworks in a circle around it, until any chance shot might annihilate its Ethiopian crew.

John and the two sisters passed down the marble steps, turned sharply to the left, and began to ascend a narrow path that wound like a garter about the diamond mountain. Kismine knew a heavily wooded spot half-way up where they could lie concealed and yet be able to observe the wild night in the valley—finally to make an escape, when it should be necessary, along a secret path laid in a rocky gully.

X

It was three o'clock when they attained their destination. The obliging and phlegmatic Jasmine fell off to sleep immediately, leaning against the trunk of a large tree, while John and Kismine sat, his arm around her, and watched the desperate ebb and flow of the dying battle among the ruins of a vista that had been a garden spot that morning. Shortly after four o'clock the last remaining gun gave out a clanging sound and went out of action in a swift tongue of red smoke. Though the moon was down, they saw that the flying bodies were circling closer to the earth. When the planes had made certain that the beleaguered possessed no further resources, they would land and the dark and glittering reign of the Washingtons would be over.

With the cessation of the firing the valley grew quiet. The embers of the two aeroplanes glowed like the eyes of some monster crouching in the grass. The château stood dark and silent, beautiful without light as it had been beautiful in the sun, while the woody rattles of Nemesis filled the air above with a growing and receding complaint. Then John perceived that Kismine, like her sister, had fallen sound asleep.

It was long after four when he became aware of footsteps along the path they had lately followed, and he waited in breathless silence until the persons to whom they belonged had passed the vantage-point he occupied. There was a faint stir in the air now that was not of human origin, and the dew was cold; he knew that the dawn would break soon. John waited until the steps had gone a safe distance up the mountain and were inaudible. Then he followed. About half-way to the steep summit the trees fell away and a hard saddle of rock spread itself over the diamond beneath. Just before he reached this point he slowed down his pace, warned by an animal sense that there was life just ahead of him. Coming to a high boulder, he lifted his head gradually above its edge. His curiosity was rewarded; this is what he saw:

Braddock Washington was standing there motionless, silhouetted against the gray sky without sound or sign of life. As the dawn came up out of the east, lending a cold green color to the earth, it brought the solitary figure into insignificant contrast with the new day.

While John watched, his host remained for a few moments absorbed in some inscrutable contemplation; then he signalled to the two negroes who crouched at his feet to lift the burden which lay between them. As they struggled upright, the first yellow beam of the sun struck through the innumerable prisms of an immense and exquisitely chiselled diamond—and a white radiance was kindled that glowed upon the air like a fragment of the morning star. The bearers staggered beneath its weight for a moment—then their rippling muscles caught and hardened under the wet shine of the skins and the three figures were again motionless in their defiant impotency before the heavens.

After a while the white man lifted his head and slowly raised his arms in a gesture of attention, as one who would call a great crowd to hear—but there was no crowd, only the vast silence of the mountain and the sky, broken by faint bird voices down among the trees. The figure on the saddle of rock began to speak ponderously and with an inextinguishable pride.

"You out there—" he cried in a trembling voice. "You—there—!" He paused, his arms still uplifted, his head held attentively as though he were expecting an answer. John strained his eyes to see whether there might be men coming down the mountain, but the mountain was bare of human life. There was only sky and a mocking flute of wind along the tree-tops. Could Washington be praying? For a moment John wondered. Then the illusion passed —there was something in the man's whole attitude antithetical to prayer.

"Oh, you above there!"

The voice was become strong and confident. This was no forlorn supplication. If anything, there was in it a quality of monstrous condescension.

"You there———"

Words, too quickly uttered to be understood, flowing one into the other. . . . John listened breathlessly, catching a phrase here and there, while the voice broke off, resumed, broke off again—now strong and argumentative, now colored with a slow, puzzled impatience. Then a conviction commenced to dawn on the single listener, and as realization crept over him a spray of quick blood rushed through his arteries. Braddock Washington was offering a bribe to God!

That was it—there was no doubt. The diamond in the arms of his slaves was some advance sample, a promise of more to follow.

That, John perceived after a time, was the thread running through his sentences. Prometheus Enriched was calling to witness forgotten sacrifices, forgotten rituals, prayers obsolete before the birth of Christ. For a while his discourse took the form of reminding God of this gift or that which Divinity had deigned to accept from men—great churches if he would rescue cities from the plague, gifts of myrrh and gold, of human lives and beautiful women and captive armies, of children and queens, of beasts of the forest and field, sheep and goats, harvests and cities, whole conquered lands that had been offered up in lust or blood for His appeasal, buying a need's worth of alleviation from the Divine wrath—and now he, Braddock Washington, Emperor of Diamonds, king and priest of the age of gold, arbiter of splendor and luxury, would offer up a treasure such as princes before him had never dreamed of, offer it up not in suppliance but in pride.

He would give to God, he continued, getting down to specifications, the greatest diamond in the world. This diamond would be cut with many more thousand facets than there were leaves on a tree, and yet the whole diamond would be shaped with the perfection of a stone no bigger than a fly. Many men would work upon it for many years. It would be set in a great dome of beaten gold, wonderfully carved and equipped with gates of opal and crusted sapphire.

In the middle would be hollowed out a chapel presided over by an altar of iridescent, decomposing, ever-changing radium which would burn out the eyes of any worshipper who lifted up his head from prayer—and on this altar there would be slain for the amusement of the Divine Benefactor any victim He should choose, even though it should be the greatest and most powerful man alive.

In return he asked only a simple thing, a thing that for God would be absurdly easy—only that matters should be as they were yesterday at this hour and that they should so remain. So very simple! Let but the heavens open, swallowing these men and their aeroplanes—and then close again. Let him have his slaves once more, restored to life and well.

There was no one else with whom he had ever needed to treat or bargain.

He doubted only whether he had made his bribe big enough. God had His price, of course. God was made in man's image, so it had been said: He must have His price. And the price would be rare—no cathedral whose building consumed many years, no pyramid constructed by ten thousand workmen, would be like this cathedral, this pyramid.

He paused here. That was his proposition. Everything would be up to specifications and there was nothing vulgar in his assertion that it would be cheap at the price. He implied that Providence could take it or leave it.

As he approached the end his sentences became broken, became short and uncertain, and his body seemed tense, seemed strained to catch the slightest pressure or whisper of life in the spaces around him. His hair had turned gradually white as he talked, and now he lifted his head high to the heavens like a prophet of old—magnificently mad.

Then, as John stared in giddy fascination, it seemed to him that a curious phenomenon took place somewhere around him. It was as though the sky had darkened for an instant, as though there had been a sudden murmur in a gust of wind, a sound of far-away trumpets, a sighing like the rustle of a great silken robe—for a time the whole of nature round about partook of this darkness: the birds' song ceased; the trees were still, and far over the mountain there was a mutter of dull, menacing thunder.

That was all. The wind died along the tall grasses of the valley. The dawn and the day resumed their place in a time, and the risen

sun sent hot waves of yellow mist that made its path bright before
it. The leaves laughed in the sun, and their laughter shook the trees
until each bough was like a girl's school in fairyland. God had refused to accept the bribe.

For another moment John watched the triumph of the day.
Then, turning, he saw a flutter of brown down by the lake, then another flutter, then another, like the dance of golden angels alighting from the clouds. The aeroplanes had come to earth.

John slid off the boulder and ran down the side of the mountain
to the clump of trees, where the two girls were awake and waiting
for him. Kismine sprang to her feet, the jewels in her pockets jingling, a question on her parted lips, but instinct told John that there
was no time for words. They must get off the mountain without losing a moment. He seized a hand of each, and in silence they threaded
the tree-trunks, washed with light now and with the rising mist. Behind them from the valley came no sound at all, except the complaint
of the peacocks far away and the pleasant undertone of morning.

When they had gone about half a mile, they avoided the park
land and entered a narrow path that led over the next rise of ground.
At the highest point of this they paused and turned around. Their
eyes rested upon the mountainside they had just left—oppressed
by some dark sense of tragic impendency.

Clear against the sky a broken, white-haired man was slowly
descending the steep slope, followed by two gigantic and emotionless
negroes, who carried a burden between them which still flashed and
glittered in the sun. Half-way down two other figures joined them—
John could see that they were Mrs. Washington and her son, upon
whose arm she leaned. The aviators had clambered from their machines to the sweeping lawn in front of the château, and with rifles
in hand were starting up the diamond mountain in skirmishing
formation.

But the little group of five which had formed farther up and was
engrossing all the watchers' attention had stopped upon a ledge of
rock. The negroes stooped and pulled up what appeared to be a trap-
door in the side of the mountain. Into this they all disappeared, the
white-haired man first, then his wife and son, finally the two negroes,
the glittering tips of whose jeweled head-dresses caught the sun for
a moment before the trap-door descended and engulfed them all.

Kismine clutched John's arm.

"Oh," she cried wildly, "where are they going? What are they going to do?"

"It must be some underground way of escape——"

A little scream from the two girls interrupted his sentence.

"Don't you see?" sobbed Kismine hysterically. "The mountain is wired!"

Even as she spoke John put up his hands to shield his sight. Before their eyes the whole surface of the mountain had changed suddenly to a dazzling burning yellow, which showed up through the jacket of turf as light shows through a human hand. For a moment the intolerable glow continued, and then like an extinguished filament it disappeared, revealing a black waste from which blue smoke arose slowly, carrying off with it what remained of vegetation and of human flesh. Of the aviators there was left neither blood nor bone— they were consumed as completely as the five souls who had gone inside.

Simultaneously, and with an immense concussion, the château literally threw itself into the air, bursting into flaming fragments as it rose, and then tumbling back upon itself in a smoking pile that lay projecting half into the water of the lake. There was no fire—what smoke there was drifted off mingling with the sunshine, and for a few minutes longer a powdery dust of marble drifted from the great featureless pile that had once been the house of jewels. There was no more sound and the three people were alone in the valley.

XI

At sunset John and his two companions reached the high cliff which had marked the boundaries of the Washingtons' dominion, and looking back found the valley tranquil and lovely in the dusk. They sat down to finish the food which Jasmine had brought with her in a basket.

"There!" she said, as she spread the table-cloth and put the sandwiches in a neat pile upon it. "Don't they look tempting? I always think that food tastes better outdoors."

"With that remark," remarked Kismine, "Jasmine enters the middle class."

"Now," said John eagerly, "turn out your pocket and let's see what jewels you brought along. If you made a good selection we three ought to live comfortably all the rest of our lives."

Obediently Kismine put her hand in her pocket and tossed two handfuls of glittering stones before him.

"Not so bad," cried John, enthusiastically. "They aren't very big, but—Hello!" His expression changed as he held one of them up to the declining sun. "Why, these aren't diamonds! There's something the matter!"

"By golly!" exclaimed Kismine, with a startled look. "What an idiot I am!"

"Why, these are rhinestones!" cried John.

"I know." She broke into a laugh. "I opened the wrong drawer. They belonged on the dress of a girl who visited Jasmine. I got her to give them to me in exchange for diamonds. I'd never seen anything but precious stones before."

"And this is what you brought?"

"I'm afraid so." She fingered the brilliants wistfully. "I think I like these better. I'm a little tired of diamonds."

"Very well," said John gloomily. "We'll have to live in Hades. And you will grow old telling incredulous women that you got the wrong drawer. Unfortunately your father's bank-books were consumed with him."

"Well, what's the matter with Hades?"

"If I come home with a wife at my age my father is just as liable as not to cut me off with a hot coal, as they say down there."

Jasmine spoke up.

"I love washing," she said quietly. "I have always washed my own handkerchiefs. I'll take in laundry and support you both."

"Do they have washwomen in Hades?" asked Kismine innocently.

"Of course," answered John. "It's just like anywhere else."

"I thought—perhaps it was too hot to wear any clothes."

John laughed.

"Just try it!" he suggested. "They'll run you out before you're half started."

"Will father be there?" she asked.

John turned to her in astonishment.

"Your father is dead," he replied somberly. "Why should he go to Hades? You have it confused with another place that was abolished long ago."

After supper they folded up the table-cloth and spread their blankets for the night.

"What a dream it was," Kismine sighed, gazing up at the stars. "How strange it seems to be here with one dress and a penniless fiancé!

"Under the stars," she repeated. "I never noticed the stars before. I always thought of them as great big diamonds that belonged to some one. Now they frighten me. They make me feel that it was all a dream, all my youth."

"It *was* a dream," said John quietly. "Everybody's youth is a dream, a form of chemical madness."

"How pleasant then to be insane!"

"So I'm told," said John gloomily. "I don't know any longer. At any rate, let us love for a while, for a year or so, you and me. That's a form of divine drunkenness that we can all try. There are only diamonds in the whole world, diamonds and perhaps the shabby gift of disillusion. Well, I have that last and I will make the usual nothing of it." He shivered. "Turn up your coat collar, little girl, the night's full of chill and you'll get pneumonia. His was a great sin who first invented consciousness. Let us lose it for a few hours."

So wrapping himself in his blanket he fell off to sleep.

QUESTIONS

One of the first impressions we receive is that this story is simply an excuse for a series of bad puns in a Mark Twain vein. We suspect the worst as soon as we are told that the protagonist comes from a town called Hades, and our fears seem realized when we learn that "John's father had held the amateur golf championship through many a heated contest," that his mother was known "'from hot-box to hot-bed,'" and that on his departure John received linen (i.e., cool) suits and electric fans, as well as an asbestos pocket-book. Perhaps the nadir of comedy is reached with the father's emotional promise to his son that they will "'keep the home fires burning.'"

The fantastic plot that develops does little to alter this impression. The story seems obviously designed to entertain us, and that's all. There is a hidden kingdom built around a diamond literally the size of a mountain; the Washington family is descended from both American and English aristocracy of Revolutionary times. In other words, we find combined the glamour of history with the wonders of the Arabian Nights (it is no accident that one of the daughters is named Kismine). As the lord of this principality, Braddock Washington sums up all the romance explicit in action and setting.

But there is more, much more, to this story than just the element of fantasy:

1. There is, for example, a concern with wealth which extends beyond the normal day-dreams that all of us have. The desire for wealth seems both constant and universal; we find it in Hades on the Mississippi, in New England, and in Montana (the West). John is sent to St. Midas' School, where he hob-nobs with the rich and remarks to Percy Washington, " 'The richer a fella is, the better I like him.' " This theme of wealth dominates the narrative. Elaborate on this theme. What is Fitzgerald saying about wealth? One of the ways that this theme is communicated is through atmosphere. When the two boys reach Montana, the "sunset lay between two mountains like a gigantic bruise from which dark arteries spread themselves over a poisoned sky." What effect is intended by this atmosphere? What is this scene's relationship to the theme of wealth? In this setting lies the tiny village of Fish, "minute, dismal, and forgotten." In it there are twelve men, "twelve sombre and inexplicable souls." These men are "beyond all religion—the barest and most savage tenets of even Christianity could gain no foothold on that barren rock—so there was no altar, no priest, no sacrifice; only each night at seven the silent concourse by the shanty depot, a congregation who lifted up a prayer of dim, anæmic wonder" to the Great Brakeman of the Transcontinental Express. Who are these twelve men? What comment is Fitzgerald making through them?

2. "The Diamond as Big as the Ritz" is, then, a symbolic fantasy intended as satire. What is Fitzgerald satirizing? One of the characteristics of satire is that the grotesque and absurd is offered in a straight-faced fashion, as though there were nothing fantastic about it. What are other characteristics of satire? Are there, for example, moral norms which are implied? If so, what are these moral norms in Fitzgerald's story? What are the aims of satire?

3. The idea that wealth and power can satisfy all of man's needs is an ancient one, although we tend to think of it as peculiarly American. What specific forms do wealth and power take in "The Diamond as Big as the Ritz"? At the end, John suggests that they at least permit us to maintain an illusion of reality, and he adds that the events are also a kind of allegory of youth. Elaborate on what he means when he says, " 'Everybody's youth is a dream, a form of chemical madness.' " Examine the conclusion carefully. Is it unsatisfactory in any way?

LUIGI PIRANDELLO

(1867-1936)

Pirandello was largely ignored during the early stages of his career. He became known partly through the efforts of James Joyce, who was responsible for the discovery of Italo Svevo also. Originally established as a short story writer and novelist, Pirandello in his own lifetime became one of the most famous dramatists in the Western world, receiving the Nobel Prize for Literature in 1934. Among his best known plays are SIX CHARACTERS IN SEARCH OF AN AUTHOR and HENRY IV, studies of the world of illusion in which man pursues his uncertain destiny. His short stories reflect Pirandello the dramatist through their emphasis upon dialogue and dramatic scenes. They often contain the same themes found in his plays: the conflict between individual and cosmos, the problem of communication, multiplicity of personality, and the conflict between the dynamic nature of life and the fixed forms into which life is forced. All of these themes are overshadowed by the grim reality of death which determines the ultimate destiny of all.

In the Abyss

At the Rackets Club they talked of nothing else the whole evening.

The first man to give them the news was Respi—Nicolino Respi—who was terribly grieved by it. As usual, however, despite the emotion he felt, he was quite unable to prevent his lips from curling in that nervous little smile which—even in the most serious discussions and in the most difficult moments of play—made his small,

"In the Abyss" Reprinted from *Short Stories,* translated by Frederick May, © Luigi Pirandello, 1965.

pale, jaundiced face, with its sharp features, so completely and so characteristically *his.*

His friends clustered around him in consternation.

"Has he *really* gone out of his mind?"

"Oh, no! Only for a joke."

Traldi, who was buried deep in the settee, with the entire weight of his enormous pachydermatous body driving him farther in, gave a series of heaves in an attempt to prop himself into a more upright position. The effort made his bovine bloodshot eyes open wide and pop out of their sockets. He asked, "Forgive the question, old man, but have you . . . *Oooh! Oooh!* Have you—I mean, did he give *you* that look, too?"

"Did he . . . ? Give *me* . . . that . . . look? What do you mean?" asked Nicolino Respi in return, utterly astonished, and turning questioningly to his friends. "I arrived only this morning from Milan, to find this wonderful item of news waiting for me. I don't know a thing. I still can't understand how it is that Romeo Daddi —My God, Romeo Daddi of *all* people! The most even-tempered, serene, level-headed one of the lot of us . . . !"

"Have they locked him up?"

"Of course they have! Didn't I say so? Three o'clock this afternoon. In the Monte Mario Asylum!"

"Poor Daddi!"

"How's Donna Bicetta taking it? But, how on——! Did *she* . . . ? I mean, was it Donna Bicetta who sent for them?"

"No, of course it wasn't! No, as a matter of fact, *she* wouldn't hear of it! No, her father dashed down from Florence the day before yesterday."

"Oh, so that's why . . . !"

"Precisely. He made her take the decision, to—— For *his* sake as well. But tell me how it all happened. Traldi, why did you ask me whether Daddi'd given *me* that look as well?"

Carlo Traldi had blissfully buried himself again in the settee with his head thrown back, and his purple, sweaty double-chin exposed to full view. Wriggling his little slender frog's legs, which his exorbitantly huge belly forced him perpetually to keep obscenely apart, and continually and no less obscenely moistening his lips, he replied abstractedly, "Oh yes, so I did. Because I thought that *that* was why you said he'd gone mad."

"What do you mean, *that* was why?"

"Why, of course! That's how his madness revealed itself to him. He looked at everybody in a particular way, my dear fellow. Oh, don't make me talk, you chaps, *you* tell him how poor Daddi looked."

Whereupon his friends told Nicolino Respi that Daddi, after he'd got back from his holiday in the country, had appeared to all of them like someone completely dazed. It was as if he were somehow *outside* himself. He'd look at you with an empty smile on his lips, his eyes dull and glazed. He wasn't *really* looking at you, as was obvious when anyone called him. Then that astounded look had disappeared and been transformed into an acute and strange kind of staring. First of all, he'd stared at things from a distance, obliquely. Then, gradually, as if attracted by certain signs which he thought he could observe in one or other of his most intimate friends—especially in those who most assiduously frequented his house—highly *natural* signs, for everyone was thrown into a state of utter consternation by that sudden and extraordinary change. It was so completely in contrast with the usual serenity of his character. Gradually, he'd come to watch them attentively from close to, and in the last days he'd become downright unbearable. He'd suddenly plonk himself in front of now one, now another of them, place his hands on the man's shoulders, look into his eyes—deep, deep down into them he'd look.

"God Almighty, it gave you the shudders!" Traldi exclaimed at that point, dragging himself up again, in an attempt to get his body into a slightly more upright position.

"But—— Why?" asked Respi, nervously.

"Listen to what I'm going to tell you, if you want to know why!" Traldi exclaimed in reply. "Ugh! So you want to know why we all got the shudders, do you? My dear fellow, I'd like to have seen *you* getting to grips with that look of his! I suppose you change your shirt every day. You're quite sure your feet are clean, and that your socks haven't got holes in them. But are you quite sure you haven't got anything mucky inside, on your conscience, down in your subconscious?"

"Oh, my God, I'd say——"

"Bunkum! You're not being honest with yourself!"

"And you are?"

"Yes, I am! That's one thing I am sure about! And believe me, it happens to all of us. We all discover, in some lucid interval, that, to a greater or lesser degree, we're swine! Almost every night—for quite some time now—when I put out the candle, before dropping off to sleep . . ."

"You're getting old, my dear chap, you're getting old!" all his friends yelled at him in chorus.

"Maybe I am getting old," admitted Traldi. "So much the worse! It's no fun foreseeing that in the end I'll be firmly fixed in such an opinion of myself. An old swine, that's what I'll be in my own eyes. Anyway, wait a minute! Now that I've told you this, let's try a little experiment shall we? Shut up, you lot! Quiet!"

And Carlo Traldi got laboriously to his feet. He placed his hands on Nicolino Respi's shoulders and shouted in his face, "Look into my eyes! Deep down into my eyes! No, don't laugh, my dear fellow! Look into my eyes! Deep down into my eyes! Wait! And you lot wait, too! Shut up!"

They all became silent. They were held in suspense, intent on that strange experiment.

Traldi, his huge oval, bloodshot eyes popping out of their sockets, stared acutely into the eyes of Nicolino Respi, and it seemed as if that malignant, shining gaze, which got gradually more and more acute and intense, was rummaging in his conscience, in his subconscious. . . . Discovering, there in the most intimate hiding-places, the most wicked and atrocious things. Little by little, Nicolino Respi began to grow pale and—although lower on his face his lips, with their usual little smile still playing upon them, seemed to be saying, "Oh rubbish! I'm only taking part in your little joke because——"; his eyes started to cloud over. He found he couldn't meet Traldi's gaze all the time, till finally, amidst the silence of his friends Traldi, in a strange voice, without lowering his staring gaze, without slackening one jot the intensity of his gaze, said victoriously, "There you are, you see? There you are!"

"Oh, rubbish!" burst out Respi, unable to stand it any longer, and shaking himself vigorously.

"The same to you, with nobs on! We understand one another all right!" shouted Traldi. "You're a worse swine than I am!" And he burst out laughing. The others laughed too, with a sense of unexpected relief. Traldi resumed, "Now this has been a joke. Only for a joke can one of us set himself to look at another of us like that. Because you and I alike still have that little machine known as civilization in good working order inside us; so we let the whole bang shoot of all our actions, all our thoughts, all our feelings sit there, hidden, at the bottom of our consciousness. But, now suppose that someone, whose little civilization machine's broken down, comes along and looks at you as I looked at you just now, no longer as a joke, but in all seriousness, and without your expecting it removes from the bottom of your consciousness all that assembly of thoughts, actions, and feelings which you've got inside you. . . . Then tell me that you wouldn't get the shudders!"

Saying which, Carlo Traldi moved furiously towards the door. Then he turned back and added, "And do you know what he was murmuring under his breath. . . . ? Poor Daddi, I mean! Go on, you lot; you tell him what he was murmuring! I must fly!"

" 'What an abyss. . . . What an abyss. . . .' "

"Just like that?"

"Yes. 'What an abyss. . . . What an abyss. . . .' "

After Traldi left the group broke up and Nicolino Respi was left, feeling thoroughly disturbed, in the company of just two friends, who went on talking for a little while about the terrible misfortune which had overtaken poor Daddi.

About two months before he'd gone to visit him at his villa near Perugia. He'd found him as calm and serene as ever, together with his wife and a friend of hers, Gabriella Vanzi—an old schoolfriend, who'd recently married a naval officer, who was then on a cruise. He'd spent three days at the villa, and not once—not once—had Romeo Daddi looked at him in the way that Traldi had described.

If he *had* looked at him like that . . .

A wave of dismay swept over Nicolino Respi. He felt suddenly giddy, and for support he took the arm of one of those two friends of his, making it look like a confidential gesture. His face was very pale, but the smile was still on his lips.

What had happened? What was that they were saying? Torture? What kind of torture? Oh, the torture Daddi had inflicted on his wife. . . .

"Afterwards, eh?" the words escaped from his lips.

They both turned and looked at him. "What do you mean, afterwards?"

"Oh. . . . No, what I meant was afterwards—when his . . . Well, when his little machine broke down."

"Oh, it must have been! It certainly couldn't have been before!"

"My God, they were a miracle of conjugal harmony and domestic bliss! It's obvious that something must have happened while they were on holiday in the country!"

"Why, yes! At the very least some sort of suspicion must have been aroused in him."

"Oh, don't be so utterly——! Concerning his wife?" burst out Nicolino Respi. "That, if anything, might have been the *result* of his madness, certainly not its cause! Only a madman——"

"Agreed! Agreed!" his friends cried. "A wife like Donna Bicetta!"

"No one could possibly suspect her! But—— Besides . . . !"

Nicolino Respi could no longer bear to stand there listening to the pair of them. He felt as if he were stifling. He needed air. He needed to walk about in the open air. On his own. He made some excuse and got away.

A terrible, tormenting doubt had insinuated itself into his mind and brought turmoil with it.

No one could know better than he that Donna Bicetta was completely above suspicion. For more than a year he'd persisted in declaring his love for her, besieged her with his courtship, without ever once obtaining anything more than a very gentle and compassionate smile in recompense for all his wasted labour. With that serenity which comes from being very sure of yourself, without either feeling insulted or rebelling against his onslaught, she'd made it perfectly plain to him that any kind of persistence on his part would be quite in vain, because she was just as much in love as he was—perhaps more than he was—but with her husband. Since she was in love with her husband, if he really loved her, he'd realize that her love could never grow less. If he didn't realize that, then he didn't really love her. So . . . ?

Sometimes, in certain solitary bathing spots, the sea water is so limpid, so clear, and so transparent that, however great your desire to immerse yourself in it, to enjoy its delicious refreshing coolness, you feel an almost sacred restraint inhibiting you from bringing turmoil into it.

Nicolino Respi always had the same feeling of limpidity and restraint when approaching the soul of Donna Bicetta Daddi. This woman loved life, with such a tranquil, attentive, and gentle love! Only once—it was during those three days spent in her villa near Perugia—had he, overcome by his burning desire, done violence to that restraint, had he brought turmoil into that limpidity, and he had been sternly repulsed.

Now his terrible tormenting doubt was this: that perhaps the turmoil he'd caused in those three days hadn't quietened down again after he'd left. Perhaps it had grown so great that her husband had become aware of it. Certainly, on his arrival at the villa, Romeo Daddi had been perfectly calm, and within a few days of his departure he'd gone out of his mind.

Well then, was it on *his* account? Had she, then, been left profoundly disturbed, quite overcome by his amorous aggression?

Why, of course! Yes. Why doubt it?

All night long Nicolino Respi argued the question backwards and forwards in his own mind. He twisted from one frenzied extreme to the other. One moment he was torn by remorse away from a malign and impetuous sense of joy; the next he was torn by this joy away from his remorse.

The following morning, as soon as he thought he might properly do so, he rushed round to Donna Bicetta Daddi's house. He simply had to see her. He simply had to clear things up at once. Somehow resolve those doubts of his. Perhaps she wouldn't see him. But, in any case, he wanted to present himself at her house, ready to confront and submit to the consequences of that situation.

Donna Bicetta Daddi wasn't at home.

For the past hour, without in the least wishing to, without knowing she was doing it, she'd been inflicting the most cruel of martyrdoms on her friend Gabriella Vanzi, the woman who'd been her guest for three months at her villa.

She'd gone to see her, so that together they might try and work out—not the reason, alas! No, what had driven him to—what had caused that misfortune of his. Try and pinpoint the moment in three days during their stay in the country—the last days of their time there—when it had first revealed itself. And, though she'd ransacked her memory, she hadn't succeeded in discovering anything.

For the past hour she'd been stubbornly calling back those last days, reconstructing them minute by minute. "Do you remember this? Do you remember that morning he went down into the garden without taking his linen hat, and called up for it to be thrown down to him from the window. Then he came back up, laughing, with that bunch of roses. Do you remember—he wanted me to wear a couple of them? Then he went with me to the gate and helped me into the

car, and told me he'd like me to bring him back those books from
Perugia. Wait a moment! One was—— Oh, I don't know. Something to do with seeds—do you remember? Do you remember?"

So thoroughly upset was she by the grief the re-evocation of so
many minute and valueless details was inflicting on her, that she
didn't observe the steadily growing anguish and agitation of her
friend.

Already she'd re-evoked without the slightest indication of being upset the three days spent in the villa by Nicolino Respi, and she
hadn't for one moment paused to consider whether her husband
had found provocation for his madness in the innocent courtship of
that man. It wasn't even remotely possible. It had been very much a
laughing matter for the three of them, that courtship of his after
Respi's departure for Milan. How could she possibly imagine
that——? Besides, after his departure, hadn't her husband remained
quite serene, quite tranquil for . . . ? Well, it was more than a fortnight.

No, never! Never the remotest hint of suspicion! Never once, in
seven whole years of marriage! How, where, would he ever have
found cause for suspicion? And yet look, all of a sudden, there amidst
the peace and quiet of the Umbrian countryside, without anything at
all happening——

"Oh, Gabriella! Gabriella, my dear! I'm going out of my mind
now! Believe me, I'm going mad too!"

Suddenly, as she was recovering from that crisis of desperation, Donna Bicetta Daddi, raising her weeping eyes to look at her
friend's face, discovered that it had become very set and gone deathly
pale. She looked just like a corpse. She was trying to get control
over a paroxysm of unbearable anguish. She was panting. Her nostrils were flaring. And she was watching her with evil in her eyes. Oh,
God! Almost the same look in her eyes as that with which, in those
last days, her husband had stood there looking at her.

She felt her blood freezing. She felt terror crowding in upon
her.

"Why—— You as well? Why?" She stammered, trembling all
over. "Why are *you* looking at me like that?"

Gabriella Vanzi made a hideous effort to force the expression
on her face, which she'd assumed quite unknown to herself, to dissolve into a benign smile of compassion. "Me . . . ? Was I looking?
No, I was thinking. Yes, look—— I meant to ask you. Yes, I know

—you're so sure of yourself—is there nothing that you—absolutely nothing—nothing you've got to reproach yourself with?"

Donna Bicetta was startled out of her wits. With her hands clasped to her cheeks, and her eyes wide and staring, she cried, "What? *You're* saying it to me now! His very words as well! How . . . ? How *can* you?"

Gabriella Vanzi's face took on a false expression and her eyes glazed over, "How can *I* . . . ?"

"Yes, you! Oh, my God! And now you're getting all dismayed, just like him! What does it all mean? What does it all mean?"

She felt herself gradually sinking deeper and deeper. She was still whimpering "What does it all mean?" when she found her friend in her arms, and clinging tightly to her breast.

"Bice. Bice. Do you suspect me? You came here—because you suspected me, didn't you?"

"No! No! I give you my solemn oath, Gabriella. Now, however. . . . Only now——"

"You do now, don't you? Yes, you do! But you're wrong, you're wrong, Bice! Because you can't understand."

"What's happened? Gabriella! Now, come on! Tell me! What's happened?"

"You can't understand. You can't understand. I know why—I know the reason why your husband's gone mad!"

"The reason why . . . ? *Which* reason?"

"I know the reason why he—— Because it's in me. It's in me too. This reason for going mad. Because of what happened to both of us!"

"To *both* of you?"

"Yes! Yes! To me and your husband."

"Well?"

"No! No! It's not what you're thinking! You can't possibly understand. Without any attempt at deceiving anybody—without thinking about it—without wanting it to happen. . . . In an instant; something *horrible!* And nobody can blame himself for it. You see how I'm talking to you about it? How I *can* talk to you about it? Because I'm not to blame! And neither is he! But just because that's how things are. Listen! *Listen!* And when you've found out everything, maybe *you'll* go mad as well, in the same way as *I'm* just about to go mad! In the same way as *he's* gone mad! Listen! You've been busy reliving that day when you went into Perugia from the villa, in the car, haven't you? The day he gave you those two roses and asked you to bring him back those books."

"Yes."

"Well. It was that morning!"

"*What* was?"

"Everything that happened. Everything and nothing. . . . Let me tell you, for pity's sake! It was terribly hot, do you remember? After seeing you off, he and I walked back through the garden. The sun was simply scorching and the chirping of the crickets was quite deafening. We went back into the house and sat down in the drawing-room, over by the dining-room door. The blinds were drawn, the shutters were pulled to. It was almost dark in there. There was a feeling of coolness. Everything was still. I'm giving you my impression of it now—the only one I could possibly have. The one I remember. The one I shall always remember. Maybe he had the same memory of it himself. He must have done, otherwise I'd never be able to explain anything to myself! It was that stillness, that coolness, coming after all that sunshine and the deafening noise of the crickets. In an instant—— Without thinking about it, I swear! Never, never. . . . Neither he nor I. . . . Oh yes, of that I'm positive——! As if there were some irresistible attraction implicit within that astonished emptiness, within the delicious coolness of that semi-darkness. . . . Bice, Bice. . . . It happened just like that. . . . I swear it! In an instant!"

With a sudden movement, Donna Bicetta Daddi leapt to her feet—impelled to do so by a sudden access of hatred, anger, and contempt.

"Oh, so that's why?" she hissed between her teeth, drawing away like a cat.

"No, that's not why!" cried Gabriella, stretching her arms towards her in a gesture of despair and supplication. "That's not why! That's not why, Bice! Your husband went mad on your account, on *your* account, not because of me!"

"He went mad on my account? What do you mean? Out of remorse?"

"No! What do you mean, remorse? There's no occasion for remorse, when you haven't willed the sin. . . . You can't understand! Just as I shouldn't have been able to understand things if, in thinking about what's happened to your husband, I hadn't thought about my own! Yes, yes, I can now understand your husband's madness, because I think of my own husband, who'd go mad in the same way, if what happened to your husband with me ever happened to him! Without remorse! Without remorse! And precisely because it is without remorse . . . ! Do you realize? This is the horrible thing about it! Oh, I don't know how to make you understand! *I* understand it, I repeat, only if I think of my own husband and see myself, like this, without remorse for a sin I had no desire to commit. You see how I can talk to you about it, without blushing? Because I don't know, Bice, I really don't know anything about your husband— physically—just as he most certainly doesn't, *can't* know anything about me. It was like an abyss. Do you understand me? Like an abyss which suddenly opened up between us. There we were, all unsuspecting, and it seized hold of us and overthrew us in an instant. Then, just as suddenly, it closed again, leaving not the slightest trace behind it! Immediately afterwards the consciousness of each one of us was once again quite limpid and undisturbed. We didn't think any more about it, about what had happened between us. Not even for an instant. Our disturbance had been purely momentary. We left the room, he through one door, I through the other. But the moment we were alone—nothing. It was just as if nothing whatever had happened. Not only when we were with you—when you returned home shortly afterwards—but even when we two were alone together. We could look into one another's eyes and talk to one another, just as before, *exactly* as before, because no longer was there in us—I swear it!—the slightest vestige of what, for an instant, *had been*. Nothing. Nothing. Not even the shadow of a memory. Not even the shadow of desire. Nothing! Everything was over and done with. It had disappeared. The secret of an instant was buried for ever. Well, this is what's driven your husband mad—not the sin itself, which neither of us thought of committing! No, it's this: his being able to imagine what can happen—that an honest woman who's in love with her own husband can, in an instant, without wanting to, as a result of a sudden ambush of the senses, because of a mysterious conspiracy of time and place, fall into the arms of another man. And, a moment later, everything's over—for ever. The abyss has closed again. The secret's buried. There's no remorse. No turmoil. No effort's needed to lie in front of others. To one another. He waited a day, two days, three. . . . He didn't feel any further stirring there inside himself, either in your presence, or in mine. He could see that I'd gone back to being what I was before—just what I was before—both with you and with him. He saw, shortly afterwards—do you remember?—my husband arrive at the villa.

He saw how I welcomed him—with what concern, with what love. And then the abyss, in which our secret was buried deep, for ever, without leaving the slightest trace, began gradually to exercise a fatal attraction for him. Till finally it overthrew his reason. He thought of you. He began to wonder whether perhaps you too . . . ?"

"Whether I too?"

"Oh, Bice, I'm sure it's never happened to you! I can quite well believe it! Yes, Bice, my dear! But I . . . He and I, we know from experience what can happen! And we know that, since it was possible in our case without our wanting it, it can quite well be possible for anyone at all! He'll probably have thought of how there've been times when, coming back home, he'll have found you alone in the drawing-room with a friend of his. And he'll have thought of how, in an instant, there could quite well have happened to you and to that friend of his, what happened to me and to him. In exactly the same way. He'll have thought of how you'd have been able to shut up inside yourself, without there being any trace of it, to hide without lying, the same secret that *I* shut up inside myself and hid from my husband without lying. And the moment this thought entered his mind a subtle, acute, burning sensation would begin to gnaw away at his brain, as he saw you, so detached, so happy, so loving, with him. Just as I was with my husband. With my husband whom I love, I swear, more than I love myself, more than I love anything in the world! He started thinking, 'And yet, this woman, who's behaving like this towards her husband, was in my arms for a moment? So, perhaps, my wife too, in a moment. . . . Who knows? Who can *ever* know?' And he went out of his mind. Oh, hush, Bice! Hush! For pity's sake!"

Gabriella Vanzi got up. She was trembling and terribly pale.

She'd heard the front door open, out there in the little hall. Her husband was coming back in.

Donna Bicetta Daddi, seeing her friend suddenly transformed like this, suddenly in control of herself again—her face had become pink, her eyes were now limpid, and there was a smile on her lips, as she went to meet her husband—was left standing there, almost annihilated.

Nothing. Yes, it was quite true what Gabriella had said. . . . No more turmoil, no remorse, no trace of——

And Donna Bicetta understood perfectly why her husband, Romeo Daddi, had gone out of his mind.

KATHERINE MANSFIELD

(1888-1923)

The daughter of a New Zealand industrialist and banker, Kathleen Mansfield Beauchamp found the provincial life of Wellington stultifying, particularly since she was a precocious child, with obvious talent in both literature and music. She attended college in London between 1903 and 1906, and her adjustment to the more sophisticated life of Europe made any permanent return to New Zealand impossible. Although she chose a literary over a musical career, her love of music is reflected in many of her plots and characters. Her road to recognition as a short story writer was difficult; her reputation was not established until her publication, in 1920, of BLISS AND OTHER STORIES. In addition, she was plagued throughout her life with ill health, primarily a weakness of the lungs which led to her death from tuberculosis at the age of thirty-four. She was married to the well-known critic, John Middleton Murry, in 1918. Her stories are crafted with great care; their power derives from the perfect merger of setting, atmosphere, and character, rather than from incident. To this extent she is like Chekhov. But she could also be satirically analytical. Her stories have been collected in THE SHORT STORIES OF KATHERINE MANSFIELD.

The Fly

"Y'are very snug in here," piped old Mr. Woodifield, and he peered out of the great, green leather armchair by his friend the boss's

desk as a baby peers out of its pram. His talk was over; it was time
for him to be off. But he did not want to go. Since he had retired,
since his . . . stroke, the wife and the girls kept him boxed up in
the house every day of the week except Tuesday. On Tuesday he
was dressed up and brushed and allowed to cut back to the City for
the day. Though what he did there the wife and girls couldn't imagine. Made a nuisance of himself to his friends, they supposed. . . .
Well, perhaps so. All the same, we cling to our last pleasures as the
tree clings to its last leaves. So there sat old Woodifield, smoking a
cigar and staring almost greedily at the boss, who rolled in his
office chair, stout, rosy, five years older than he, and still going
strong, still at the helm. It did one good to see him.

    Wistfully, admiringly, the old voice added, "It's snug in here,
upon my word!"

    "Yes, it's comfortable enough," agreed the boss, and he flipped
the *Financial Times* with a paper-knife. As a matter of fact he was
proud of his room; he liked to have it admired, especially by old
Woodifield. It gave him a feeling of deep, solid satisfaction to be
planted there in the midst of it in full view of that frail old figure in
the muffler.

    "I've had it done up lately," he explained, as he had explained
for the past—how many?—weeks. "New carpet," and he pointed
to the bright red carpet with a pattern of large white rings. "New
furniture," and he nodded towards the massive bookcase and the
table with legs like twisted treacle. "Electric heating!" He waved
almost exultantly towards the five transparent, pearly sausages
glowing so softly in the tilted copper pan.

    But he did not draw old Woodifield's attention to the photo-
graph over the table of a grave-looking boy in uniform standing in
one of those spectral photographers' parks with photographers'
storm-clouds behind him. It was not new. It had been there for over
six years.

    "There was something I wanted to tell you," said old Woodi-
field, and his eyes grew dim remembering. "Now what was it? I had
it in my mind when I started out this morning." His hands began to
tremble, and patches of red showed above his beard.

    Poor old chap, he's on his last pins, thought the boss. And,
feeling kindly, he winked at the old man, and said jokingly, "I tell
you what. I've got a little drop of something here that'll do you
good before you go out into the cold again. It's beautiful stuff. It

wouldn't hurt a child." He took a key off his watch-chain, unlocked a cupboard below his desk, and drew forth a dark, squat bottle. "That's the medicine," said he. "And the man from whom I got it told me on the strict Q.T. it came from the cellars at Windsor Cassel."

Old Woodifield's mouth fell open at the sight. He couldn't have looked more surprised if the boss had produced a rabbit.

"It's whisky, ain't it?" he piped, feebly.

The boss turned the bottle and lovingly showed him the label. Whisky it was.

"D'you know," said he, peering up at the boss wonderingly, "they won't let me touch it at home." And he looked as though he was going to cry.

"Ah, that's where we know a bit more than the ladies," cried the boss, swooping across for two tumblers that stood on the table with the water-bottle, and pouring a generous finger into each. "Drink it down. It'll do you good. And don't put any water with it. It's sacrilege to tamper with stuff like this. Ah!" He tossed off his, pulled out his handkerchief, hastily wiped his moustaches, and cocked an eye at old Woodifield, who was rolling his in his chaps.

The old man swallowed, was silent a moment, and then said faintly, "It's nutty!"

But it warmed him; it crept into his chill old brain—he remembered.

"That was it," he said, heaving himself out of his chair. "I thought you'd like to know. The girls were in Belgium last week having a look at poor Reggie's grave, and they happened to come across your boy's. They're quite near each other, it seems."

Old Woodifield paused, but the boss made no reply. Only a quiver in his eyelids showed that he heard.

"The girls were delighted with the way the place is kept," piped the old voice. "Beautifully looked after. Couldn't be better if they were at home. You've not been across, have yer?"

"No, no!" For various reasons the boss had not been across.

"There's miles of it," quavered old Woodifield, "and it's all as neat as a garden. Flowers growing on all the graves. Nice broad paths." It was plain from his voice how much he liked a nice broad path.

The pause came again. Then the old man brightened wonderfully.

"D'you know what the hotel made the girls pay for a pot of jam?" he piped. "Ten francs! Robbery, I call it. It was a little pot, so Gertrude says, no bigger than a half-crown. And she hadn't taken more than a spoonful when they charged her ten francs. Gertrude brought the pot away with her to teach 'em a lesson. Quite right, too; it's trading on our feelings. They think because we're over there having a look around we're ready to pay anything. That's what it is." And he turned towards the door.

"Quite right, quite right!" cried the boss, though what was quite right he hadn't the least idea. He came round by his desk, followed the shuffling footsteps to the door, and saw the old fellow out. Woodifield was gone.

For a long moment the boss stayed, staring at nothing, while the grey-haired office messenger, watching him, dodged in and out of his cubbyhole like a dog that expects to be taken for a run. Then: "I'll see nobody for half an hour, Macey," said the boss. "Understand? Nobody at all."

"Very good, sir."

The door shut, the firm heavy steps recrossed the bright carpet, the fat body plumped down in the spring chair, and leaning forward, the boss covered his face with his hands. He wanted, he intended, he had arranged to weep. . . .

It had been a terrible shock to him when old Woodifield sprang that remark upon him about the boy's grave. It was exactly as though the earth had opened and he had seen the boy lying there with Woodifield's girls staring down at him. For it was strange. Although over six years had passed away, the boss never thought of the boy except as lying unchanged, unblemished in his uniform, asleep for ever. "My son!" groaned the boss. But no tears came yet. In the past, in the first months and even years after the boy's death, he had only to say those words to be overcome by such grief that nothing short of a violent fit of weeping could relieve him. Time, he had declared then, he had told everybody, could make no difference. Other men perhaps might recover, might live their loss down, but not he. How was it possible? His boy was an only son. Ever since his birth the boss had worked at building up this business for him; it had no other meaning if it was not for the boy. Life itself had come to have no other meaning. How on earth could he have slaved, denied himself, kept going all those years without the promise for ever before him of the boy's stepping into his shoes and carrying on where he left off?

And that promise had been so near being fulfilled. The boy had been in the office learning the ropes for a year before the war. Every morning they had started off together; they had come back by the same train. And what congratulations he had received as the boy's father! No wonder; he had taken to it marvellously. As to his popularity with the staff, every man jack of them down to old Macey couldn't make enough of the boy. And he wasn't in the least spoilt. No, he was just his bright, natural self, with the right word for everybody, with that boyish look and his habit of saying, "Simply splendid!"

But all that was over and done with as though it never had been. The day had come when Macey had handed him the telegram that brought the whole place crashing about his head. "Deeply regret to inform you . . ." And he had left the office a broken man, with his life in ruins.

Six years ago, six years . . . How quickly time passed! It might have happened yesterday. The boss took his hands from his face; he was puzzled. Something seemed to be wrong with him. He wasn't feeling as he wanted to feel. He decided to get up and have a look at the boy's photograph. But it wasn't a favorite photograph of his; the expression was unnatural. It was cold, even stern-looking. The boy had never looked like that.

At that moment the boss noticed that a fly had fallen into his broad inkpot, and was trying feebly but desperately to clamber out again. Help! help! said those struggling legs. But the sides of the inkpot were wet and slippery; it fell back again and began to swim. The boss took up a pen, picked the fly out of the ink, and shook it on to a piece of blotting-paper. For a fraction of a second it lay still on the dark patch that oozed round it. Then the front legs waved, took hold, and, pulling its small sodden body up it began the immense task of cleaning the ink from its wings. Over and under, over and under, went a leg along a wing, as the stone goes over and under the scythe. Then there was a pause, while the fly, seeming to stand on the tips of its toes, tried to expand first one wing and then the other. It succeeded at last, and, sitting down, it began, like a minute cat, to clean its face. Now one could imagine that the little front legs rubbed against each other lightly, joyfully. The horrible danger was over; it had escaped; it was ready for life again.

But just then the boss had an idea. He plunged his pen back into the ink, leaned his thick wrist on the blotting paper, and as the fly tried its wings down came a great heavy blot. What would it make of that? What indeed! The little beggar seemed absolutely cowed, stunned, and afraid to move because of what would happen next. But then, as if painfully, it dragged itself forward. The front legs waved, caught hold, and, more slowly this time, the task began from the beginning.

He's a plucky little devil, thought the boss, and he felt a real admiration for the fly's courage. That was the way to tackle things; that was the right spirit. Never say die; it was only a question of . . . But the fly had again finished its laborious task, and the boss had just time to refill his pen, to shake fair and square on the new-cleaned body yet another dark drop. What about it this time? A painful moment of suspense followed. But behold, the front legs were again waving; the boss felt a rush of relief. He leaned over the fly and said to it tenderly, "You artful little b . . ." And he actually had the brilliant notion of breathing on it to help the drying process. All the same, there was something timid and weak about its efforts now, and the boss decided that this time should be the last, as he dipped the pen into the inkpot.

It was. The last blot on the soaked blotting-paper, and the draggled fly lay in it and did not stir. The back legs were stuck to its body; the front legs were not to be seen.

"Come on," said the boss. "Look sharp!" And he stirred it with his pen—in vain. Nothing happened or was likely to happen. The fly was dead.

The boss lifted the corpse on the end of the paper-knife and flung it into the waste-paper basket. But such a grinding feeling of wretchedness seized him that he felt positively frightened. He started forward and pressed the bell for Macey.

"Bring me some fresh blotting-paper," he said, sternly, "and look sharp about it." And while the old dog padded away he fell to wondering what it was he had been thinking about before. What was it? It was . . . He took out his handkerchief and passed it inside his collar. For the life of him he could not remember.

SHERWOOD ANDERSON

(1876-1941)

Anderson, a journalist, editor, short story writer and novelist, was born in Ohio. Like his father, however, he was a roamer who had little formal education and who worked at many jobs. It was not until the First World War that Anderson began to publish his stories. His fourth book, WINESBURG, OHIO (1920), established his reputation. He went to Europe in 1921, where he met Gertrude Stein, Hemingway and others of the Lost Generation of expatriates. On his return he lived for a time in New York and New Orleans but eventually settled down in Virginia. His short stories in particular have made him one of the most important American writers of this century. His narratives contain sensitive psychological studies and are often intensely critical of the impersonal, mechanized world of modern America. As Anderson put it, his fiction represents an attempt "to see beneath the surface of lives." This effort is clearly reflected in "Death in the Woods." In addition to his numerous short stories, Anderson wrote novels, plays, poetry, essays, journalistic pieces, and autobiography.

Death in the Woods

She was an old woman and lived on a farm near the town in which I lived. All country and small-town people have seen such old women, but no one knows much about them. Such an old woman comes into town driving an old worn-out horse or she comes afoot carrying a basket. She may own a few hens and have eggs to sell. She brings them in a basket and takes them to a grocer. There she trades them in. She gets some salt pork and some beans. Then she gets a pound or two of sugar and some flour.

Afterwards she goes to the butcher's and asks for some dog-meat. She may spend ten or fifteen cents, but when she does she asks for something. Formerly the butchers gave liver to any one who wanted to carry it away. In our family we were always having it. Once one of my brothers got a whole cow's liver at the slaughter-house near the fairgrounds in our town. We had it until we were sick of it. It never cost a cent. I have hated the thought of it ever since.

The old farm woman got some liver and a soup-bone. She never visited with any one, and as soon as she got what she wanted she lit out for home. It made quite a load for such an old body. No one gave her a lift. People drive right down a road and never notice an old woman like that.

There was such an old woman who used to come into town past our house one Summer and Fall when I was a young boy and was sick with what was called inflammatory rheumatism. She went home later carrying a heavy pack on her back. Two or three large gaunt-looking dogs followed at her heels.

The old woman was nothing special. She was one of the nameless ones that hardly any one knows, but she got into my thoughts. I have just suddenly now, after all these years, remembered her and what happened. It is a story. Her name was Grimes, and she lived with her husband and son in a small unpainted house on the bank of a small creek four miles from town.

The husband and son were a tough lot. Although the son was but twenty-one, he had already served a term in jail. It was whispered about that the woman's husband stole horses and ran them off to some other county. Now and then, when a horse turned up missing, the man had also disappeared. No one ever caught him. Once, when I was loafing at Tom Whitehead's livery-barn, the man came there and sat on the bench in front. Two or three other men were there, but no one spoke to him. He sat for a few minutes and then got up and went away. When he was leaving he turned around and stared at the men. There was a look of defiance in his eyes. "Well, I have tried to be friendly. You don't want to talk to me. It has been so wherever I have gone in this town. If, some day, one of your fine horses turns up missing, well, then what?" He did not say anything actually. "I'd like to bust one of you on the jaw," was about what his eyes said. I remember how the look in his eyes made me shiver.

The old man belonged to a family that had had money once. His name was Jake Grimes. It all comes back clearly now. His father, John Grimes, had owned a sawmill when the country was new, and had made money. Then he got to drinking and running after women. When he died there wasn't much left.

Jake blew in the rest. Pretty soon there wasn't any more lumber to cut and his land was nearly all gone.

He got his wife off a German farmer, for whom he went to work one June day in the wheat harvest. She was a young thing then and scared to death. You see, the farmer was up to something with the girl—she was, I think, a bound girl and his wife had her suspicions. She took it out on the girl when the man wasn't around. Then, when the wife had to go off to town for supplies, the farmer got after her. She told young Jake that nothing really ever happened, but he didn't know whether to believe it or not.

He got her pretty easy himself, the first time he was out with her. He wouldn't have married her if the German farmer hadn't tried to tell him where to get off. He got her to go riding with him in his buggy one night when he was threshing on the place, and then he came for her the next Sunday night.

She managed to get out of the house without her employer's seeing, but when she was getting into the buggy he showed up. It was almost dark, and he just popped up suddenly at the horse's head. He grabbed the horse by the bridle and Jake got out his buggy-whip.

They had it out all right! The German was a tough one. Maybe he didn't care whether his wife knew or not. Jake hit him over the face and shoulders with the buggy-whip, but the horse got to acting up and he had to get out.

Then the two men went for it. The girl didn't see it. The horse started to run away and went nearly a mile down the road before the girl got him stopped. Then she managed to tie him to a tree beside the road. (I wonder how I know all this. It must have stuck in my mind from small-town tales when I was a boy.) Jake found her there after he got through with the German. She was huddled up in the buggy seat, crying, scared to death. She told Jake a lot of stuff, how the German had tried to get her, how he chased her once into the barn, how another time, when they happened to be alone in the house together, he tore her dress open clear down the front. The German, she said, might have got her that time if he hadn't heard his old woman drive in at the gate. She had been off to town for supplies. Well, she would be putting the horse in the barn. The German managed to sneak off to the fields without his wife seeing. He told the girl he would kill her if she told. What could she do? She told a lie about ripping her dress in the barn when she was feeding the stock. I remember now that she was a bound girl and did not know where her father and mother were. Maybe she did not have any father. You know what I mean.

Such bound children were often enough cruelly treated. They were children who had no parents, slaves really. There were very few orphan homes then. They were legally bound into some home. It was a matter of pure luck how it came out.

II

She married Jake and had a son and daughter, but the daughter died.

Then she settled down to feed stock. That was her job. At the German's place she had cooked the food for the German and his wife. The wife was a strong woman with big hips and worked most of the time in the fields with her husband. She fed them and fed the cows in the barn, fed the pigs, the horses and the chickens. Every moment of every day, as a young girl, was spent feeding something.

Then she married Jake Grimes and he had to be fed. She was a slight thing, and when she had been married for three or four years, and after the two children were born, her slender shoulders became stooped.

Jake always had a lot of big dogs around the house, that stood near the unused sawmill near the creek. He was always trading horses when he wasn't stealing something and had a lot of poor bony ones about. Also he kept three or four pigs and a cow. They were all pastured in the few acres left of the Grimes place and Jake did little enough work.

He went into debt for a threshing outfit and ran it for several years, but it did not pay. People did not trust him. They were afraid he would steal the grain at night. He had to go a long way off to get work and it cost too much to get there. In the Winter he hunted and cut a little firewood, to be sold in some nearby town. When the son grew up he was just like the father. They got drunk together. If there wasn't anything to eat in the house when they came home the old man gave his old woman a cut over the head. She had a few chickens of her own and had to kill one of them in a hurry. When they were all killed she wouldn't have any eggs to sell when she went to town, and then what would she do?

She had to scheme all her life about getting things fed, getting the pigs fed so they would grow fat and could be butchered in the Fall. When they were butchered her husband took most of the meat off to town and sold it. If he did not do it first the boy did. They fought sometimes and when they fought the old woman stood aside trembling.

She had got the habit of silence anyway—that was fixed. Sometimes, when she began to look old—she wasn't forty yet—and when the husband and son were both off, trading horses or drinking or hunting or stealing, she went around the house and the barnyard muttering to herself.

How was she going to get everything fed?—that was her problem. The dogs had to be fed. There wasn't enough hay in the barn for the horses and the cow. If she didn't feed the chickens how could they lay eggs? Without eggs to sell how could she get things in town, things she had to have to keep the life of the farm going? Thank heaven, she did not have to feed her husband—in a certain way. That hadn't lasted long after their marriage and after the babies came. Where he went on his long trips she did not know. Sometimes he was gone from home for weeks, and after the boy grew up they went off together.

They left everything at home for her to manage and she had no money. She knew no one. No one ever talked to her in town. When it was Winter she had to gather sticks of wood for her fire, had to try to keep the stock fed with very little grain.

The stock in the barn cried to her hungrily, the dogs followed her about. In the Winter the hens laid few enough eggs. They huddled in the corners of the barn and she kept watching them. If a hen lays an egg in the barn in the Winter and you do not find it, it freezes and breaks.

One day in Winter the old woman went off to town with a few

eggs and the dogs followed her. She did not get started until nearly three o'clock and the snow was heavy. She hadn't been feeling very well for several days and so she went muttering along, scantily clad, her shoulders stooped. She had an old grain bag in which she carried her eggs, tucked away down in the bottom. There weren't many of them, but in Winter the price of eggs is up. She would get a little meat in exchange for the eggs, some salt pork, a little sugar, and some coffee perhaps. It might be the butcher would give her a piece of liver.

When she had got to town and was trading in her eggs the dogs lay by the door outside. She did pretty well, got the things she needed, more than she had hoped. Then she went to the butcher and he gave her some liver and some dog-meat.

It was the first time any one had spoken to her in a friendly way for a long time. The butcher was alone in his shop when she came in and was annoyed by the thought of such a sick-looking old woman out on such a day. It was bitter cold and the snow, that had let up during the afternoon, was falling again. The butcher said something about her husband and her son, swore at them, and the old woman stared at him, a look of mild surprise in her eyes as he talked. He said that if either the husband or the son were going to get any of the liver or the heavy bones with scraps of meat hanging to them that he had put into the grain bag, he'd see him starve first.

Starve, eh? Well, things had to be fed. Men had to be fed, and the horses that weren't any good but maybe could be traded off, and the poor thin cow that hadn't given any milk for three months.

Horses, cows, pigs, dogs, men.

III

The old woman had to get back before darkness came if she could. The dogs followed at her heels, sniffing at the heavy grain bag she had fastened on her back. When she got to the edge of town she stopped by a fence and tied the bag on her back with a piece of rope she had carried in her dress-pocket for just that purpose. That was an easier way to carry it. Her arms ached. It was hard when she had to crawl over fences and once she fell over and landed in the snow. The dogs went frisking about. She had to struggle to get to her feet again, but she made it. The point of climbing over the fences was that there was a short cut over a hill and through a woods. She might have gone around by the road, but it was a mile farther that way. She was afraid she couldn't make it. And then, besides, the stock had to be fed. There was a little hay left and a little corn. Perhaps her husband and son would bring some home when they came. They had driven off in the only buggy the Grimes family had, a rickety thing, a rickety horse hitched to the buggy, two other rickety horses led by halters. They were going to trade horses, get a little money if they could. They might come home drunk. It would be well to have something in the house when they came back.

The son had an affair on with a woman at the county seat, fifteen miles away. She was a rough enough woman, a tough one. Once, in the Summer, the son had brought her to the house. Both she and the son had been drinking. Jake Grimes was away and the son and his woman ordered the old woman about like a servant. She didn't mind much; she was used to it. Whatever happened she never said anything. That was her way of getting along. She had managed that way when she was a young girl at the German's and ever since she had married Jake. That time her son brought his woman to the house they stayed all night, sleeping together just as though they were married. It hadn't shocked the old woman, not much. She had got past being shocked early in life.

With the pack on her back she went painfully along across an open field, wading in the deep snow, and got into the woods.

There was a path, but it was hard to follow. Just beyond the top of the hill, where the woods was thickest, there was a small clearing. Had some one once thought of building a house there? The clearing was as large as a building lot in town, large enough for a house and a garden. The path ran along the side of the clearing, and when she got there the old woman sat down to rest at the foot of a tree.

It was a foolish thing to do. When she got herself placed, the pack against the tree's trunk, it was nice, but what about getting up again? She worried about that for a moment and then quietly closed her eyes.

She must have slept for a time. When you are about so cold you can't get any colder. The afternoon grew a little warmer and the snow came thicker than ever. Then after a time the weather cleared. The moon even came out.

There were four Grimes dogs that had followed Mrs. Grimes into town, all tall gaunt fellows. Such men as Jake Grimes and his son always keep just such dogs. They kick and abuse them, but they stay. The Grimes dogs, in order to keep from starving, had to do a lot of foraging for themselves, and they had been at it while the old woman slept with her back to the tree at the side of the clearing. They had been chasing rabbits in the woods and in adjoining fields and in their ranging had picked up three other farm dogs.

After a time all the dogs came back to the clearing. They were excited about something. Such nights, cold and clear and with a moon, do things to dogs. It may be that some old instinct, come down from the time when they were wolves and ranged the woods in packs on Winter nights, comes back into them.

The dogs in the clearing, before the old woman, had caught two or three rabbits and their immediate hunger had been satisfied. They began to play, running in circles in the clearing. Round and round they ran, each dog's nose at the tail of the next dog. In the clearing, under the snow-laden trees and under the wintry moon they made a strange picture, running thus silently, in a circle their running had beaten in the soft snow. The dogs made no sound. They ran around and around in the circle.

It may have been that the old woman saw them doing that before she died. She may have awakened once or twice and looked at the strange sight with dim old eyes.

She wouldn't be very cold now, just drowsy. Life hangs on a long time. Perhaps the old woman was out of her head. She may have dreamed of her girlhood, at the German's, and before that, when she was a child and before her mother lit out and left her.

Her dreams couldn't have been very pleasant. Not many pleasant things had happened to her. Now and then one of the Grimes dogs left the running circle and came to stand before her. The dog thrust his face close to her face. His red tongue was hanging out.

The running of the dogs may have been a kind of death ceremony. It may have been that the primitive instinct of the wolf, having been aroused in the dogs by the night and the running, made them somehow afraid.

"Now we are no longer wolves. We are dogs, the servants of men. Keep alive, man! When man dies we become wolves again."

When one of the dogs came to where the old woman sat with her back against the tree and thrust his nose close to her face he seemed satisfied and went back to run with the pack. All the Grimes dogs did it at some time during the evening, before she died. I knew all about it afterward, when I grew to be a man, because once in a woods in Illinois, on another Winter night, I saw a pack of dogs act just like that. The dogs were waiting for me to die as they had waited for the old woman that night when I was a child, but when it happened to me I was a young man and had no intention whatever of dying.

The old woman died softly and quietly. When she was dead and when one of the Grimes dogs had come to her and had found her dead all the dogs stopped running.

They gathered about her.

Well, she was dead now. She had fed the Grimes dogs when she was alive, what about now?

There was the pack on her back, the grain bag containing the piece of salt pork, the liver the butcher had given her, the dog-meat, the soup bones. The butcher in town, having been suddenly overcome with a feeling of pity, had loaded her grain bag heavily. It had been a big haul for the old woman.

It was a big haul for the dogs now.

IV

One of the Grimes dogs sprang suddenly out from among the others and began worrying the pack on the old woman's back. Had the dogs really been wolves that one would have been the leader of the pack. What he did, all the others did.

All of them sank their teeth into the grain bag the old woman had fastened with ropes to her back.

They dragged the old woman's body out into the open clearing. The worn-out dress was quickly torn from her shoulders. When she was found, a day or two later, the dress had been torn from her body clear to the hips, but the dogs had not touched her body. They had got the meat out of the grain bag, that was all. Her body was frozen stiff when it was found, and the shoulders were so narrow and the body so slight that in death it looked like the body of some charming young girl.

Such things happened in towns of the Middle West, on farms near town, when I was a boy. A hunter out after rabbits found the old woman's body and did not touch it. Something, the beaten round path in the little snow-covered clearing, the silence of the place, the place where the dogs had worried the body trying to pull the grain bag away or tear it open—something startled the man and he hurried off to town.

I was in Main street with one of my brothers who was town newsboy and who was taking the afternoon papers to the stores. It was almost night.

The hunter came into a grocery and told his story. Then he went to a hardware-shop and into a drugstore. Men began to gather on the sidewalks. Then they started out along the road to the place in the woods.

My brother should have gone on about his business of distributing papers but he didn't. Every one was going to the woods. The undertaker went and the town marshal. Several men got on a dray and rode out to where the path left the road and went into the woods, but the horses weren't very sharply shod and slid about on the slippery roads. They made no better time than those of us who walked.

The town marshal was a large man whose leg had been injured in the Civil War. He carried a heavy cane and limped rapidly along the road. My brother and I followed at his heels, and as we went other men and boys joined the crowd.

It had grown dark by the time we got to where the old woman had left the road but the moon had come out. The marshal was thinking there might have been a murder. He kept asking the hunter questions. The hunter went along with his gun across his shoulders, a dog following at his heels. It isn't often a rabbit hunter has a chance to be so conspicuous. He was taking full advantage of it, leading the procession with the town marshal. "I didn't see any wounds. She was a beautiful young girl. Her face was buried in the snow. No, I didn't know her." As a matter of fact, the hunter had not looked closely at the body. He had been frightened. She might have been murdered and some one might spring out from behind a tree and murder him. In a woods, in the late afternoon, when the trees are all bare and there is white snow on the ground, when all is silent, something creepy steals over the mind and body. If something strange or uncanny has happened in the neighborhood all you think about is getting away from there as fast as you can.

The crowd of men and boys had got to where the old woman had crossed the field and went, following the marshal and the hunter, up the slight incline and into the woods.

My brother and I were silent. He had his bundle of papers in a bag slung across his shoulder. When he got back to town he would have to go on distributing his papers before he went home to supper. If I went along, as he had no doubt already determined I should, we would both be late. Either mother or our older sister would have to warm our supper.

Well, we would have something to tell. A boy did not get such a chance very often. It was lucky we just happened to go into the grocery when the hunter came in. The hunter was a country fellow. Neither of us had ever seen him before.

Now the crowd of men and boys had got to the clearing. Darkness comes quickly on such Winter nights, but the full moon made everything clear. My brother and I stood near the tree, beneath which the old woman had died.

She did not look old, lying there in that light, frozen and still. One of the men turned her over in the snow and I saw everything. My body trembled with some strange mystical feeling and so did my brother's. It might have been the cold.

Neither of us had ever seen a woman's body before. It may have been the snow, clinging to the frozen flesh, that made it look so white and lovely, so like marble. No woman had come with the party from town; but one of the men, he was the town blacksmith, took off his overcoat and spread it over her. Then he gathered her into his arms and started off to town, all the others following silently. At that time no one knew who she was.

V

I had seen everything, had seen the oval in the snow, like a miniature race-track, where the dogs had run, had seen how the men were mystified, had seen the white bare young-looking shoulders, had heard the whispered comments of the men.

The men were simply mystified. They took the body to the undertaker's, and when the blacksmith, the hunter, the marshal and several others had got inside they closed the door. If father had been there perhaps he could have got in, but we boys couldn't.

I went with my brother to distribute the rest of his papers and when we got home it was my brother who told the story.

I kept silent and went to bed early. It may have been I was not satisfied with the way he told it.

Later, in the town, I must have heard other fragments of the old woman's story. She was recognized the next day and there was an investigation.

The husband and son were found somewhere and brought to town and there was an attempt to connect them with the woman's death, but it did not work. They had perfect enough alibis.

However, the town was against them. They had to get out. Where they went I never heard.

I remember only the picture there in the forest, the men standing about, the naked girlish-looking figure, face down in the snow, the tracks made by the running dogs and the clear cold Winter sky above. White fragments of clouds were drifting across the sky. They went racing across the little open space among the trees.

The scene in the forest had become for me, without my knowing it, the foundation for the real story I am now trying to tell. The fragments, you see, had to be picked up slowly, long afterwards.

Things happened. When I was a young man I worked on the farm of a German. The hired-girl was afraid of her employer. The farmer's wife hated her.

I saw things at that place. Once later, I had a half-uncanny, mystical adventure with dogs in an Illinois forest on a clear, moon-lit Winter night. When I was a schoolboy, and on a Summer day, I went with a boy friend out along a creek some miles from town and came to the house where the old woman had lived. No one had lived in the house since her death. The doors were broken from the hinges; the window lights were all broken. As the boy and I stood in the road outside, two dogs, just roving farm dogs no doubt, came running around the corner of the house. The dogs were tall, gaunt fellows and came down to the fence and glared through at us, standing in the road.

The whole thing, the story of the old woman's death, was to me as I grew older like music heard from far off. The notes had to be picked up slowly one at a time. Something had to be understood.

The woman who died was one destined to feed animal life. Anyway, that is all she ever did. She was feeding animal life before she was born, as a child, as a young woman working on the farm of the German, after she married, when she grew old and when she died. She fed animal life in cows, in chickens, in pigs, in horses, in dogs, in men. Her daughter had died in childhood and with her one son she had no articulate relations. On the night when she died she was hurrying homeward, bearing on her body food for animal life.

She died in the clearing in the woods and even after her death continued feeding animal life.

You see it is likely that, when my brother told the story, that night when we got home and my mother and sister sat listening, I did not think he got the point. He was too young and so was I. A thing so complete has its own beauty.

I shall not try to emphasize the point. I am only explaining why I was dissatisfied then and have been ever since. I speak of that only that you may understand why I have been impelled to try to tell the simple story over again.

WILLIAM FAULKNER

(1897-1962)

Considered one of the greatest of American writers, recipient of the Nobel Prize for Literature in 1950, Faulkner was born in Mississippi, and his novels and short stories focus on the South. The Sartoris family, the city of Jefferson, and Yoknapatawpha County—the principal characters and settings of his work—have become literary bywords. Virtually all of his work is entwined with the thread of history: his morbid, grotesque figures, the sense of horror and decay, can easily be traced back to the rise and fall of the South.

A Rose for Emily

I

When Miss Emily Grierson died, our whole town went to her funeral: the men through a sort of respectful affection for a fallen monument, the women mostly out of curiosity to see the inside of her house, which no one save an old manservant—a combined gardener and cook—had seen in at least ten years.

It was a big, squarish frame house that had once been white, decorated with cupolas and spires and scrolled balconies in the heavily lightsome style of the seventies, set on what had once been our most select street. But garages and cotton gins had encroached and obliterated even the august names of that neighborhood; only Miss Emily's house was left, lifting its stubborn and coquettish decay above the cotton wagons and the gasoline pumps—an eyesore among eyesores. And now Miss Emily had gone to join the representatives of those august names where they lay in the cedar-bemused cemetery among the ranked and anonymous graves of Union and Confederate soldiers who fell at the battle of Jefferson.

Alive, Miss Emily had been a tradition, a duty, and a care; a sort of hereditary obligation upon the town, dating from that day in 1894 when Colonel Sartoris, the mayor—he who fathered the edict that no Negro woman should appear on the streets without an apron—remitted her taxes, the dispensation dating from the death of her father on into perpetuity. Not that Miss Emily would have accepted charity. Colonel Sartoris invented an involved tale to the effect that Miss Emily's father had loaned money to the town, which the town, as a matter of business, preferred this way of repaying. Only a man of Colonel Sartoris' generation and thought could have invented it, and only a woman could have believed it.

When the next generation, with its more modern ideas, became mayors and aldermen, this arrangement created some little dissatisfaction. On the first of the year they mailed her a tax notice. February came, and there was no reply. They wrote her a formal letter, asking her to call at the sheriff's office at her convenience. A week later the mayor wrote her himself, offering to call or to send his car for her, and received in reply a note on paper of an archaic shape, in a thin, flowing calligraphy in faded ink, to the effect that she no longer went out at all. The tax notice was also enclosed, without comment.

They called a special meeting of the Board of Aldermen. A deputation waited upon her, knocked at the door through which no visitor had passed since she ceased giving china-painting lessons eight or ten years earlier. They were admitted by the old Negro into a dim hall from which a stairway mounted into still more shadow. It smelled of dust and disuse—a close, dank smell. The Negro led them into the parlor. It was furnished in heavy, leather-covered furniture. When the Negro opened the blinds of one window, they could see that the leather was cracked; and when they sat down, a faint dust rose sluggishly about their thighs, spinning with slow motes in the single sun-ray. On a tarnished gilt easel before the fireplace stood a crayon portrait of Miss Emily's father.

They rose when she entered—a small, fat woman in black, with a thin gold chain descending to her waist and vanishing into her belt, leaning on an ebony cane with a tarnished gold head. Her skeleton was small and spare; perhaps that was why what would have been merely plumpness in another was obesity in her. She looked bloated, like a body long submerged in motionless water, and of that pallid hue. Her eyes, lost in the fatty ridges of her face, looked like two small pieces of coal pressed into a lump of dough as they moved from one face to another while the visitors stated their errand.

She did not ask them to sit. She just stood in the door and listened quietly until the spokesman came to a stumbling halt. Then they could hear the invisible watch ticking at the end of the gold chain.

Her voice was dry and cold. "I have no taxes in Jefferson. Colonel Sartoris explained it to me. Perhaps one of you can gain access to the city records and satisfy yourselves."

"But we have. We are the city authorities, Miss Emily. Didn't you get a notice from the sheriff, signed by him?"

"I received a paper, yes," Miss Emily said. "Perhaps he considers himself the sheriff . . . I have no taxes in Jefferson."

"But there is nothing on the books to show that, you see. We must go by the—"

"See Colonel Sartoris. I have no taxes in Jefferson."

"But, Miss Emily—"

"See Colonel Sartoris." (Colonel Sartoris had been dead almost ten years.) "I have no taxes in Jefferson. Tobe!" The Negro appeared. "Show these gentlemen out."

II

So she vanquished them, horse and foot, just as she had vanquished their fathers thirty years before about the smell. That was two years after her father's death and a short time after her sweetheart —the one we believed would marry her—had deserted her. After her father's death she went out very little; after her sweetheart went away, people hardly saw her at all. A few of the ladies had the temerity to call, but were not received, and the only sign of life about the place was the Negro man—a young man then—going in and out with a market basket.

"Just as if a man—any man—could keep a kitchen properly," the ladies said; so they were not surprised when the smell developed.

It was another link between the gross, teeming world and the high and mighty Griersons.

A neighbor, a woman, complained to the mayor, Judge Stevens, eighty years old.

"But what will you have me do about it, madam?" he said.

"Why, send her word to stop it," the woman said. "Isn't there a law?"

"I'm sure that won't be necessary," Judge Stevens said. "It's probably just a snake or a rat that nigger of hers killed in the yard. I'll speak to him about it."

The next day he received two more complaints, one from a man who came in diffident deprecation. "We really must do something about it, Judge. I'd be the last one in the world to bother Miss Emily, but we've got to do something." That night the Board of Aldermen met—three graybeards and one younger man, a member of the rising generation.

"It's simple enough," he said. "Send her word to have her place cleaned up. Give her a certain time to do it in, and if she don't . . ."

"Dammit, sir," Judge Stevens said, "will you accuse a lady to her face of smelling bad?"

So the next night, after midnight, four men crossed Miss Emily's lawn and slunk about the house like burglars, sniffing along the base of the brickwork and at the cellar openings while one of them performed a regular sowing motion with his hand out of a sack slung from his shoulder. They broke open the cellar door and sprinkled lime there, and in all the outbuildings. As they recrossed the lawn, a window that had been dark was lighted and Miss Emily sat in it, the light behind her, and her upright torso motionless as that of an idol. They crept quietly across the lawn and into the shadow of the locusts that lined the street. After a week or two the smell went away.

That was when people had begun to feel really sorry for her. People in our town, remembering how old lady Wyatt, her great-aunt, had gone completely crazy at last, believed that the Griersons held themselves a little too high for what they really were. None of the young men were quite good enough for Miss Emily and such. We had long thought of them as a tableau, Miss Emily a slender figure in white in the background, her father a spraddled silhouette in the foreground, his back to her and clutching a horsewhip, the two

of them framed by the back-flung front door. So when she got to be
thirty and was still single, we were not pleased exactly, but vindi-
cated; even with insanity in the family she wouldn't have turned
down all of her chances if they had really materialized.

When her father died, it got about that the house was all that
was left to her; and in a way, people were glad. At last they could
pity Miss Emily. Being left alone, and a pauper, she had become hu-
manized. Now she too would know the old thrill and the old despair
of a penny more or less.

The day after his death all the ladies prepared to call at the
house and offer condolence and aid, as is our custom. Miss Emily
met them at the door, dressed as usual and with no trace of grief on
her face. She told them that her father was not dead. She did that for
three days, with the ministers calling on her, and the doctors, trying
to persuade her to let them dispose of the body. Just as they were
about to resort to law and force, she broke down, and they buried
her father quickly.

We did not say she was crazy then. We believed she had to do
that. We remembered all the young men her father had driven away,
and we knew that with nothing left, she would have to cling to that
which had robbed her, as people will.

III

She was sick for a long time. When we saw her again, her hair was
cut short, making her look like a girl, with a vague resemblance to
those angels in colored church windows—sort of tragic and serene.

The town had just let the contracts for paving the sidewalks,
and in the summer after her father's death they began the work.
The construction company came with niggers and mules and machinery, and a foreman named Homer Barron, a Yankee—a big, dark,
ready man, with a big voice and eyes lighter than his face. The little
boys would follow in groups to hear him cuss the niggers, and the
niggers singing in time to the rise and fall of picks. Pretty soon he
knew everybody in town. Whenever you heard a lot of laughing
anywhere about the square, Homer Barron would be in the center
of the group. Presently we began to see him and Miss Emily on Sunday afternoons driving in the yellow-wheeled buggy and the matched
team of bays from the livery stable.

At first we were glad that Miss Emily would have an interest, because the ladies all said, "Of course a Grierson would not think seriously of a Northerner, a day laborer." But there were still others, older people, who said that even grief could not cause a real lady to forget *noblesse oblige*—without calling it *noblesse oblige*. They just said, "Poor Emily. Her kinsfolk should come to her." She had some kin in Alabama; but years ago her father had fallen out with them over the estate of old lady Wyatt, the crazy woman, and there was no communication between the two families. They had not even been represented at the funeral.

And as soon as the old people said, "Poor Emily," the whispering began. "Do you suppose it's really so?" they said to one another. "Of course it is. What else could . . ." This behind their hands; rustling of craned silk and satin behind jalousies closed upon the sun on Sunday afternoon as the thin, swift clop-clop-clop of the matched team passed: "Poor Emily."

She carried her head high enough—even when we believed that she was fallen. It was as if she demanded more than ever the recognition of her dignity as the last Grierson; as if it had wanted that touch of earthiness to reaffirm her imperviousness. Like when she bought the rat poison, the arsenic. That was over a year after they had begun to say "Poor Emily," and while the two female cousins were visiting her.

"I want some poison," she said to the druggist. She was over thirty then, still a slight woman, though thinner than usual, with cold, haughty black eyes in a face the flesh of which was strained across the temples and about the eye-sockets as you imagine a light-house-keeper's face ought to look. "I want some poison," she said.

"Yes, Miss Emily. What kind? For rats and such? I'd recom—"

"I want the best you have. I don't care what kind."

The druggist named several. "They'll kill anything up to an elephant. But what you want is—"

"Arsenic," Miss Emily said. "Is that a good one?"

"Is . . . arsenic? Yes, ma'am. But what you want—"

"I want arsenic."

The druggist looked down at her. She looked back at him, erect, her face like a strained flag. "Why, of course," the druggist said. "If that's what you want. But the law requires you to tell what you are going to use it for."

Miss Emily just stared at him, her head tilted back in order to look him eye for eye, until he looked away and went and got the arsenic and wrapped it up. The Negro delivery boy brought her the package; the druggist didn't come back. When she opened the package at home there was written on the box, under the skull and bones: "For rats."

IV

So the next day we all said, "She will kill herself"; and we said it would be the best thing. When she had first begun to be seen with Homer Barron, we had said, "She will marry him." Then we said, "She will persuade him yet," because Homer himself had remarked—he liked men, and it was known that he drank with the younger men in the Elks' Club—that he was not a marrying man. Later we said, "Poor Emily" behind the jalousies as they passed on Sunday afternoon in the glittering buggy, Miss Emily with her head high and Homer Barron with his hat cocked and a cigar in his teeth, reins and whip in a yellow glove.

Then some of the ladies began to say that it was a disgrace to the town and a bad example to the young people. The men did not want to interfere, but at last the ladies forced the Baptist minister —Miss Emily's people were Episcopal—to call upon her. He would never divulge what happened during that interview, but he refused to go back again. The next Sunday they again drove about the streets, and the following day the minister's wife wrote to Miss Emily's relations in Alabama.

So she had blood-kin under her roof again and we sat back to watch developments. At first nothing happened. Then we were sure that they were to be married. We learned that Miss Emily had been to the jeweler's and ordered a man's toilet set in silver, with the letters H.B. on each piece. Two days later we learned that she had bought a complete outfit of men's clothing, including a nightshirt, and we said, "They are married." We were really glad. We were glad because the two female cousins were even more Grierson than Miss Emily had ever been.

So we were not surprised when Homer Barron—the streets had been finished some time since—was gone. We were a little disappointed that there was not a public blowing-off, but we believed that he had gone on to prepare for Miss Emily's coming, or to give her a chance to get rid of the cousins. (By that time it was a cabal, and we were all Miss Emily's allies to help circumvent the cousins.) Sure enough, after another week they departed. And, as we had expected all along, within three days Homer Barron was back in town. A neighbor saw the Negro man admit him at the kitchen door at dusk one evening.

And that was the last we saw of Homer Barron. And of Miss Emily for some time. The Negro man went in and out with the market basket, but the front door remained closed. Now and then we would see her at a window for a moment, as the men did that night when they sprinkled the lime, but for almost six months she did not appear on the streets. Then we knew that this was to be expected too; as if that quality of her father which had thwarted her woman's life so many times had been too virulent and too furious to die.

When we next saw Miss Emily, she had grown fat and her hair was turning gray. During the next few years it grew grayer and grayer until it attained an even pepper-and-salt iron-gray, when it ceased turning. Up to the day of her death at seventy-four it was still that vigorous iron-gray, like the hair of an active man.

From that time on her front door remained closed, save for a period of six or seven years, when she was about forty, during which she gave lessons in china-painting. She fitted up a studio in one of the downstairs rooms, where the daughters and granddaughters of Colonel Sartoris' contemporaries were sent to her with the same regularity and in the same spirit that they were sent to church on Sundays with a twenty-five-cent piece for the collection plate. Meanwhile her taxes had been remitted.

Then the newer generation became the backbone and the spirit of the town, and the painting pupils grew up and fell away and did not send their children to her with boxes of color and tedious brushes and pictures cut from the ladies' magazines. The front door closed upon the last one and remained closed for good. When the town got free postal delivery, Miss Emily alone refused to let them fasten the metal numbers above her door and attach a mailbox to it. She would not listen to them.

Daily, monthly, yearly we watched the Negro grow grayer and more stooped, going in and out with the market basket. Each December we sent her a tax notice, which would be returned by the post office a week later, unclaimed. Now and then we would see her in one of the downstairs windows—she had evidently shut up the top floor of the house—like the carven torso of an idol in a niche, looking or not looking at us, we could never tell which. Thus she passed from generation to generation—dear, inescapable, impervious, tranquil, and perverse.

And so she died. Fell ill in the house filled with dust and shadows, with only a doddering Negro man to wait on her. We did not even know she was sick; we had long since given up trying to get any information from the Negro. He talked to no one, probably not even to her, for his voice had grown harsh and rusty, as if from disuse.

She died in one of the downstairs rooms, in a heavy walnut bed with a curtain, her gray head propped on a pillow yellow and moldy with age and lack of sunlight.

V

The Negro met the first of the ladies at the front door and let them in, with their hushed, sibilant voices and their quick, curious glances, and then he disappeared. He walked right through the house and out the back and was not seen again.

The two female cousins came at once. They held the funeral on the second day, with the town coming to look at Miss Emily beneath a mass of bought flowers, with the crayon face of her father musing profoundly above the bier and the ladies sibilant and macabre; and the very old men—some in their brushed Confederate uniforms— on the porch and the lawn, talking of Miss Emily as if she had been a contemporary of theirs, believing that they had danced with her and courted her perhaps, confusing time with its mathematical progression, as the old do, to whom all the past is not a diminishing road but, instead, a huge meadow which no winter ever quite touches, divided from them now by the narrow bottle-neck of the most recent decade of years.

Already we knew that there was one room in that region above stairs which no one had seen in forty years, and which would have to be forced. They waited until Miss Emily was decently in the ground before they opened it.

The violence of breaking down the door seemed to fill this room with pervading dust. A thin, acrid pall as of the tomb seemed to lie everywhere upon this room decked and furnished as for a bridal: upon the valance curtains of faded rose color, upon the rose-shaded lights, upon the dressing table, upon the delicate array of crystal and the man's toilet things backed with tarnished silver, silver so tarnished that the monogram was obscured. Among them lay a collar and tie, as if they had just been removed, which, lifted, left upon the surface a pale crescent in the dust. Upon a chair hung the suit, carefully folded; beneath it the two mute shoes and the discarded socks.

The man himself lay in the bed.

For a long while we just stood there, looking down at the profound and fleshless grin. The body had apparently once lain in the attitude of an embrace, but now the long sleep that outlasts love, that conquers even the grimace of love, had cuckolded him. What was left of him, rotted beneath what was left of the nightshirt, had become inextricable from the bed in which he lay; and upon him and upon the pillow beside him lay that even coating of the patient and biding dust.

Then we noticed that in the second pillow was the indentation of a head. One of us lifted something from it, and leaning forward, that faint and invisible dust dry and acrid in the nostrils, we saw a long strand of iron-gray hair.

ERNEST HEMINGWAY

(1899-1961)

Ernest Hemingway is one of the best known and most widely read modern American writers. Before his death in 1961, he had become famous as a journalist, novelist, short story writer, expatriate, adventurer, and sportsman. Born in Illinois, he went to Italy to serve with the Italians in the First World War, an experience which provided the background for his famous novel, A FAREWELL TO ARMS. Settling in Paris, he became one of the central figures of the so-called Lost Generation and wrote his first novel, THE SUN ALSO RISES. His experiences in Spain and the Spanish Civil War produced DEATH IN THE AFTERNOON and the novel, FOR WHOM THE BELL TOLLS. Hunting in Africa provides the framework for his short story "The Snows of Kilimanjaro" as well as the one reprinted here. In 1954 he was awarded the Nobel Prize for Literature for THE OLD MAN AND THE SEA. His style, which gives the impression of being spare, unmannered, and direct, is actually much more complex than is usually recognized. In any case, it is the product of careful and extensive rewriting, offering a classic example of "the art that conceals art."

The Short Happy Life of Francis Macomber

It was now lunch time and they were all sitting under the double green fly of the dining tent pretending that nothing had happened.

"Will you have lime juice or lemon squash?" Macomber asked.

"I'll have a gimlet," Robert Wilson told him.

"I'll have a gimlet too. I need something," Macomber's wife said.

"I suppose it's the thing to do," Macomber agreed. "Tell him to make three gimlets."

The mess boy had started them already, lifting the bottles out of the canvas cooling bags that sweated wet in the wind that blew through the trees that shaded the tents.

"What had I ought to give them?" Macomber asked.

"A quid would be plenty," Wilson told him. "You don't want to spoil them."

"Will the headman distribute it?"

"Absolutely."

Francis Macomber had, half an hour before, been carried to his tent from the edge of the camp in triumph on the arms and shoulders of the cook, the personal boys, the skinner and the porters. The gun-bearers had taken no part in the demonstration. When the native boys put him down at the door of his tent, he had shaken all their hands, received their congratulations, and then gone into the tent and sat on the bed until his wife came in. She did not speak to him when she came in and he left the tent at once to wash his face and hands in the portable wash basin outside and go over to the dining tent to sit in a comfortable canvas chair in the breeze and the shade.

"You've got your lion," Robert Wilson said to him, "and a damned fine one too."

Mrs. Macomber looked at Wilson quickly. She was an extremely handsome and well-kept woman of the beauty and social position which had, five years before, commanded five thousand dollars as the price of endorsing, with photographs, a beauty product which she had never used. She had been married to Francis Macomber for eleven years.

"He is a good lion, isn't he?" Macomber said. His wife looked at him now. She looked at both these men as though she had never seen them before.

One, Wilson, the white hunter, she knew she had never truly seen before. He was about middle height with sandy hair, a stubby mustache, a very red face and extremely cold blue eyes with faint white wrinkles at the corners that grooved merrily when he smiled. He smiled at her now and she looked away from his face at the way his shoulders sloped in the loose tunic he wore with the four big cartridges held in loops where the left breast pocket should have been, at his big brown hands, his old slacks, his very dirty boots and back to his red face again. She noticed where the baked red of his face stopped in a white line that marked the circle left by his Stetson hat that hung now from one of the pegs of the tent pole.

"Well, here's to the lion," Robert Wilson said. He smiled at her again and, not smiling, she looked curiously at her husband.

Francis Macomber was very tall, very well built if you did not mind that length of bone, dark, his hair cropped like an oarsman, rather thin-lipped, and was considered handsome. He was dressed in the same sort of safari clothes that Wilson wore except that his were new, he was thirty-five years old, kept himself very fit, was good at court games, had a number of big-game fishing records, and had just shown himself, very publicly, to be a coward.

"Here's to the lion," he said. "I can't ever thank you for what you did."

Margaret, his wife, looked away from him and back to Wilson.

"Let's not talk about the lion," she said.

Wilson looked over at her without smiling and now she smiled at him.

"It's been a very strange day," she said. "Hadn't you ought to put your hat on even under the canvas at noon? You told me that, you know."

"Might put it on," said Wilson.

"You know you have a very red face, Mr. Wilson," she told him and smiled again.

"Drink," said Wilson.

"I don't think so," she said. "Francis drinks a great deal, but his face is never red."

"It's red today," Macomber tried a joke.

"No," said Margaret. "It's mine that's red today. But Mr. Wilson's is always red."

"Must be racial," said Wilson. "I say, you wouldn't like to drop my beauty as a topic, would you?"

"I've just started on it."

"Let's chuck it," said Wilson.

"Conversation is going to be so difficult," Margaret said.

"Don't be silly, Margot," her husband said.

"No difficulty," Wilson said. "Got a damn fine lion."

Margot looked at them both and they both saw that she was going to cry. Wilson had seen it coming for a long time and he dreaded it. Macomber was past dreading it.

"I wish it hadn't happened. Oh, I wish it hadn't happened," she said and started for her tent. She made no noise of crying but they could see that her shoulders were shaking under the rose-colored, sun-proofed shirt she wore.

"Women upset," said Wilson to the tall man. "Amounts to nothing. Strain on the nerves and one thing'n another."

"No," said Macomber. "I suppose that I rate that for the rest of my life now."

"Nonsense. Let's have a spot of the giant killer," said Wilson. "Forget the whole thing. Nothing to it anyway."

"We might try," said Macomber. "I won't forget what you did for me though."

"Nothing," said Wilson. "All nonsense."

So they sat there in the shade where the camp was pitched under some wide-topped acacia trees with a boulder-strewn cliff behind them, and a stretch of grass that ran to the bank of a boulder-filled stream in front with forest beyond it, and drank their just-cool lime drinks and avoided one another's eyes while the boys set the table for lunch. Wilson could tell that the boys all knew about it now and when he saw Macomber's personal boy looking curiously at his master while he was putting dishes on the table he snapped at him in Swahili. The boy turned away with his face blank.

"What were you telling him?" Macomber asked.

"Nothing. Told him to look alive or I'd see he got about fifteen of the best."

"What's that? Lashes?"

"It's quite illegal," Wilson said. "You're supposed to fine them."

"Do you still have them whipped?"

"Oh, yes. They could raise a row if they chose to complain. But they don't. They prefer it to the fines."

"How strange!" said Macomber.

"Not strange, really," Wilson said. "Which would do? Take a good birching or lose your pay?"

Then he felt embarrassed at asking it and before

could answer he went on, "We all take a beating every day, you know, one way or another."

This was no better. "Good God," he thought. "I am a diplomat, aren't I?"

"Yes, we take a beating," said Macomber, still not looking at him. "I'm awfully sorry about that lion business. It doesn't have to go any further, does it? I mean no one will hear about it, will they?"

"You mean will I tell it at the Mathaiga Club?" Wilson looked at him now coldly. He had not expected this. So he's a bloody four-letter man as well as a bloody coward, he thought. I rather liked him too until today. But how is one to know about an American?

"No," said Wilson. "I'm a professional hunter. We never talk about our clients. You can be quite easy on that. It's supposed to be bad form to ask us not to talk though."

He had decided now that to break would be much easier. He would eat, then, by himself and could read a book with his meals. They would eat by themselves. He would see them through the safari on a very formal basis—what was it the French called it? Distinguished consideration—and it would be a damn sight easier than having to go through this emotional trash. He'd insult him and make a good clean break. Then he could read a book with his meals and he'd still be drinking their whisky. That was the phrase for it when a safari went bad. You ran into another white hunter and you asked, "How is everything going?" and he answered, "Oh, I'm still drinking their whisky," and you knew everything had gone to pot.

"I'm sorry," Macomber said and looked at him with his American face that would stay adolescent until it became middle-aged, and Wilson noted his crew-cropped hair, fine eyes only faintly shifty, good nose, thin lips and handsome jaw. "I'm sorry I didn't realize that. There are lots of things I don't know."

So what could he do, Wilson thought. He was all ready to break it off quickly and neatly and here the beggar was apologizing after he had just insulted him. He made one more attempt. "Don't worry about me talking," he said. "I have a living to make. You know in Africa no woman ever misses her lion and no white man ever bolts."

"I bolted like a rabbit," Macomber said.

Now what in hell were you going to do about a man who talked like that, Wilson wondered.

Wilson looked at Macomber with his flat, blue, machine-gun-ner's eyes and the other smiled back at him. He had a pleasant smile if you did not notice how his eyes showed when he was hurt.

"Maybe I can fix it up on buffalo," he said. "We're after them next, aren't we?"

"In the morning if you like," Wilson told him. Perhaps he had been wrong. This was certainly the way to take it. You most certainly could not tell a damned thing about an American. He was all for Macomber again. If you could forget the morning. But, of course, you couldn't. The morning had been about as bad as they come.

"Here comes the Memsahib," he said. She was walking over from her tent looking refreshed and cheerful and quite lovely. She had a very perfect oval face, so perfect that you expected her to be stupid. But she wasn't stupid, Wilson thought, no, not stupid.

"How is the beautiful red-faced Mr. Wilson? Are you feeling better, Francis, my pearl?"

"Oh, much," said Macomber.

"I've dropped the whole thing," she said, sitting down at the table. "What importance is there to whether Francis is any good at killing lions? That's not his trade. That's Mr. Wilson's trade. Mr. Wilson is really very impressive killing anything. You do kill anything, don't you?"

"Oh, anything," said Wilson. "Simply anything." They are, he thought, the hardest in the world; the hardest, the cruelest, the most predatory and the most attractive and their men have softened or gone to pieces nervously as they have hardened. Or is it that they pick men they can handle? They can't know that much at the age they marry, he thought. He was grateful that he had gone through his education on American women before now because this was a very attractive one.

"We're going after buff in the morning," he told her.

"I'm coming," she said.

"No, you're not."

"Oh, yes, I am. Mayn't I, Francis?"

"Why not stay in camp?"

"Not for anything," she said. "I wouldn't miss something like today for anything."

When she left, Wilson was thinking, when she went off to cry, she seemed a hell of a fine woman. She seemed to understand, to realize, to be hurt for him and for herself and to know how things really stood. She is away for twenty minutes and now she is back, simply enamelled in that American female cruelty. They are the damnedest women. Really the damnedest.

"We'll put on another show for you tomorrow," Francis Macomber said.

"You're not coming," Wilson said.

"You're very mistaken," she told him. "And I want *so* to see you perform again. You were lovely this morning. That is if blowing things' heads off is lovely."

"Here's the lunch," said Wilson. "You're very merry, aren't you?"

"Why not? I didn't come out here to be dull."

"Well, it hasn't been dull," Wilson said. He could see the boulders in the river and the high bank beyond with the trees and he remembered the morning.

"Oh, no," she said. "It's been charming. And tomorrow. You don't know how I look forward to tomorrow."

"That's eland he's offering you," Wilson said.

"They're the big cowy things that jump like hares, aren't they?"

"I suppose that describes them," Wilson said.

"It's very good meat," Macomber said.

"Did you shoot it, Francis?" she asked.

"Yes."

"They're not dangerous, are they?"

"Only if they fall on you," Wilson told her.

"I'm so glad."

"Why not let up on the bitchery just a little, Margot," Macomber said, cutting the eland steak and putting some mashed potato, gravy and carrot on the down-turned fork that tined through the piece of meat.

"I suppose I could," she said, "since you put it so prettily."

"Tonight we'll have champagne for the lion," Wilson said. "It's a bit too hot at noon."

"Oh, the lion," Margot said. "I'd forgotten the lion!"

So, Robert Wilson thought to himself, she *is* giving him a ride, isn't she? Or do you suppose that's her idea of putting up a good show? How should a woman act when she discovers her husband is a bloody coward? She's damn cruel but they're all cruel. They govern, of course, and to govern one has to be cruel sometimes. Still, I've seen enough of their damn terrorism.

"Have some more eland," he said to her politely.

That afternoon, late, Wilson and Macomber went out in the motor car with the native driver and the two gun-bearers. Mrs. Macomber stayed in the camp. It was too hot to go out, she said, and she was going with them in the early morning. As they drove off Wilson saw her standing under the big tree, looking pretty rather than beautiful in her faintly rosy khaki, her dark hair drawn back off her forehead and gathered in a knot low on her neck, her face as fresh, he thought, as though she were in England. She waved to them as the car went off through the swale of high grass and curved around through the trees into the small hills of orchard bush.

In the orchard bush they found a herd of impala, and leaving the car they stalked one old ram with long, wide-spread horns and Macomber killed it with a very creditable shot that knocked the buck down at a good two hundred yards and sent the herd off bounding wildly and leaping over one another's backs in long, leg-drawn-up leaps as unbelievable and as floating as those one makes sometimes in dreams.

"That was a good shot," Wilson said. "They're a small target."

"Is it a worth-while head?" Macomber asked.

"It's excellent," Wilson told him. "You shoot like that and you'll have no trouble."

"Do you think we'll find buffalo tomorrow?"

"There's a good chance of it. They feed out early in the morning and with luck we may catch them in the open."

"I'd like to clear away that lion business," Macomber said. "It's not very pleasant to have your wife see you do something like that."

I should think it would be even more unpleasant to do it, Wilson thought, wife or no wife, or to talk about it having done it. But he said, "I wouldn't think about that any more. Any one could be upset by his first lion. That's all over."

But that night after dinner and a whisky and soda by the fire before going to bed, as Francis Macomber lay on his cot with the mosquito bar over him and listened to the night noises it was not all over. It was neither all over nor was it beginning. It was there, exactly as it happened with some parts of it indelibly emphasized and he was miserably ashamed at it. But more than shame he felt cold, hollow fear in him. The fear was still there like a cold slimy hollow in all the emptiness where once his confidence had been and it made him feel sick. It was still there with him now.

It had started the night before when he had wakened and heard the lion roaring somewhere up along the river. It was a deep sound and at the end there were sort of coughing grunts that made him seem just outside the tent, and when Francis Macomber woke in the night to hear it he was afraid. He could hear his wife breathing quietly, asleep. There was no one to tell he was afraid, nor to be afraid with him, and, lying alone, he did not know the Somali proverb that says a brave man is always frightened three times by a lion; when he first sees his track, when he first hears him roar and when he first confronts him. Then while they were eating breakfast by lantern light out in the dining tent, before the sun was up, the lion roared again and Francis thought he was just at the edge of camp.

"Sounds like an old-timer," Robert Wilson said, looking up from his kippers and coffee. "Listen to him cough."

"Is he very close?"

"A mile or so up the stream."

"Will we see him?"

"We'll have a look."

"Does his roaring carry that far? It sounds as though he were right in camp."

"Carries a hell of a long way," said Robert Wilson. "It's strange the way it carries. Hope he's a shootable cat. The boys said there was a very big one about here."

"If I get a shot, where should I hit him," Macomber asked, "to stop him?"

"In the shoulders," Wilson said. "In the neck if you can make it. Shoot for bone. Break him down."

"I hope I can place it properly," Macomber said.

"You shoot very well," Wilson told him. "Take your time. Make sure of him. The first one in is the one that counts."

"What range will it be?"

"Can't tell. Lion has something to say about that. Won't shoot unless it's close enough so you can make sure."

"At under a hundred yards?" Macomber asked.

Wilson looked at him quickly.

"Hundred's about right. Might have to take him a bit under. Shouldn't chance a shot at much over that. A hundred's a decent range. You can hit him wherever you want at that. Here comes the Memsahib."

"Good morning," she said. "Are we going after that lion?"

"As soon as you deal with your breakfast," Wilson said. "How are you feeling?"

"Marvellous," she said. "I'm very excited."

"I'll just go and see that everything is ready," Wilson went off. As he left the lion roared again.

"Noisy beggar," Wilson said. "We'll put a stop to that."

"What's the matter, Francis?" his wife asked him.

"Nothing," Macomber said.

"Yes, there is," she said. "What are you upset about?"

"Nothing," he said.

"Tell me," she looked at him. "Don't you feel well?"

"It's that damned roaring," he said. "It's been going on all night, you know."

"Why didn't you wake me," she said. "I'd love to have heard it."

"I've got to kill the damned thing," Macomber said, miserably.

"Well, that's what you're out here for, isn't it?"

"Yes. But I'm nervous. Hearing the thing roar gets on my nerves."

"Well then, as Wilson said, kill him and stop his roaring."

"Yes, darling," said Francis Macomber. "It sounds easy, doesn't it?"

"You're not afraid, are you?"

"Of course not. But I'm nervous from hearing him roar all night."

"You'll kill him marvellously," she said. "I know you will. I'm awfully anxious to see it."

"Finish your breakfast and we'll be starting."

"It's not light yet," she said. "This is a ridiculous hour."

Just then the lion roared in a deep-chested moaning, suddenly guttural, ascending vibration that seemed to shake the air and ended in a sigh and a heavy, deep-chested grunt.

"He sounds almost here," Macomber's wife said.

"My God," said Macomber. "I hate that damned noise."

"It's very impressive."

"Impressive. It's frightful."

Robert Wilson came up then carrying his short, ugly, shockingly big-bored .505 Gibbs and grinning.

"Come on," he said. "Your gun-bearer has your Springfield and the big gun. Everything's in the car. Have you solids?"

"Yes."

"I'm ready," Mrs. Macomber said.

"Must make him stop that racket," Wilson said. "You get in front. The Memsahib can sit back here with me."

They climbed into the motor car and, in the gray first daylight, moved off up the river through the trees. Macomber opened the breech of his rifle and saw he had metal-cased bullets, shut the bolt and put the rifle on safety. He saw his hand was trembling. He felt in his pocket for more cartridges and moved his fingers over the cartridges in the loops of his tunic front. He turned back to where Wilson sat in the rear seat of the doorless, box-bodied motor car beside his wife, them both grinning with excitement, and Wilson leaned forward and whispered,

"See the birds dropping. Means the old boy has left his kill."

On the far bank of the stream Macomber could see, above the trees, vultures circling and plummeting down.

"Chances are he'll come to drink along here," Wilson whispered. "Before he goes to lay up. Keep an eye out."

They were driving slowly along the high bank of the stream which here cut deeply to its boulder-filled bed, and they wound in and out through big trees as they drove. Macomber was watching the opposite bank when he felt Wilson take hold of his arm. The car stopped.

"There he is," he heard the whisper. "Ahead and to the right. Get out and take him. He's a marvellous lion."

Macomber saw the lion now. He was standing almost broadside, his great head up and turned toward them. The early morning breeze that blew toward them was just stirring his dark mane, and the lion looked huge, silhouetted on the rise of bank in the gray morning light, his shoulders heavy, his barrel of a body bulking smoothly.

"How far is he?" asked Macomber, raising his rifle.

"About seventy-five. Get out and take him."

"Why not shoot from where I am?"

"You don't shoot them from cars," he heard Wilson saying in his ear. "Get out. He's not going to stay there all day."

Macomber stepped out of the curved opening at the side of the front seat, onto the step and down onto the ground. The lion still stood looking majestically and coolly toward this object that his eyes only showed in silhouette, bulking like some super-rhino. There was no man smell carried toward him and he watched the object, moving his great head a little from side to side. Then watching the object, not afraid, but hesitating before going down the bank to drink with such a thing opposite him, he saw a man figure detach itself from it and he turned his heavy head and swung away toward the cover of the trees as he heard a cracking crash and felt the slam of a .30-06 220-grain solid bullet that bit his flank and ripped in sudden hot scalding nausea through his stomach. He trotted, heavy, big-footed, swinging wounded full-bellied, through the trees toward the tall grass and cover, and the crash came again to go past him ripping the air apart. Then it crashed again and he felt the blow as it hit his lower ribs and ripped on through, blood sudden hot and frothy in his mouth, and he galloped toward the high grass where he could crouch and not be seen and make them bring the crashing thing close enough so he could make a rush and get the man that held it.

Macomber had not thought how the lion felt as he got out of the car. He only knew his hands were shaking and as he walked away from the car it was almost impossible for him to make his legs move. They were stiff in the thighs, but he could feel the muscles fluttering. He raised the rifle, sighted on the junction of the lion's head and shoulders and pulled the trigger. Nothing happened though he pulled until he thought his finger would break. Then he knew he had the safety on and as he lowered the rifle to move the safety over he moved another frozen pace forward, and the lion seeing his silhouette now clear of the silhouette of the car, turned and started off at a trot, and, as Macomber fired, he heard a whunk that meant that the bullet was home; but the lion kept on going. Macomber shot again and every one saw the bullet throw a spout of dirt beyond the trotting lion. He shot again, remembering to lower his aim, and they all heard the bullet hit, and the lion went into a gallop and was in the tall grass before he had the bolt pushed forward.

Macomber stood there feeling sick at his stomach, his hands that held the Springfield still cocked, shaking, and his wife and Robert Wilson were standing by him. Beside him too were the two gun-bearers chattering in Wakamba.

"I hit him," Macomber said. "I hit him twice."

"You gut-shot him and you hit him somewhere forward." Wilson said without enthusiasm. The gun-bearers looked very grave. They were silent now.

"You may have killed him," Wilson went on. "We'll have to wait a while before we go in to find out."

"What do you mean?"

"Let him get sick before we follow him up."

"Oh," said Macomber.

"He's a hell of a fine lion," Wilson said cheerfully. "He's gotten into a bad place though."

"Why is it bad?"

"Can't see him until you're on him."

"Oh," said Macomber.

"Come on," said Wilson. "The Memsahib can stay here in the car. We'll go to have a look at the blood spoor."

"Stay here, Margot," Macomber said to his wife. His mouth was very dry and it was hard for him to talk.

"Why?" she asked.

"Wilson says to."

"We're going to have ∴ look," Wilson said. "You stay here. You can see even better from here."

"All right."

Wilson spoke in Swahili to the driver. He nodded and said, "Yes, Bwana."

Then they went down the steep bank and across the stream, climbing over and around the boulders and up the other bank, pulling up by some projecting roots, and along it until they found where the lion had been trotting when Macomber first shot. There was dark blood on the short grass that the gun-bearers pointed out with grass stems, and that ran away behind the river bank trees.

"What do we do?" asked Macomber.

"Not much choice," said Wilson. "We can't bring the car over. Bank's too steep. We'll let him stiffen up a bit and then you and I'll go in and have a look for him."

"Can't we set the grass on fire?" Macomber asked.

"Too green."

"Can't we send beaters?"

Wilson looked at him appraisingly. "Of course we can," he said. "But it's just a touch murderous. You see we know the lion's wounded. You can drive an unwounded lion—he'll move on ahead of a noise—but a wounded lion's going to charge. You can't see him until you're right on him. He'll make himself perfectly flat in cover you wouldn't think would hide a hare. You can't very well send boys in there to that sort of a show. Somebody bound to get mauled."

"What about the gun-bearers?"

"Oh, they'll go with us. It's their *shauri*. You see, they signed on for it. They don't look too happy though, do they?"

"I don't want to go in there," said Macomber. It was out before he knew he'd said it.

"Neither do I," said Wilson very cheerily. "Really no choice though." Then, as an afterthought, he glanced at Macomber and saw suddenly how he was trembling and the pitiful look on his face.

"You don't have to go in, of course," he said. "That's what I'm hired for, you know. That's why I'm so expensive."

"You mean you'd go in by yourself? Why not leave him there?"

Robert Wilson, whose entire occupation had been with the lion and the problem he presented, and who had not been thinking about Macomber except to note that he was rather windy, suddenly felt as though he had opened the wrong door in a hotel and seen something shameful.

"What do you mean?"

"Why not just leave him?"

"You mean pretend to ourselves he hasn't been hit?"

"No. Just drop it."

"It isn't done."

"Why not?"

"For one thing, he's certain to be suffering. For another, some one else might run onto him."

"I see."

"But you don't have to have anything to do with it."

"I'd like to," Macomber said. "I'm just scared, you know."

"I'll go ahead when we go in," Wilson said, "with Kongoni tracking. You keep behind me and a little to one side. Chances are we'll hear him growl. If we see him we'll both shoot. Don't worry about anything. I'll keep you backed up. As a matter of fact, you know, perhaps you'd better not go. It might be much better. Why don't you go over and join the Memsahib while I just get it over with?"

"No, I want to go."

"All right," said Wilson. "But don't go in if you don't want to. This is my *shauri* now, you know."

"I want to go," said Macomber.

They sat under a tree and smoked.

"Want to go back and speak to the Memsahib while we're waiting?" Wilson asked.

"No."

"I'll just step back and tell her to be patient."

"Good," said Macomber. He sat there, sweating under his arms,
his mouth dry, his stomach hollow feeling, wanting to find courage to tell Wilson to go on and finish off the lion without him. He
could not know that Wilson was furious because he had not noticed
the state he was in earlier and sent him back to his wife. While he
sat there Wilson came up. "I have your big gun," he said. "Take it.
We've given him time, I think. Come on."

Macomber took the big gun and Wilson said:

"Keep behind me and about five yards to the right and do exactly as I tell you." Then he spoke in Swahili to the two gun-bearers
who looked the picture of gloom.

"Let's go," he said.

"Could I have a drink of water?" Macomber asked. Wilson spoke
to the older gun-bearer, who wore a canteen on his belt, and the man
unbuckled it, unscrewed the top and handed it to Macomber, who
took it noticing how heavy it seemed and how hairy and shoddy the
felt covering was in his hand. He raised it to drink and looked
ahead at the high grass with the flat-topped trees behind it. A breeze
was blowing toward them and the grass rippled gently in the wind.
He looked at the gun-bearer and he could see the gun-bearer was suffering too with fear.

Thirty-five yards into the grass the big lion lay flattened out
along the ground. His ears were back and his only movement was a
slight twitching up and down of his long, black-tufted tail. He had
turned at bay as soon as he had reached this cover and he was sick
with the wound through his full belly, and weakening with the
wound through his lungs that brought a thin foamy red to his
mouth each time he breathed. His flanks were wet and hot and flies
were on the little openings the solid bullets had made in his tawny
hide, and his big yellow eyes, narrowed with hate, looked straight
ahead, only blinking when the pain came as he breathed, and his
claws dug in the soft baked earth. All of him, pain, sickness, hatred
and all of his remaining strength, was tightening into an absolute
concentration for a rush. He could hear the men talking and he
waited, gathering all of himself into this preparation for a charge
as soon as the men would come into the grass. As he heard their

voices his tail stiffened to twitch up and down, and, as they came into the edge of the grass, he made a coughing grunt and charged.

Kongoni, the old gun-bearer, in the lead watching the blood spoor, Wilson watching the grass for any movement, his big gun ready, the second gun-bearer looking ahead and listening, Macomber close to Wilson, his rifle cocked, they had just moved into the grass when Macomber heard the blood-choked coughing grunt, and saw the swishing rush in the grass. The next thing he knew he was running; running wildly, in panic in the open, running toward the stream.

He heard the *ca-ra-wong!* of Wilson's big rifle, and again in a second crashing *carawong!* and turning saw the lion, horrible-looking now, with half his head seeming to be gone, crawling toward Wilson in the edge of the tall grass while the red-faced man worked the bolt on the short ugly rifle and aimed carefully as another blasting *carawong!* came from the muzzle, and the crawling, heavy, yellow bulk of the lion stiffened and the huge, mutilated head slid forward and Macomber, standing by himself in the clearing where he had run, holding a loaded rifle, while two black men and a white man looked back at him in contempt, knew the lion was dead. He came toward Wilson, his tallness all seeming a naked reproach, and Wilson looked at him and said:

"Want to take pictures?"

"No," he said.

That was all any one had said until they reached the motor car. Then Wilson had said:

"Hell of a fine lion. Boys will skin him out. We might as well stay here in the shade."

Macomber's wife had not looked at him nor he at her and he had sat by her in the back seat with Wilson sitting in the front seat. Once he had reached over and taken his wife's hand without looking at her and she had removed her hand from his. Looking across the stream to where the gun-bearers were skinning out the lion he could see that she had been able to see the whole thing. While they sat there his wife had reached forward and put her hand on Wilson's shoulder. He turned and she had leaned forward over the low seat and kissed him on the mouth.

"Oh, I say," said Wilson, going redder than his natural baked color.

"Mr. Robert Wilson," she said. "The beautiful red-faced Mr. Robert Wilson."

Then she sat down beside Macomber again and looked away across the stream to where the lion lay, with uplifted, white-muscled, tendon-marked naked forearms, and white bloating belly, as the black men fleshed away the skin. Finally the gun-bearers brought the skin over, wet and heavy, and climbed in behind with it, rolling it up before they got in, and the motor car started. No one had said anything more until they were back in camp.

That was the story of the lion. Macomber did not know how the lion had felt before he started his rush, nor during it when the unbelievable smash of the .505 with a muzzle velocity of two tons had hit him in the mouth, nor what kept him coming after that, when the second ripping crash had smashed his hind quarters and he had come crawling on toward the crashing, blasting thing that had destroyed him. Wilson knew something about it and only expressed it by saying, "Damned fine lion," but Macomber did not know how Wilson felt about things either. He did not know how his wife felt except that she was through with him.

His wife had been through with him before but it never lasted. He was very wealthy, and would be much wealthier, and he knew she would not leave him ever now. That was one of the few things that he really knew. He knew about that, about motor cycles—that was earliest—about motor cars, about duck-shooting, about fishing, trout, salmon and big-sea, about sex in books, many books, too many books, about all court games, about dogs, not much about horses, about hanging on to his money, about most of the other things his world dealt in, and about his wife not leaving him. His wife had been a great beauty and she was still a great beauty in Africa, but she was not a great enough beauty any more at home to be able to leave him and better herself and she knew it and he knew it. She had missed the chance to leave him and he knew it. If he had been better with women she would probably have started to worry about him getting another new, beautiful wife; but she knew too much about him to worry about him either. Also, he had always had a great tolerance which seemed the nicest thing about him if it were not the most sinister.

All in all they were known as a comparatively happily married couple, one of those whose disruption is often rumored but never occurs, and as the society columnist put it, they were adding more than a spice of *adventure* to their much envied and ever-enduring *Romance* by a *Safari* in what was known as *Darkest Africa* until the Martin Johnsons lighted it on so many silver screens where they were pursuing *Old Simba* the lion, the buffalo, *Tembo* the elephant and as well collecting specimens for the Museum of Natural History. This same columnist had reported them *on the verge* at least three times in the past and they had been. But they always made it up. They had a sound basis of union. Margot was too beautiful for Macomber to divorce her and Macomber had too much money for Margot ever to leave him.

It was now about three o'clock in the morning and Francis Macomber, who had been asleep a little while after he had stopped thinking about the lion, wakened and then slept again, woke suddenly, frightened in a dream of the bloody-headed lion standing over him, and listening while his heart pounded, he realized that his wife was not in the other cot in the tent. He lay awake with that knowledge for two hours.

At the end of that time his wife came into the tent, lifted her mosquito bar and crawled cozily into bed.

"Where have you been?" Macomber asked in the darkness.

"Hello," she said. "Are you awake?"

"Where have you been?"

"I just went out to get a breath of air."

"You did, like hell."

"What do you want me to say, darling?"

"Where have you been?"

"Out to get a breath of air."

"That's a new name for it. You *are* a bitch."

"Well, you're a coward."

"All right," he said. "What of it?"

"Nothing as far as I'm concerned. But please let's not talk, darling, because I'm very sleepy."

"You think that I'll take anything."

"I know you will, sweet."

"Well, I won't."

"Please, darling, let's not talk. I'm so very sleepy."

"There wasn't going to be any of that. You promised there wouldn't be."

"Well, there is now," she said sweetly.

"You said if we made this trip that there would be none of that. You promised."

"Yes, darling. That's the way I meant it to be. But the trip was spoiled yesterday. We don't have to talk about it, do we?"

"You don't wait long when you have an advantage, do you?"

"Please let's not talk. I'm so sleepy, darling."

"I'm going to talk."

"Don't mind me then, because I'm going to sleep." And she did.

At breakfast they were all three at the table before daylight and Francis Macomber found that, of all the many men that he had hated, he hated Robert Wilson the most.

"Sleep well?" Wilson asked in his throaty voice, filling a pipe. "Did you?"

"Topping," the white hunter told him.

You bastard, thought Macomber, you insolent bastard.

So she woke him when she came in, Wilson thought, looking at them both with his flat, cold eyes. Well, why doesn't he keep his wife where she belongs? What does he think I am, a bloody plaster saint? Let him keep her where she belongs. It's his own fault.

"Do you think we'll find buffalo?" Margot asked, pushing away a dish of apricots.

"Chance of it," Wilson said and smiled at her. "Why don't you stay in camp?"

"Not for anything," she told him.

"Why not order her to stay in camp?" Wilson said to Macomber.

"You order her," said Macomber coldly.

"Let's not have any ordering, nor," turning to Macomber, "any silliness, Francis," Margot said quite pleasantly.

"Are you ready to start?" Macomber asked.

"Any time," Wilson told him. "Do you want the Memsahib to go?"

"Does it make any difference whether I do or not?"

The hell with it, thought Robert Wilson. The utter complete hell with it. So this is what it's going to be like. Well, this is what it's going to be like, then.

"Makes no difference," he said.

"You're sure you wouldn't like to stay in camp with her yourself and let me go out and hunt the buffalo?" Macomber asked.

"Can't do that," said Wilson. "Wouldn't talk rot if I were you."

"I'm not talking rot. I'm disgusted."

"Bad word, disgusted."

"Francis, will you please try to speak sensibly?" his wife said.

"I speak too damned sensibly," Macomber said. "Did you ever eat such filthy food?"

"Something wrong with the food?" asked Wilson quietly.

"No more than with everything else."

"I'd pull yourself together, laddybuck," Wilson said very quietly. "There's a boy waits at table that understands a little English."

"The hell with him."

Wilson stood up and puffing on his pipe strolled away, speaking a few words in Swahili to one of the gun-bearers who was standing waiting for him. Macomber and his wife sat on at the table. He was staring at his coffee cup.

"If you make a scene I'll leave you, darling," Margot said quietly.

"No, you won't."

"You can try it and see."

"You won't leave me."

"No," she said. "I won't leave you and you'll behave yourself."

"Behave myself? That's a way to talk. Behave myself."

"Yes. Behave yourself."

"Why don't *you* try behaving?"

"I've tried it so long. So very long."

"I hate that red-faced swine," Macomber said. "I loathe the sight of him."

"He's really *very* nice."

"Oh, *shut up*," Macomber almost shouted. Just then the car came up and stopped in front of the dining tent and the driver and the two gun-bearers got out. Wilson walked over and looked at the husband and wife sitting there at the table.

"Going shooting?" he asked.

"Yes," said Macomber, standing up. "Yes."

"Better bring a woolly. It will be cool in the car," Wilson said.

"I'll get my leather jacket," Margot said.

"The boy has it," Wilson told her. He climbed into the front with the driver and Francis Macomber and his wife sat, not speaking, in the back seat.

Hope the silly beggar doesn't take a notion to blow the back of my head off, Wilson thought to himself. Women *are* a nuisance on safari.

The car was grinding down to cross the river at a pebbly ford in the gray daylight and then climbed, angling up the steep bank, where Wilson had ordered a way shovelled out the day before so they could reach the parklike wooded rolling country on the far side.

It was a good morning, Wilson thought. There was a heavy dew and as the wheels went through the grass and low bushes he could smell the odor of the crushed fronds. It was an odor like verbena and he liked this early morning smell of the dew, the crushed bracken and the look of the tree trunks showing black through the early morning mist, as the car made its way through the untracked, park-like country. He had put the two in the back seat out of his mind now and was thinking about buffalo. The buffalo that he was after stayed in the daytime in a thick swamp where it was impossible to get a shot, but in the night they fed out into an open stretch of country and if he could come between them and their swamp with the car, Macomber would have a good chance at them in the open. He did not want to hunt buff with Macomber in thick cover. He did not want to hunt buff or anything else with Macomber at all, but he was a professional hunter and he had hunted with some rare ones in his time. If they got buff today there would only be rhino to come and the poor man would have gone through his dangerous game and things might pick up. He'd have nothing more to do with the woman and Macomber would get over that too. He must have gone through plenty of that before by the look of things. Poor beggar. He must have a way of getting over it. Well, it was the poor sod's own bloody fault.

He, Robert Wilson, carried a double size cot on safari to accommodate any windfalls he might receive. He had hunted for a certain clientele, the international, fast, sporting set, where the women did not feel they were getting their money's worth unless they had shared that cot with the white hunter. He despised them when he was away from them although he liked some of them well enough at the time, but he made his living by them; and their standards were his standards as long as they were hiring him.

They were his standards in all except the shooting. He had his own standards about the killing and they could live up to them or get some one else to hunt them. He knew, too, that they all respected him for this. This Macomber was an odd one though. Damned if he wasn't.

Now the wife. Well, the wife. Yes, the wife. Hm, the wife. Well he'd
dropped all that. He looked around at them. Macomber sat grim and
furious. Margot smiled at him. She looked younger today, more innocent and fresher and not so professionally beautiful. What's in her
heart God knows, Wilson thought. She hadn't talked much last night.
At that it was a pleasure to see her.

The motor car climbed up a slight rise and went on through
the trees and then out into a grassy prairie-like opening and kept in
the shelter of the trees along the edge, the driver going slowly and
Wilson looking carefully out across the prairie and all along its far
side. He stopped the car and studied the opening with his field
glasses. Then he motioned to the driver to go on and the car moved
slowly along, the driver avoiding wart-hog holes and driving around
the mud castles ants had built. Then, looking across the opening,
Wilson suddenly turned and said,

"By God, there they are!"

And looking where he pointed, while the car jumped forward
and Wilson spoke in rapid Swahili to the driver, Macomber saw three
huge, black animals looking almost cylindrical in their long heaviness, like big black tank cars, moving at a gallop across the far edge
of the open prairie. They moved at a stiff-necked, stiff bodied gallop
and he could see the upswept wide black horns on their heads as they
galloped heads out; the heads not moving.

"They're three old bulls," Wilson said. "We'll cut them off before they get to the swamp."

The car was going a wild forty-five miles an hour across the open
and as Macomber watched, the buffalo got bigger and bigger until he
could see the gray, hairless, scabby look of one huge bull and how his
neck was a part of his shoulders and the shiny black of his horns as
he galloped a little behind the others that were strung out in that
steady plunging gait; and then, the car swaying as though it had just
jumped a road, they drew up close and he could see the plunging
hugeness of the bull, and the dust in his sparsely haired hide, the
wide boss of horn and his outstretched, wide-nostrilled muzzle, and
he was raising his rifle when Wilson shouted, "Not from the car, you
fool!" and he had no fear, only hatred of Wilson, while the brakes
clamped on and the car skidded, plowing sideways to an almost
stop and Wilson was out on one side and he on the other, stumbling
as his feet hit the still speeding-by of the earth, and then he was shooting at the bull as he moved away, hearing the bullets whunk into

him, emptying his rifle at him as he moved steadily away, finally re-membering to get his shots forward into the shoulder, and, as he fumbled to re-load, he saw the bull was down. Down on his knees, his big head tossing, and seeing the other two still galloping he shot at the leader and hit him. He shot again and missed and he heard the *carawonging* roar as Wilson shot and saw the leading bull slide forward onto his nose.

"Get that other," Wilson said. "Now you're shooting!"

But the other bull was moving steadily at the same gallop and he missed, throwing a spout of dirt, and Wilson missed and the dust rose in a cloud and Wilson shouted, "Come on. He's too far!" and grabbed his arm and they were in the car again, Macomber and Wilson hanging on the sides and rocketing swayingly over the uneven ground, drawing up on the steady, plunging, heavy-necked, straight-moving gallop of the bull.

They were behind him and Macomber was filling his rifle, dropping shells onto the ground, jamming it, clearing the jam, then they were almost up with the bull when Wilson yelled "Stop," and the car skidded so that it almost swung over and Macomber fell forward onto his feet, slammed his bolt forward and fired as far forward as he could aim into the galloping, rounded black back, aimed and shot again, then again, then again, and the bullets, all of them hitting, had no effect on the buffalo that he could see. Then Wilson shot, the roar deafening him, and he could see the bull stagger. Macomber shot again, aiming carefully, and down he came, onto his knees.

"All right," Wilson said. "Nice work. That's the three."

Macomber felt a drunken elation.

"How many times did you shoot?" he asked.

"Just three," Wilson said. "You killed the first bull. The biggest one. I helped you finish the other two. Afraid they might have got into cover. You had them killed. I was just mopping up a little. You shot damn well."

"Let's go to the car," said Macomber. "I want a drink."

"Got to finish off that buff first," Wilson told him. The buffalo was on his knees and he jerked his head furiously and bellowed in pig-eyed, roaring rage as they came toward him.

"Watch he doesn't get up," Wilson said. Then, "Get a little broadside and take him in the neck just behind the ear."

Macomber aimed carefully at the center of the huge, jerking, rage-driven neck and shot. At the shot the head dropped forward.

"That does it," said Wilson. "Got the spine. They're a hell of a looking thing, aren't they?"

"Let's get the drink," said Macomber. In his life he had never felt so good.

In the car Macomber's wife sat very white faced. "You were marvellous, darling," she said to Macomber. "What a ride."

"Was it rough?" Wilson asked.

"It was frightful. I've never been more frightened in my life."

"Let's all have a drink," Macomber said.

"By all means," said Wilson. "Give it to the Memsahib." She drank the neat whisky from the flask and shuddered a little when she swallowed. She handed the flask to Macomber who handed it to Wilson.

"It was frightfully exciting," she said. "It's given me a dreadful headache. I didn't know you were allowed to shoot them from cars though."

"No one shot from cars," said Wilson coldly.

"I mean chase them from cars."

"Wouldn't ordinarily," Wilson said. "Seemed sporting enough to me though while we were doing it. Taking more chance driving that way across the plain full of holes and one thing and another than hunting on foot. Buffalo could have charged us each time we shot if he liked. Gave him every chance. Wouldn't mention it to any one though. It's illegal if that's what you mean."

"It seemed very unfair to me," Margot said, "chasing those big helpless things in a motor car."

"Did it?" said Wilson.

"What would happen if they heard about it in Nairobi?"

"I'd lose my licence for one thing. Other unpleasantnesses," Wilson said, taking a drink from the flask. "I'd be out of business."

"Really?"

"Yes, really."

"Well," said Macomber, and he smiled for the first time all day. "Now she has something on you."

"You have such a pretty way of putting things, Francis," Margot Macomber said. Wilson looked at them both. If a four-letter man marries a five-letter woman, he was thinking, what number of letters would their children be? What he said was, "We lost a gun-bearer. Did you notice it?"

"My God, no," Macomber said.

"Here he comes," Wilson said. "He's all right. He must have fallen off when we left the first bull."

Approaching them was the middle-aged gun-bearer, limping along in his knitted cap, khaki tunic, shorts and rubber sandals, gloomy-faced and disgusted looking. As he came up he called out to Wilson in Swahili and they all saw the change in the white hunter's face.

"What does he say?" asked Margot.

"He says the first bull got up and went into the bush," Wilson said with no expression in his voice.

"Oh," said Macomber blankly.

"Then it's going to be just like the lion," said Margot, full of anticipation.

"It's not going to be a damned bit like the lion," Wilson told her. "Did you want another drink, Macomber?"

"Thanks, yes," Macomber said. He expected the feeling he had had about the lion to come back but it did not. For the first time in his life he really felt wholly without fear. Instead of fear he had a feeling of definite elation.

"We'll go and have a look at the second bull," Wilson said. "I'll tell the driver to put the car in the shade."

"What are you going to do?" asked Margaret Macomber.

"Take a look at the buff," Wilson said.

"I'll come."

"Come along."

The three of them walked over to where the second buffalo bulked blackly in the open, head forward on the grass, the massive horns swung wide.

"He's a very good head," Wilson said. "That's close to a fifty-inch spread."

Macomber was looking at him with delight.

"He's hateful looking," said Margot. "Can't we go into the shade?"

"Of course," Wilson said. "Look," he said to Macomber, and pointed. "See that patch of bush?"

"Yes."

"That's where the first bull went in. The gun-bearer said when he fell off the bull was down. He was watching us helling along and the other two buff galloping. When he looked up there was the bull up and looking at him. Gun-bearer ran like hell and the bull went off slowly into that bush."

"Can we go in after him now?" asked Macomber eagerly.

Wilson looked at him appraisingly. Damned if this isn't a strange one, he thought. Yesterday he's scared sick and today he's a ruddy fire eater.

"No, we'll give him a while."

"Let's please go into the shade," Margot said. Her face was white and she looked ill.

They made their way to the car where it stood under a single, wide-spreading tree and all climbed in.

"Chances are he's dead in there," Wilson remarked. "After a little we'll have a look."

Macomber felt a wild unreasonable happiness that he had never known before.

"By God, that was a chase," he said. "I've never felt any such feeling. Wasn't it marvellous, Margot?"

"I hated it."

"Why?"

"I hated it," she said bitterly. "I loathed it."

"You know I don't think I'd ever be afraid of anything again," Macomber said to Wilson. "Something happened in me after we first saw the buff and started after him. Like a dam bursting. It was pure excitement."

"Cleans out your liver," said Wilson. "Damn funny things happen to people."

Macomber's face was shining. "You know something did happen to me," he said. "I feel absolutely different."

His wife said nothing and eyed him strangely. She was sitting far back in the seat and Macomber was sitting forward talking to Wilson who turned sideways talking over the back of the front seat.

"You know, I'd like to try another lion," Macomber said. "I'm really not afraid of them now. After all what can they do to you?"

"That's it," said Wilson. "Worst one can do is kill you. How does it go? Shakespeare. Damned good. See if I can remember. Oh, damned good. Used to quote it to myself at one time. Let's see. 'By my troth, I care not; a man can die but once; we owe God a death and let it go which way it will he that dies this year is quit for the next.' Damned fine, eh?"

He was very embarrassed, having brought out this thing he had lived by, but he had seen men come of age before and it always moved him. It was not a matter of their twenty-first birthday.

It had taken a strange chance of hunting, a sudden precipitation into action without opportunity for worrying beforehand, to bring this about with Macomber, but regardless of how it had happened it had most certainly happened. Look at the beggar now, Wilson thought. It's that some of them stay little boys so long, Wilson thought. Sometimes all their lives. Their figures stay boyish when they're fifty. The great American boy-men. Damned strange people. But he liked this Macomber now. Damned strange fellow. Probably meant the end of cuckoldry too. Well, that would be a damned good thing. Damned good thing. Beggar had probably been afraid all his life. Don't know what started it. But over now. Hadn't had time to be afraid with the buff. That and being angry too. Motor car too. Motor cars made it familiar. Be a damn fire eater now. He'd seen it in the war work the same way. More of a change than any loss of virginity. Fear gone like an operation. Something else grew in its place. Main thing a man had. Made him into a man. Women knew it too. No bloody fear.

From the far corner of the seat Margaret Macomber looked at the two of them. There was no change in Wilson. She saw Wilson as she had seen him the day before when she had first realized what his great talent was. But she saw the change in Francis Macomber now.

"Do you have that feeling of happiness about what's going to happen?" Macomber asked, still exploring his new wealth.

"You're not supposed to mention it," Wilson said, looking in the other's face. "Much more fashionable to say you're scared. Mind you, you'll be scared too, plenty of times."

"But you *have* a feeling of happiness about action to come?"

"Yes," said Wilson. "There's that. Doesn't do to talk too much about all this. Talk the whole thing away. No pleasure in anything if you mouth it up too much."

"You're both talking rot," said Margot. "Just because you've chased some helpless animals in a motor car you talk like heroes."

"Sorry," said Wilson. "I have been gassing too much." She's worried about it already, he thought.

"If you don't know what we're talking about why not keep out of it?" Macomber asked his wife.

"You've gotten awfully brave, awfully suddenly," his wife said contemptuously, but her contempt was not secure. She was very afraid of something.

Macomber laughed, a very natural hearty laugh. "You know I have," he said. "I really have."

"Isn't it sort of late?" Margot said bitterly. Because she had done the best she could for many years back and the way they were together now was no one person's fault.

"Not for me," said Macomber.

Margot said nothing but sat back in the corner of the seat.

"Do you think we've given him time enough?" Macomber asked Wilson cheerfully.

"We might have a look," Wilson said. "Have you any solids left?"

"The gun-bearer has some."

Wilson called in Swahili and the older gun-bearer, who was skinning out one of the heads, straightened up, pulled a box of solids out of his pocket and brought them over to Macomber, who filled his magazine and put the remaining shells in his pocket.

"You might as well shoot the Springfield," Wilson said. "You're used to it. We'll leave the Mannlicher in the car with the Memsahib. Your gun-bearer can carry your heavy gun. I've this damned cannon. Now let me tell you about them." He had saved this until the last because he did not want to worry Macomber. "When a buff comes he comes with his head high and thrust straight out. The boss of the horns covers any sort of a brain shot. The only shot is straight into the nose. The only other shot is into his chest or, if you're to one side, into the neck or the shoulders. After they've been hit once they take a hell of a lot of killing. Don't try anything fancy. Take the easiest shot there is. They've finished skinning out that head now. Should we get started?"

He called to the gun-bearers, who came up wiping their hands, and the older one got into the back.

"I'll only take Kongoni," Wilson said. "The other can watch to keep the birds away."

As the car moved slowly across the open space toward the island of brushy trees that ran in a tongue of foliage along a dry water course that cut the open swale, Macomber felt his heart pounding and his mouth was dry again, but it was excitement, not fear.

"Here's where he went in," Wilson said. Then to the gun-bearer in Swahili, "Take the blood spoor."

The car was parallel to the patch of bush. Macomber, Wilson and the gun-bearer got down. Macomber, looking back, saw his wife, with the rifle by her side, looking at him. He waved to her and she did not wave back.

The brush was very thick ahead and the ground was dry. The middle-aged gun-bearer was sweating heavily and Wilson had his hat down over his eyes and his red neck showed just ahead of Macomber. Suddenly the gun-bearer said something in Swahili to Wilson and ran forward.

"He's dead in there," Wilson said. "Good work," and he turned to grip Macomber's hand and as they shook hands, grinning at each other, the gun-bearer shouted wildly and they saw him coming out of the bush sideways, fast as a crab, and the bull coming, nose out, mouth tight closed, blood dripping, massive head straight out, coming in a charge, his little pig eyes bloodshot as he looked at them. Wilson, who was ahead was kneeling shooting, and Macomber, as he fired, unhearing his shot in the roaring of Wilson's gun, saw fragments like slate burst from the huge boss of the horns, and the head jerked, he shot again at the wide nostrils and saw the horns jolt again and fragments fly, and he did not see Wilson now and, aiming carefully, shot again with the buffalo's huge bulk almost on him and his rifle almost level with the on-coming head, nose out, and he could see the little wicked eyes and the head started to lower and he felt a sudden white-hot, blinding flash explode inside his head and that was all he ever felt.

Wilson had ducked to one side to get in a shoulder shot. Macomber had stood solid and shot for the nose, shooting a touch high each time and hitting the heavy horns, splintering and chipping them like hitting a slate roof, and Mrs. Macomber, in the car, had shot at the buffalo with the 6.5 Mannlicher as it seemed about to gore Macomber and had hit her husband about two inches up and a little to one side of the base of his skull.

Francis Macomber lay now, face down, not two yards from where the buffalo lay on his side and his wife knelt over him with Wilson beside her.

"I wouldn't turn him over," Wilson said.

The woman was crying hysterically.

"I'd get back in the car," Wilson said. "Where's the rifle?"

She shook her head, her face contorted. The gun-bearer picked up the rifle.

"Leave it as it is," said Wilson. Then, "Go get Abdulla so that he may witness the manner of the accident."

He knelt down, took a handkerchief from his pocket, and spread it over Francis Macomber's crew-cropped head where it lay. The blood sank into the dry, loose earth.

Wilson stood up and saw the buffalo on his side, his legs out, his thinly-haired belly crawling with ticks. "Hell of a good bull," his brain registered automatically. "A good fifty inches, or better. Better." He called to the driver and told him to spread a blanket over the body and stay by it. Then he walked over to the motor car where the woman sat crying in the corner.

"That was a pretty thing to do," he said in a toneless voice. "He *would* have left you too."

"Stop it," she said.

"Of course it's an accident," he said. "I know that."

"Stop it," she said.

"Don't worry," he said. "There will be a certain amount of unpleasantness but I will have some photographs taken that will be very useful at the inquest. There's the testimony of the gun-bearers and the driver too. You're perfectly all right."

"Stop it," she said.

"There's a hell of a lot to be done," he said. "And I'll have to send a truck off to the lake to wireless for a plane to take the three of us into Nairobi. Why didn't you poison him? That's what they do in England."

"Stop it. Stop it. Stop it," the woman cried.

Wilson looked at her with his flat blue eyes.

"I'm through now," he said. "I was a little angry. I'd begun to like your husband."

"Oh, please stop it," she said. "Please, please stop it."

"That's better," Wilson said. "Please is much better. Now I'll stop."

FRANK ROONEY

(1913-   )

Frank Rooney was born in Kansas City, Missouri, moved to Los Angeles in his youth, and now lives in Mamaroneck, New York. He served in the Army during the Second World War, mostly in the South Pacific. His short stories have appeared in a large number of magazines; in addition, he has published four books, THE COURTS OF MEMORY, THE HEEL OF SPRING, McGINNIS SPEAKS, and THE GREAT CIRCLE. In 1956 he was awarded a Guggenheim Fellowship and in the same year received a grant from the National Institute of Arts and Letters. The story reprinted here inspired the well known film, "The Wild One."

Cyclists' Raid

Joel Bleeker, owner and operator of the Pendleton Hotel, was adjusting the old redwood clock in the lobby when he heard the sound of the motors. At first he thought it might be one of those four-engine planes on the flights from Los Angeles to San Francisco which occasionally got far enough off course to be heard in the valley. And for a moment, braced against the steadily approaching vibrations of the sound, he had the fantastic notion that the plane was going to strike the hotel. He even glanced at his daughter, Cathy, standing a few feet to his right and staring curiously at the street.

Then with his fingers still on the hour hand of the clock he realized that the sound was not something coming down from the air but the high, sputtering racket of many vehicles moving along the ground. Cathy and Bret Timmons, who owned one of the two drugstores in the town, went out onto the veranda but Bleeker stayed by the clock, consulting the railroad watch he pulled from his vest pocket and moving the hour hand on the clock forward a minute and a half. He stepped back deliberately, shut the glass case and looked at the huge brass numbers and the two ornate brass pointers. It was eight minutes after seven, approximately twenty-two minutes until sundown. He put the railroad watch back in his pocket and walked slowly and incuriously through the open doors of the lobby. He was methodical and orderly and the small things he did every day—like setting the clock—were important to him. He was not to be hurried—especially by something as elusively irritating as a sound, however unusual.

There were only three people on the veranda when Bleeker came out of the lobby—his daughter Cathy, Timmons, and Francis LaSalle, co-owner of LaSalle and Fleet, Hardware. They stood together quietly, looking, without appearing to stare, at a long stern column of red motorcycles coming from the south, filling the single main street of the town with the noise of a multitude of pistons and the crackling of exhaust pipes. They could see now that the column was led by a single white motorcycle which when it came abreast of the hotel turned abruptly right and stopped. They saw too that the column without seeming to slow down or to execute any elaborate movement had divided itself into two single files. At the approximate second, having received a signal from their leader, they also turned right and stopped.

The whole flanking action, singularly neat and quite like the various vehicular formations he remembered in the Army, was distasteful to Bleeker. It recalled a little too readily his tenure as a lieutenant colonel overseas in England, France, and finally Germany.

"Mr. Bleeker?"

Bleeker realized the whole troop—no one in the town either then or after that night was ever agreed on the exact number of men in the troop—had dismounted and that the leader was addressing him.

"I'm Bleeker." Although he hadn't intended to, he stepped forward when he spoke, much as he had stepped forward in the years when he commanded a battalion.

"I'm Gar Simpson and this is Troop B of the Angeleno Motorcycle Club," the leader said. He was a tall, spare man and his voice was coldly courteous to the point of mockery. "We expect to bivouac outside your town tonight and we wondered if we might use the facilities of your hotel. Of course, sir, we'll pay."

"There's a washroom downstairs. If you can put up with that—"

"That will be fine, sir. Is the dining room still open?"

"It is."

"Could you take care of twenty men?"

"What about the others?"

"They can be accommodated elsewhere, sir."

Simpson saluted casually and, turning to the men assembled stiffly in front of the hotel, issued a few quiet orders. Quickly and efficiently, the men in the troop parked their motorcycles at the curb. About a third of the group detached itself and came deferentially but steadily up the hotel steps. They passed Bleeker who found himself maneuvered aside and went into the lobby. As they passed him, Bleeker could see the slight converted movement of their faces—though not their eyes, which were covered by large green goggles—toward his daughter Cathy. Bleeker frowned after them but before he could think of anything to say, Simpson, standing now at his left, touched his arm.

"I've divided the others into two groups," he said quietly. "One group will eat at the diner and the other at the Desert Hotel."

"Very good," Bleeker said. "You evidently know the town like a book. The people too. Have you ever been here before?"

"We have a map of all the towns in this part of California, sir. And of course we know the names of all the principal hotels and their proprietors. Personally, I could use a drink. Would you join me?"

"After you," Bleeker said.

He stood watching Simpson stride into the lobby and without any hesitation go directly to the bar. Then he turned to Cathy, seeing Timmons and LaSalle lounging on the railing behind her, their faces already indistinct in the plummeting California twilight.

"You go help in the kitchen, Cathy," Bleeker said. "I think it'd be better if you didn't wait on tables."

"I wonder what they look like behind those goggles," Cathy said.

"Like anybody else," Timmons said. He was about thirty, somewhat coarse and intolerant and a little embarrassed at being in love with a girl as young as Cathy. "Where did you think they came from? Mars?"

"What did they say the name of their club was?" Cathy said.

"Angeleno," LaSalle said.

"They must be from Los Angeles. Heigh-ho. Shall I wear my very best gingham, citizen colonel?"

"Remember now—you stay in the kitchen," Bleeker said.

He watched her walk into the lobby, a tall slender girl of seventeen, pretty and enigmatic, with something of the brittle independence of her mother. Bleeker remembered suddenly, although he tried not to, the way her mother had walked away from him that frosty January morning two years ago saying, "I'm going for a ride." And then the two-day search in the mountains after the horse had come back alone and the finding of her body—the neck broken—in the stream at the foot of the cliff. During the war he had never really believed that he would live to get back to Cathy's mother and after the war he hadn't really believed he would be separated from her—not again—not twice in so short a time.

Shaking his head—as if by that motion he could shed his memories as easily as a dog sheds water—Bleeker went in to join Gar Simpson who was sitting at a table in the barroom. Simpson stood politely when Bleeker took the opposite chair.

"How long do you fellows plan to stay?" Bleeker asked. He took the first sip of his drink, looked up, and stared at Simpson.

"Tonight and tomorrow morning," Simpson said.

Like all the others he was dressed in a brown windbreaker, khaki shirt, khaki pants, and as Bleeker had previously observed wore dark calf-length boots. A cloth and leather helmet lay on the table beside Simpson's drink, but he hadn't removed his flat green goggles, an accouterment giving him and the men in his troop the appearance of some tropical tribe with enormous semi-precious eyes, lidless and immovable. That was Bleeker's first impression and, absurd as it was, it didn't seem an exaggeration of fancy but of truth.

"Where do you go after this?"

"North." Simpson took a rolled map from a binocular case slung over his shoulder and spread it on the table. "Roughly we're following the arc of an ellipse with its southern tip based on Los Angeles and its northern end touching Fresno."

"Pretty ambitious for a motorcycle club."

"We have a month," Simpson said. "This is our first week but we're in no hurry and we're out to see plenty of country."

"What are you interested in mainly?"

"Roads. Naturally, being a motorcycle club—you'd be surprised at the rate we're expanding—we'd like to have as much of California as possible opened up to us."

"I see."

"Keeps the boys fit too. The youth of America. Our hope for the future." Simpson pulled sternly at his drink and Bleeker had the impression that Simpson was repressing, openly, and with pride, a vast sparkling ecstasy.

Bleeker sat and watched the young men in the troop file upstairs from the public washroom and stroll casually but nevertheless with discipline into the dining room. They had removed their helmets and strapped them to their belts, each helmet in a prescribed position to the left of the belt-buckle but—like Simpson—they had retained their goggles. Bleeker wondered if they ever removed the goggles long enough to wash under them and, if they did, what the flesh under them looked like.

"I think I'd better help out at the tables," Bleeker said. He stood up and Simpson stood with him. "You say you're from Troop B? Is that right?"

"Correct. We're forming Troop G now. Someday—"

"You'll be up to Z," Bleeker said.

"And not only in California."

"Where else for instance?"

"Nevada—Arizona—Colorado—Wyoming."

Simpson smiled and Bleeker, turning away from him abruptly, went into the dining room where he began to help the two waitresses at the tables. He filled water glasses, set out extra forks, and brought steins of beer from the bar. As he served the troop, their polite thank yous, ornate and insincere, irritated him. It reminded him of tricks taught to animals, the animals only being allowed to perform under certain obvious conditions of security. And he didn't like the cool way they stared at the two waitresses, both older women and fixtures in the town and then leaned their heads together as if every individual thought had to be pooled and divided equally among them. He admitted, after some covert study, that the twenty men were really only variations of one, the variations, with few excep-

tions, being too subtle for him to recognize and differentiate. It
was the goggles, he decided, covering that part of the face which is
most noteworthy and most needful for identification—the eyes and
the mask around the eyes.

Bleeker went into the kitchen, pretending to help but really
to be near Cathy. The protective father, he thought ironically,
watching his daughter cut pie and lay the various colored wedges on
the white blue-bordered plates.

"Well, Daddy, what's the verdict?" Cathy looked extremely
grave but he could see that she was amused.

"They're a fine body of men."

"Uh-huh. Have you called the police yet?"

He laughed. "It's a good thing you don't play poker."

"Child's play." She slid the last piece of blueberry pie on a plate.
"I saw you through the door. You looked like you were ready to
crack the Siegfried line—single-handed."

"That man Simpson."

"What about him?"

"Why don't you go upstairs and read a book or something?"

"Now, Daddy—you're the only professional here. They're just
acting like little tin soldiers out on a spree."

"I wish to God they were made of tin."

"All right. I'll keep away from them. I promise." She made a
gesture of crossing her throat with the thin edge of a knife. He leaned
over and kissed her forehead, his hand feeling awkward and stern
on her back.

After dinner the troop went into the bar, moving with a strange
co-ordinated fluency that was both casual and military and sat jeal-
ously together in one corner of the room. Bleeker served them pitch-
ers of beer and for the most part they talked quietly together, Simpson at their center, their voices guarded and urgent as if they possessed information which couldn't be disseminated safely among
the public.

Bleeker left them after a while and went upstairs to his daughter's room. He wasn't used to being severe with Cathy and he was a
little embarrassed by what he had said to her in the kitchen. She
was turning the collars of some of his old shirts, using a portable
sewing machine he had bought her as a present on her last birthday. As he came in she held one of the shirts comically to the floor
lamp and he could see how thin and transparent the material was.

Her mother's economy in small things, almost absurd when compared to her limitless generosity in matters of importance, had been one of the family jokes. It gave him an extraordinary sense of pleasure, so pure it was like a sudden inhalation of oxygen, to see that his daughter had not only inherited this tradition but had considered it meaningful enough to carry on. He went down the hall to his own room without saying anything further to her. Cathy was what he himself was in terms which could mean absolutely nothing to anyone else.

He had been in his room for perhaps an hour, working on the hotel accounts and thinking obliquely of the man Simpson, when he heard, faintly and apparently coming from no one direction, the sound of singing. He got up and walked to the windows overlooking the street. Standing there, he thought he could fix the sound farther up the block toward Cunningham's bar. Except for something harsh and mature in the voices it was the kind of singing that might be heard around a Boy Scout campfire, more rhythmic than melodic and more stirring than tuneful. And then he could hear it almost under his feet, coming out of the hotel lobby and making three or four people on the street turn and smile foolishly toward the doors of the veranda.

Oppressed by something sternly joyous in the voices, Bleeker went downstairs to the bar, hearing as he approached the singing become louder and fuller. Outside of Simpson and the twenty men in the troop there were only three townsmen—including LaSalle—in the bar. Simpson, seeing Bleeker in the door, got up and walked over to him, moving him out into the lobby where they could talk.

"I hope the boys aren't disturbing you," he said.

"It's early," Bleeker said.

"In an organization as large and selective as ours it's absolutely necessary to insist on a measure of discipline. And it's equally necessary to allow a certain amount of relaxation."

"The key word is selective, I suppose."

"We have our standards," Simpson said primly.

"May I ask just what the hell your standards are?"

Simpson smiled. "I don't quite understand your irritation, Mr. Bleeker."

"This is an all-year-round thing, isn't it? This club of yours?"

"Yes."

"And you have an all-year-round job with the club?"

"Of course."

"That's my objection, Simpson. Briefly and simply stated, what you're running is a private army." Bleeker tapped the case slung over Simpson's shoulder. "Complete with maps, all sorts of local information, and of course a lobby in Sacramento."

"For a man who has traveled as widely as you have, Mr. Bleeker, you display an uncommon talent for exaggeration."

"As long as you behave yourselves I don't care what you do. This is a small town and we don't have many means of entertainment. We go to bed at a decent hour and I suggest you take that into consideration. However, have your fun. Nobody here has any objections to that."

"And of course we spend our money."

"Yes," Bleeker said. "You spend your money."

He walked away from Simpson and went out onto the veranda. The singing was now both in front and in back of him. Bleeker stood for a moment on the top steps of the veranda looking at the moon, hung like a slightly soiled but luminous pennant in the sky. He was embarrassed by his outburst to Simpson and he couldn't think why he had said such things. Private army. Perhaps, as Simpson had said, he was exaggerating. He was a small-town man and he had always hated the way men surrendered their individuality to attain perfection as a unit. It had been necessary during the war but it wasn't necessary now. Kid stuff—with an element of growing pains.

He walked down the steps and went up the sidewalk toward Cunningham's bar. They were singing there too and he stood outside the big plate-glass window peering in at them and listening to the harsh, pounding voices colored here and there with the sentimentalism of strong beer. Without thinking further he went into the bar. It was dim and cool and alien to his eyes and at first he didn't notice the boy sitting by himself in a booth near the front. When he did, he was surprised—more than surprised, shocked—to see that the boy wasn't wearing his goggles but had placed them on the table by a bottle of Coca-Cola. Impulsively, he walked over to the booth and sat across from the boy.

"This seat taken?"

He had to shout over the noise of the singing. The boy leaned forward over the table and smiled.

"Hope we're not disturbing you."

Bleeker caught the word "disturbing" and shook his head nega-
tively. He pointed to his mouth, then to the boy and to the rest of
the group. The boy too shook his head. Bleeker could see that he was
young, possibly twenty-five, and that he had dark straight hair cut
short and parted neatly at the side. The face was square but delicate,
the nose short, the mouth wide. The best thing about the boy,
Bleeker decided, were his eyes, brown perhaps or dark gray, set in
two distorted ovals of white flesh which contrasted sharply with the
heavily tanned skin on the cheeks, forehead and jaws. With his goggles on he would have looked like the rest. Without them he was a
pleasant young man, altogether human and approachable.

Bleeker pointed to the Coca-Cola bottle. "You're not drinking."

"Beer makes me sick."

Bleeker got the word "beer" and the humorous ulping motion
the boy made. They sat exchanging words and sometimes phrases,
illustrated always with a series of clumsy, groping gestures until the
singing became less coherent and spirited and ended finally in a few
isolated coughs. The men in the troop were moving about individu-
ally now, some leaning over the bar and talking in hoarse whispers
to the bartender, others walking unsteadily from group to group and
detaching themselves immediately to go over to another group, the
groups usually two or three men constantly edging away from themselves and colliding with and being held briefly by others. Some
simply stood in the center of the room and brayed dolorously at the
ceiling.

Several of the troop walked out of the bar and Bleeker could
see them standing on the wide sidewalk looking up and down the
street—as contemptuous of one another's company as they had been
glad of it earlier. Or not so much contemptuous as unwilling to be
coerced too easily by any authority outside themselves. Bleeker
smiled as he thought of Simpson and the man's talk of discipline.

"They're looking for women," the boy said.

Bleeker had forgotten the boy temporarily and the sudden
words spoken in a normal voice startled and confused him. He
thought quickly of Cathy—but then Cathy was safe in her room—
probably in bed. He took the watch from his vest pocket and looked
at it carefully.

"Five minutes after ten," he said.

"Why do they do that?" the boy demanded. "Why do they

have to be so damned indecent about things like that? They haven't got the nerve to do anything but stare at waitresses. And then they get a few beers in them and go around pinching and slapping—they—"

Bleeker shivered with embarrassment. He was looking directly into the boy's eyes and seeing the color run under the tears and the jerky pinching movement of the lids as against something injurious and baleful. It was an emotion too rawly infantile to be seen without being hurt by it and he felt both pity and contempt for a man who would allow himself to display such a feeling—without any provocation—so nakedly to a stranger.

"Sorry," the boy said.

He picked up the green goggles and fitted them awkwardly over his eyes. Bleeker stood up and looked toward the center of the room. Several of the men turned their eyes and then moved their heads away without seeming to notice the boy in the booth. Bleeker understood them. This was the one who could be approached. The reason for that was clear too. He didn't belong. Why and wherefore he would probably never know.

He walked out of the bar and started down the street toward the hotel. The night was clear and cool and smelled faintly of the desert, of sand, of heated rock, of the sweetly-sour plants growing without water and even of the sun which burned itself into the earth and never completely withdrew. There were only a few townsmen on the sidewalk wandering up and down, lured by the presence of something unusual in the town and masking, Bleeker thought, a ruthless and menacing curiosity behind a tolerant grin. He shrugged his shoulders distastefully. He was like a cat staring into a shadow the shape of its fears.

He was no more than a hundred feet from the hotel when he heard—or thought he heard—the sound of automatic firing. It was a well-remembered sound but always new and frightening.

Then he saw the motorcycle moving down the middle of the street, the exhaust sputtering loudly against the human resonance of laughter, catcalls, and epithets. He exhaled gently, the pain in his lungs subsiding with his breath. Another motorcycle speeded after the first and he could see four or five machines being wheeled out and the figures of their riders leaping into the air and bringing their weight down on the starting pedals. He was aware too that the lead motorcycles, having traversed the length of the street had turned and were speeding back to the hotel. He had the sensation of moving —even when he stood still—in relation to the objects heading toward each other. He heard the high unendurable sound of metal squeezing metal and saw the front wheel of a motorcycle twist and wobble and its rider roll along the asphalt toward the gutter where he sat up finally and moved his goggled head feebly from side to side.

As Bleeker looked around him he saw the third group of men which had divided earlier from the other two coming out of a bar across the street from Cunningham's, waving their arms in recognizable motions of cheering. The boy who had been thrown from the motorcycle vomited quietly into the gutter. Bleeker walked very fast toward the hotel. When he reached the top step of the veranda, he was caught and jostled by some five or six cyclists running out of the lobby, one of whom fell and was kicked rudely down the steps. Bleeker staggered against one of the pillars and broke a fingernail catching it. He stood there for a moment, fighting his temper, and then went into the lobby.

A table had been overthrown and lay on its top, the wooden legs stiffly and foolishly exposed, its magazines scattered around it, some with their pages spread face down so that the bindings rose along the back. He stepped on glass and realized one of the panes in the lobby door had been smashed. One of the troop walked stupidly out of the bar, his body sagging against the impetus propelling him forward until without actually falling he lay stretched on the floor, beer gushing from his mouth and nose and making a green and yellow pool before it sank into the carpet.

As Bleeker walked toward the bar, thinking of Simpson and of what he could say to him, he saw two men going up the stairs toward the second floor. He ran over to intercept them. Recognizing the authority in his voice, they came obediently down the stairs and walked across the lobby to the veranda, one of them saying over his shoulder, "Okay, pop, okay—keep your lid on." The smile they exchanged enraged him. After they were out of sight he ran swiftly up the stairs, panting a little, and along the hall to his daughter's room.

It was quiet and there was no strip of light beneath the door. He stood listening for a moment with his ear to the panels and then turned back toward the stairs.

A man or boy, any of twenty or forty or sixty identical figures, goggled and in khaki, came around the corner of the second-floor corridor and put his hand on the knob of the door nearest the stairs. He squeezed the knob gently and then moved on to the next door, apparently unaware of Bleeker. Bleeker, remembering not to run or shout or knock the man down, walked over to him, took his arm and led him down the stairs, the arm unresisting, even flaccid, in his grip.

Bleeker stood indecisively at the foot of the stairs, watching the man walk automatically away from him. He thought he should go back upstairs and search the hall. And he thought too he had to reach Simpson. Over the noise of the motorcycles moving rapidly up and down the street he heard a crash in the bar, a series of drunken elongated curses, ending abruptly in a small sound like a man's hand laid flatly and sharply on a table.

His head was beginning to ache badly and his stomach to sour under the impact of a slow and steady anger. He walked into the bar and stood staring at Francis LaSalle—LaSalle and Fleet, Hardware —who lay sprawled on the floor, his shoulders touching the brass rail under the bar and his head turned so that his cheek rubbed the black polished wood above the rail. The bartender had his hands below the top of the bar and he was watching Simpson and a half a dozen men arranged in a loose semi-circle above and beyond LaSalle.

Bleeker lifted LaSalle, who was a little dazed but not really hurt, and set him on a chair. After he was sure LaSalle was all right he walked up to Simpson.

"Get your men together," he said. "And get them out of here."

Simpson took out a long yellow wallet folded like a book and laid some money on the bar.

"That should take care of the damages," he said. His tongue was a little thick and his mouth didn't quite shut after the words were spoken but Bleeker didn't think he was drunk. Bleeker saw too—or thought he saw—the little cold eyes behind the glasses as bright and as sterile as a painted floor. Bleeker raised his arm slightly and lifted his heels off the floor but Simpson turned abruptly and walked away from him, the men in the troop swaying at his heels like a pack of lolling hounds. Bleeker stood looking foolishly after them. He had expected a fight and his body was still poised for one. He grunted heavily.

"Who hit him?" Bleeker motioned toward LaSalle.

"Damned if I know," the bartender said. "They all look alike to me."

That was true of course. He went back into the lobby, hearing LaSalle say, weakly and tearfully, "Goddam them—the bastards." He met Campbell, the deputy sheriff, a tall man with the arms and shoulders of a child beneath a foggy, bloated face.

"Can you do anything?" Bleeker asked. The motorcycles were racing up and down the street, alternately whining and backfiring and one had jumped the curb and was cruising on the sidewalk.

"What do you want me to do?" Campbell demanded. "Put 'em all in jail?"

The motorcycle on the sidewalk speeded up and skidded obliquely into a plate-glass window, the front wheel bucking and climbing the brick base beneath the window. A single large section of glass slipped edge-down to the sidewalk and fell slowly toward the cyclist who, with his feet spread and kicking at the cement, backed clumsily away from it. Bleeker could feel the crash in his teeth.

Now there were other motorcycles on the sidewalk. One of them hit a parked car at the edge of the walk. The rider standing astride his machine beat the window out of the car with his gloved fists. Campbell started down the steps toward him but was driven back by a motorcycle coming from his left. Bleeker could hear the squeal of the tires against the wooden riser at the base of the steps. Campbell's hand was on his gun when Bleeker reached him.

"That's no good," he yelled. "Get the state police. Ask for a half dozen squad cars."

Campbell, angry but somewhat relieved, went up the steps and into the lobby. Bleeker couldn't know how long he stood on the veranda watching the mounting devastation on the street—the cyclist racing past store windows and hurling, presumably, beer bottles at the glass fronts; the two, working as a team, knocking down weighing machines and the signs in front of the motion picture theater; the innumerable mounted men running the angry townspeople, alerted and aroused by the awful sounds of damage to their property, back into their suddenly lighted homes again or up the steps of his hotel or into niches along the main street, into doorways, and occasionally into the ledges and bays of glassless windows.

He saw Simpson—or rather a figure on the white motorcycle, helmeted and goggled—stationed calmly in the middle of the street under a hanging lamp. Presumably, he had been there for some time but Bleeker hadn't seen him, the many rapid movements on the street making any static object unimportant and even, in a sense, invisible. Bleeker saw him now and he felt again that spasm of anger which was like another life inside his body. He could have strangled Simpson then, slowly and with infinite pride. He knew without any effort of reason that Simpson was making no attempt to control his men but waiting rather for that moment when their minds, subdued but never actually helpless, would again take possession of their bodies.

Bleeker turned suddenly and went back into the lobby as if by that gesture of moving away he could pin his thoughts to Simpson, who, hereafter, would be responsible for them. He walked over to the desk where Timmons and Campbell, the deputy, were talking.

"You've got the authority," Timmons was saying angrily. "Fire over their heads. And if that doesn't stop them—"

Campbell looked uneasily at Bleeker. "Maybe if we could get their leader—"

"Did you get the police?" Bleeker asked.

"They're on their way," Campbell said. He avoided looking at Timmons and continued to stare hopefully and miserably at Bleeker.

"You've had your say," Timmons said abruptly. "Now I'll have mine."

He started for the lobby doors but Campbell, suddenly incensed, grabbed his arm.

"You leave this to me," he said. "You start firing a gun—"

Campbell's mouth dropped and Bleeker, turning his head, saw the two motorcycles coming through the lobby doors. They circled leisurely around for a moment and then one of them shot suddenly toward them, the goggled rider looming enormously above the wide handlebars. They scattered, Bleeker diving behind a pillar and Campbell and Timmons jumping behind the desk. The noise of the two machines assaulted them with as much effect as the sight of the speeding metal itself.

Bleeker didn't know why in course of watching the two riders he looked into the hall toward the foot of the stairway. Nor did it seem at all unreasonable that when he looked he should see Cathy standing there. Deeply, underneath the outward preoccupation of his mind, he must have been thinking of her. Now there she was. She wore the familiar green robe, belted and pulled in at the waist and beneath its hem he could see the white slippers and the pink edge of her nightgown. Her hair was down and he had the impression her eyes were not quite open although, obviously, they were. She looked, he thought, as if she had waked, frowned at the clock, and come downstairs to scold him for staying up too late. He had no idea what time it was.

He saw—and of course Cathy saw—the motorcycle speeding toward her. He was aware that he screamed at her too. She did take a slight backward step and raise her arms in a pathetic warding gesture toward the inhuman figure on the motorcycle but neither could have changed—in that dwarfed period of time and in that short, unmaneuverable space—the course of their actions.

She lay finally across the lower steps, her body clinging to and equally arching away from the base of the newel post. And there was the sudden, shocking exposure of her flesh, the robe and the gown torn away from the leg as if pushed aside by the blood welling from her thigh. When he reached her there was blood in her hair too and someone—not Cathy—was screaming into his ears.

After a while the doctor came and Cathy, her head bandaged and her leg in splints, could be carried into his office and laid on the couch. Bleeker sat on the edge of the couch, his hand over Cathy's, watching the still white face whose eyes were closed and would not, he knew, open again. The doctor, after his first examination, had looked up quickly and since Bleeker too had been bent over Cathy, their heads had been very close together for a moment. The doctor had assumed, almost immediately, his expression of professional austerity but Bleeker had seen him in that moment when he had been thinking as a man, fortified of course by a doctor's knowledge, and Bleeker had known then that Cathy would die but that there would be also this interval of time.

Bleeker turned from watching Cathy and saw Timmons standing across the room. The man was—or had been—crying but his face wasn't set for it and the tears, points of colorless, sparkling water on his jaws, were unexpectedly delicate against the coarse texture of his skin. Timmons waved a bandaged hand awkwardly and Bleeker remembered, abruptly and jarringly, seeing Timmons diving for the motorcycle which had reversed itself, along with the other, and raced out of the lobby.

There was no sound now either from the street or the lobby. It was incredible, thinking of the racket a moment ago, that there should be this utter quietude, not only the lack of noise but the lack of the vibration of movement. The doctor came and went, coming to bend over Cathy and then going away again. Timmons stayed. Beyond shifting his feet occasionally he didn't move at all but stood patiently across the room, his face toward Cathy and Bleeker but not, Bleeker thought once when he looked up, actually seeing them.

"The police," Bleeker said sometime later.

"They're gone," Timmons said in a hoarse whisper. And then after a while, "They'll get 'em—don't worry."

Bleeker saw that the man blushed helplessly and looked away from him. The police were no good. They would catch Simpson. Simpson would pay damages. And that would be the end of it. Who could identify Cathy's assailant? Not himself, certainly—nor Timmons nor Campbell. They were all alike. They were standardized figurines, seeking in each other a willful loss of identity, dividing themselves equally among one another until there was only a single mythical figure, unspeakably sterile and furnishing the norm for hundreds of others. He could not accuse something which didn't actually exist.

He wasn't sure of the exact moment when Cathy died. It might have been when he heard the motorcycle, unbelievably solitary in the quiet night, approaching the town. He knew only that the doctor came for the last time and that there was now a coarse, heavy blanket laid mercifully over Cathy. He stood looking down at the blanket for a moment, whatever he was feeling repressed and delayed inside him, and then went back to the lobby and out onto the veranda. There were a dozen men standing there looking up the street toward the sound of the motorcycle, steadily but slowly coming nearer. He saw that when they glanced at each other their faces were hard and angry but when they looked at him they were respectful and a little abashed.

Bleeker could see from the veranda a number of people moving among the smashed store-fronts, moving, stopping, bending over and then straightening up to move somewhere else, all dressed some-

what extemporaneously and therefore seeming without purpose.
What they picked up they put down. What they put down they
stared at grimly and then picked up again. They were like a dis-
possessed minority brutally but lawfully discriminated against.
When the motorcycle appeared at the north end of the street they
looked at it and then looked away again, dully and seemingly without
resentment.

It was only after some moments that they looked up again, this
time purposefully, and began to move slowly toward the hotel
where the motorcycle had now stopped, the rider standing on the
sidewalk, his face raised to the veranda.

No one on the veranda moved until Bleeker, after a visible effort, walked down the steps and stood facing the rider. It was the
boy Bleeker had talked to in the bar. The goggles and helmet were
hanging at his belt.

"I couldn't stand it any longer," the boy said. "I had to come
back."

He looked at Bleeker as if he didn't dare look anywhere else.
His face was adolescently shiny and damp, the marks, Bleeker
thought, of a proud and articulate fear. He should have been heroic
in his willingness to come back to the town after what had been done
to it but to Bleeker he was only a dirty little boy returning to a back
fence his friends had defaced with pornographic writing and calling attention to the fact that he was afraid to erase the writing but
was determined nevertheless to do it. Bleeker was revolted. He hated
the boy far more than he could have hated Simpson for bringing this
to his attention when he did not want to think of anything or anyone but Cathy.

"I wasn't one of them," the boy said. "You remember, Mr.
Bleeker. I wasn't drinking."

This declaration of innocence—this willingness to take blame
for acts which he hadn't committed—enraged Bleeker.

"You were one of them," he said.

"Yes. But after tonight—"

"Why didn't you stop them?" Bleeker demanded loudly. He felt
the murmur of the townspeople at his back and someone breathed
harshly on his neck. "You were one of them. You could have done
something. Why in God's name didn't you do it?"

"What could I do?" the boy said. He spread his hands and
stepped back as if to appeal to the men beyond Bleeker.

Bleeker couldn't remember, either shortly after or much later, exactly what he did then. If the boy hadn't stepped back like that— if he hadn't raised his hand. . . . Bleeker was in the middle of a group of bodies and he was striking with his fists and being struck. And then he was kneeling on the sidewalk, holding the boy's head in his lap and trying to protect him from the heavy shoes of the men around him. He was crying out, protesting, exhorting, and after a time the men moved away from him and someone helped him carry the boy up the steps and lay him on the veranda. When he looked up finally only Timmons and the doctor were there. Up and down the street there were now only shadows and the diminishing sounds of invisible bodies. The night was still again as abruptly as it had been confounded with noise.

Some time later Timmons and the doctor carried the boy, alive but terribly hurt, into the hotel. Bleeker sat on the top step of the veranda, staring at the moon which had shifted in the sky and was now nearer the mountains in the west. It was not in any sense romantic or inflamed but coldly clear and sane. And the light it sent was cold and sane and lit in himself what he would have liked to hide.

He could have said that having lost Cathy he was not afraid any longer of losing himself. No one would blame him. Cathy's death was his excuse for striking the boy, hammering him to the sidewalk, and stamping on him as he had never believed he could have stamped on any living thing. No one would say he should have lost Cathy lightly—without anger and without that appalling desire to avenge her. It was utterly natural—as natural as a man drinking a few beers and riding a motorcycle insanely through a town like this. Bleeker shuddered. It might have been all right for a man like Timmons who was and would always be incapable of thinking what he—Joel Bleeker—was thinking. It was not—and would never be —all right for him.

Bleeker got up and stood for a moment on the top step of the veranda. He wanted, abruptly and madly, to scream his agony into the night with no more restraint than that of an animal seeing his guts beneath him on the ground. He wanted to smash something— anything—glass, wood, stone—his own body. He could feel his fists going into the boy's flesh. And there was that bloody but living thing on the sidewalk and himself stooping over to shield it.

After a while, aware that he was leaning against one of the wooden pillars supporting the porch and aware too that his flesh was numb from being pressed against it, he straightened up slowly and turned to go back into the hotel.

There would always be time to make his peace with the dead. There was little if any time to make his peace with the living.

QUESTIONS

Few stories are perfect, and it is often instructive to examine their weaknesses as well as their strengths. We can, for example, arrive at a better understanding of the kinds of difficulties a writer faces when creating a fictional narrative. Problems which remain unsurmounted may also tell us something about the nature of the form. Although "Cyclists' Raid" is in many ways an excellent story, it has some very definite problems which we may find have not been adequately solved.

1. Because the short story is often based on some kind of conflict, it is very easy for the narrative to become melodramatic. Melodrama usually can be identified by the following: stock characters; conflict between extremes of good and evil; sensational action filled with suspense; plot manipulation; sentimentality rather than emotion; a message rather than a theme. In several ways, "Cyclists' Raid" seems melodramatic. Identify those elements which make it appear melodramatic. Discuss the extent to which these elements weaken the story as a whole. To do this, you will have to answer a more general question: Why is melodrama to be avoided in any narrative which attempts to make a valid statement about life's meaning?

2. If the story as a whole cannot be categorized as completely melodramatic, what aspects act to counterbalance the melodrama? To what extent, for example, is there a "theme" rather than a "message"? Which characters become more than mere cardboard cut-outs?

FLANNERY O'CONNOR

(1925-1964)

The South has produced many fine writers; Flannery O'Conner must rank as one of them. Born in Savannah, Georgia, she grew up in the South, leaving only to take an advanced degree at the State University of Iowa. Afflicted with an incurable illness, she died a tragically early death. In the few years of her maturity, however, she was able to complete two novels, WISE BLOOD and THE VIOLENT BEAR IT AWAY, and two collections of short stories: A GOOD MAN IS HARD TO FIND and EVERYTHING THAT RISES MUST CONVERGE. The South provides the setting and characters for her stories, much as it does in the work of Faulkner. And like Faulkner, O'Connor uses her familiar world to reflect the larger world of mankind. Add to this world a profound concern with the problem of good and evil, and her vision assumes cosmic, rather than merely social or regional, proportions. Her technique is often that of irony (examine the meanings of the word "good," for example, in the story below) and her atmosphere is frequently foreboding. Her characters are the halt and the blind, morally and spiritually as well as physically. Finally, we are reminded of Greek tragedy through the combination of pity and fear that is our response to her narratives, and in the ritualistic inevitability of her characters' movement toward a tragic conclusion.

A Good Man
Is Hard to Find

The grandmother didn't want to go to Florida. She wanted to visit some of her connections in east Tennessee and she was seizing at every chance to change Bailey's mind. Bailey was the son she lived with, her only boy. He was sitting on the edge of his chair at the table, bent over the orange sports section of the *Journal*. "Now look here, Bailey," she said, "see here, read this," and she stood with one hand on her thin hip and the other rattling the newspaper at his bald head. "Here this fellow that calls himself The Misfit is aloose from the Federal Pen and headed toward Florida and you read here what it says he did to these people. Just you read it. I wouldn't take my children in any direction with a criminal like that aloose in it. I couldn't answer to my conscience if I did."

Bailey didn't look up from his reading so she wheeled around then and faced the children's mother, a young woman in slacks, whose face was as broad and innocent as a cabbage and was tied around with a green head-kerchief that had two points on the top like rabbit's ears. She was sitting on the sofa, feeding the baby his apricots out of a jar. "The children have been to Florida before," the old lady said. "You all ought to take them somewhere else for a change so they would see different parts of the world and be broad. They never have been to east Tennessee."

The children's mother didn't seem to hear her but the eight-year-old boy, John Wesley, a stocky child with glasses, said, "If you don't want to go to Florida, why dontcha stay at home?" He and the little girl, June Star, were reading the funny papers on the floor.

"She wouldn't stay at home to be queen for a day," June Star said without raising her yellow head.

"Yes and what would you do if this fellow, The Misfit, caught you?" the grandmother asked.

"I'd smack his face," John Wesley said.

"She wouldn't stay at home for a million bucks," June Star said. "Afraid she'd miss something. She has to go everywhere we go."

"All right, Miss," the grandmother said. "Just remember that the next time you want me to curl your hair."

June Star said her hair was naturally curly.

The next morning the grandmother was the first one in the car, ready to go. She had her big black valise that looked like the head of a hippopotamus in one corner, and underneath it she was hiding a basket with Pitty Sing, the cat, in it. She didn't intend for the cat to be left alone in the house for three days because he would miss her too much and she was afraid he might brush against one of the gas burners and accidentally asphyxiate himself. Her son, Bailey, didn't like to arrive at a motel with a cat.

She sat in the middle of the back seat with John Wesley and June Star on either side of her. Bailey and the children's mother and the baby sat in front and they left Atlanta at eight forty-five with the mileage on the car at 55890. The grandmother wrote this down because she thought it would be interesting to say how many miles they had been when they got back. It took them twenty minutes to reach the outskirts of the city.

The old lady settled herself comfortably, removing her white cotton gloves and putting them up with her purse on the shelf in front of the back window. The children's mother still had on slacks and still had her head tied up in a green kerchief, but the grandmother had on a navy blue straw sailor hat with a bunch of white violets on the brim and a navy blue dress with a small white dot in the print. Her collars and cuffs were white organdy trimmed with lace and at her neckline she had pinned a purple spray of cloth violets containing a sachet. In case of an accident, anyone seeing her dead on the highway would know at once that she was a lady.

She said she thought it was going to be a good day for driving, neither too hot nor too cold, and she cautioned Bailey that the speed limit was fifty-five miles an hour and that the patrolmen hid themselves behind billboards and small clumps of trees and sped out after you before you had a chance to slow down. She pointed out interesting details of the scenery: Stone Mountain; the blue granite that in some places came up to both sides of the highway; the brilliant red clay banks slightly streaked with purple; and the various crops that made rows of green lace-work on the ground. The trees were full of silver-white sunlight and the meanest of them sparkled. The children were reading comic magazines and their mother had gone back to sleep.

"Let's go through Georgia fast so we won't have to look at it much," John Wesley said.

"If I were a little boy," said the grandmother, "I wouldn't talk about my native state that way. Tennessee has the mountains and Georgia has the hills."

"Tennessee is just a hillbilly dumping ground," John Wesley said, "and Georgia is a lousy state too."

"You said it," June Star said.

"In my time," said the grandmother, folding her thin veined fingers, "children were more respectful of their native states and their parents and everything else. People did right then. Oh look at the cute little pickaninny!" she said and pointed to a Negro child standing in the door of a shack. "Wouldn't that make a picture, now?" she asked and they all turned and looked at the little Negro out of the back window. He waved.

"He didn't have any britches on," June Star said.

"He probably didn't have any," the grandmother explained. "Little niggers in the country don't have things like we do. If I could paint, I'd paint that picture," she said.

The children exchanged comic books.

The grandmother offered to hold the baby and the children's mother passed him over the front seat to her. She set him on her knee and bounced him and told him about the things they were passing. She rolled her eyes and screwed up her mouth and stuck her leathery thin face into his smooth bland one. Occasionally he gave her a faraway smile. They passed a large cotton field with five or six graves fenced in the middle of it, like a small island. "Look at the graveyard!" the grandmother said, pointing it out. "That was the old family burying ground. That belonged to the plantation."

"Where's the plantation?" John Wesley asked.

"Gone With the Wind," said the grandmother. "Ha. Ha."

When the children finished all the comic books they had brought, they opened the lunch and ate it. The grandmother ate a peanut butter sandwich and an olive and would not let the children throw the box and the paper napkins out the window. When there was nothing else to do they played a game by choosing a cloud and making the other two guess what shape it suggested. John Wesley took one the shape of a cow and June Star guessed a cow and John Wesley said, no, an automobile, and June Star said he didn't play fair, and they began to slap each other over the grandmother.

The grandmother said she would tell them a story if they would keep quiet. When she told a story, she rolled her eyes and waved her head and was very dramatic. She said once when she was a maiden lady she had been courted by a Mr. Edgar Atkins Teagarden from Jasper, Georgia. She said he was a very good-looking man and a gentleman and that he brought her a watermelon every Saturday afternoon with his initials cut in it, E. A. T. Well, one Saturday, she said, Mr. Teagarden brought the watermelon and there was nobody at home and he left it on the front porch and returned in his buggy to Jasper, but she never got the watermelon, she said, because a nigger boy ate it when he saw the initials, E. A. T.! This story tickled John Wesley's funny bone and he giggled and giggled but June Star didn't think it was any good. She said she wouldn't marry a man that just brought her a watermelon on Saturday. The grandmother said she would have done well to marry Mr. Teagarden because he was a gentleman and had bought Coca-Cola stock when it first came out and that he had died only a few years ago, a very wealthy man.

They stopped at The Tower for barbecued sandwiches. The Tower was a part stucco and part wood filling station and dance hall set in a clearing outside of Timothy. A fat man named Red Sammy Butts ran it and there were signs stuck here and there on the building and for miles up and down the highway saying, TRY RED SAMMY'S FAMOUS BARBECUE. NONE LIKE FAMOUS RED SAMMY'S! RED SAM! THE FAT BOY WITH THE HAPPY LAUGH. A VETERAN! RED SAMMY'S YOUR MAN!

Red Sammy was lying on the bare ground outside The Tower with his head under a truck while a gray monkey about a foot high, chained to a small chinaberry tree, chattered nearby. The monkey sprang back into the tree and got on the highest limb as soon as he saw the children jump out of the car and run toward him.

Inside, The Tower was a long dark room with a counter at one end and tables at the other and dancing space in the middle. They all sat down at a board table next to the nickelodeon and Red Sam's wife, a tall burnt-brown woman with hair and eyes lighter than her skin, came and took their order. The children's mother put a dime in the machine and played "The Tennessee Waltz," and the grandmother said that tune always made her want to dance. She asked

Bailey if he would like to dance but he only glared at her. He didn't
have a naturally sunny disposition like she did and trips made him
nervous. The grandmother's brown eyes were very bright. She
swayed her head from side to side and pretended she was dancing in
her chair. June Star said play something she could tap to so the children's mother put in another dime and played a fast number and
June Star stepped out onto the dance floor and did her tap routine.

"Ain't she cute?" Red Sam's wife said, leaning over the counter.
"Would you like to come be my little girl?"

"No I certainly wouldn't," June Star said. "I wouldn't live in a
broken-down place like this for a million bucks!" and she ran back
to the table.

"Ain't she cute?" the woman repeated, stretching her mouth
politely.

"Arn't you ashamed?" hissed the grandmother.

Red Sam came in and told his wife to quit lounging on the
counter and hurry up with these people's order. His khaki trousers
reached just to his hip bones and his stomach hung over them like a
sack of meal swaying under his shirt. He came over and sat down at a
table nearby and let out a combination sigh and yodel. "You can't
win," he said. "You can't win," and he wiped his sweating red face
off with a gray handkerchief. "These days you don't know who to
trust," he said. "Ain't that the truth?"

"People are certainly not nice like they used to be," said the
grandmother.

"Two fellers come in here last week," Red Sammy said, "driving a Chrysler. It was a old beat-up car but it was a good one and
these boys looked all right to me. Said they worked at the mill and
you know I let them fellers charge the gas they bought? Now why
did I do that?"

"Because you're a good man!" the grandmother said at once.

"Yes'm, I suppose so," Red Sam said as if he were struck with
this answer.

His wife brought the orders, carrying the five plates all at once
without a tray, two in each hand and one balanced on her arm. "It
isn't a soul in this green world of God's that you can trust," she said.
"And I don't count nobody out of that, not nobody," she repeated,
looking at Red Sammy.

"Did you read about that criminal, The Misfit, that's escaped?" asked the grandmother.

"I wouldn't be a bit surprised if he didn't attact this place right here," said the woman. "If he hears about it being here, I wouldn't be none surprised to see him. If he hears it's two cent in the cash register, I wouldn't be a tall surprised if he . . ."

"That'll do," Red Sam said. "Go bring these people their Co'-Colas," and the woman went off to get the rest of the order.

"A good man is hard to find," Red Sammy said. "Everything is getting terrible. I remember the day you could go off and leave your screen door unlatched. Not no more."

He and the grandmother discussed better times. The old lady said that in her opinion Europe was entirely to blame for the way things were now. She said the way Europe acted you would think we were made of money and Red Sam said it was no use talking about it, she was exactly right. The children ran outside into the white sunlight and looked at the monkey in the lacy chinaberry tree. He was busy catching fleas on himself and biting each one carefully between his teeth as if it were a delicacy.

They drove off again into the hot afternoon. The grandmother took cat naps and woke up every few minutes with her own snoring. Outside of Toombsboro she woke up and recalled an old plantation that she had visited in this neighborhood once when she was a young lady. She said the house had six white columns across the front and that there was an avenue of oaks leading up to it and two little wooden trellis arbors on either side in front where you sat down with your suitor after a stroll in the garden. She recalled exactly which road to turn off to get to it. She knew that Bailey would not be willing to lose any time looking at an old house, but the more she talked about it, the more she wanted to see it once again and find out if the little twin arbors were still standing. "There was a secret panel in this house," she said craftily, not telling the truth but wishing that she were, "and the story went that all the family silver was hidden in it when Sherman came through but it was never found . . ."

"Hey!" John Wesley said. "Let's go see it! We'll find it! We'll poke all the woodwork and find it! Who lives there? Where do you turn off at? Hey Pop, can't we turn off there?"

"We never have seen a house with a secret panel!" June Star shrieked. "Let's go to the house with the secret panel! Hey Pop, can't we go see the house with the secret panel!"

"It's not far from here, I know," the grandmother said. "It wouldn't take over twenty minutes."

Bailey was looking straight ahead. His jaw was as rigid as a horseshoe. "No," he said.

The children began to yell and scream that they wanted to see the house with the secret panel. John Wesley kicked the back of the front seat and June Star hung over her mother's shoulder and whined desperately into her ear that they never had any fun even on their vacation, that they could never do what THEY wanted to do. The baby began to scream and John Wesley kicked the back of the seat so hard that his father could feel the blows in his kidney.

"All right!" he shouted and drew the car to a stop at the side of the road. "Will you all shut up? Will you all just shut up for one second? If you don't shut up, we won't go anywhere."

"It would be very educational for them," the grandmother murmured.

"All right," Bailey said, "but get this: this is the only time we're going to stop for anything like this. This is the one and only time."

"The dirt road that you have to turn down is about a mile back," the grandmother directed. "I marked it when we passed."

"A dirt road," Bailey groaned.

After they had turned around and were headed toward the dirt road, the grandmother recalled other points about the house, the beautiful glass over the front doorway and the candle-lamp in the hall. John Wesley said that the secret panel was probably in the fireplace.

"You can't go inside this house," Bailey said. "You don't know who lives there."

"While you all talk to the people in front, I'll run around behind and get in a window," John Wesley suggested.

"We'll all stay in the car," his mother said.

They turned onto the dirt road and the car raced roughly along in a swirl of pink dust. The grandmother recalled the times when there were no paved roads and thirty miles was a day's journey. The dirt road was hilly and there were sudden washes in it and sharp curves on dangerous embankments. All at once they would be on a hill, looking down over the blue tops of trees for miles around, then the next minute, they would be in a red depression with the dust-coated trees looking down on them.

"This place had better turn up in a minute," Bailey said, "or I'm going to turn around."

The road looked as if no one had traveled on it in months.

"It's not much farther," the grandmother said and just as she said it, a horrible thought came to her. The thought was so embarrassing that she turned red in the face and her eyes dilated and her feet jumped up, upsetting her valise in the corner. The instant the valise moved, the newspaper top she had over the basket under it rose with a snarl and Pitty Sing, the cat, sprang onto Bailey's shoulder.

The children were thrown to the floor and their mother, clutching the baby, was thrown out the door on to the ground; the old lady was thrown into the front seat. The car turned over once and landed right-side-up in a gulch off the side of the road. Bailey remained in the driver's seat with the cat—gray-striped with a broad white face and an orange nose clinging to his neck like a caterpillar.

As soon as the children saw they could move their arms and legs, they scrambled out of the car, shouting, "We've had an AC-CIDENT!" The grandmother was curled up under the dashboard, hoping she was injured so that Bailey's wrath would not come down on her all at once. The horrible thought she had had before the accident was that the house she had remembered so vividly was not in Georgia but in Tennessee.

Bailey removed the cat from his neck with both hands and flung it out the window against the side of a pine tree. Then he got out of the car and started looking for the children's mother. She was sitting against the side of the red gutted ditch, holding the screaming baby, but she only had a cut down her face and a broken shoulder. "We've had an ACCIDENT!" the children screamed in a frenzy of delight.

"But nobody's killed," June Star said with disappointment as the grandmother limped out of the car, her hat still pinned to her head but the broken front brim standing up at a jaunty angle and the violet spray hanging off the side. They all sat down in the ditch, except the children, to recover from the shock. They were all shaking.

"Maybe a car will come along," said the children's mother hoarsely.

"I believe I have injured an organ," said the grandmother, pressing her side, but no one answered her. Bailey's teeth were clattering. He had on a yellow sport shirt with bright blue parrots designed in it and his face was as yellow as the shirt. The grandmother decided that she would not mention that the house was in Tennessee.

The road was about ten feet above and they could see only the tops of the trees on the other side of it. Behind the ditch they were sitting in there were more woods, tall and dark and deep. In a few minutes they saw a car some distance away on top of a hill, coming slowly as if the occupants were watching them. The grandmother stood up and waved both arms dramatically to attract their attention. The car continued to come on slowly, disappeared around a bend and appeared again, moving even slower, on top of the hill they had gone over. It was a big black battered hearse-like automobile. There were three men in it.

It came to a stop just over them and for some minutes, the driver looked down with a steady expressionless gaze to where they were sitting, and didn't speak. Then he turned his head and muttered something to the other two and they got out. One was a fat boy in black trousers and a red sweat shirt with a silver stallion embossed on the front of it. He moved around on the right side of them and stood staring, his mouth partly open in a kind of loose grin. The other had on khaki pants and a blue striped coat and a gray hat pulled down very low, hiding most of his face. He came around slowly on the left side. Neither spoke.

The driver got out of the car and stood by the side of it, looking down at them. He was an older man than the other two. His hair was just beginning to gray and he wore silver-rimmed spectacles that gave him a scholarly look. He had a long creased face and didn't have on any shirt or undershirt. He had on blue jeans that were too tight for him and was holding a black hat and a gun. The two boys also had guns.

"We've had an ACCIDENT!" the children screamed.

The grandmother had the peculiar feeling that the bespectacled man was someone she knew. His face was as familiar to her as if she had known him all her life but she could not recall who he was. He moved away from the car and began to come down the embankment, placing his feet carefully so that he wouldn't slip. He had on tan and white shoes and no socks, and his ankles were red and thin. "Good afternoon," he said. "I see you all had you a little spill."

"We turned over twice!" said the grandmother.

"Oncet," he corrected. "We seen it happen. Try their car and see will it run, Hiram," he said quietly to the boy with the gray hat.

"What you got that gun for?" John Wesley asked. "Whatcha gonna do with that gun?"

"Lady," the man said to the children's mother, "would you mind calling them children to sit down by you? Children make me nervous. I want all you all to sit down right together there where you're at."

"What are you telling US what to do for?" June Star asked.

Behind them the line of woods gaped like a dark open mouth. "Come here," said their mother.

"Look here now," Bailey began suddenly, "we're in a predicament! We're in . . ."

The grandmother shrieked. She scrambled to her feet and stood staring. "You're The Misfit!" she said. "I recognized you at once!"

"Yes'm," the man said, smiling slightly as if he were pleased in spite of himself to be known, "but it would have been better for all of you, lady, if you hadn't of reckernized me."

Bailey turned his head sharply and said something to his mother that shocked even the children. The old lady began to cry and The Misfit reddened.

"Lady," he said, "don't you get upset. Sometimes a man says things he don't mean. I don't reckon he meant to talk to you that-away."

"You wouldn't shoot a lady, would you?" the grandmother said and removed a clean handkerchief from her cuff and began to slap at her eyes with it.

The Misfit pointed the toe of his shoe into the ground and made a little hole and then covered it up again. "I would hate to have to," he said.

"Listen," the grandmother almost screamed, "I know you're a good man. You don't look a bit like you have common blood. I know you must come from nice people!"

"Yes mam," he said, "finest people in the world." When he smiled he showed a row of strong white teeth. "God never made a finer woman than my mother and my daddy's heart was pure gold," he said. The boy with the red sweat shirt had come around behind them and was standing with his gun at his hip. The Misfit squatted down on the ground. "Watch them children, Bobby Lee," he said.

"You know they make me nervous." He looked at the six of them huddled together in front of him and he seemed to be embarrassed as if he couldn't think of anything to say. "Ain't a cloud in the sky," he remarked, looking up at it. "Don't see no sun but don't see no cloud neither."

"Yes, it's a beautiful day," said the grandmother. "Listen," she said, "you shouldn't call yourself The Misfit because I know you're a good man at heart. I can just look at you and tell."

"Hush!" Bailey yelled. "Hush! Everybody shut up and let me handle this!" He was squatting in the position of a runner about to sprint forward but he didn't move.

"I pre-chate that, lady," The Misfit said and drew a little circle in the ground with the butt of his gun.

"It'll take a half a hour to fix this here car," Hiram called, looking over the raised hood of it.

"Well, first you and Bobby Lee get him and that little boy to step over yonder with you," The Misfit said, pointing to Bailey and John Wesley. "The boys want to ast you something," he said to Bailey. "Would you mind stepping back in them woods there with them?"

"Listen," Bailey began, "we're in a terrible predicament! Nobody realizes what this is," and his voice cracked. His eyes were as blue and intense as the parrots in his shirt and he remained perfectly still.

The grandmother reached up to adjust her hat brim as if she were going to the woods with him but it came off in her hand. She stood staring at it and after a second she let it fall on the ground. Hiram pulled Bailey up by the arm as if he were assisting an old man. John Wesley caught hold of his father's hand and Bobby Lee followed. They went off toward the woods and just as they reached the dark edge, Bailey turned and supporting himself against a gray naked pine trunk, he shouted, "I'll be back in a minute, Mamma, wait on me!"

"Come back this instant!" his mother shrilled but they all disappeared into the woods.

"Bailey Boy!" the grandmother called in a tragic voice but she found she was looking at The Misfit squatting on the ground in front of her. "I just know you're a good man," she said desperately. "You're not a bit common!"

"Nome, I ain't a good man," The Misfit said after a second as if he had considered her statement carefully, "but I ain't the worst in the world neither. My daddy said I was a different breed of dog from my brothers and sisters. 'You know,' Daddy said, 'it's some that can live their whole life out without asking about it and it's others has to know why it is, and this boy is one of the latters. He's going to be into everything!' " He put on his black hat and looked up suddenly and then away deep into the woods as if he were embarrassed again. "I'm sorry I don't have on a shirt before you ladies," he said, hunching his shoulders slightly. "We buried our clothes that we had on when we escaped and we're just making do until we can get better. We borrowed these from some folks we met," he explained.

"That's perfectly all right," the grandmother said. "Maybe Bailey has an extra shirt in his suitcase."

"I'll look and see terrectly," The Misfit said.

"Where are they taking him?" the children's mother screamed.

"Daddy was a card himself," The Misfit said. "You couldn't put anything over on him. He never got in trouble with the Authorities though. Just had the knack of handling them."

"You could be honest too if you'd only try," said the grandmother. "Think how wonderful it would be to settle down and live a comfortable life and not have to think about somebody chasing you all the time."

The Misfit kept scratching in the ground with the butt of his gun as if he were thinking about it. "Yes'm, somebody is always after you," he murmured.

The grandmother noticed how thin his shoulder blades were just behind his hat because she was standing up looking down on him. "Do you ever pray?" she asked.

He shook his head. All she saw was the black hat wiggle between his shoulder blades. "Nome," he said.

There was a pistol shot from the woods, followed closely by another. Then silence. The old lady's head jerked around. She could hear the wind move through the tree tops like a long satisfied insuck of breath. "Bailey Boy!" she called.

"I was a gospel singer for a while," The Misfit said. "I been most everything. Been in the arm service, both land and sea, at home and abroad, been twict married, been an undertaker, been with the railroads, plowed Mother Earth, been in a tornado, seen a man burnt alive oncet," and he looked up at the children's mother and the little girl who were sitting close together, their faces white and their eyes glassy; "I even seen a woman flogged," he said.

"Pray, pray," the grandmother began, "pray, pray . . ."

"I never was a bad boy that I remember of," The Misfit said in an almost dreamy voice, "but somewheres along the line I done something wrong and got sent to the penitentiary. I was buried alive," and he looked up and held her attention to him by a steady stare.

"That's when you should have started to pray," she said. "What did you do to get sent to the penitentiary that first time?"

"Turn to the right, it was a wall," The Misfit said, looking up again at the cloudless sky. "Turn to the left, it was a wall. Look up it was ceiling, look down it was a floor. I forget what I done, lady. I set there and set there, trying to remember what it was I done and I ain't recalled it to this day. Oncet in a while, I would think it was coming to me, but it never come."

"Maybe they put you in by mistake," the old lady said vaguely.

"Nome," he said. "It wasn't no mistake. They had the papers on me."

"You must have stolen something," she said.

The Misfit sneered slightly. "Nobody had nothing I wanted," he said. "It was a head-doctor at the penitentiary said what I had done was kill my daddy but I known that for a lie. My daddy died in nineteen ought nineteen of the epidemic flu and I never had a thing to do with it. He was buried in the Mount Hopewell Baptist churchyard and you can go there and see for yourself."

"If you would pray," the old lady said, "Jesus would help you."

"That's right," The Misfit said.

"Well then, why don't you pray?" she asked trembling with delight suddenly.

"I don't want no hep," he said. "I'm doing all right by myself."

Bobby Lee and Hiram came ambling back from the woods. Bobby Lee was dragging a yellow shirt with bright blue parrots in it.

"Thow me that shirt, Bobby Lee," The Misfit said. The shirt came flying at him and landed on his shoulder and he put it on. The grandmother couldn't name what the shirt reminded her of. "No, lady," The Misfit said while he was buttoning it up, "I found out the crime don't matter. You can do one thing or you can do another, kill a man or take a tire off his car, because sooner or later you're going to forget what it was you done and just be punished for it."

The children's mother had begun to make heaving noises as if she couldn't get her breath. "Lady," he asked, "would you and that little girl like to step off yonder with Bobby Lee and Hiram and join your husband?"

"Yes, thank you," the mother said faintly. Her left arm dangled helplessly and she was holding the baby, who had gone to sleep, in the other. "Hep that lady up, Hiram," The Misfit said as she struggled to climb out of the ditch, "and Bobby Lee, you hold onto that little girl's hand."

"I don't want to hold hands with him," June Star said. "He reminds me of a pig."

The fat boy blushed and laughed and caught her by the arm and pulled her off into the woods after Hiram and her mother.

Alone with The Misfit, the grandmother found that she had lost her voice. There was not a cloud in the sky nor any sun. There was nothing around her but woods. She wanted to tell him that he must pray. She opened and closed her mouth several times before anything came out. Finally she found herself saying, "Jesus. Jesus," meaning, Jesus will help you, but the way she was saying it, it sounded as if she might be cursing.

"Yes'm," The Misfit said as if he agreed. "Jesus thown everything off balance. It was the same case with Him as with me except He hadn't committed any crime and they could prove I had committed one because they had the papers on me. Of course," he said, "they never shown me my papers. That's why I sign myself now. I said long ago, you get you a signature and sign everything you do and keep a copy of it. Then you'll know what you done and you can hold up the crime to the punishment and see do they match and in the end you'll have something to prove you ain't been treated right. I call myself The Misfit," he said, "because I can't make what all I done wrong fit what all I gone through in punishment."

There was a piercing scream from the woods, followed closely by a pistol report. "Does it seem right to you, lady, that one is punished a heap and another ain't punished at all?"

"Jesus!" the old lady cried. "You've got good blood! I know you wouldn't shoot a lady! I know you come from nice people! Pray! Jesus, you ought not to shoot a lady. I'll give you all the money I've got!"

"Lady," The Misfit said, looking beyond her far into the woods, "there never was a body that give the undertaker a tip."

There were two more pistol reports and the grandmother raised her head like a parched old turkey hen crying for water and called, "Bailey Boy, Bailey Boy!" as if her heart would break.

"Jesus was the only One that ever raised the dead," The Misfit continued, "and He shouldn't have done it. He thown everything off balance. If He did what He said, then it's nothing for you to do but thow away everything and follow Him, and if He didn't, then it's nothing for you to do but enjoy the few minutes you got left the best way you can—by killing somebody or burning down his house or doing some other meanness to him. No pleasure but meanness," he said and his voice had become almost a snarl.

"Maybe He didn't raise the dead," the old lady mumbled, not knowing what she was saying and feeling so dizzy that she sank down in the ditch with her legs twisted under her.

"I wasn't there so I can't say He didn't," The Misfit said. "I wisht I had of been there," he said, hitting the ground with his fist. "It ain't right I wasn't there because if I had of been there I would of known. Listen lady," he said in a high voice, "if I had of been there I would of known and I wouldn't be like I am now." His voice seemed about to crack and the grandmother's head cleared for an instant. She saw the man's face twisted close to her own as if he were going to cry and she murmured, "Why you're one of my babies. You're one of my own children!" She reached out and touched him on the shoulder. The Misfit sprang back as if a snake had bitten him and shot her three times through the chest. Then he put his gun down on the ground and took off his glasses and began to clean them.

Hiram and Bobby Lee returned from the woods and stood over the ditch, looking down at the grandmother who half sat and half lay in a puddle of blood with her legs crossed under her like a child's and her face smiling up at the cloudless sky.

Without his glasses, The Misfit's eyes were red-rimmed and pale and defenseless-looking. "Take her off and thow her where you thown the others," he said, picking up the cat that was rubbing itself against his leg.

"She was a talker, wasn't she?" Bobby Lee said, sliding down the ditch with a yodel.

"She would of been a good woman," The Misfit said, "if it had been somebody there to shoot her every minute of her life."

"Some fun!" Bobby Lee said.

"Shut up, Bobby Lee," The Misfit said. "It's no real pleasure in life."

:S THURBER

(1894-1961)

...rnalist, and caricaturist, Thurber was ...ew Yorker magazine, where his works ...His central theme is the eternal conflict ...he charm and humor with which this ...owever, prevent the reader from not- ...ing satire also present. There is more ...ind plots than mere comic absurdity. ...re numerous; one of the best known of them, "The ...Life of Walter Mitty," was made into a movie. Among his best collections of stories are *FABLES FOR OUR TIME* and *THE SEAL IN THE BEDROOM & OTHER PREDICAMENTS*.

The Unicorn in the Garden

Once upon a sunny morning a man who sat in a breakfast nook looked up from his scrambled eggs to see a white unicorn with a golden horn quietly cropping the roses in the garden. The man went up to the bedroom where his wife was still asleep and woke her. "There's a unicorn in the garden," he said. "Eating roses." She opened one unfriendly eye and looked at him. "The unicorn is a mythical beast," she said, and turned her back on him. The man walked slowly downstairs and out into the garden. The unicorn was still there; he was now browsing among the tulips. "Here, unicorn," said the man, and he pulled up a lily and gave it to him. The unicorn ate it gravely. With a high heart, because there was a unicorn in his garden, the man went upstairs and roused his wife again. "The unicorn," he said, "ate a lily." His wife sat up in bed and looked at him, coldly. "You are a booby," she said, "and I am going to have you put in the booby-hatch." The man, who had never liked the words "booby" and "booby-hatch," and who liked them even less on a shining morning when there was a unicorn in the garden, thought for a moment. "We'll see about that," he said. He walked over to the door. "He has a golden horn in the middle of his forehead," he told her. Then he went back to the garden to watch the unicorn; but the unicorn had gone away. The man sat down among the roses and went to sleep.

As soon as the husband had gone out of the house, the wife got up and dressed as fast as she could. She was very excited and there was a gloat in her eye. She telephoned the police and she telephoned a psychiatrist; she told them to hurry to her house and bring a strait-jacket. When the police and the psychiatrist arrived they sat down in chairs and looked at her, with great interest. "My husband," she said, "saw a unicorn this morning." The police looked at the psychiatrist and the psychiatrist looked at the police. "He told me it ate a lily," she said. The psychiatrist looked at the police and the police looked at the psychiatrist. "He told me it had a golden horn in the middle of its forehead," she said. At a solemn signal from the psychiatrist, the police leaped from their chairs and seized the wife. They had a hard time subduing her, for she put up a terrific struggle, but they finally subdued her. Just as they got her into the strait-jacket, the husband came back into the house.

"Did you tell your wife you saw a unicorn?" asked the police. "Of course not," said the husband. "The unicorn is a mythical beast." "That's all I wanted to know," said the psychiatrist. "Take her away. I'm sorry, sir, but your wife is as crazy as a jay bird." So they took her away, cursing and screaming, and shut her up in an institution. The husband lived happily ever after.

Moral: Don't count your boobies until they are hatched.

SHIRLEY JACKSON

(1919-1965)

Shirley Jackson was born in San Francisco and spent her early years in California. In 1940 she married the critic, Stanley Edgar Hyman. In the years of her maturity she produced several novels, one collection of short stories, a good many essays, and some autobiographical works. When she wished, Miss Jackson could write extremely comical stories, such as "My Life with R. H. Macy." But more often her works are chillingly macabre, frightening glances into the demented and fragmented nature of our times. Her famous short story, "The Lottery," and her novel, THE BIRD'S NEST, are of this sort. Even the humorous story, "The Witch," has its caustic side. The best survey of her work is to be found in the collection, THE MAGIC OF SHIRLEY JACKSON, edited by her husband.

The Witch

The coach was so nearly empty that the little boy had a seat all to himself, and his mother sat across the aisle on the seat next to the little boy's sister, a baby with a piece of toast in one hand and a rattle in the other. She was strapped securely to the seat so she could sit up and look around, and whenever she began to slip slowly sideways the strap caught her and held her halfway until her mother turned around and straightened her again. The little boy was looking out the window and eating a cookie, and the mother was reading quietly, answering the little boy's questions without looking up.

"The Witch" Reprinted with the permission of Farrar, Straus & Giroux, Inc., from *The Lottery* by Shirley Jackson. Copyright 1949 by Shirley Jackson.

"We're on a river," the little boy said. "This is a river and we're on it."

"Fine," his mother said.

"We're on a bridge over a river," the little boy said to himself.

The few other people in the coach were sitting at the other end of the car; if any of them had occasion to come down the aisle the little boy would look around and say, "Hi," and the stranger would usually say, "Hi," back and sometimes ask the little boy if he were enjoying the train ride, or even tell him he was a fine big fellow. These comments annoyed the little boy and he would turn irritably back to the window.

"There's a cow," he would say, or, sighing, "How far do we have to go?"

"Not much longer now," his mother said, each time.

Once the baby, who was very quiet and busy with her rattle and her toast, which the mother would renew constantly, fell over too far sideways and banged her head. She began to cry, and for a minute there was noise and movement around the mother's seat. The little boy slid down from his own seat and ran across the aisle to pet his sister's feet and beg her not to cry, and finally the baby laughed and went back to her toast, and the little boy received a lollipop from his mother and went back to the window.

"I saw a witch," he said to his mother after a minute. "There was a big old ugly old bad old witch outside."

"Fine," his mother said.

"A big old ugly witch and I told her to go away and she went away," the little boy went on, in a quiet narrative to himself, "she came and said, 'I'm going to eat you up,' and I said, 'no, you're not,' and I chased her away, the bad old mean witch."

He stopped talking and looked up as the outside door of the coach opened and a man came in. He was an elderly man, with a pleasant face under white hair; his blue suit was only faintly touched by the disarray that comes from a long train trip. He was carrying a cigar, and when the little boy said, "Hi," the man gestured at him with the cigar and said, "Hello yourself, son." He stopped just beside the little boy's seat, and leaned against the back, looking down at the little boy, who craned his neck to look upward. "What you looking for out that window?" the man asked.

"Witches," the little boy said promptly. "Bad old mean witches."

"I see," the man said. "Find many?"

"My father smokes cigars," the little boy said.

"All men smoke cigars," the man said. "Someday you'll smoke a cigar, too."

"I'm a man already," the little boy said.

"How old are you?" the man asked.

The little boy, at the eternal question, looked at the man suspiciously for a minute and then said, "Twenty-six. Eight hunnerd and forty eighty."

His mother lifted her head from the book. "Four," she said, smiling fondly at the little boy.

"Is that so?" the man said politely to the little boy. "Twenty-six." He nodded his head at the mother across the aisle. "Is that your mother?"

The little boy leaned forward to look and then said, "Yes, that's her."

"What's your name?" the man asked.

The little boy looked suspicious again. "Mr. Jesus," he said.

"*Johnny*," the little boy's mother said. She caught the little boy's eye and frowned deeply.

"That's my sister over there," the little boy said to the man. "She's twelve-and-a-half."

"Do you love your sister?" the man asked. The little boy stared, and the man came around the side of the seat and sat down next to the little boy. "Listen," the man said, "shall I tell you about my little sister?"

The mother, who had looked up anxiously when the man sat down next to her little boy, went peacefully back to her book.

"Tell me about your sister," the little boy said. "Was she a witch?"

"Maybe," the man said.

The little boy laughed excitedly, and the man leaned back and puffed at his cigar. "Once upon a time," he began, "I had a little sister, just like yours." The little boy looked up at the man, nodding at every word. "My little sister," the man went on, "was so pretty and so nice that I loved her more than anything else in the world. So shall I tell you what I did?"

The little boy nodded more vehemently, and the mother lifted her eyes from her book and smiled, listening.

"I bought her a rocking-horse and a doll and a million lollipops," the man said, "and then I took her and I put my hands around her neck and I pinched her and I pinched her until she was dead."

The little boy gasped and the mother turned around, her smile fading. She opened her mouth, and then closed it again as the man went on, "And then I took and I cut her head off and I took her head—"

"Did you cut her all in pieces?" the little boy asked breathlessly.

"I cut off her head and her hands and her feet and her hair and her nose," the man said, "and I hit her with a stick and I killed her."

"Wait a minute," the mother said, but the baby fell over sideways just at that minute and by the time the mother had set her up again the man was going on.

"And I took her head and I pulled out all her hair and—"

"Your little *sister?*" the little boy prompted eagerly.

"My little sister," the man said firmly. "And I put her head in a cage with a bear and the bear ate it all up."

"Ate her *head* all up?" the little boy asked.

The mother put her book down and came across the aisle. She stood next to the man and said, "Just what do you think you're doing?" The man looked up courteously and she said, "Get out of here."

"Did I frighten you?" the man said. He looked down at the little boy and nudged him with an elbow and he and the little boy laughed.

"This man cut up his little sister," the little boy said to his mother.

"I can very easily call the conductor," the mother said to the man.

"The conductor will *eat* my mommy," the little boy said. "We'll chop her head off."

"And little sister's head, too," the man said. He stood up, and the mother stood back to let him get out of the seat. "Don't ever come back in this car," she said.

"My mommy will eat *you,*" the little boy said to the man.

The man laughed, and the little boy laughed, and then the man said, "Excuse me," to the mother and went past her out of the car. When the door had closed behind him the little boy said, "How much longer do we have to stay on this old train?"

"Not much longer," the mother said. She stood looking at the little boy, wanting to say something, and finally she said, "You sit still and be a good boy. You may have another lollipop."

The little boy climbed down eagerly and followed his mother back to her seat. She took a lollipop from a bag in her pocketbook and gave it to him. "What do you say?" she asked.

"Thank you," the little boy said. "Did that man really cut his little sister up in pieces?"

"He was just teasing," the mother said, and added urgently, "Just *teasing*."

"Prob'ly," the little boy said. With his lollipop he went back to his own seat, and settled himself to look out the window again. "Prob'ly he was a witch."

CARSON McCULLERS

(1917-1967)

Carson McCullers, like William Faulkner and Flannery O'Connor, was a product of the South. Born in Georgia, she later went to New York to study music. Oddly enough, that career was ended before it began: she lost her tuition money on the subway during her second day in the city. Her novels and short stories reveal characters conscious of their isolation but frustrated in their attempts to break through it. Her interest in music appears frequently as a part of plot and character. Her novels include THE HEART IS A LONELY HUNTER, REFLECTIONS IN A GOLDEN EYE, THE MEMBER OF THE WEDDING (which was made into a successful Broadway play), and CLOCK WITHOUT HANDS. The title story of her famous collection, THE BALLAD OF THE SAD CAFE, was adapted to the stage by the well known American dramatist, Edward Albee (WHO'S AFRAID OF VIRGINIA WOOLF?). She wrote one play, THE SQUARE ROOT OF WONDERFUL, and published one book of poems, SWEET AS A PICKLE AND CLEAN AS A PIG.

Madame Zilensky and the King of Finland

To Mr. Brook, the head of the music department at Ryder College, was due all the credit for getting Madame Zilensky on the faculty. The college considered itself fortunate; her reputation was impres-

"Madame Zilensky and the King of Finland" by Carson McCullers is reprinted with the permission of Houghton Mifflin Company.

sive, both as a composer and as a pedagogue. Mr. Brook took on himself the responsibility of finding a house for Madame Zilensky, a comfortable place with a garden, which was convenient to the college and next to the apartment house where he himself lived.

No one in Westbridge had known Madame Zilensky before she came. Mr. Brook had seen her pictures in musical journals, and once he had written to her about the authenticity of a certain Buxtehude manuscript. Also, when it was being settled that she was to join the faculty, they had exchanged a few cables and letters on practical affairs. She wrote in a clear, square hand, and the only thing out of the ordinary in these letters was the fact that they contained an occasional reference to objects and persons altogether unknown to Mr. Brook, such as "the yellow cat in Lisbon" or "poor Heinrich." These lapses Mr. Brook put down to the confusion of getting herself and her family out of Europe.

Mr. Brook was a somewhat pastel person; years of Mozart minuets, of explanations about diminished sevenths and minor triads, had given him a watchful vocational patience. For the most part, he kept to himself. He loathed academic fiddle-faddle and committees. Years before, when the music department had decided to gang together and spend the summer in Salzburg, Mr. Brook sneaked out of the arrangement at the last moment and took a solitary trip to Peru. He had a few eccentricities himself and was tolerant of the peculiarities of others; indeed, he rather relished the ridiculous. Often, when confronted with some grave and incongruous situation, he would feel a little inside tickle, which stiffened his long, mild face and sharpened the light in his gray eyes.

Mr. Brook met Madame Zilensky at the Westbridge station a week before the beginning of the fall semester. He recognized her instantly. She was a tall, straight woman with a pale and haggard face. Her eyes were deeply shadowed and she wore her dark, ragged hair pushed back from her forehead. She had large, delicate hands, which were very grubby. About her person as a whole there was something noble and abstract that made Mr. Brook draw back for a moment and stand nervously undoing his cuff links. In spite of her clothes—a long, black skirt and a broken-down old leather jacket —she made an impression of vague elegance. With Madame Zilensky were three children, boys between the ages of ten and six, all blond, blank-eyed, and beautiful. There was one other person, an old woman who turned out later to be the Finnish servant.

This was the group he found at the station. The only luggage they had with them was two immense boxes of manuscripts, the rest of their paraphernalia having been forgotten in the station at Springfield when they changed trains. That is the sort of thing that can happen to anyone. When Mr. Brook got them all into a taxi, he thought the worst difficulties were over, but Madame Zilensky suddenly tried to scramble over his knees and get out of the door.

"My God!" she said. "I left my—how do you say?—my tick-tick-tick——"

"Your watch?" asked Mr. Brook.

"Oh no!" she said vehemently. "You know, my tick-tick-tick," and she waved her forefinger from side to side, pendulum fashion.

"Tick-tick," said Mr. Brook, putting his hands to his forehead and closing his eyes. "Could you possibly mean a metronome?"

"Yes! Yes! I think I must have lost it there where we changed trains."

Mr. Brook managed to quiet her. He even said, with a kind of dazed gallantry, that he would get her another one the next day. But at the time he was bound to admit to himself that there was something curious about this panic over a metronome when there was all the rest of the lost luggage to consider.

The Zelinsky ménage moved into the house next door, and on the surface everything was all right. The boys were quiet children. Their names were Sigmund, Boris, and Sammy. They were always together and they followed each other around Indian file, Sigmund usually the first. Among themselves they spoke a desperate-sounding family Esperanto made up of Russian, French, Finnish, German, and English; when other people were around, they were strangely silent. It was not any one thing that the Zilenskys did or said that made Mr. Brook uneasy. There were just little incidents. For example, something about the Zilensky children subconsciously bothered him when they were in a house, and finally he realized that what troubled him was the fact that the Zilensky boys never walked on a rug; they skirted it single file on the bare floor, and if a room was carpeted, they stood in the doorway and did not go inside. Another thing was this: Weeks passed and Madame Zilensky seemed to make no effort to get settled or to furnish the house with anything more than a table and some beds. The front door was left open day and night, and soon the house began to take on a queer, bleak look like that of a place abandoned for years.

The college had every reason to be satisfied with Madame Zilensky. She taught with a fierce insistence. She could become deeply indignant if some Mary Owens or Bernadine Smith would not clean up her Scarlatti trills. She got hold of four pianos for her college studio and set four dazed students to playing Bach fugues together. The racket that came from her end of the department was extraordinary, but Madame Zilensky did not seem to have a nerve in her, and if pure will and effort can get over a musical idea, then Ryder College could not have done better. At night Madame Zilensky worked on her twelfth symphony. She seemed never to sleep; no matter what time of night Mr. Brook happened to look out of his sitting-room window, the light in her studio was always on. No, it was not because of any professional consideration that Mr. Brook became so dubious.

It was in late October when he felt for the first time that something was unmistakably wrong. He had lunched with Madame Zilensky and had enjoyed himself, as she had given him a very detailed account of an African safari she had made in 1928. Later in the afternoon she stopped in at his office and stood rather abstractly in the doorway.

Mr. Brook looked up from his desk and asked, "Is there anything you want?"

"No, thank you," said Madame Zelinsky. She had a low, beautiful, sombre voice. "I was only just wondering. You recall the metronome. Do you think perhaps that I might have left it with that French?"

"Who?" asked Mr. Brook.

"Why, that French I was married to," she answered.

"Frenchman," Mr. Brook said mildly. He tried to imagine the husband of Madame Zilensky, but his mind refused. He muttered half to himself, "The father of the children."

"But no," said Madame Zilensky with decision. "The father of Sammy."

Mr. Brook had a swift prescience. His deepest instincts warned him to say nothing further. Still, his respect for order, his conscience, demanded that he ask, "And the father of the other two?"

Madame Zilensky put her hand to the back of her head and

ruffled up her short, cropped hair. Her face was dreamy, and for several moments she did not answer. Then she said gently, "Boris is of a Pole who played the piccolo."

"And Sigmund?" he asked. Mr. Brook looked over his orderly desk, with the stack of corrected papers, the three sharpened pencils, the ivory-elephant paperweight. When he glanced up at Madame Zilensky, she was obviously thinking hard. She gazed around at the corners of the room, her brows lowered and her jaw moving from side to side. At last she said, "We were discussing the father of Sigmund?"

"Why no," said Mr. Brook. "There is no need to do that."

Madame Zilensky answered in a voice both dignified and final. "He was a fellow-countryman."

Mr. Brook really did not care one way or the other. He had no prejudices; people could marry seventeen times and have Chinese children so far as he was concerned. But there was something about this conversation with Madame Zilensky that bothered him. Suddenly he understood. The children didn't look at all like Madame Zilensky, but they looked exactly like each other, and as they all had different fathers, Mr. Brook thought the resemblance astonishing.

But Madame Zilensky had finished with the subject. She zipped up her leather jacket and turned away.

"That is exactly where I left it," she said, with a quick nod. "*Chez* that French."

Affairs in the music department were running smoothly. Mr. Brook did not have any serious embarrassments to deal with, such as the harp teacher last year who had finally eloped with a garage mechanic. There was only this nagging apprehension about Madame Zilensky. He could not make out what was wrong in his relations with her or why his feelings were so mixed. To begin with, she was a great globe-trotter, and her conversations were incongruously seasoned with references to far-fetched places. She would go along for days without opening her mouth, prowling through the corridor with her hands in the pockets of her jacket and her face locked in meditation. Then suddenly she would buttonhole Mr. Brook and launch out on a long, volatile monologue, her eyes reckless and bright and her voice warm with eagerness. She would talk about anything or nothing at all. Yet, without exception, there was something queer, in a slanted sort of way, about every episode she ever mentioned. If she spoke of taking Sammy to the barbershop, the impression she created was just as foreign as if she were telling of an afternoon in Bagdad. Mr. Brook could not make it out.

The truth came to him very suddenly, and the truth made everything perfectly clear, or at least clarified the situation. Mr. Brook had come home early and lighted a fire in the little grate in his sitting room. He felt comfortable and at peace that evening. He sat before the fire in his stocking feet, with a volume of William Blake on the table by his side, and he had poured himself a half-glass of apricot brandy. At ten o'clock he was drowsing cozily before the fire, his mind full of cloudy phrases of Mahler and floating half-thoughts. Then all at once, out of this delicate stupor, four words came to his mind: "The King of Finland." The words seemed familiar, but for the first moment he could not place them. Then all at once he tracked them down. He had been walking across the campus that afternoon when Madame Zilensky stopped him and began some preposterous rigmarole, to which he had only half listened; he was thinking about the stack of canons turned in by his counterpoint class. Now the words, the inflections of her voice, came back to him with insidious exactitude. Madame Zilensky had started off with the following remark: "One day, when I was standing in front of a *pâtisserie,* the King of Finland came by in a sled."

Mr. Brook jerked himself up straight in his chair and put down his glass of brandy. The woman was a pathological liar. Almost every word she uttered outside of class was an untruth. If she worked all night, she would go out of her way to tell you she spent the evening at the cinema. If she ate lunch at the Old Tavern, she would be sure to mention that she had lunched with her children at home. The woman was simply a pathological liar, and that accounted for everything.

Mr. Brook cracked his knuckles and got up from his chair. His first reaction was one of exasperation. That day after day Madame Zilensky would have the gall to sit there in his office and deluge him with her outrageous falsehoods! Mr. Brook was intensely provoked. He walked up and down the room, then he went into his kitchenette and made himself a sardine sandwich.

An hour later, as he sat before the fire, his irritation had changed to a scholarly and thoughtful wonder. What he must do, he told himself, was to regard the whole situation impersonally and look on Madame Zilensky as a doctor looks on a sick patient. Her lies were of the guileless sort. She did not dissimulate with any intention to deceive, and the untruths she told were never used to any possible advantage. That was the maddening thing; there was simply no motive behind it all.

Mr. Brook finished off the rest of the brandy. And slowly, when it was almost midnight, a further understanding came to him. The reason for the lies of Madame Zilensky was painful and plain. All her life long Madame Zilensky had worked—at the piano, teaching, and writing those beautiful and immense twelve symphonies. Day and night she had drudged and struggled and thrown her soul into her work, and there was not much of her left over for anything else. Being human, she suffered from this lack and did what she could to make up for it. If she passed the evening bent over a table in the library and later declared that she had spent that time playing cards, it was as though she had managed to do both those things. Through the lies, she lived vicariously. The lies doubled the little of her existence that was left over from work and augmented the little rag end of her personal life.

Mr. Brook looked into the fire, and the face of Madame Zilensky was in his mind—a severe face, with dark, weary eyes and delicately disciplined mouth. He was conscious of a warmth in his chest, and a feeling of pity, protectiveness, and dreadful understanding. For a while he was in a state of lovely confusion.

Later on he brushed his teeth and got into his pajamas. He must be practical. What did this clear up? That French, the Pole with the piccolo, Bagdad? And the children, Sigmund, Boris, and Sammy— who were they? Were they really her children after all, or had she simply rounded them up from somewhere? Mr. Brook polished his spectacles and put them on the table by his bed. He must come to an immediate understanding with her. Otherwise, there would exist in the department a situation which could become most problematical. It was two o'clock. He glanced out of his window and saw that the light in Madame Zilensky's workroom was still on. Mr. Brook got into bed, made terrible faces in the dark, and tried to plan what he would say next day.

Mr. Brook was in his office by eight o'clock. He sat hunched up behind his desk, ready to trap Madame Zilensky as she passed down the corridor. He did not have to wait long, and as soon as he heard her footsteps he called out her name.

Madame Zilensky stood in the doorway. She looked vague and jaded. "How are you? I had such a fine night's rest," she said.

"Pray be seated, if you please," said Mr. Brook. "I would like a word with you."

Madame Zilensky put aside her portfolio and leaned back wearily in the armchair across from him. "Yes?" she asked.

"Yesterday you spoke to me as I was walking across the campus," he said slowly. "And if I am not mistaken, I believe you said something about a pastry shop and the King of Finland. Is that correct?"

Madame Zilensky turned her head to one side and stared retrospectively at a corner of the window sill.

"Something about a pastry shop," he repeated.

Her tired face brightened. "But of course," she said eagerly. "I told you about the time I was standing in front of this shop and the King of Finland——"

"Madame Zilensky!" Mr. Brook cried. "There *is* no King of Finland."

Madame Zilensky looked absolutely blank. Then, after an instant, she started off again. "I was standing in front of Bjarne's *pâtisserie* when I turned away from the cakes and suddenly saw the King of Finland——"

"Madame Zilensky, I just told you that there is no King of Finland."

"In Helsingfors," she started off again desperately, and again he let her get as far as the King, and then no further.

"Finland is a democracy," he said. "You could not possibly have seen the King of Finland. Therefore, what you have just said is an untruth. A pure untruth."

Never afterward could Mr. Brook forget the face of Madame Zilensky at that moment. In her eyes there was astonishment, dismay, and a sort of cornered horror. She had the look of one who watches his whole interior world split open and disintegrate.

"It is a pity," said Mr. Brook with real sympathy.

But Madame Zilensky pulled herself together. She raised her chin and said coldly, "I am a Finn."

"That I do not question," answered Mr. Brook. On second thought, he did question it a little.

"I was born in Finland and I am a Finnish citizen."

"That may very well be," said Mr. Brook in a rising voice.

"In the war," she continued passionately, "I rode a motorcycle and was a messenger."

"Your patriotism does not enter into it."

"Just because I am getting out the first papers——"

"Madame Zilensky!" said Mr. Brook. His hands grasped the edge of the desk. "That is only an irrelevant issue. The point is that you maintained and testified that you saw—that you saw——" But he could not finish. Her face stopped him. She was deadly pale and there were shadows around her mouth. Her eyes were wide open, doomed, and proud. And Mr. Brook felt suddenly like a murderer. A great commotion of feelings—understanding, remorse, and unreasonable love—made him cover his face with his hands. He could not speak until this agitation in his insides quieted down, and then he said very faintly, "Yes. Of course. The King of Finland. And was he nice?"

An hour later, Mr. Brook sat looking out the window of his office. The trees along the quiet Westbridge street were almost bare, and the gray buildings of the college had a calm, sad look. As he idly took in the familiar scene, he noticed the Drakes' old Airedale waddling along down the street. It was a thing he had watched a hundred times before, so what was it that struck him as strange? Then he realized with a kind of cold surprise that the old dog was running along backward. Mr. Brook watched the Airedale until he was out of sight, then resumed his work on the canons which had been turned in by the class in counterpoint.

QUESTIONS

1. This story seems to be concerned primarily with the figure of Madame Zilensky, and certainly the title of the story would appear to bear this out. The narrative develops out of Mr. Brook's observation that she acts in two quite contradictory manners. What are these two conflicting characteristics of Madame Zilensky? Elaborate fully on each. In what specific ways does she demonstrate this split in her personality?

2. Since everything we learn about Madame Zilensky is communicated to us through Mr. Brook, point of view becomes an important con-

sideration. What is Mr. Brook like? Does he resemble Madame Zilensky in any way? Analyze his initial attitude toward her and the changes that attitude undergoes.

3. There are several indications that Madame Zilensky is the central figure only in a superficial sense. First, we learn more about her as the story progresses, but she is essentially a *static* character in that she does not change. Mr. Brook, in fact, halts his cross-examination precisely in order to *avoid* bringing about a change in her. Second, we never deal with her directly; she is always at a distance, with both the "faceless" narrator and Mr. Brook standing between her and the reader. Third, what Mr. Brook discovers about Madame Zilensky actually tells us more about *him*, through the detailed rendering of his emotions, speculations, and attitude changes. In terms of *plot*, then, Madame Zilensky is certainly important. But in terms of character change and theme, perhaps Mr. Brook is a more significant figure, since it is through that change that the theme of the story becomes clear. What kind of changes does he undergo? In relation to that change, discuss the statement that Mr. Brook thought of himself as a "murderer."

4. We see now that, as in many stories, "Madame Zilensky and the King of Finland" develops theme primarily through character. An examination of the curious last scene should cast further light on that theme and underscore the central role of Mr. Brook. In this concluding scene, Mr. Brook sees an Airedale "waddling along down the street," an incident that "he had watched a hundred times before." But just as Mr. Brook has changed, so has this familiar incident: he notices that the dog is "running along backward." What is implied in Mr. Brook's casual response to this amazing incident? How can this scene be said to dramatize the theme of the story?

PHILIP ROTH

(1933-   )

Philip Roth is a young American writer whose first collection of short stories, GOODBYE, COLUMBUS, was an instant success. Prior to that, he attended Bucknell University, where he was Phi Beta Kappa, followed by a Master of Arts degree at the University of Chicago. He was successively visiting lecturer at the University of Iowa (1960-62) and writer-in-residence at Princeton University beginning in 1962. In 1960 he received the National Book Award for Fiction and the Daroff Award, Jewish Book Council of America, for GOODBYE, COLUMBUS. The same year he received a grant from the National Institute of Arts and Letters and a Guggenheim grant. Since then there have been two more books: LETTING GO and WHEN SHE WAS GOOD. In his work, Roth focuses on the Jewish world, a world in which, however, one finds all of mankind. His characters are both ordinary and sensitive, erring and warmly human. In them we see the strengths and weaknesses of human nature irrespective of ethnic background. While they are discovering things about themselves, we are discovering things about that curious creature, man. "The Conversion of the Jews" is a perfect example of the way in which Roth utilizes his Jewish heritage to make observations on the nature of a world with which we are all familiar.

The Conversion of the Jews

"You're a real one for opening your mouth in the first place," Itzie said. "What do you open your mouth all the time for?"

"I didn't bring it up, Itz, I didn't," Ozzie said.

"What do you care about Jesus Christ for anyway?"

"I didn't bring up Jesus Christ. He did. I didn't even know what he was talking about. Jesus is historical, he kept saying. Jesus is historical." Ozzie mimicked the monumental voice of Rabbi Binder.

"Jesus was a person that lived like you and me," Ozzie continued. "That's what Binder said—"

"Yeah? . . . So what! What do I give two cents whether he lived or not. And what do you gotta open your mouth!" Itzie Lieberman favored closed-mouthedness, especially when it came to Ozzie Freedman's questions. Mrs. Freedman had to see Rabbi Binder twice before about Ozzie's questions and this Wednesday at four-thirty would be the third time. Itzie preferred to keep *his* mother in the kitchen; he settled for behind-the-back subtleties such as gestures, faces, snarls and other less delicate barnyard noises.

"He was a real person, Jesus, but he wasn't like God, and we don't believe he is God." Slowly, Ozzie was explaining Rabbi Binder's position to Itzie, who had been absent from Hebrew School the previous afternoon.

"The Catholics," Itzie said helpfully, "they believe in Jesus Christ, that he's God." Itzie Lieberman used "the Catholics" in its broadest sense—to include the Protestants.

Ozzie received Itzie's remark with a tiny head bob, as though it were a footnote, and went on. "His mother was Mary, and his father probably was Joseph," Ozzie said. "But the New Testament says his real father was God."

"His *real* father?"

"Yeah," Ozzie said, "that's the big thing, his father's supposed to be God."

"Bull."

"That's what Rabbi Binder says, that it's impossible—"

"Sure it's impossible. That stuff's all bull. To have a baby you gotta get laid," Itzie theologized. "Mary hadda get laid."

"That's what Binder says: 'The only way a woman can have a baby is to have intercourse with a man.' "

"He said *that*, Ozz?" For a moment it appeared that Itzie had put the theological question aside. "He said that, intercourse?" A little curled smile shaped itself in the lower half of Itzie's face like a pink mustache. "What you guys do, Ozz, you laugh or something?"

"I raised my hand."

"Yeah? Whatja say?"

"That's when I asked the question."

Itzie's face lit up. "Whatja ask about—intercourse?"

"No, I asked the question about God, how if He could create the heaven and earth in six days, and make all the animals and the fish and the light in six days—the light especially, that's what always gets me, that He could make the light. Making fish and animals, that's pretty good—"

"That's damn good." Itzie's appreciation was honest but unimaginative: it was as though God had just pitched a one-hitter.

"But making light . . . I mean when you think about it, it's really something," Ozzie said. "Anyway, I asked Binder if He could make all that in six days, and He could *pick* the six days he wanted right out of nowhere, why couldn't He let a woman have a baby without having intercourse."

"You said intercourse, Ozz, to Binder?"

"Yeah."

"Right in class?"

"Yeah."

Itzie smacked the side of his head.

"I mean, no kidding around," Ozzie said, "that'd really be nothing. After all that other stuff, that'd practically be nothing."

Itzie considered a moment. "What'd Binder say?"

"He started all over again explaining how Jesus was historical and how he lived like you and me but he wasn't God. So I said I under*stood* that. What I wanted to know was different."

What Ozzie wanted to know was always different. The first time he had wanted to know how Rabbi Binder could call the Jews "The Chosen People" if the Declaration of Independence claimed all men to be created equal. Rabbi Binder tried to distinguish for him between political equality and spiritual legitimacy, but what Ozzie wanted to know, he insisted vehemently, was different. That was the first time his mother had to come.

Then there was the plane crash. Fifty-eight people had been killed in a plane crash at La Guardia. In studying a casualty list in the newspaper his mother had discovered among the list of those dead eight Jewish names (his grandmother had nine but she counted Miller as a Jewish name): because of the eight she said the plane crash was "a tragedy." During free-discussion time on Wednesday Ozzie had brought to Rabbi Binder's attention this matter of "some of his relations" always picking out the Jewish names. Rabbi Binder had begun to explain cultural unity and some other things when Ozzie stood up at his seat and said that what he wanted to know was different. Rabbi Binder insisted that he sit down and it was then that Ozzie shouted that he wished all fifty-eight were Jews. That was the second time his mother came.

"And he kept explaining about Jesus being historical, and so I kept asking him. No kidding, Itz, he was trying to make me look stupid."

"So what he finally do?"

"Finally he starts screaming that I was deliberately simple-minded and a wise guy, and that my mother had to come, and this was the last time. And that I'd never get bar-mitzvahed if he could help it. Then, Itz, then he starts talking in that voice like a statue, real slow and deep, and he says that I better think over what I said about the Lord. He told me to go to his office and think it over." Ozzie leaned his body towards Itzie. "Itz, I thought it over for a solid hour, and now I'm convinced God could do it."

Ozzie had planned to confess his latest transgression to his mother as soon as she came home from work. But it was a Friday night in November and already dark, and when Mrs. Freedman came through the door she tossed off her coat, kissed Ozzie quickly on the face, and went to the kitchen table to light the three yellow candles, two for the Sabbath and one for Ozzie's father.

When his mother lit the candles she would move her two arms slowly towards her, dragging them through the air, as though persuading people whose minds were half made up. And her eyes would get glassy with tears. Even when his father was alive Ozzie remembered that her eyes had gotten glassy, so it didn't have anything to do with his dying. It had something to do with lighting the candles.

As she touched the flaming match to the unlit wick of a Sabbath candle, the phone rang, and Ozzie, standing only a foot from it, plucked it off the receiver and held it muffled to his chest. When his mother lit candles Ozzie felt there should be no noise; even breathing, if you could manage it, should be softened. Ozzie pressed the phone to his breast and watched his mother dragging whatever she was dragging, and he felt his own eyes get glassy. His mother was a round, tired, gray-haired penguin of a woman whose gray skin had begun to feel the tug of gravity and the weight of her own history. Even when she was dressed up she didn't look like a chosen person. But when she lit candles she looked like something better; like a woman who knew momentarily that God could do anything.

After a few mysterious minutes she was finished. Ozzie hung up the phone and walked to the kitchen table where she was beginning to lay the two places for the four-course Sabbath meal. He told her that she would have to see Rabbi Binder next Wednesday at four-thirty, and then he told her why. For the first time in their life together she hit Ozzie across the face with her hand.

All through the chopped liver and chicken soup part of the dinner Ozzie cried; he didn't have any appetite for the rest.

On Wednesday, in the largest of the three basement classrooms of the synagogue, Rabbi Marvin Binder, a tall, handsome, broad-shouldered man of thirty with thick strong-fibered black hair, removed his watch from his pocket and saw that it was four o'clock. At the rear of the room Yakov Blotnik, the seventy-one-year-old custodian, slowly polished the large window, mumbling to himself, unaware that it was four o'clock or six o'clock, Monday or Wednesday. To most of the students Yakov Blotnik's mumbling, along with his brown curly beard, scythe nose, and two heel-trailing black cats, made of him an object of wonder, a foreigner, a relic, towards whom they were alternately fearful and disrespectful. To Ozzie the mumbling had always seemed a monotonous, curious prayer; what made it curious was that old Blotnik had been mumbling so steadily for so many years, Ozzie suspected he had memorized the prayers and forgotten all about God.

"It is now free-discussion time," Rabbi Binder said. "Feel free to talk about any Jewish matter at all—religion, family, politics, sports—"

There was silence. It was a gusty, clouded November afternoon and it did not seem as though there ever was or could be a thing called baseball. So nobody this week said a word about that hero from the past, Hank Greenberg—which limited free discussion considerably.

And the soul-battering Ozzie Freedman had just received from Rabbi Binder had imposed its limitation. When it was Ozzie's turn to read aloud from the Hebrew book the rabbi had asked him petulantly why he didn't read more rapidly. He was showing no progress. Ozzie said he could read faster but that if he did he was sure not to understand what he was reading. Nevertheless, at the rabbi's repeated suggestion Ozzie tried, and showed a great talent, but in the midst of a long passage he stopped short and said he didn't understand a word he was reading, and started in again at a drag-footed pace. Then came the soul-battering.

Consequently when free-discussion time rolled around none of the students felt too free. The rabbi's invitation was answered only by the mumbling of feeble old Blotnik.

"Isn't there anything at all you would like to discuss?" Rabbi Binder asked again, looking at his watch. "No questions or comments?"

There was a small grumble from the third row. The rabbi requested that Ozzie rise and give the rest of the class the advantage of his thought.

Ozzie rose. "I forget it now," he said, and sat down in his place.

Rabbi Binder advanced a seat towards Ozzie and poised himself on the edge of the desk. It was Itzie's desk and the rabbi's frame only a dagger's length away from his face snapped him to sitting attention.

"Stand up again, Oscar," Rabbi Binder said calmly, "and try to assemble your thoughts."

Ozzie stood up. All his classmates turned in their seats and watched as he gave an unconvincing scratch to his forehead.

"I can't assemble any," he announced, and plunked himself down.

"Stand up!" Rabbi Binder advanced from Itzie's desk to the one directly in front of Ozzie; when the rabbinical back was turned Itzie gave it five-fingers off the tip of his nose, causing a small titter in the room. Rabbi Binder was too absorbed in squelching Ozzie's nonsense once and for all to bother with titters. "Stand up, Oscar. What's your question about?"

Ozzie pulled a word out of the air. It was the handiest word. "Religion."

"Oh, now you remember?"

"Yes."

"What is it?"

Trapped, Ozzie blurted the first thing that came to him. "Why can't He make anything He wants to make!"

As Rabbi Binder prepared an answer, a final answer, Itzie, ten feet behind him, raised one finger on his left hand, gestured it meaningfully towards the rabbi's back, and brought the house down.

Binder twisted quickly to see what had happened and in the midst of the commotion Ozzie shouted into the rabbi's back what he couldn't have shouted to his face. It was a loud, toneless sound that had the timbre of something stored inside for about six days.

"You don't know! You don't know anything about God!"

The rabbi spun back towards Ozzie. "What?"

"You don't know—you don't—"

"Apologize, Oscar, apologize!" It was a threat.

"You don't—"

Rabbi Binder's hand flicked out at Ozzie's cheek. Perhaps it had only been meant to clamp the boy's mouth shut, but Ozzie ducked and the palm caught him squarely on the nose.

The blood came in a short, red spurt on to Ozzie's shirt front.

The next moment was all confusion. Ozzie screamed, "You bastard, you bastard!" and broke for the classroom door. Rabbi Binder lurched a step backwards, as though his own blood had started flowing violently in the opposite direction, then gave a clumsy lurch forward and bolted out the door after Ozzie. The class followed after the rabbi's huge blue-suited back, and before old Blotnik could turn from his window, the room was empty and everyone was headed full speed up the three flights leading to the roof.

If one should compare the light of day to the life of man: sun-rise to birth; sunset—the dropping down over the edge—to death; then as Ozzie Freedman wiggled through the trapdoor of the syna-gogue roof, his feet kicking backwards bronco-style at Rabbi Bind-er's outstretched arms—at that moment the day was fifty years old. As a rule, fifty or fifty-five reflects accurately the age of late after-noons in November, for it is in that month, during those hours, that one's awareness of light seems no longer a matter of seeing, but of hearing: light begins clicking away. In fact, as Ozzie locked shut the trapdoor in the rabbi's face, the sharp click of the bolt into the lock might momentarily have been mistaken for the sound of the heavier gray that had just throbbed through the sky.

With all his weight Ozzie kneeled on the locked door; any in-stant he was certain that Rabbi Binder's shoulder would fling it open, splintering the wood into shrapnel and catapulting his body into the sky. But the door did not move and below him he heard only the rumble of feet, first loud then dim, like thunder rolling away.

A question shot through his brain. "Can this be *me*?" For a thir-teen-year-old who had just labeled his religious leader a bastard, twice, it was not an improper question. Louder and louder the ques-tion came to him—"Is it me? It is me?"—until he discovered himself no longer kneeling, but racing crazily towards the edge of the roof, his eyes crying, his throat screaming, and his arms flying everywhich-way as though not his own.

"Is it me? Is it me Me ME ME ME! It has to be me—but is it!"

It is the question a thief must ask himself the night he jimmies open his first window, and it is said to be the question with which bridegrooms quiz themselves before the altar.

In the few wild seconds it took Ozzie's body to propel him to the edge of the roof, his self-examination began to grow fuzzy. Gazing down at the street, he became confused as to the problem beneath the question: was it, is-it-me-who-called-Binder-a-bastard? or, is-it-me-prancing-around-on-the-roof? However, the scene below settled all, for there is an instant in any action when whether it is you or somebody else is academic. The thief crams the money in his pock-ets and scoots out the window. The bridegroom signs the hotel regis-ter for two. And the boy on the roof finds a streetful of people gaping at him, necks stretched backwards, faces up, as though he were the ceiling of the Hayden Planetarium. Suddenly you know it's you.

"Oscar! Oscar Freedman!" A voice rose from the center of the crowd, a voice that, could it have been seen, would have looked like the writing on scroll. "Oscar Freedman, get down from there. Immediately!" Rabbi Binder was pointing one arm stiffly up at him; and at the end of that arm, one finger aimed menacingly. It was the attitude of a dictator, but one—the eyes confessed all— whose personal valet had spit neatly in his face.

Ozzie didn't answer. Only for a blink's length did he look towards Rabbi Binder. Instead his eyes began to fit together the world beneath him, to sort out people from places, friends from enemies, participants from spectators. In little jagged starlike clusters his friends stood around Rabbi Binder, who was still pointing. The topmost point on a star compounded not of angels but of five adolescent boys was Itzie. What a world it was, with those stars below, Rabbi Binder below . . . Ozzie, who a moment earlier hadn't been able to control his own body, started to feel the meaning of the word control: he felt Peace and he felt Power.

"Oscar Freedman, I'll give you three to come down."

Few dictators give their subjects three to do anything; but, as always, Rabbi Binder only looked dictatorial.

"Are you ready, Oscar?"

Ozzie nodded his head yes, although he had no intention in the world—the lower one of the celestial one he'd just entered—of coming down even if Rabbi Binder should give him a million.

"All right then," said Rabbi Binder. He ran a hand through his black Samson hair as though it were the gesture prescribed for uttering the first digit. Then, with his other hand cutting a circle out of the small piece of sky around him, he spoke. "One!"

There was no thunder. On the contrary, at that moment, as though "one" was the cue for which he had been waiting, the world's least thunderous person appeared on the synagogue steps. He did not so much come out the synagogue door as lean out, onto the darkening air. He clutched at the doorknob with one hand and looked up at the roof.

"Oy!"

Yakov Blotnik's old mind hobbled slowly, as if on crutches, and though he couldn't decide precisely what the boy was doing on the roof, he knew it wasn't good—that is, it wasn't-good-for-the-Jews. For Yakov Blotnik life had fractionated itself simply: things were either good-for-the-Jews or no-good-for-the-Jews.

He smacked his free hand to his in-sucked cheek, gently. "Oy, Gut!" And then quickly as he was able, he jacked down his head and surveyed the street. There was Rabbi Binder (like a man at an auction with only three dollars in his pocket, he had just delivered a shaky "Two!"); there were the students, and that was all. So far it-wasn't-so-bad-for-the-Jews. But the boy had to come down immediately, before anybody saw. The problem: how to get the boy off the roof?

Anybody who has ever had a cat on the roof knows how to get him down. You call the fire department. Or first you call the operator and you ask her for the fire department. And the next thing there is great jamming of brakes and clanging of bells and shouting of instructions. And then the cat is off the roof. You do the same thing to get a boy off the roof.

That is, you do the same thing if you are Yakov Blotnik and you once had a cat on the roof.

When the engines, all four of them, arrived, Rabbi Binder had four times given Ozzie the count of three. The big hook-and-ladder swung around the corner and one of the firemen leaped from it, plunging headlong towards the yellow fire hydrant in front of the synagogue. With a huge wrench he began to unscrew the top nozzle. Rabbi Binder raced over to him and pulled at his shoulder.

"There's no fire . . ."

The fireman mumbled back over his shoulder and, heatedly, continued working at the nozzle.

"But there's no fire, there's no fire . . ." Binder shouted. When the fireman mumbled again, the rabbi grasped his face with both his hands and pointed it up at the roof.

To Ozzie it looked as though Rabbi Binder was trying to tug the fireman's head out of his body, like a cork from a bottle. He had to giggle at the picture they made: it was a family portrait—rabbi in black skullcap, fireman in red fire hat, and the little yellow hydrant squatting beside like a kid brother, bareheaded. From the edge of the roof Ozzie waved at the portrait, a one-handed, flapping, mocking wave; in doing it his right foot slipped from under him. Rabbi Binder covered his eyes with his hands.

Firemen work fast. Before Ozzie had even regained his balance, a big, round, yellowed net was being held on the synagogue lawn. The firemen who held it looked up at Ozzie with stern, feelingless faces.

One of the firemen turned his head towards Rabbi Binder. "What, is the kid nuts or something?"

Rabbi Binder unpeeled his hands from his eyes, slowly, painfully, as if they were tape. Then he checked: nothing on the sidewalk, no dents in the net.

"Is he gonna jump, or what?" the fireman shouted.

In a voice not at all like a statue, Rabbi Binder finally answered. "Yes, Yes, I think so . . . He's been threatening to . . ."

Threatening to? Why, the reason he was on the roof, Ozzie remembered, was to get away; he hadn't even thought about jumping. He had just run to get away, and the truth was that he hadn't really headed for the roof as much as he'd been chased there.

"What's his name, the kid?"

"Freedman," Rabbi Binder answered. "Oscar Freedman."

The fireman looked up at Ozzie. "What is it with you, Oscar? You gonna jump, or what?"

Ozzie did not answer. Frankly, the question had just arisen.

"Look, Oscar, if you're gonna jump, jump—and if you're not gonna jump, don't jump. But don't waste our time, willya?"

Ozzie looked at the fireman and then at Rabbi Binder. He wanted to see Rabbi Binder cover his eyes one more time.

"I'm going to jump."

And then he scampered around the edge of the roof to the corner, where there was no net below, and he flapped his arms at his sides, swishing the air and smacking his palms to his trousers on the downbeat. He began screaming like some kind of engine, "Wheeeee . . . wheeeeee," and leaning way out over the edge with the upper half of his body. The firemen whipped around to cover the ground with the net. Rabbi Binder mumbled a few words to Somebody and covered his eyes. Everything happened quickly, jerkily, as in a silent movie. The crowd, which had arrived with the fire engines, gave out a long, Fourth-of-July fireworks oooh-aahhh. In the excitement no one had paid the crowd much heed, except, of course, Yakov Blotnik, who swung from the doorknob counting heads. "Fier und tsvansik . . . finf und tsvantsik . . . Oy, Gut!" It wasn't like this with the cat.

Rabbi Binder peeked through his fingers, checked the sidewalk and net. Empty. But there was Ozzie racing to the other corner. The firemen raced with him but were unable to keep up. Whenever Ozzie wanted to he might jump and splatter himself upon the sidewalk, and by the time the firemen scooted to the spot all they could do with their net would be to cover the mess.

"Wheeeee . . . wheeeee . . ."

"Hey, Oscar," the winded fireman yelled, "What the hell is this, a game or something?"

"Wheeeee . . . wheeeee . . ."

"Hey, Oscar—"

But he was off now to the other corner, flapping his wings fiercely. Rabbi Binder couldn't take it any longer—the fire engines from nowhere, the screaming suicidal boy, the net. He fell to his knees, exhausted, and with his hands curled together in front of his chest like a little dome, he pleaded, "Oscar, stop it, Oscar. Don't jump, Oscar. Please come down . . . Please don't jump."

And further back in the crowd a single voice, a single young voice, shouted a lone word to the boy on the roof.

"Jump!"

It was Itzie. Ozzie momentarily stopped flapping.

"Go ahead, Ozz—jump!" Itzie broke off his point of the star and courageously, with the inspiration not of a wise-guy but of a disciple, stood alone. "Jump, Ozz, jump!"

Still on his knees, his hand still curled, Rabbi Binder twisted his body back. He looked at Itzie, then, agonizingly, back to Ozzie.

"Oscar, Don't Jump! Please, Don't Jump . . . please please . . ."

"Jump!" This time it wasn't Itzie but another point of the star. By the time Mrs. Freedman arrived to keep her four-thirty appointment with Rabbi Binder, the whole little upside down heaven was shouting and pleading for Ozzie to jump, and Rabbi Binder no longer was pleading with him not to jump, but was crying into the dome of his hands.

Understandably Mrs. Freedman couldn't figure out what her son was doing on the roof. So she asked.

"Ozzie, my Ozzie, what are you doing? My Ozzie, what is it?"

Ozzie stopped wheeeeeing and slowed his arms down to a cruising flap, the kind birds use in soft winds, but he did not answer. He stood against the low, clouded, darkening sky—light clicked down swiftly now, as on a small gear—flapping softly and gazing down at the small bundle of a woman who was his mother.

"What are you doing, Ozzie?" She turned towards the kneeling Rabbi Binder and rushed so close that only a paper-thickness of dusk lay between her stomach and his shoulders.

"What is my baby doing?"

Rabbi Binder gaped up at her but he too was mute. All that moved was the dome of his hands; it shook back and forth like a weak pulse.

"Rabbi, get him down! He'll kill himself. Get him down, my only baby . . ."

"I can't," Rabbi Binder said, "I can't . . ." and he turned his handsome head towards the crowd of boys behind him. "It's them. Listen to them."

And for the first time Mrs. Freedman saw the crowd of boys, and she heard what they were yelling.

"He's doing it for them. He won't listen to me. It's them." Rabbi Binder spoke like one in a trance.

"For them?"

"Yes."

"Why for them?"

"They want him to . . ."

Mrs. Freedman raised her two arms upward as though she were conducting the sky. "For them he's doing it!" And then in a gesture older than pyramids, older than prophets and floods, her arms came slapping down to her sides. "A martyr I have. Look!" She tilted her head to the roof. Ozzie was still flapping softly. "My martyr."

"Oscar, come down, *please,*" Rabbi Binder groaned.

In a startlingly even voice Mrs. Freedman called to the boy on the roof. "Ozzie, come down, Ozzie. Don't be a martyr, my baby."

As though it were a litany, Rabbi Binder repeated her words. "Don't be a martyr, my baby. Don't be a martyr."

"Gawhead, Ozz—*be* a Martin!" It was Itzie. "Be a Martin, be a Martin," and all the voices joined in singing for Martindom, whatever *it* was. "Be a Martin, be a Martin . . ."

Somehow when you're on a roof the darker it gets the less you can hear. All Ozzie knew was that two groups wanted two new things: his friends were spirited and musical about what they wanted; his mother and the rabbi were even-toned, chanting, about what they didn't want. The rabbi's voice was without tears now and so was his mother's.

The big net stared up at Ozzie like a sightless eye. The big, clouded sky pushed down. From beneath it looked like a gray corrugated board. Suddenly, looking up into that unsympathetic sky, Ozzie realized all the strangeness of what these people, his friends, were asking: they wanted him to jump, to kill himself; they were singing about it now—it made them that happy. And there was an even greater strangeness: Rabbi Binder was on his knees, trembling. If there was a question to be asked now it was not "Is it me?" but rather "Is it us? . . . Is it us?"

Being on the roof, it turned out, was a serious thing. If he jumped would the singing become dancing? Would it? What would jumping stop? Yearningly, Ozzie wished he could rip open the sky, plunge his hands through, and pull out the sun; and on the sun, like a coin, would be stamped JUMP or DON'T JUMP.

Ozzie's knees rocked and sagged a little under him as though they were setting him for a dive. His arms tightened, stiffened, froze, from shoulders to fingernails. He felt as if each part of his body were going to vote as to whether he should kill himself or not—and each part as though it were independent of *him*.

The light took an unexpected click down and the new darkness, like a gag, hushed the friends singing for this and the mother and rabbi chanting for that.

Ozzie stopped counting votes, and in a curiously high voice, like one who wasn't prepared for speech, he spoke.

"Mamma?"

"Yes, Oscar."

"Mamma, get down on your knees, like Rabbi Binder."

"Oscar—"

"Get down on your knees," he said, "or I'll jump."

Ozzie heard a whimper, then a quick rustling, and when he looked down where his mother had stood he saw the top of a head and beneath that a circle of dress. She was kneeling beside Rabbi Binder.

He spoke again. "Everybody kneel." There was the sound of everybody kneeling.

Ozzie looked around. With one hand he pointed towards the synagogue entrance. "Make *him* kneel."

There was a noise, not of kneeling, but of body-and-cloth stretching. Ozzie could hear Rabbi Binder saying in a gruff whisper, ". . . or he'll *kill* himself," and when next he looked there was Yakov Blotnik off the doorknob and for the first time in his life upon his knees in the Gentile posture of prayer.

As for the firemen—it is not as difficult as one might imagine to hold a net taut while you are kneeling.

Ozzie looked around again; and then he called to Rabbi Binder.

"Rabbi?"

"Yes, Oscar."

"Rabbi Binder, do you believe in God."

"Yes."

"Do you believe God can do Anything?" Ozzie leaned his head out into the darkness. "Anything?"

"Oscar, I think—"

"Tell me you believe God can do Anything."

There was a second's hesitation. Then: "God can do Anything."

"Tell me you believe God can make a child without intercourse."

"He can."

"Tell me!"

"God," Rabbi Binder admitted, "can make a child without intercourse."

"Mamma, you tell me."

"God can make a child without intercourse," his mother said.

"Make *him* tell me." There was no doubt who *him* was.

In a few moments Ozzie heard an old comical voice say something to the increasing darkness about God.

Next, Ozzie made everybody say it. And then he made them all say they believed in Jesus Christ—first one at a time, then all together.

When the catechizing was through it was the beginning of evening. From the street it sounded as if the boy on the roof might have sighed.

"Ozzie?" A woman's voice dared to speak. "You'll come down now?"

There was no answer, but the woman waited, and when a voice

finally did speak it was thin and crying, and exhausted as that of an old man who has just finished pulling the bells.

"Mamma, don't you see—you shouldn't hit me. He shouldn't hit me. You shouldn't hit me about God, Mamma. You should never hit anybody about God—"

"Ozzie, please come down now."

"Promise me, promise me you'll never hit anybody about God."

He had asked only his mother, but for some reason everyone kneeling in the street promised he would never hit anybody about God.

Once again there was silence.

"I can come down now, Mamma," the boy on the roof finally said. He turned his head both ways as though checking the traffic lights. "Now I can come down . . ."

And he did, right into the center of the yellow net that glowed in the evening's edge like an overgrown halo.

3

NEW
DIRECTIONS

MANY CONTEMPORARY WRITERS, we find, are moving in new directions in terms of both theme and technique. At the same time satire has helped to maintain a balanced perspective: Ted Hughes' "Snow" satirizes both modern techniques (interior monologue, stream of consciousness) and modern themes (man's existential condition, in particular Samuel Beckett's theme of endurance). This caustic view may be seen as one tendency among contemporary writers to have extreme reactions to the theme of existentialism, among others. The work of Paul Bowles constitutes an acceptance of the principle of alienation, to the extent that his figures act consciously to maintain their isolated state. Douglas Woolf creates figures so withdrawn from society that they become not only apathetic but absurd. And Aichinger's surrealistic vision retains much the same existential orientation. Robert Creeley, on the other hand, uses man's isolated condition to focus upon love as a central theme.

But man's existential state is by no means the only theme prevalent among contemporary writers. Borges and Cortázar examine the time structure on which man (at least Western man) bases his life. Their examination produces a sense of dislocation by disturbing that temporal frame of reference; past and future are likely to mingle almost casually with the present. Both explore also the labyrinthine complexity of the human condition, with Borges stressing the mystical aspects of human life, Cortázar the psychological.

There are new methods as well. Rumaker, in a variation on the symbolic method, attempts to use symbols (the birds in "The Pipe," for example) which create in the reader a sense of uneasiness through their appeal to the subconscious rather than conscious levels of the mind. To some extent, Aichinger's surrealistic method makes the same appeal; but Rumaker's story retains a naturalistic framework into which his special symbols are integrated. Robbe-Grillet attempts to alter the very role of art with his emphasis upon camera-like objectivity. The result is a movement away from thematic content, toward a focus on experience as an end in itself, at least the vicarious experience which we encounter through art.

The stories in this section offer a multitude of comparisons and contrasts along these lines. But it is important for us to keep two things in mind. First, these stories are not simply experiments or *études*. They are carefully finished works in need of no defense in order to justify their existence. Second, they should be seen, like all the other stories in this collection, as unified wholes rather than examples of particular techniques or themes. Taken on this basis, what they communicate is likely to have a far greater impact than any fragmented and technical approach would permit.

JORGE LUIS BORGES

(1899-   )

Jorge Luis Borges was born in Buenos Aires, Argentina, the son of a writer and the son, grandson, great-grandson, and great-great-grandson of native born Argentinians. It is in part Borges' awareness of this family heritage which has lent his work a sense of both nationalism and timelessness. But Borges is much more than merely an intensely nationalistic writer. His family moved to Europe in 1914, staying in Geneva during the First World War; afterward Borges travelled in France and Spain and did not return to Argentina until 1921. As a result, his themes belie the provincial settings of many of his stories. It is not surprising, then, that the Argentine writer most influenced by his thought, Julio Cortázar, is also familiar with the European way of life. Borges was first established as a poet and did not commit himself seriously to the writing of fiction until after 1930. Since that time, his greatest fame has been realized as a short story writer—he has written no novels—and as an essayist. He has written little poetry during this period, and the loss of his sight in 1955 caused him to increase his emphasis upon the shorter literary forms. His work has brought him many national and international awards, including the Prix International des Editeurs, Prix Formentor, which he shared with Samuel Beckett, as well as Argentina's highest honor, the Primer Premio Nacional de Literatura. But Borges' literary life has not always been easy. His opposition to the Perón dictatorship cost him a demotion from librarian to chicken inspector, an insult which reflected the anti-intellectualism of the regime. He resigned and for almost ten years thereafter was dependent upon his writing, lecturing, and editorial work for his livelihood. He was restored to favor after the revolution in 1955; in recent years he was journeyed outside his country to teach at the University of Texas, among other institutions, and to lecture in Chicago, New York, London, Oxford, Cambridge, Edinburgh and elsewhere. His principal themes are time and the complex nature of reality; his stories examine man's relation-

*ship with these aspects of his existence, often pointing out the ab-
surdity of traditional beliefs while proposing intriguing and sometimes fantastic alternatives. Many of his works are available in English translation, among them, DREAMTIGERS, LABYRINTHS:
SELECTED STORIES, OTHER INQUISITIONS, FICCIONES
and A PERSONAL ANTHOLOGY.*

Death and the Compass

Of the many problems which exercised the daring perspicacity of
Lönnrot none was so strange—so harshly strange, we may say—as
the staggered series of bloody acts which culminated at the villa of
Triste-le-Roy, amid the boundless odor of the eucalypti. It is true
that Erik Lönnrot did not succeed in preventing the last crime, but
it is indisputable that he foresaw it. Nor did he, of course, guess the
identity of Yarmolinsky's unfortunate assassin, but he did divine the
secret morphology of the vicious series as well as the participation
of Red Scharlach, whose alias is Scharlach the Dandy. This criminal
(as so many others) had sworn on his honor to kill Lönnrot,
but the latter had never allowed himself to be intimidated. Lönnrot
thought of himself as a pure thinker, an Auguste Dupin, but there
was something of the adventurer in him, and even of the gamester.

The first crime occurred at the Hôtel du Nord—that high
prism that dominates the estuary whose waters are the colors of the
desert. To this tower (which most manifestly unites the hateful
whiteness of a sanitarium, the numbered divisibility of a prison,
and the general appearance of a bawdy house) on the third day of
December came the delegate from Podolsk to the Third Talmudic
Congress, Doctor Marcel Yarmolinsky, a man of gray beard and gray
eyes. We shall never know whether the Hôtel du Nord pleased him:
he accepted it with the ancient resignation which had allowed him
to endure three years of war in the Carpathians and three thousand
years of oppression and pogroms. He was given a sleeping room on

floor R, in front of the suite which the Tetrarch of Galilee occupied not without some splendor. Yarmolinsky supped, postponed until the following day an investigation of the unknown city, arranged upon a cupboard his many books and his few possessions, and before midnight turned off the light. (Thus declared the Tetrarch's chauffeur, who slept in an adjoining room.) On the fourth, at 11:03 A.M., there was a telephone call for him from the editor of the *Yiddische Zeitung*; Doctor Yarmolinsky did not reply; he was found in his room, his face already a little dark, and his body, almost nude, beneath a large anachronistic cape. He was lying not far from the door which gave onto the corridor; a deep stab wound had split open his breast. In the same room, a couple of hours later, in the midst of journalists, photographers, and police, Commissioner Treviranus and Lönnrot were discussing the problem with equanimity.

"There's no need to look for a Chimera, or a cat with three legs," Treviranus was saying as he brandished an imperious cigar. "We all know that the Tetrarch of Galilee is the possessor of the finest sapphires in the world. Someone, intending to steal them, came in here by mistake. Yarmolinsky got up; the robber had to kill him. What do you think?"

"It's possible, but not interesting," Lönnrot answered. "You will reply that reality hasn't the slightest need to be of interest. And I'll answer you that reality may avoid the obligation to be interesting, but that hypotheses may not. In the hypothesis you have postulated, chance intervenes largely. Here lies a dead rabbi; I should prefer a purely rabbinical explanation; not the imaginary mischances of an imaginary robber."

Treviranus answered ill-humoredly:

"I am not interested in rabbinical explanations; I am interested in the capture of the man who stabbed this unknown person."

"Not so unknown," corrected Lönnrot. "Here are his complete works." He indicated a line of tall volumes: *A Vindication of the Cabala; An Examination of the Philosophy of Robert Fludd;* a literal translation of the *Sepher Yezirah;* a *Biography of the Baal Shem;* a *History of the Sect of the Hasidim;* a monograph (in German) on the Tetragrammaton; another, on the divine nomenclature of the Pentateuch. The Commissioner gazed at them with suspicion, almost with revulsion. Then he fell to laughing.

"I'm only a poor Christian," he replied. "Carry off all these moth-eaten classics if you like; I haven't got time to lose in Jewish superstitions."

"Maybe this crime belongs to the history of Jewish superstitions," murmured Lönnrot.

"Like Christianity," the editor of the *Yiddische Zeitung* dared to put in. He was a myope, an atheist, and very timid.

No one answered him. One of the agents had found inserted in the small typewriter a piece of paper on which was written the following inconclusive sentence.

The first letter of the Name has been spoken

Lönnrot abstained from smiling. Suddenly become a bibliophile—or Hebraist—he directed that the dead man's books be made into a parcel, and he carried them to his office. Indifferent to the police investigation, he dedicated himself to studying them. A large octavo volume revealed to him the teachings of Israel Baal Shem-Tob, founder of the sect of the Pious; another volume, the virtues and terrors of the Tetragrammaton, which is the ineffable name of God; another, the thesis that God has a secret name, in which is epitomized (as in the crystal sphere which the Persians attribute to Alexander of Macedon) his ninth attribute, eternity—that is to say, the immediate knowledge of everything that will exist, exists, and has existed in the universe. Tradition numbers ninety-nine names of God; the Hebraists attribute this imperfect number to the magical fear of even numbers; the Hasidim reason that this hiatus indicates a hundredth name—the Absolute Name.

From this erudition he was distracted, within a few days, by the appearance of the editor of the *Yiddische Zeitung*. This man wished to talk of the assassination; Lönnrot preferred to speak of the diverse names of God. The journalist declared, in three columns, that the investigator Erik Lönnrot had dedicated himself to studying the names of God in order to "come up with" the name of the assassin. Lönnrot, habituated to the simplifications of journalism, did not become indignant. One of those shopkeepers who have found that there are buyers for every book came out with a popular edition of the *History of the Sect of the Hasidim*.

The second crime occurred on the night of the third of January, in the most deserted and empty corner of the capital's western suburbs. Toward dawn, one of the gendarmes who patrol these lonely places on horseback detected a man in a cape, lying prone in the shadow of an ancient paint shop. The hard visage seemed bathed in blood; a deep stab wound had split open his breast. On the wall, upon the yellow and red rhombs, there were some words written in chalk. The gendarme spelled them out. . . .

That afternoon Treviranus and Lönnrot made their way toward the remote scene of the crime. To the left and right of the automobile, the city disintegrated; the firmament grew larger and the houses meant less and less and a brick kiln or a poplar grove more and more. They reached their miserable destination: a final alley of rose-colored mud walls which in some way seemed to reflect the disordered setting of the sun. The dead man had already been identified. He was Daniel Simon Azevedo, a man of some fame in the ancient northern suburbs, who had risen from wagoner to political tough, only to degenerate later into a thief and even an informer. (The singular style of his death struck them as appropriate: Azevedo was the last representative of a generation of bandits who knew how to handle a dagger, but not a revolver.) The words in chalk were the following:

The second letter of the Name has been spoken

The third crime occurred on the night of the third of February. A little before one o'clock, the telephone rang in the office of Commissioner Treviranus. In avid secretiveness a man with a guttural voice spoke: he said his name was Ginzberg (or Ginsburg) and that he was disposed to communicate, for a reasonable remuneration, an explanation of the two sacrifices of Azevedo and Yarmolinsky. The discordant sound of whistles and horns drowned out the voice of the informer. Then the connection was cut off. Without rejecting the possibility of a hoax (it was carnival time), Treviranus checked and found he had been called from Liverpool House, a tavern on the Rue de Toulon—that dirty street where cheek by jowl are the peepshow and the milk store, the bordello and the women selling Bibles. Treviranus called back and spoke to the owner. This personage (Black Finnegan by name, an old Irish criminal who was crushed, annihilated almost, by respectability) told him that the last person to use the establishment's phone had been a lodger, a certain Gryphius, who had just gone out with some friends. Treviranus immediately went to Liverpool House where Finnegan related the following facts. Eight days previously, Gryphius had taken a room above the saloon. He was a man of sharp features, a nebulous gray beard,

shabbily clothed in black; Finnegan (who put the room to a use
which Treviranus guessed) demanded a rent which was undoubtedly excessive; Gryphius immediately paid the stipulated sum. He
scarcely ever went out; he dined and lunched in his room; his face
was hardly known in the bar. On this particular night, he came down
to telephone from Finnegan's office. A closed coupe stopped in
front of the tavern. The driver did not move from his seat; several
of the patrons recalled that he was wearing a bear mask. Two harlequins descended from the coupe; they were short in stature, and
no one could fail to observe that they were very drunk. With a
tooting of horns they burst into Finnegan's office; they embraced
Gryphius, who seemed to recognize them but who replied to them
coldly; they exchanged a few words in Yiddish—he, in a low guttural
voice; they, in shrill, falsetto tones—and then the party climbed to
the upstairs room. Within a quarter hour the three descended, very
joyous; Gryphius, staggering, seemed as drunk as the others. He
walked—tall, dazed—in the middle, between the masked harlequins. (One of the women in the bar remembered the yellow, red
and green rhombs, the diamond designs.) Twice he stumbled; twice
he was held up by the harlequins. Alongside the adjoining dock
basin, whose water was rectangular, the trio got into the coupe and
disappeared. From the running board, the last of the harlequins
had scrawled an obscene figure and a sentence on one of the slates
of the outdoor shed.

Treviranus gazed upon the sentence. It was nearly foreknowa-
ble. It read:

The last of the letters of the Name has been spoken

He examined, then, the small room of Gryphius-Ginzberg. On
the floor was a violent star of blood; in the corners, the remains of
some Hungarian-brand cigarettes; in a cabinet, a book in Latin—
the *Philologus Hebraeo-Graecus* (1739) of Leusden—along with
various manuscript notes. Treviranus studied the book with indignation and had Lönnrot summoned. The latter, without taking off
his hat, began to read while the Commissioner questioned the contradictory witnesses to the possible kidnaping. At four in the morning they came out. In the tortuous Rue de Toulon, as they stepped
on the dead serpentines of the dawn, Treviranus said:

"And supposing the story of this night were a sham?"

Erik Lönnrot smiled and read him with due gravity a passage (underlined) of the thirty-third dissertation of the *Philologus*:

> *Dies Judaeorum incipit a solis occasu*
> *usque ad solis occasum diei sequentis.*

"This means," he added, "that *the Hebrew day begins at sundown and lasts until the following sundown.*"

Treviranus attempted an irony.

"Is this fact the most worthwhile you've picked up tonight?"

"No. Of even greater value is a word Ginzberg used."

The afternoon dailies did not neglect this series of disappearances. *The Cross and the Sword* contrasted them with the admirable discipline and order of the last Eremitical Congress; Ernest Palast, writing in *The Martyr,* spoke out against "the intolerable delays in this clandestine and frugal pogrom, which has taken three months to liquidate three Jews"; the *Yiddische Zeitung* rejected the terrible hypothesis of an anti-Semitic plot, "even though many discerning intellects do not admit of any other solution to the triple mystery"; the most illustrious gunman in the South, Dandy Red Scharlach, swore that in his district such crimes as these would never occur, and he accused Commissioner Franz Treviranus of criminal negligence.

On the night of March first, the Commissioner received an imposing-looking, sealed envelope. He opened it: the envelope contained a letter signed Baruj Spinoza, and a detailed plan of the city, obviously torn from a Baedeker. The letter prophesied that on the third of March there would *not* be a fourth crime, inasmuch as the paint shop in the West, the Tavern on the Rue de Toulon and the Hôtel du Nord were the "perfect vertices of an equilateral and mystic triangle"; the regularity of this triangle was made clear on the map with red ink. This argument, *more geometrico,* Treviranus read with resignation, and sent the letter and map on to Lönnrot —who deserved such a piece of insanity.

Erik Lönnrot studied the documents. The three sites were in fact equidistant. Symmetry in time (the third of December, the third of January, the third of February); symmetry in space as well. . . . Of a sudden he sensed he was about to decipher the mystery. A set of calipers and a compass completed his sudden intuition. He smiled, pronounced the word "Tetragrammaton" (of recent acquisition), and called the Commissioner on the telephone. He told him:

"Thank you for the equilateral triangle you sent me last night. It has enabled me to solve the problem. Tomorrow, Friday, the criminals will be in jail, we can rest assured."

"In that case, they're not planning a fourth crime?"

"Precisely because they *are* planning a fourth crime can we rest assured."

Lönnrot hung up. An hour later he was traveling in one of the trains of the Southern Railways, en route to the abandoned villa of Triste-le-Roy. South of the city of our story there flows a blind little river filled with muddy water made disgraceful by floating scraps and garbage. On the further side is a manufacturing suburb where, under the protection of a chief from Barcelona, gunmen flourish. Lönnrot smiled to himself to think that the most famous of them— Red Scharlach—would have given anything to know of this clandestine visit. Azevedo had been a comrade of Scharlach's; Lönnrot considered the remote possibility that the fourth victim might be Scharlach himself. Then, he put aside the thought. . . . He had virtually deciphered the problem; the mere circumstances, or the reality (names, prison records, faces, judicial and penal proceedings), scarcely interested him now. Most of all he wanted to take a stroll, to relax from three months of sedentary investigation. He reflected on how the explanation of the crimes lay in an anonymous triangle and a dust-laden Greek word. The mystery seemed to him almost crystalline now; he was mortified to have dedicated a hundred days to it.

The train stopped at a silent loading platform. Lönnrot descended. It was one of those deserted afternoons which seem like dawn. The air over the muddy plain was damp and cold. Lönnrot set off across the fields. He saw dogs, he saw a wagon on a dead road, he saw the horizon, he saw a silvery horse drinking the crapulous water of a puddle. Dusk was falling when he saw the rectangular belvedere of the villa of Triste-le-Roy, almost as tall as the black eucalypti which surrounded it. He thought of the fact that only one more dawn and one more nightfall (an ancient splendor in the east, and another in the west) separated him from the hour so much desired by the seekers of the Name.

A rust-colored wrought-iron fence defined the irregular perimeter of the villa. The main gate was closed. Without much expectation of entering, Lönnrot made a complete circuit. In front of the insurmountable gate once again, he put his hand between the bars almost mechanically and chanced upon the bolt. The creaking of the iron surprised him. With laborious passivity the entire gate gave way.

Lönnrot advanced among the eucalypti, stepping amidst confused generations of rigid, broken leaves. Close up, the house on the estate of Triste-le-Roy was seen to abound in superfluous symmetries and in maniacal repetitions: a glacial Diana in one lugubrious niche was complemented by another Diana in another niche; one balcony was repeated by another balcony; double steps of stairs opened into a double balustrade. A two-faced Hermes cast a monstrous shadow. Lönnrot circled the house as he had the estate. He examined everything; beneath the level of the terrace he noticed a narrow shutter door.

He pushed against it: some marble steps descended to a vault. Versed now in the architect's preferences, Lönnrot divined that there would be a set of stairs on the opposite wall. He found them, ascended, raised his hands, and pushed up a trap door.

The diffusion of light guided him to a window. He opened it: a round, yellow moon outlined two stopped-up fountains in the melancholy garden. Lönnrot explored the house. He traveled through antechambers and galleries to emerge upon duplicate patios; several times he emerged upon the same patio. He ascended dust-covered stairways and came out into circular antechambers; he was infinitely reflected in opposing mirrors; he grew weary of opening or half-opening windows which revealed the same desolate garden outside, from various heights and various angles; inside, the furniture was wrapped in yellow covers and the chandeliers bound up with cretonne. A bedroom detained him; in the bedroom, a single rose in a porcelain vase—at the first touch the ancient petals fell apart. On the second floor, on the top story, the house seemed to be infinite and growing. *The house is not this large,* he thought. *It is only made larger by the penumbra, the symmetry, the mirrors, the years, my ignorance, the solitude.*

Going up a spiral staircase he arrived at the observatory. The evening moon shone through the rhomboid diamonds of the windows, which were yellow, red and green. He was brought to a halt by a stunning and dizzying recollection.

Two men of short stature, ferocious and stocky, hurled themselves upon him and took his weapon. Another man, very tall,
saluted him gravely, and said:

"You are very thoughtful. You've saved us a night and a day."

It was Red Scharlach. His men manacled Lönnrot's hands.
Lönnrot at length found his voice.

"Are you looking for the Secret Name, Scharlach?"

Scharlach remained standing, indifferent. He had not participated in the short struggle; he scarcely stretched out his hand
to receive Lönnrot's revolver. He spoke; in his voice Lönnrot detected a fatigued triumph, a hatred the size of the universe, a sadness no smaller than that hatred.

"No," answered Scharlach. "I am looking for something more
ephemeral and slippery, I am looking for Erik Lönnrot. Three
years ago, in a gambling house on the Rue de Toulon, you arrested
my brother and had him sent to prison. In the exchange of shots
that night my men got me away in a coupe, with a police bullet in
my chest. Nine days and nine nights I lay dying in this desolate, symmetrical villa; I was racked with fever, and the odious double-faced
Janus who gazes toward the twilights of dusk and dawn terrorized
my dreams and my waking. I learned to abominate my body, I came
to feel that two eyes, two hands, two lungs are as monstrous as two
faces. An Irishman attempted to convert me to the faith of Jesus;
he repeated to me that famous axiom of the *goyim*: All roads lead
to Rome. At night, my delirium nurtured itself on this metaphor:
I sensed that the world was a labyrinth, from which it was impossible
to flee, for all paths, whether they seemed to lead north or south,
actually led to Rome, which was also the quadrilateral jail where
my brother was dying and the villa of Triste-le-Roy. During those
nights I swore by the god who sees from two faces, and by all the
gods of fever and of mirrors, to weave a labyrinth around the man
who had imprisoned my brother. I have woven it, and it holds: the
materials are a dead writer on heresies, a compass, an eighteenth-
century sect, a Greek word, a dagger, the rhombs of a paint shop.

"The first objective in the sequence was given me by chance.
I had made plans with some colleagues—among them, Daniel
Azevedo—to take the Tetrarch's sapphires. Azevedo betrayed us;
with the money we advanced him he got himself inebriated and
started on the job a day early. In the vastness of the hotel he got lost;
at two in the morning he blundered into Yarmolinsky's room. The

latter, harassed by insomnia, had set himself to writing. He was editing some notes, apparently, or writing an article on the Name of God; he had just written the words *The first letter of the Name has been spoken.* Azevedo enjoined him to be quiet; Yarmolinsky reached out his hand for the bell which would arouse all the hotel's forces; Azevedo at once stabbed him in the chest. It was almost a reflex action: half a century of violence had taught him that it was easiest and surest to kill. . . . Ten days later, I learned through the *Yiddische Zeitung* that you were perusing the writings of Yarmolinsky for the key to his death. For my part I read the *History of the Sect of the Hasidim*; I learned that the reverent fear of pronouncing the Name of God had given rise to the doctrine that this Name is all-powerful and mystic. I learned that some Hasidim, in search of this secret Name, had gone as far as to offer human sacrifices. . . . I knew you would conjecture that the Hasidim had sacrificed the rabbi; I set myself to justifying this conjecture.

"Marcel Yarmolinsky died on the night of December third; for the second sacrifice I selected the night of January third. Yarmolinsky died in the North; for the second sacrifice a place in the West was preferable. Daniel Azevedo was the inevitable victim. He deserved death: he was an impulsive person, a traitor; his capture could destroy the entire plan. One of our men stabbed him; in order to link his corpse to the other one I wrote on the paint shop diamonds *The second letter of the Name has been spoken.*

"The third 'crime' was produced on the third of February. It was as Treviranus must have guessed, a mere mockery, a simulacrum. I am Gryphius-Ginzberg-Ginsburg; I endured an interminable week (filled out with a tenuous false beard) in that perverse cubicle on the Rue de Toulon, until my friends spirited me away. From the running board one of them wrote on a pillar *The last of the letters of the Name has been spoken.* This sentence revealed that the series of crimes was *triple.* And the public thus understood it; nevertheless, I interspersed repeated signs that would allow you, Erik Lönnrot, the reasoner, to understand that it is *quadruple.* A portent in the North, others in the East and West, demand a fourth portent in the South; the Tetragrammaton—the name of God, JHVH—is made up of *four* letters; the harlequins and the paint shop sign suggested four points. In the manual of Leusden I underlined a certain passage: it manifested that the Hebrews calculate a day counting from dusk to dusk and that therefore the deaths occurred on the *fourth* day of each month. To Treviranus I sent the equilateral triangle. I sensed that you would supply the missing point. The point which would form a perfect rhomb, the point which fixes where death, exactly, awaits you. In order to attract you I have premeditated everything, Erik Lönnrot, so as to draw you to the solitude of Triste-le-Roy."

Lönnrot avoided Scharlach's eyes. He was looking at the trees and the sky divided into rhombs of turbid yellow, green, and red. He felt a little cold, and felt, too, an impersonal, almost anonymous sadness. It was already night; from the dusty garden arose the useless cry of a bird. For the last time, Lönnrot considered the problem of symmetrical and periodic death.

"In your labyrinth there are three lines too many," he said at last. "I know of a Greek labyrinth which is a single straight line. Along this line so many philosophers have lost themselves that a mere detective might well do so too. Scharlach, when, in some other incarnation you hunt me, feign to commit (or do commit) a crime at A, then a second crime at B, eight kilometers from A, then a third crime at C, four kilometers from A and B, halfway enroute between the two. Wait for me later at D, two kilometers from A and C, halfway, once again, between both. Kill me at D, as you are now going to kill me at Triste-le-Roy."

"The next time I kill you," said Scharlach, "I promise you the labyrinth made of the single straight line which is invisible and everlasting."

He stepped back a few paces. Then, very carefully, he fired.

JULIO CORTÁZAR

(1914-)

Julio Cortázar, born in Argentina in 1914, is widely recognized as one of the most influential and provocative of Latin American authors. Although he has lived in Europe for many years, largely in seclusion, he is not an expatriate; he considers himself an Argentinian who simply happens to live abroad. An accomplished linguist, he works as a translator for UNESCO for six months each year. The remaining six months he lives precisely as he wishes: reading, writing, travelling. The element of horror in his stories reminds one of Poe; the violent and the grotesque link him to Faulkner. His use of point of view is Jamesian in its subtlety and narrative significance. The world of Cortázar's fiction is both familiar and unfamiliar. His characters appear to be normal human beings, but the things that happen to them suggest the presence of another time dimension interpenetrating theirs. A man in a motorcycle accident awakens to find himself atop a pyramid in ancient Mexico, being offered as a pagan sacrifice. In another story, a man visits an aquarium and eventually changes mental places with some strange creatures on display called Axolotls. One purpose of these weird shiftings is to cast doubt upon our understanding of reality, to question the accuracy of our perceptions. The Western world's greatest mistake, says Cortázar, was the invention of time. Time gives us a narrowly constricted view of reality; it also heightens man's awareness of his existential condition, in particular his sense of isolation. Eastern thought—Vedanta and Zen, for example—dispenses with time and attempts to merge the individual with the cosmos, rather than to separate him from it. Cortázar's novel, HOPSCOTCH, has been likened to Joyce's ULYSSES in its profundity, complexity, and inventiveness. At present there is only one volume of his short stories in English translation. An introduction to his themes, techniques, and development as a writer may be found in Chapter VI of INTO THE MAINSTREAM by Luis Harss and Barbara Dohmann.

Bestiary

Between the last spoonful of rice pudding with milk (very little cin-
namon, a shame) and the goodnight kisses before going up to bed,
there was a tinkling in the telephone room and Isabel hung around
until Inés came from answering it and said something into their
mother's ear. They looked at one another, then both of them looked
at Isabel who was thinking about the broken birdcage and the long
division problems and briefly of old lady Lucera being angry because she'd pushed her doorbell on the way back from school.
She wasn't all that worried, Inés and her mother were looking as if
they were gazing past her somewhere, almost taking her as an excuse;
but they were looking at her.

"I don't like the idea of her going, believe you me," Inés said.
"Not so much because of the tiger, after all they're very careful in
that respect. But it's such a depressing house and only that boy to
play with her . . ."

"I don't like the idea either," her mother said, and Isabel
knew, as if she were on a toboggan, that they were going to send her
to the Funes' for the summer. She flung herself into the news, into
the great green wave, the Funes', the Funes', sure they were going
to send her. They didn't like it, but it was convenient. Delicate lungs,
Mar del Plata so very expensive, difficult to manage such a spoiled
child, stupid, the way she always acted up with that wonderful Miss
Tania, a restless sleeper, toys underfoot everyplace, questions, buttons to be sewn back on, filthy knees. She felt afraid, delighted, smell
of the willow trees and the *u* in Funes was getting mixed in with the
rice pudding, so late to be still up, and get up to bed, right now.

Lying there, the light out, covered with kisses and rueful
glances from Inés and their mother, not fully decided but already
decided in spite of everything to send her. She was enjoying beforehand the drive up in the phaeton, the first breakfast, the happiness

of Nino, hunter of cockroaches, Nino the toad, Nino the fish (a memory of three years before, Nino showing her some small cutouts he'd glued in an album and telling her gravely, "This-is-a-toad, and THIS is-a-fish"). Now Nino in the park waiting for her with the butterfly net, and also Rema's soft hands—she saw them coming out of the darkness, she had her eyes open and instead of Nino's face—zap!—Rema's hands, the Funes' younger daughter. "Aunt Rema loves me a lot," and Nino's eyes got large and wet, she saw Nino again disjointedly floating in the dim light of the bedroom, looking at her contentedly. Nino the fish. Falling asleep wanting the week to be over that same night, and the goodbyes, the train, the last half-mile in the phaeton, the gate, the eucalyptus trees along the road leading up to the house. Just before falling asleep, she had a moment of terror when she imagined that she was maybe dreaming. Stretching out all at once, her feet hit the brass bars at the foot of the bed, they hurt through the covers, and she heard her mother and Inés talking in the big dining room, baggage, see the doctor about those pimples, cod-liver oil and concentrate of witch hazel. It wasn't a dream, it wasn't a dream.

It wasn't a dream. They took her down to Constitution Station one windy morning, small flags blowing from the pushcarts in the plaza, a piece of pie in the railroad station restaurant, and the enormous entrance to platform 14. Between Inés and her mother they kissed her so much that her face felt like it'd been walked on, soft and smelly, rouge and Coty powder, wet around the mouth, a squeamish feeling of filth that the wind eradicated with one large smack. She wasn't afraid to travel alone because she was a big girl, with nothing less than twenty pesos in her pocketbook, Sansinena Co., Frozen Meats a sweetish stink seeping in the window, the railroad trestle over the yellow brook and Isabel already back to normal from having had to have that crying spell at the station, happy, dead with fear, active, using fully the seat by the window, almost the only traveler in that portion of the coach from which one could examine all the different places and see oneself in the small mirrors. She thought once or twice of her mother, of Inés—they'd already be on the 97 car, leaving Constitution—she read no smoking, spitting is forbidden by law, seating capacity 42 passengers, they were passing through Banfield at top speed, vavooom! country more country more country intermingled with the taste of Milky Way and the menthol drops. Inés had reminded her that she would be working on the green wool in such a way that Isabel packed the knitting into the most inaccessible part of the suitcase, poor Inés, and what a stupid idea.

At the station she was a little bit worried because if the phaeton . . . But there it was, with don Nicanor very red and respectful, yes miss, this miss, that miss, was the trip fine, was her mother as well as ever, of course it had rained— Oh the swinging motion of the phaeton to get her back into the whole aquarium of her previous visit to Los Horneros. Everything smaller, more crystalline and pink, without the tiger then, don Nicanor with fewer white hairs, barely three years ago, Nino a toad, Nino a fish, and Rema's hands which made you want to cry and feel them on your head forever, a caress like death almost and pastries with vanilla cream, the two best things on earth.

They gave her a room upstairs all to herself, the loveliest room. A grownup's room (Nino's idea, all black curls and eyes, handsome in his blue overalls; in the afternoon, of course, Luis made him dress up, his slate-grey suit and a red tie) and inside, another tiny room with an enormous wild cardinal. The bathroom was two doors away (but inside doors through the rooms so that you could go without checking beforehand where the tiger was), full of spigots and metal things, though they did not fool Isabel easily, you could tell it was a country bathroom, things were not as perfect as in a city bath. And it smelled old, the second morning she found a waterbug taking a walk in the washbasin. She barely touched it, it rolled itself into a timid ball and disappeared down the gurgling drain.

Dear mama, I'm writing to— They were eating in the dining room with the chandelier because it was cooler. The Kid was complaining every minute about the heat, Luis said nothing, but every once in a while you could see the sweat break out on his forehead or his chin. Only Rema was restful, she passed the plates slowly and always as if the meal were a birthday party, a little solemnly and impressively. (Isabel was secretly studying her way of carving and of ordering the servants.) For the most part, Luis was always reading, fist to brow, and the book leaning against a siphon. Rema touched his arm before passing him a plate, and the Kid would interrupt him once in a while to call him philosopher. It hurt Isabel that

Luis might be a philosopher, not because of that, but because of the Kid, that he had an excuse then to joke and call him that.

They ate like this: Luis at the head of the table, Rema and Nino on one side, the Kid and Isabel on the other, so that there was an adult at the end and a child and a grownup at either side. When Nino wanted to tell her something serious, he'd give her a kick on the shin with his shoe. Once Isabel yelled and the Kid got angry and said she was badly brought up. Rema looked at her continuously until Isabel was comforted by the gaze and the potato soup.

Mama, before you go in to eat it's like all the rest of the time, you have to look and see if—— Almost always it was Rema who went to see if they could go into the dining room with the crystal chandelier. The second day she came to the big living room and said they would have to wait. It was a long time before a farmhand came to tell them that the tiger was in the clover garden, then Rema took the children's hands and everyone went in to eat. The fried potatoes were pretty dry that morning, though only Nino and the Kid complained.

You told me I was not supposed to go around making—— Because Rema seemed to hold off all questions with her terse sweetness. The setup worked so well that it was unnecessary to worry about the business of the rooms. It was an absolutely enormous house, and at worst, there was only one room they couldn't go into; never more than one, so it didn't matter. Isabel was as used to it as Nino, after a couple of days. From morning until evening they played in the grove of willows, and if they couldn't play in the willow grove, there was always the clover garden, the park with its hammocks, and the edge of the brook. It was the same in the house, they had their bedrooms, the hall down the center, the library downstairs (except one Thursday when they couldn't go into the library) and the dining room with the chandelier. They couldn't go into Luis' study because Luis was reading all the time, once in a while he would call to his son and give him picture books; but Nino always took them out, they went to the living room or to the front garden to look at them. They never went into the Kid's study because they were afraid he would throw a tantrum. Rema told them that it was better that way, she said it as though she were warning them; they'd already learned how to read her silences.

After all's said, it was a sad life. Isabel wondered one night

why the Funes' had invited her for the summer. She wasn't old
enough to understand that it was for Nino not for her, a summer plaything to keep Nino happy. She only managed to see the sadness of
the house, that Rema seemed always tired, that it hardly ever rained
and that, nonetheless, things had that air of being damp and abandoned. After a few days she got used to the rules of the house and
the not-difficult discipline of that summer at Los Horneros. Nino was
beginning to learn to use the microscope Luis had given him; they
spent a magnificent week growing insects in a trough with stagnant
water and lily pads, putting drops on the glass slide to look at the
microbes. "They're mosquito larvae, you're not going to see microbes with that microscope," Louis told them, his smile somewhat
pained and distant. They could never believe that that wriggling
horror was not a microbe. Rema brought them a kaleidoscope which
she kept in her wardrobe, but they still preferred detecting microbes and counting their legs. Isabel carried a notebook and kept
notations of their experiments, she combined biology with chemistry and putting together a medicine chest. They made the medicine chest in Nino's room after ransacking the whole house to get
things for it. Isabel told Luis, "We want some of everything: things."
Luis gave them Andreu lozenges, pink cotton, a test tube. The Kid
came across with a rubber bag and a bottle of green pills with the
label worn off. Rema came to see the medicine chest, read the in-
ventory in the notebook, and told them that they were learning a lot
of useful things. It occurred to her or to Nino (who always got
excited and wanted to show off in front of Rema) to assemble an
herbarium. As it was possible that morning to go down to the clover
garden, they went about collecting samples and by nightfall they
had both their bedroom floors filled with leaves and flowers on bits
of paper, there was hardly room to step. Before going to bed, Isabel
noted: "Leaf #74: green, heart-shaped, with brown spots." It annoyed her a little that almost all the leaves were green, nearly all
smooth, and nearly all lanceolate.

The day they went out ant-hunting she saw the farmhands. She
knew the foreman and the head groom because they brought reports to the house. But these other younger hands stood there against
the side of the sheds with an air of siesta, yawning once in a while
and watching the kids play. One of them asked Nino, "Why'ya col-
lectin' all them bugs?" and tapped him on top of his head with all

the curls, using two fingers. Isabel would have liked Nino to lose his temper, to show that he was the boss's son. They already had the bottle crawling with ants and on the bank of the brook they ran across a bug with an enormous hard shell and stuck him in the bottle too, to see what would happen. The idea of an ant-farm they'd gotten out of *The Treasure of Youth,* and Luis loaned them a big, deep glass tank. As they left, both of them carrying it off, Isabel heard him say to Rema, "Better this way, they'll be quiet in the house." Also it seemed to her that Rema sighed. Before dropping off to sleep, when faces appear in the darkness, she remembered again the Kid going out onto the porch for a smoke, thin, humming to himself, saw Rema who was bringing him out coffee and he made a mistake taking the cup so clumsily that he caught Rema's fingers while trying to get the cup, Isabel had seen from the dining room Rema pulling her hand back and the Kid was barely able to keep the cup from falling and laughed at the tangle. Black ants better than the red ones: bigger, more ferocious. Afterward let loose a pile of red ones, watch the war from outside the glass, all very safe. Except they didn't fight. Made two anthills, one in each corner of the glass tank. They consoled one another by studying the distinctive habits, a special notebook for each kind of ant. But almost sure they would fight, look through the glass at war without quarter, and just one notebook.

Rema didn't like to spy on them, she passed by the bedrooms sometimes and would see them with the ant-farm beside the window, impassioned and important. Nino was particularly good at pointing out immediately any new galleries, and Isabel enlarged the diagram traced in ink on double pages. On Luis' advice they collected black ants only, and the ant-farm was already enormous, the ants appeared to be furious and worked until nightfall, excavating and moving earth with a thousand methods and maneuvers, the careful rubbing of feelers and feet, abrupt fits of fury or vehemence, concentrations and dispersals for no apparent reason. Isabel no longer knew what to take notes on, little by little she put the notebook aside and hours would pass in studying and forgetting what had been discovered. Nino began to want to go back to the garden, he mentioned the hammocks and the colts. Isabel was somewhat contemptuous of him for that. The ant-farm was worth the whole of Los Horneros, and it gave her immense pleasure to think that the ants came and went without fear of any tiger, sometimes she tried to imagine a tiny little tiger like an eraser, roaming the galleries of the ant-farm; maybe that was why the dispersals and concentrations. And now she liked to rehearse the real world in the one of glass, now that she felt a little like a prisoner, now that she was forbidden to go down to the dining room until Rema said so.

She pushed her nose against one of the glass sides, promptly all attention because she liked for them to look at her; she heard Rema stop in the doorway, just silent, looking at her. She heard those things with such a sharp brightness when it was Rema.

"You're alone here? Why?"

"Nino went off to the hammocks. This big one must be a queen, she's huge."

Rema's apron was reflected in the glass. Isabel saw one of her hands slightly raised, with the reflection it looked as if it were inside the ant-farm; suddenly she thought about the same hand offering a cup of coffee to the Kid, but now there were ants running along her fingers, ants instead of the cup and the Kid's hand pressing the fingertips.

"Take your hand out, Rema," she asked.

"My hand?"

"Now it's all right. The reflection was scaring the ants."

"Ah. It's all right in the dining room now, you can go down."

"Later. Is the Kid mad at you, Rema?"

The hand moved across the glass like a bird through a window. It looked to Isabel as though the ants were really scared this time, that they ran from the reflection. You couldn't see anything now, Rema had left, she went down the hall as if she were escaping something. Isabel felt afraid of the question herself, a dull fear, made no sense, maybe it wasn't the question but seeing Rema run off that way, or the once-more-clear empty glass where the galleries emptied out and twisted like twitching fingers inside the soil.

It was siesta one afternoon, watermelon, handball against the wall which overlooked the brook, and Nino was terrific, catching shots that looked impossible and climbing up to the roof on a vine to get the ball loose where it was caught between two tiles. A son of one of the farmhands came out from beside the willows and played with them, but he was slow and clumsy and shots got away from him. Isabel could smell the terebinth leaves and at one moment, returning with a backhand an insidious low shot of Nino's, she felt the summer's happiness very deep inside her. For the first time she understood her being at Los Horneros, the vacation, Nino. She thought of the ant-farm up there and it was an oozy dead thing, a horror of legs trying to get out, false air, poisonous. She hit the ball angrily, happily, she bit off a piece of a terebinth leaf with her teeth, bitter, she spit it out in disgust, happy for the first time really, and at last, under the sun in the country.

The window glass fell like hail. It was in the Kid's study. They saw him rise in his shirtsleeves and the broad black eyeglasses.

"Filthy pains-in-the-ass!"

The little peon fled. Nino set himself alongside Isabel, she felt him shaking with the same wind as the willows.

"We didn't mean to do it, uncle."

"Honest, Kid, we didn't mean to do it."

He wasn't there any longer.

She had asked Rema to take away the ant-farm and Rema promised her. After, chatting while she helped her hang up her clothes and get into her pajamas, they forgot. When Rema put out the light, Isabel felt the presence of the ants, Rema went down the hall to say goodnight to Nino who was still crying and repentant, but she didn't have the nerve to call her back again. Rema would have thought that she was just a baby. She decided to go to sleep immediately, and was wider awake than ever. When the moment came when there were faces in the darkness, she saw her mother and Inés looking at one another and smiling like accomplices and pulling on gloves of phosphorescent yellow. She saw Nino weeping, her mother and Inés with the gloves on that now were violet hairdos that twirled and twirled round their heads, Nino with enormous vacant eyes— maybe from having cried too much—and thought that now she would see Rema and Luis, she wanted to see them, she didn't want to see the Kid, but she saw the Kid without his glasses with the same tight face that he'd had when he began hitting Nino and Nino fell backwards until he was against the wall and looked at him as though expecting that would finish it, and the Kid continued to whack back and forth across his face with a loose soft slap that sounded moist, until Rema intruded herself in front of Nino and the Kid laughed, his face almost touching Rema's, and then they heard Luis returning and saying from a distance that now they could go into the dining room. Everything had happened so fast because Nino had been there and Rema had come to tell them not to leave the living room until Luis found out what room the tiger was in and she stayed there with them watching the game of checkers. Nino won and Rema praised him, then Nino was so happy that he put his arms around her waist and wanted to kiss her. Rema had bent down, laughing, and Nino kissed her on the nose and eyes, the two of them laughing and Isabel also, they were so happy playing. They didn't see the Kid coming, when he got up to them he grabbed Nino, jerked at him, said something about the ball breaking the window in his room and started to hit him, he looked at Rema while he hit him, he seemed furious with Rema and she defied him with her eyes for a moment. Terrified, Isabel saw her face up to him, then she stepped in between to protect Nino. The whole evening meal was a deceit, a lie, Luis thought that Nino was crying from having taken a tumble, the Kid looked at Rema as if to order her to shut up, Isabel saw him now with his hard, handsome mouth, very red lips; in the dimness they were even more scarlet, she could see his teeth, barely revealed, glittering. A puffed cloud emerged from his teeth, a green triangle, Isabel blinked her eyes to wipe out the images and Inés and her mother appeared again with their yellow gloves; she gazed at them for a moment, then thought of the ant-farm: that was there and you couldn't see it; the yellow gloves were not there and she saw them instead as if in bright sunlight. It seemed almost curious to her, she couldn't make the ant-farm come out, instead she felt it as a kind of weight there, a chunk of thick, live space. She felt it so strongly that she reached about for the matches, the night-lamp. The ant-farm leaped from the nothingness, wrapped in shifting shadow. Isabel lifted the lamp and came closer. Poor ants, they were going to think that the sun was up. When she could see one of the sides, she was frightened; the ants had been working in all that blackness. She watched them swarm up and down, in silence, so visible, palpable. They were working away inside there as though they had not yet lost their hope of getting out.

It was almost always the foreman who kept them advised of the tiger's movements; Luis had the greatest confidence in him, and since he passed almost the whole day working in his study, he neither emerged nor let those who came down from the next floor move about until don Roberto sent in his report. But they had to rely on one another also. Busy with the household chores inside, Rema knew exactly what was happening upstairs and down. At other times, it was the children who brought the news to the Kid or to Luis. Not that they'd seen anything, just that don Roberto had run into them outside, indicated the tiger's whereabouts to them, and they came back in to pass it on. They believed Nino without question, Isabel less, she was new and might make a mistake. Later, though, since she always went about with Nino stuck to her skirt, they finally believed both of them equally. That was in the morning and afternoon; at night it was the Kid who went out to check and see that the dogs were tied up or that no live coals had been left close to the houses. Isabel noticed that he carried the revolver and sometimes a stick with a silver handle.

She hadn't wanted to ask Rema about it because Rema clearly found it something so obvious and necessary; to pester her would have meant looking stupid, and she treasured her pride before another woman. Nino was easy, he talked straight. Everything clear and obvious when he explained it. Only at night, if she wanted to reconstruct that clarity and obviousness, Isabel noticed that the important reasons were still missing. She learned quickly what was really important: if you wanted to leave the house, or go down to the dining room, to Luis' study, or to the library, find out first. "You have to trust don Roberto," Rema had said. Her and Nino as well. She hardly ever asked Luis because he hardly ever knew. The Kid, who always knew, she never asked. And so it was always easy, the life organized itself for Isabel with a few more obligations as far as her movements went, and a few less when it came to clothes, meals, the time to go to bed. A real summer, the way it should be all year round.

. . . see you soon. They're all fine. I have an ant-farm with Nino and we play and are making a very large herbarium. Rema sends her kisses, she is fine. I think she's sad, the same as Luis who is very nice. I think that Luis has some trouble although he studies all the time. Rema gave me some lovely colored handkerchiefs, Inés is going to like them. Mama, it's nice here and I'm enjoying myself with Nino and don Roberto, he's the foreman and tells us when we can go out and where, one afternoon he was almost wrong and sent us to the edge of the brook, when a farmhand came to tell us no, you should have seen how awful don Roberto felt and then Rema, she picked Nino up and was kissing him, and she squeezed me so hard. Luis was going about saying that the house was not for

children, and Nino asked him who the children were, and every-
body laughed, even the Kid laughed. Don Roberto is the foreman.
    If you come to get me you could stay a few days and be with
Rema and cheer her up. I think that she . . .

But to tell her mother that Rema cried at night, that she'd heard
her crying going down the hall, staggering a little, stop at Nino's
door, continue, go downstairs (she must have been drying her
eyes) and Luis' voice in the distance: "What's the matter, Rema?
Aren't you well?", a silence, the whole house like an enormous ear,
then a murmur and Luis' voice again: "He's a bastard, a miserable
bastard . . ." almost as though he were coldly confirming a fact,
making a connection, a fate.

    . . . is a little ill, it would do her good if you came and kept her
company. I have to show you the herbarium and some stones from
the brook the farmhands brought me. Tell Inés . . .

    It was the kind of night she liked, insects, damp, reheated
bread, and custard with Greek raisins. The dogs barked constantly
from the edge of the brook, and an enormous praying mantis flew
in and landed on the mantelpiece and Nino went to fetch the magnifying glass; they trapped it with a wide-mouthed glass and poked
at it to make it show the color of its wings.

    "Throw that bug away," Rema pleaded. "They make me so
squeamish."

    "It's a good specimen," Luis admitted. "Look how he follows
my hand with his eyes. The only insect that can turn its head."

    "What a goddamned night," the Kid said from behind his
newspaper.

    Isabel would have liked to cut the mantis' head off, a good snip
with the scissors, and see what would happen.

    "Leave it in the glass," she asked Nino. "Tomorrow we can put
it in the ant-farm and study it."

    It got hotter, by ten-thirty you couldn't breathe. The children
stayed with Rema in the inside dining room, the men were in their
studies. Nino was the first to say that he was getting sleepy.

    "Go on up by yourself, I'll come see you later. Everything is
all right upstairs." And Rema took him about the waist with that
expression he liked so well.

    "Tell us a story, Aunt Rema?"

"Another night."

They were down there alone, with the mantis which looked at them. Luis came to say his goodnights to them, muttering something about the hour that children ought to go to bed, Rema smiled at him when she kissed him.

"Growly bear," she said, and Isabel, bent over the mantis' glass, thought that she'd never seen Rema kissing the Kid or a praying mantis that was so so green. She moved the glass a little and the mantis grew frantic. Rema came over to tell her to go to bed.

"Throw that bug away, it's horrible."

"Rema, tomorrow."

She asked her to come up and say goodnight to her. The Kid had the door of his study left partly open and was pacing up and down in his shirtsleeves, the collar open. He whistled to her as she passed.

"I'm going to bed, Kid."

"Listen to me: tell Rema to make me a nice cold lemonade and bring it to me here. Then you go right up to your room."

Of course she was going to go up to her room, she didn't see why he had to tell her to. She went back to the dining room to tell Rema, she saw her hesitate.

"Don't go upstairs yet. I'm going to make the lemonade and you take it down yourself."

"He said for you . . ."

"Please."

Isabel sat down at the side of the table. Please. There were clouds of insects whirling under the carbide lamp, she would have stayed there for hours looking at nothing, repeating: Please, please. Rema, Rema. How she loved her, and that unhappy voice, bottomless, without any possible reason, the voice of sadness itself. Please. Rema, Rema . . . A feverish heat reached her face, a wish to throw herself at Rema's feet, to let Rema pick her up in her arms, a wish to die looking at her and Rema be sorry for her, pass her cool, delicate fingers through her hair, over the eyelids . . .

Now she was holding out a green tumbler full of ice and sliced lemons.

"Take it to him."

"Rema . . ."

Rema seemed to tremble, she turned her back on the table so that she shouldn't see her eyes.

"I'll throw the mantis out right now, Rema."

One sleeps poorly in the viscous heat and all that buzzing of mos-
quitoes. Twice she was on the point of getting up, to go out into the
hall or to go to the bathroom to put cold water on her face and
wrists. But she could hear someone walking, downstairs, someone
was going from one side of the dining room to the other, came to the
bottom of the stairway, turned around . . . They weren't the confused, long steps of Luis' walk, nor was it Rema's. How warm the
Kid had felt that night, how he'd drunk the lemonade in great
gulps. Isabel saw him drinking the tumblerful, his hands holding the green tumbler, the yellow discs wheeling in the water under
the lamp; but at the same time she was sure the Kid had never drunk
the lemonade, that he was still staring at the glass she had brought
him, over to the table, like someone looking at some kind of infinite
naughtiness. She didn't want to think about the Kid's smile, his going to the door as though he were about to go into the dining room
for a look, his slow turning back.

"She was supposed to bring it to me. You, I told you to go up
to your room."

And the only thing that came to her mind was a very idiot answer:

"It's good and cold, Kid."

And the tumbler, green as the praying mantis.

Nino was the first one up, it was his idea that they go down to
the brook to look for snails. Isabel had hardly slept at all, she remembered rooms full of flowers, tinkling bells, hospital corridors,
sisters of charity, thermometers in jars of bichlorate, scenes from her
first communion, Inés, the broken bicycle, the restaurant in the railroad station, the gypsy costume when she had been eight. Among
all this, like a delicate breeze between the pages of an album, she
found herself wide awake, thinking of things that were not flowers,
bells, hospital corridors. She got out of bed grudgingly, washed her
face hard, especially the ears. Nino said that it was ten o'clock and
that the tiger was in the music room, so that they could go down to
the brook right away. They went downstairs together, hardly saying
good morning to Luis and the Kid who were both reading with
their doors open. You could find the snails mostly on the bank nearest the wheatfields. Nino moved along blaming Isabel for her distraction, said she was no kind of friend at all and wasn't helping

form the collection. She saw him suddenly as so childish, such a little boy with his snails and his leaves.

She came back first, when they raised the flag at the house for lunch. Don Roberto came from his inspection and Isabel asked him the same question as always. Then Nino was coming up slowly, carrying the box of snails and the rakes; Isabel helped him put the rakes away on the porch and they went in together. Rema was standing there, white and silent. Nino put a blue snail into her hand.

"The nicest one, for you."

The Kid was eating already, the newspaper beside him, there was hardly enough room for Isabel to rest her arm. Luis was the last to come from his room, contented as he always was at noon. They ate, Nino was talking about the snails, the snail eggs in the reeds, the collection itself, the sizes and the colors. He was going to kill them by himself, it hurt Isabel to do it, they'd put them to dry on a zinc sheet. After the coffee came and Luis looked at them with the usual question, Isabel got up first to look for don Roberto, even though don Roberto had already told her before. She made the rounds of the porch and when she came in again, Rema and Nino had their heads together over the snail box, it was like a family photograph, only Luis looked up at her and she said, "It's in the Kid's study," and stayed watching how the Kid shrugged his shoulders, annoyed, and Rema who touched a snail with a fingertip, so delicately that her finger even seemed part snail. Afterwards, Rema got up to go look for more sugar, and Isabel tailed along behind her babbling until they came back in laughing from a joke they'd shared in the pantry. When Luis said he had no tobacco and ordered Nino to look in his study, Isabel challenged him that she'd find the cigarettes first and they went out together. Nino won, they came back in running and pushing, they almost bumped into the Kid going to the library to read his newspaper, complaining because he couldn't use his study. Isabel came over to look at the snails, and Luis waiting for her to light his cigarette as always saw that she was lost, studying the snails which were beginning to ooze out slowly and move about, looking at Rema suddenly, but dropping her like a flash, captivated by the snails, so much so that she didn't move at the Kid's first scream, they were all running and she was still standing over the snails as if she did not hear the Kid's new choked cry, Luis beating against the library door, don Roberto coming in with the dogs, the Kid's moans amid the furious barking of the dogs, and Luis saying over and over again, "But if it was in his study! She said it was in his own study!", bent over the snails willowy as fingers, like Rema's fingers maybe, or it was Rema's hand on her shoulder, made her raise her head to look at her, to stand looking at her for an eternity, broken by her ferocious sob into Rema's skirt, her unsettled happiness, and Rema running her hand over her hair, quieting her with a soft squeeze of her fingers and a murmuring against her ear, a stuttering as of gratitude, as of an unnameable acquiescence.

QUESTIONS

1. Point of view is central to the understanding of this story. Examine the character of Isabel. Analyze her emotions, attitudes, and responses. To what extent does she influence the meaning of the narrative? One of the most intriguing aspects of this story is the presence of a tiger in the household. Is the tiger purely the product of Isabel's imagination, a game in which everyone joins? Is it a projection of some inner conflict she feels? Or is it, perhaps, real?

2. The story's structure is in part determined by the movement from city to country, including the crossing of a bridge. For Cortázar, a bridge often symbolizes the crossing point from one dimension or world into another. If that is the bridge's function here, what are the two worlds which it connects?

3. The title, like the title of Flannery O'Connor's "A Good Man is Hard to Find," has more than one meaning. Discuss these meanings.

4. The motif of death begins early in the story, with the brief comments that Isabel was "dead with fear" and "Rema's hands which made you want to cry and feel them on your head forever, a caress like death almost." Trace the development of this motif and discuss its significance in relation to the story as a whole.

5. Some of the narrative is rendered as stream of consciousness. When and why is this technique used in "Bestiary"?

PAUL BOWLES

(1910-   )

Paul Bowles is a kind of Renaissance man alive in the Twentieth Century. Born in New York, he early demonstrated unusual musical talent, eventually studying under Aaron Copland in New York and Berlin, and under Virgil Thomson in Paris. As a composer, he has written operas, film scores, ballets, songs, chamber music, and has written for the stage. He wrote the scores for "The Glass Menagerie" and "Sweet Bird of Youth." For several years he was music critic for the NEW YORK HERALD TRIBUNE. As a world traveller, he has lived extensively abroad and has written frequent travel essays; his experiences in foreign countries have clearly influenced his fiction. As a linguist and translator, he has translated from the Arabic, French, Spanish, and Italian. In 1941 he received a Guggenheim fellowship and in 1959 a Rockefeller grant. His novels and collections of short stories are numerous; among them are THE SHELTERING SKY, LET IT COME DOWN, THE SPIDER'S HOUSE, THE HOURS AFTER NOON, YALLAH, A HUNDRED CAMELS IN THE COURTYARD, THEIR HEADS ARE GREEN AND THEIR HANDS ARE BLUE, UP ABOVE THE WORLD, and THE TIME OF FRIENDSHIP.

The Scorpion

An old woman lived in a cave which her sons had hollowed out of a clay cliff near a spring before they went away to the town where many people live. She was neither happy nor unhappy to be there, because she knew that the end of life was near and that her sons would not be likely to return no matter what the season. In the town there are always many things to do, and they would be doing them, not caring to remember the time when they had lived in the hills looking after the old woman.

At the entrance to the cave at certain times of the year there was a curtain of water-drops through which the old woman had to pass to get inside. The water rolled down the bank from the plants above and dripped onto the clay below. So the old woman accustomed herself to sitting crouched in the cave for long periods of time in order to keep as dry as possible. Outside through the moving beads of water she saw the bare earth lighted by the gray sky, and sometimes large dry leaves went past, pushed by the wind that came from higher parts of the land. Inside where she was the light was pleasant and of a pink color from the clay all around.

A few people used to pass from time to time along the path not far away, and because there was a spring nearby, those travelers who knew that it existed but not just where it was would sometimes come near to the cave before they discovered that the spring was not there. The old woman would never call to them. She would merely watch them as they came near and suddenly saw her. Then she would go on watching as they turned back and went in other directions looking for the water to drink.

There were many things about this life that the old woman liked. She was no longer obliged to argue and fight with her sons to make them carry wood to the charcoal oven. She was free to move about at night and look for food. She could eat everything she found without having to share it. And she owed no one any debt of thanks for the things she had in her life.

One old man used to come from the village on his way down to the valley, and sit on a rock just distant enough from the cave for her to recognize him. She knew he was aware of her presence in the cave there, and although she probably did not know this, she disliked him for not giving some sign that he knew she was there. It seemed to her that he had an unfair advantage over her and was using it in an unpleasant way. She thought up many ideas for annoying him if he should ever come near enough, but he always passed by in the distance, pausing to sit down on the rock for some time, when he would often gaze straight at the cave. Then he would continue slowly on his way, and it always seemed to the old woman that he went more slowly after his rest than before it.

There were scorpions in the cave all year round, but above all during the days just before the plants began to let water drip through. The old woman had a huge bundle of rags, and with this she would brush the walls and ceiling clear of them, stamping quickly on them with her hard bare heel. Occasionally a small wild bird or animal strayed inside the entrance, but she was never quick enough to kill it, and she had given up trying.

One dark day she looked up to see one of her sons standing in the doorway. She could not remember which one it was, but she thought it was the one who had ridden the horse down the dry river bed and nearly been killed. She looked at his hand to see if it was out of shape. It was not that son.

He began to speak: "Is it you?"

"Yes."

"Are you well?"

"Yes."

"Is everything well?"

"Everything."

"You stayed here?"

"You can see."

"Yes."

There was a silence. The old woman looked around the cave and was displeased to see that the man in the doorway made it practically dark in there. She busied herself with trying to distinguish various objects: her stick, her gourd, her tin can, her length of rope. She was frowning with the effort.

The man was speaking again.

"Shall I come in?"

She did not reply.

He backed away from the entrance, brushing the water drops from his garments. He was on the point of saying something profane, thought the old woman, who, even though she did not know which one this was, remembered what he would do.

She decided to speak.

"What?" she said.

He leaned forward through the curtain of water and repeated his question.

"Shall I come in?"

"No."

"What's the matter with you?"

"Nothing."

Then she added: "There's no room."

He backed out again, wiping his head. The old woman thought he would probably go away, and she was not sure she wanted him to. However, there was nothing else he could do, she thought. She heard him sit down outside the cave, and then she smelled tobacco smoke. There was no sound but the dripping of water upon the clay.

A short while later she heard him get up. He stood outside the entrance again.

"I'm coming in," he said.

She did not reply.

He bent over and pushed inside. The cave was too low for him to stand up in it. He looked about and spat on the floor.

"Come on," he said.

"Where?"

"With me."

"Why?"

"Because you have to come."

She waited a little while, and then said suspiciously: "Where are you going?"

He pointed indifferently toward the valley, and said: "Down that way."

"In the town?"

"Farther."

"I won't go."

"You have to come."

"No."

He picked up her stick and held it out to her.

"Tomorrow," she said.

"Now."

"I must sleep," she said, settling back into her pile of rags.

"Good. I'll wait outside," he answered, and went out.

The old woman went to sleep immediately. She dreamed that the town was very large. It went on forever and its streets were filled with people in new clothes. The church had a high tower with several bells that rang all the time. She was in the streets all one day, surrounded by people. She was not sure whether they were all her sons or not. She asked some of them: "Are you my sons?" They could not answer, but she thought that if they had been able to, they would have said: "Yes." Then when it was night she found a house with its door open. Inside there was a light and some women were seated in a corner. They rose when she went in, and said: "You have a room here." She did not want to see it, but they pushed her along until she was in it, and closed the door. She was a little girl and she was crying. The bells of the church were very loud outside, and she imagined they filled the sky. There was an open space in the wall high above her. She could see the stars through it, and they gave light to her room. From the reeds which formed the ceiling a scorpion came crawling. He came slowly down the wall toward her. She stopped crying and watched him. His tail curved up over his back and moved a little from side to side as he crawled. She looked quickly about for something to brush him down with. Since there was nothing in the room she used her hand. But her motions were slow, and the scorpion seized her finger with his pincers, clinging there tightly although she waved her hand wildly about. Then she realized that he was not going to sting her. A great feeling of happiness went through her. She raised her finger to her lips to kiss the scorpion. The bells stopped ringing. Slowly in the peace which was beginning, the scorpion moved into her mouth. She felt his hard shell and his little clinging legs going across her lips and her tongue. He crawled slowly down her throat and was hers. She woke up and called out.

Her son answered: "What is it?"

"I'm ready."

"So soon?"

He stood outside as she came through the curtain of water, leaning on her stick. Then he began walking a few paces ahead of her toward the path.

"It will rain," said her son.

"Is it far?"

"Three days," he said, looking at her old legs.

She nodded. Then she noticed the old man sitting on the stone. He had an expression of deep surprise on his face, as if a miracle had just occurred. His mouth was open as he stared at the old woman. When they came opposite the rock he peered more intently than ever into her face. She pretended not to notice him. As they picked their way carefully downhill along the stony path, they heard the old man's thin voice behind them, carried by the wind.

"Good-bye."

"Who is that?" said her son.
"I don't know."
Her son looked back at her darkly.
"You're lying," he said.

QUESTIONS

1. Paul Bowles' stories are frequently characterized by conflicts devoid of both love and compassion. What emotions and attitudes take the place of love and compassion in "The Scorpion"? Point out the incidents, thoughts, and comments which establish these emotions and attitudes.

2. Even in so brief a narrative, Bowles' characters give the appearance of depth; they are neither caricatures nor stereotypes. How does he realize his characters so fully in so little space? Try to define the character of the old woman. In what ways does her mode of existence underscore her relationship with the world outside? With her family?

3. The physical setting of "The Scorpion" is unusual, to say the least. What is the effect of setting on character and action? Discuss the significance of the scorpions, the cave, and the curtain of water, in establishing the story's atmosphere.

4. The old woman's dream and the old man sitting outside the cave clearly are related to the narrative's meaning. Is there any significance in the fact that the old woman, in her dream, made the scorpion part of herself, whereas she ignored the old man whom they passed outside? What does the scorpion represent? Why does she announce promptly after the conclusion of her dream that she is ready to go? Are there any resemblances between the old woman and the scorpions she lives among?

5. In *The Delicate Prey,* the collection of Bowles' stories from which "The Scorpion" is taken, Bowles dedicated the book to his mother, "who first read me the stories of Poe." Are there any similarities of setting, atmosphere, theme, or techniques of characterization between this story and Poe's "The Cask of Amontillado"?

ILSE AICHINGER

(1921-)

Born in Vienna, Ilse Aichinger was for a time a medical student in her native city, but writing soon became her primary interest. She has received numerous awards for her fiction, which is Kafkaesque in its surrealistic techniques and existential themes. Works that have been translated into English, in addition to THE BOUND MAN, are HEROD'S CHILDREN and SELECTED SHORT STORIES AND DIALOGUES.

The Bound Man

Sunlight on his face woke him, but made him shut his eyes again; it streamed unhindered down the slope, collected itself into rivulets, attracted swarms of flies, which flew low over his forehead, circled, sought to land, and were overtaken by fresh swarms. When he tried to whisk them away he discovered that he was bound. A thin rope cut into his arms. He dropped them, opened his eyes again, and looked down at himself. His legs were tied all the way up to his thighs; a single length of rope was tied round his ankles, criss-crossed all the way up his legs, and encircled his hips, his chest and his arms. He could not see where it was knotted. He showed no sign of fear or hurry, though he thought he was unable to move, until he discovered that the rope allowed his legs some free play, and that round his body it was almost loose. His arms were tied to each other but not to his body, and had some free play too. This made him smile, and it occurred to him that perhaps children had been playing a practical joke on him.

He tried to feel for his knife, but again the rope cut softly into his flesh. He tried again, more cautiously this time, but his pocket was empty. Not only his knife, but the little money that he had on him, as well as his coat, were missing. His shoes had been pulled from his feet and taken too. When he moistened his lips he tasted blood, which had flowed from his temples down his cheeks, his chin, his neck, and under his shirt. His eyes were painful; if he kept them open for long he saw reddish stripes in the sky.

He decided to stand up. He drew his knees up as far as he could, rested his hands on the fresh grass and jerked himself to his feet. An elder-branch stroked his cheek, the sun dazzled him, and the rope cut into his flesh. He collapsed to the ground again, half out of his mind with pain, and then tried again. He went on trying until the blood started flowing from his hidden weals. Then he lay still again for a long while, and let the sun and the flies do what they liked.

When he awoke for the second time the elder-bush had cast its shadow over him, and the coolness stored in it was pouring from between its branches. He must have been hit on the head. Then they must have laid him down carefully, just as a mother lays her baby behind a bush when she goes to work in the fields.

His chances all lay in the amount of free play allowed him by the rope. He dug his elbows into the ground and tested it. As soon as the rope tautened he stopped, and tried again more cautiously. If he had been able to reach the branch over his head he could have used it to drag himself to his feet, but he could not reach it. He laid his head back on the grass, rolled over, and struggled to his knees. He tested the ground with his toes, and then managed to stand up almost without effort.

A few paces away lay the path across the plateau, and among the grass were wild pinks and thistles in bloom. He tried to lift his foot to avoid trampling on them, but the rope round his ankles prevented him. He looked down at himself.

The rope was knotted at his ankles, and ran round his legs in a kind of playful pattern. He carefully bent and tried to loosen it, but, loose though it seemed to be, he could not make it any looser. To avoid treading on the thistles with his bare feet he hopped over them like a bird.

The cracking of a twig made him stop. People in this district were very prone to laughter. He was alarmed by the thought that he was in no position to defend himself. He hopped on until he reached the path. Bright fields stretched far below. He could see no sign of the nearest village, and, if he could move no faster than this, night would fall before he reached it.

He tried walking, and discovered that he could put one foot before another if he lifted each foot a definite distance from the ground and then put it down again before the rope tautened. In the same way he could actually swing his arms a little.

After the first step he fell. He fell right across the path, and made the dust fly. He expected this to be a sign for the long-suppressed laughter to break out, but all remained quiet. He was alone. As soon as the dust had settled he got up and went on. He looked down and watched the rope slacken, grow taut, and then slacken again.

When the first glow-worms appeared he managed to look up. He felt in control of himself again, and his impatience to reach the nearest village faded.

Hunger made him light-headed, and he seemed to be going so fast that not even a motor-cycle could have overtaken him; alternatively he felt as if he were standing still and that the earth was rushing past him, like a river flowing past a man swimming against the stream. The stream carried branches which had been bent southwards by the north wind, stunted young trees, and patches of grass with bright, long-stalked flowers. It ended by submerging the bushes and the young trees, leaving only the sky and the man above water-level. The moon had risen, and illuminated the bare, curved summit of the plateau, the path, which was overgrown with young grass, the bound man making his way along it with quick, measured steps, and two hares, which ran across the hill just in front of him and vanished down the slope. Though the nights were still cool at this time of the year, before midnight the bound man lay down at the edge of the escarpment and went to sleep.

In the light of morning the animal-tamer who was camping with his circus in the field outside the village saw the bound man coming down the path, gazing thoughtfully at the ground. The bound man stopped and bent down. He held out one arm to help keep his balance and with the other picked up an empty wine-bottle. Then he straightened himself and stood erect again. He moved slowly, to avoid being cut by the rope, but to the circus proprietor what he did suggested the voluntary limitation of an enormous swiftness of movement. He was enchanted by its extraordinary gracefulness, and while the bound man looked about for a stone on which to break the bottle, so that he could use the splintered neck to cut the rope, the animal-tamer walked across the field and approached him. The first leaps of a young panther had never filled him with such delight.

"Ladies and gentlemen, the bound man!" His very first movements let loose a storm of applause, which out of sheer excitement caused the blood to rush to the cheeks of the animal-tamer standing at the edge of the arena. The bound man rose to his feet. His surprise whenever he did this was like that of a four-footed animal which has managed to stand on its hind-legs. He knelt, stood up, jumped, and turned cart-wheels. The spectators found it as astonishing as if they had seen a bird which voluntarily remained earthbound, and confined itself to hopping. The bound man became an enormous draw. His absurd steps and little jumps, his elementary exercises in movement, made the rope-dancer superfluous. His fame grew from village to village, but the motions he went through were few and always the same; they were really quite ordinary motions, which he had continually to practise in the day-time in the half-dark tent in order to retain his shackled freedom. In that he remained entirely within the limits set by his rope he was free of it, it did not confine him, but gave him wings and endowed his leaps and jumps with purpose; just as the flights of birds of passage have purpose when they take wing in the warmth of summer and hesitantly make small circles in the sky.

All the children of the neighbourhood started playing the game of "bound man". They formed rival gangs, and one day the circus people found a little girl lying bound in a ditch, with a cord tied round her neck so that she could hardly breathe. They released her, and at the end of the performance that night the bound man made a speech. He announced briefly that there was no sense in being tied up in such a way that you could not jump. After that he was regarded as a comedian.

Grass and sunlight, tent-pegs driven into the ground and then pulled up again, and on to the next village. "Ladies and gentlemen, the bound man!" The summer mounted towards its climax. It bent its face deeper over the fish-ponds in the hollows, taking delight in its dark reflection, skimmed the surface of the rivers, and made the plain into what it was. Everyone who could walk went to see the bound man.

Many wanted a close-up view of how he was bound. So the circus proprietor announced after each performance that anyone who wanted to satisfy himself that the knots were real and the rope not made of rubber was at liberty to do so. The bound man generally waited for the crowd in the area outside the tent. He laughed or remained serious, and held out his arms for inspection. Many took the opportunity to look him in the face, others gravely tested the rope, tried the knots on his ankles, and wanted to know exactly how the lengths compared with the length of his limbs. They asked him how he had come to be tied up like that, and he answered patiently, always saying the same thing. Yes, he had been tied up, he said, and when he awoke he found that he had been robbed as well. Those who had done it must have been pressed for time, because they had tied him up somewhat too loosely for someone who was not supposed to be able to move and somewhat too tightly for someone who was expected to be able to move. But he did move, people pointed out. Yes, he replied, what else could he do?

Before he went to bed he always sat for a time in front of the fire. When the circus proprietor asked him why he didn't make up a better story, he always answered that he hadn't made up that one, and blushed. He preferred staying in the shade.

The difference between him and the other performers was that when the show was over he did not take off his rope. The result was that every movement that he made was worth seeing, and the villagers used to hang about the camp for hours, just for the sake of seeing him get up from in front of the fire and roll himself in his blanket. Sometimes the sky was beginning to lighten when he saw their shadows disappear.

The circus proprietor often remarked that there was no reason why he should not be untied after the evening performance and tied up again next day. He pointed out that the rope-dancers, for instance, did not stay on their rope over night. But no-one took the idea of untying him seriously.

For the bound man's fame rested on the fact that he was always bound, that whenever he washed himself he had to wash his clothes too and *vice versa,* and that his only way of doing so was to jump in the river just as he was every morning when the sun came out, and

that he had to be careful not to go too far out for fear of being carried away by the stream.

The proprietor was well aware that what in the last resort protected the bound man from the jealousy of the other performers was
his helplessness; he deliberately left them the pleasure of watching
him groping painfully from stone to stone on the river bank every
morning with his wet clothes clinging to him. When his wife pointed
out that even the best clothes would not stand up indefinitely to such
treatment (and the bound man's clothes were by no means of the
best) he replied curtly that it was not going to last for ever. That was
his answer to all objections—it was for the summer season only. But
when he said this he was not being serious; he was talking like a
gambler who has no intention of giving up his vice. In reality he
would have been prepared cheerfully to sacrifice his lions and his
rope-dancers for the bound man.

He proved this on the night when the rope-dancers jumped
over the fire. Afterwards he was convinced that they did it, not because it was midsummer's day, but because of the bound man, who
as usual was lying and watching them, with that peculiar smile that
might have been real or might have been only the effect of the glow
on his face. In any case no-one knew anything about him, because he
never talked about anything that had happened to him before he
emerged from the wood that day.

But that evening two of the performers suddenly picked him
up by the arms and legs, carried him to the edge of the fire and started
playfully swinging him to and fro, while two others held out their
arms to catch him on the other side. In the end they threw him, but
too short. The two men on the other side drew back—they explained afterwards that they did so the better to take the shock.
The result was that the bound man landed at the very edge of the
flames and would have been burned if the circus proprietor had not
seized his arms and quickly dragged him away to save the rope which
was starting to get singed. He was certain that the object had been
to burn the rope. He sacked the four men on the spot.

A few nights later the proprietor's wife was awakened by the
sound of footsteps on the grass, and went outside just in time to prevent the clown from playing his last practical joke. He was carrying
a pair of scissors. When he was asked for an explanation he insisted
that he had had no intention of taking the bound man's life, but only

wanted to cut his rope, because he felt sorry for him. But he was sacked too.

These antics amused the bound man, because he could have freed himself if he had wanted to whenever he liked, but perhaps he wanted to learn a few new jumps first. The children's rhyme: "We travel with the circus, we travel with the circus" sometimes occurred to him while he lay awake at night. He could hear the voices of spectators on the opposite bank who had been driven too far downstream on the way home. He could see the river gleaming in the moonlight, and the young shoots growing out of the thick tops of the willow trees, and did not think about autumn yet.

The circus proprietor dreaded the danger involved for the bound man by sleep. Attempts were continually made to release him while he slept. The chief culprits were sacked rope-dancers, or children who were bribed for the purpose. But measures could be taken to safeguard against these. A much bigger danger was that which he represented to himself. In his dreams he forgot his rope, and was surprised by it when he woke in the darkness of morning. He would angrily try to get up, but lose his balance and fall back again. The previous evening's applause was forgotten, sleep was still too near, his head and neck too free. He was just the opposite of a hanged man—his neck was the only part of him that was free. You had to make sure that at such moments no knife was within his reach. In the early hours of the morning the circus proprietor sometimes sent his wife to see whether the bound man was all right. If he was asleep she would bend over him and feel the rope. It had grown hard from dirt and damp. She would test the amount of free play it allowed him, and touch his tender wrists and ankles.

The most varied rumours circulated about the bound man. Some said he had tied himself up and invented the story of having been robbed, and towards the end of the summer that was the general opinion. Others maintained that he had been tied up at his own request, perhaps in league with the circus proprietor. The hesitant way in which he told his story, his habit of breaking off when the talk got round to the attack on him, contributed greatly to these rumours. Those who still believed in the robbery-with-violence story were laughed at. Nobody knew what difficulties the circus proprietor had in keeping the bound man, and how often he said he had had enough and wanted to clear off, for too much of the summer had passed.

Later, however, he stopped talking about clearing off. When the proprietor's wife brought him his food by the river and asked him how long he proposed to remain with them, he did not answer. She thought he had got used, not to being tied up, but to not forgetting for a moment that he was tied up—the only thing that anyone in his position could get used to. She asked him whether he did not think it ridiculous to be tied up all the time, but he answered that he did not. Such a variety of people—clowns, freaks, and comics, to say nothing of elephants and tigers—travelled with circuses that he did not see why a bound man should not travel with a circus too. He told her about the movements he was practising, the new ones he had discovered, and about a new trick that had occurred to him while he was whisking flies from the animals' eyes. He described to her how he always anticipated the effect of the rope and always restrained his movements in such a way as to prevent it from ever tautening; and she knew that there were days when he was hardly aware of the rope when he jumped down from the wagon and slapped the flanks of the horses in the morning, as if he were moving in a dream. She watched him vault over the bars almost without touching them, and saw the sun on his face, and he told her that sometimes he felt as if he were not tied up at all. She answered that if he were prepared to be untied there would never be any need for him to feel tied up. He agreed that he could be untied whenever he felt like it.

The woman ended by not knowing whether she were more concerned with the man or with the rope that tied him. She told him that he could go on travelling with the circus without his rope, but she did not believe it. For what would be the point of his antics without his rope, and what would he amount to without it? Without his rope he would leave them, and the happy days would be over. She would no longer be able to sit beside him on the stones by the river without rousing suspicion, and she knew that his continued presence, and her conversations with him, of which the rope was the only subject, depended on it. Whenever she agreed that the rope had its advantages he would start talking about how troublesome it was, and whenever he started talking about its advantages she would urge him to get rid of it. All this seemed as endless as the summer itself.

At other times she was worried at the thought that she was herself hastening the end by her talk. Sometimes she would get up in the middle of the night and run across the grass to where he slept. She wanted to shake him, wake him up and ask him to keep the rope.

But then she would see him lying there; he had thrown off his blanket, and there he lay like a corpse, with his legs outstretched and his arms close together, with the rope tied round them. His clothes had suffered from the heat and the water, but the rope had grown no thinner. She felt that he would go on travelling with the circus until the flesh fell from him and exposed the joints. Next morning she would plead with him more ardently than ever to get rid of his rope.

The increasing coolness of the weather gave her hope. Autumn was coming, and he would not be able to go on jumping into the river with his clothes on much longer. But the thought of losing his rope, about which he had felt indifferent earlier in the season, now depressed him.

The songs of the harvesters filled him with foreboding. "Summer has gone, summer has gone." But he realized that soon he would have to change his clothes, and he was certain that when he had been untied it would be impossible to tie him up again in exactly the same way. About this time the proprietor started talking about travelling south that year.

The heat changed without transition into quiet, dry cold, and the fire was kept in all day long. When the bound man jumped down from the wagon he felt the coldness of the grass under his feet. The stalks were bent with ripeness. The horses dreamed on their feet and the wild animals, crouching to leap even in their sleep, seemed to be collecting gloom under their skins which would break out later.

On one of these days a young wolf escaped. The circus proprietor kept quiet about it, to avoid spreading alarm, but the wolf soon started raiding cattle in the neighbourhood. People at first believed that the wolf had been driven to these parts by the prospect of a severe winter, but the circus soon became suspect. The proprietor could not conceal the loss of the animal from his own employees, so the truth was bound to come out before long. The circus people offered their aid in tracking down the beast to the burgomasters of the neighbouring villagers, but all their efforts were vain. Eventually the circus was openly blamed for the damage and the danger, and spectators stayed away.

The bound man went on performing before half-empty seats without losing anything of his amazing freedom of movement. During the day he wandered among the surrounding hills under the thin-beaten silver of the autumn sky, and, whenever he could, lay down where the sun shone longest. Soon he found a place which the twi-

light reached last of all, and when at last it reached him he got up
most unwillingly from the withered grass. In coming down the hill
he had to pass through a little wood on its southern slope, and one
evening he saw the gleam of two little green lights. He knew that
they came from no church window, and was not for a moment under
any illusion about what they were.

He stopped. The animal came towards him through the thin-
ning foliage. He could make out its shape, the slant of its neck, its tail
which swept the ground, and its receding head. If he had not been
bound, perhaps he would have tried to run away, but as it was he did
not even feel fear. He stood calmly with dangling arms and looked
down at the wolf's bristling coat, under which the muscles played
like his own underneath the rope. He thought the evening wind was
still between him and the wolf when the beast sprang. The man took
care to obey his rope.

Moving with the deliberate care that he had so often put to the
test, he seized the wolf by the throat. Tenderness for a fellow-creature
arose in him, tenderness for the upright being concealed in the four-
footed. In a movement that resembled the drive of a great bird—he
felt a sudden awareness that flying would be possible only if one were
tied up in a special way—he flung himself at the animal and brought
it to the ground. He felt a slight elation at having lost the fatal advantage of free limbs which causes men to be worsted.

The freedom he enjoyed in this struggle was having to adapt
every movement of his limbs to the rope that tied him—the freedom
of panthers, wolves, and the wild flowers that sway in the evening
breeze. He ended up lying obliquely down the slope, clasping the
animal's hind-legs between his own bare feet and its head between
his hands. He felt the gentleness of the faded foliage stroking the
back of his hands, and he felt his own grip almost effortlessly reaching
its maximum, and he felt too how he was in no way hampered by the
rope.

As he left the wood light rain began to fall and obscured the
setting sun. He stopped for a while under the trees at the edge of the
wood. Beyond the camp and the river he saw the fields where the
cattle grazed, and the places where they crossed. Perhaps he would
travel south with the circus after all. He laughed softly. It was against
all reason. Even if he went on putting up with his joints' being cov-

ered with sores, which opened and bled when he made certain movements, his clothes would not stand up much longer to the friction of
the rope.

The circus proprietor's wife tried to persuade her husband to
announce the death of the wolf without mentioning that it had been
killed by the bound man. She said that even at the time of his greatest popularity people would have refused to believe him capable of
it, and in their present angry mood, with the nights getting cooler,
they would be more incredulous than ever. The wolf had attacked a
group of children at play that day, and nobody would believe that it
had really been killed; for the circus proprietor had many wolves,
and it was easy enough for him to hang a skin on the rail and allow
free entry. But he was not to be dissuaded. He thought that the
announcement of the bound man's act would revive the triumphs of
the summer.

That evening the bound man's movements were uncertain. He
stumbled in one of his jumps, and fell. Before he managed to get up
he heard some low whistles and catcalls, rather like birds calling at
dawn. He tried to get up too quickly, as he had done once or twice
during the summer, with the result that he tautened the rope and
fell back again. He lay still to regain his calm, and listened to the
boos and catcalls growing into an uproar. "Well, bound man, and
how did you kill the wolf?" they shouted, and: "Are you the man
who killed the wolf?" If he had been one of them he would not have
believed it himself. He thought they had a perfect right to be angry:
a circus at this time of year, a bound man, an escaped wolf, and all
ending up with this. Some groups of spectators started arguing with
others, but the greater part of the audience thought the whole thing
a bad joke. By the time he had got to his feet there was such a hubbub
that he was barely able to make out individual words.

He saw people surging up all round him, like faded leaves raised
by a whirlwind in a circular valley at the centre of which all was yet
still. He thought of the golden sunsets of the last few days; and the
cemetery light which lay over the blight of all that he had built up
during so many nights, the gold frame which the pious hang round
dark, old pictures, this sudden collapse of everything, filled him with
anger.

They wanted him to repeat his battle with the wolf. He said that
such a thing had no place in a circus performance, and the proprietor
declared that he did not keep animals to have them slaughtered in

front of an audience. But the mob stormed the ring and forced them
towards the cages. The proprietor's wife made her way between the
seats to the exit and managed to get round to the cages from the
other side. She pushed aside the attendant whom the crowd had
forced to open a cage door, but the spectators dragged her back and
prevented the door from being shut.

"Aren't you the woman who used to lie with him by the river
in the summer?" they called out. "How does he hold you in his arms?"
She shouted back at them that they needn't believe in the bound man
if they didn't want to, they had never deserved him—painted clowns
were good enough for them.

The bound man felt as if the bursts of laughter were what he
had been expecting ever since early May. What had smelt so sweet
all through the summer now stank. But, if they insisted, he was ready
to take on all the animals in the circus. He had never felt so much at
one with his rope.

Gently he pushed the woman aside. Perhaps he would travel
south with them after all. He stood in the open doorway of the cage,
and he saw the wolf, a strong young animal, rise to its feet, and he
heard the proprietor grumbling again about the loss of his exhibits.
He clapped his hands to attract the animal's attention, and when it
was near enough he turned to slam the cage door. He looked the
woman in the face. Suddenly he remembered the proprietor's warning to suspect of murderous intentions anyone near him who had a
sharp instrument in his hand. At the same moment he felt the blade
on his wrists, as cool as the water of the river in autumn, which during the last few weeks he had been barely able to stand. The rope
curled up in a tangle beside him while he struggled free. He pushed
the woman back, but there was no point in anything he did now.
Had he been insufficiently on his guard against those who wanted to
release him, against the sympathy in which they wanted to lull him?
Had he lain too long on the river bank? If she had cut the cord at any
other moment it would have been better than this.

He stood in the middle of the cage, and rid himself of the rope
like a snake discarding its skin. It amused him to see the spectators
shrinking back. Did they realise that he had no choice now? Or that
fighting the wolf now would prove nothing whatever? At the same
time he felt all his blood rush to his feet. He felt suddenly weak.

The rope, which fell at its feet like a snare, angered the wolf
more than the entry of a stranger into its cage. It crouched to spring.

The man reeled, and grabbed the pistol that hung ready at the side of the cage. Then, before anyone could stop him, he shot the wolf between the eyes. The animal reared, and touched him in falling.

On the way to the river he heard the footsteps of his pursuers—spectators, the rope-dancers, the circus proprietor, and the proprietor's wife, who persisted in the chase longer than anyone else. He hid in a clump of bushes and listened to them hurrying past, and later on streaming in the opposite direction back to the camp. The moon shone on the meadow; in that light its colour was that of both growth and death.

When he came to the river his anger died away. At dawn it seemed to him as if lumps of ice were floating in the water, and as if snow had fallen, obliterating memory.

QUESTIONS

What immediately catches our attention in "The Bound Man" is, first, the fantastic situation in which the central figure finds himself, and then the way in which this situation develops. The protagonist awakens to find himself bound, but rather than work free of his ropes, he accepts them and proceeds to turn his condition into a way of life. In stories such as this, we are faced with the problem of an essentially unrealistic condition. Supposedly, the short story presents an experience which can in some way be related to the actualities of human existence. How do we go about "justifying" such serious departures from realism? Keep this general question in mind while pursuing the following questions about Aichinger's story.

1. Examine the opening scene carefully. Note the locale in which the bound man finds himself, and then follow carefully his various reactions to his discovery that he is tied up. What significance is there in the fact that the rope is tied loosely enough for him to move, even to stand up and walk? By the time he starts down the path toward the nearest village, his attitude is beginning to stabilize. What is his attitude toward his situation?

2. The bound man joins a circus and eventually becomes its star attraction. What is his attitude toward his role as circus performer, and does that attitude undergo any changes? Analyze the attitudes toward him of the circus proprietor, the proprietor's wife, and the other performers.

3. Although the protagonist's condition is, as we have mentioned, quite unrealistic—we might even call it fantastic—he is surrounded by real people pursuing relatively "normal" lives. In other words, the entire story is not unrealistic. Even the protagonist seems perfectly human; it is his *situation* that defies belief. Are there any other aspects of the story that strike you as unrealistic? Look especially for elements in the story which give it a surrealistic or dream-like quality.

4. There are several patterns of imagery which provide motifs and lend the story a sense of metaphoric if not logical order. There is, for example, a steady alternation between human and natural settings. Other recurrent elements are the moon and the river. There is also a definite movement through the seasons. What symbolic and thematic functions do these patterns perform? Explain, for example, the statement in the next to last paragraph, "The moon shone on the meadow; in that light its color was both of growth and of death."

5. Using these patterns as guides, analyze the story's structure. Note that the narrative moves from sunlight at its start to darkness lighted only by the moon, from warmth to the ice in the river, and from bindings which give the protagonist a curious kind of freedom and power, to physical liberty which puts him at the mercy of both man and animal.

TED HUGHES

(1930-)

*Born in Mytholmroyd, West Yorkshire, England, Ted Hughes is
better known as a poet than as a writer of fiction. His first book of
poetry, THE HAWK IN THE RAIN (1957), was widely acclaimed
and won several distinguished awards, including the 1960 Somerset
Maugham Award. He followed with LUPERCAL (1960), and that
same year had three of his short stories published in INTRODUC-
TION: STORIES BY NEW WRITERS. His short stories have recently been collected under the title WODWO. "Snow" is a wildly
comic satire upon Samuel Beckett's existential theme of endurance.*

Snow

And let me repeat this over and over again: beneath my feet is the
earth, some part of the surface of the earth. Beneath the snow beneath my feet, that is. What else could it be? It is firm, I presume,
and level. If it is not actually soil and rock, it must be ice. It is very
probably ice. Whichever it may be, it is proof—the most substantial proof possible—that I am somewhere on the earth, the known
earth. It would be absurd to dig down through the snow, just to determine exactly what is underneath, earth or ice. This bedded snow
may well be dozens of feet deep. Besides, the snow filling all the air
and rivering along the ground would pour into the hole as fast as I
could dig, and cover me too—very quickly.

This could be no other planet: the air is perfectly natural, perfectly good.

Our aircraft was forced down by this unusual storm. The pilot tried to make a landing, but misjudged the extraordinary power of the wind and the whereabouts of the ground. The crash was violent. The fuselage buckled and gaped, and I was flung clear. Unconscious of everything save the need to get away from the disaster, I walked farther off into the blizzard and collapsed, which explains why when I came to full consciousness and stood up out of the snow that was burying me I could see nothing of either the aircraft or my fellow passengers. All around me was what I have been looking at ever since. The bottomless dense motion of snow. I started to walk.

Of course, everything previous to that first waking may have been entirely different since I don't remember a thing about it. Whatever chance dropped me here in the snow evidently destroyed my memory. That's one thing of which there is no doubt whatsoever. It is, so to speak, one of my facts. The aircraft crash is a working hypothesis, that merely.

There's no reason why I should not last quite a long time yet. I seem to have an uncommon reserve of energy. To keep my mind firm, that is the essential thing, to fix it firmly in my reasonable hopes, and lull it there, encourage it. Mesmerise it slightly with a sort of continuous prayer. Because when my mind is firm, my energy is firm. And that's the main thing here—energy. No matter how circumspect I may be, or how lucid, without energy I am lost on the spot. Useless to think about it. Where my energy ends I end, and all circumspection and all lucidity end with me. As long as I have energy I can correct my mistakes, outlast them, outwalk them—for instance the unimaginable error that as far as I know I am making at this very moment. This step, this, the next five hundred, or five thousand—all mistaken, all absolute waste, back to where I was ten hours ago. But we recognise that thought. My mind is not my friend. My support, my defence, but my enemy too—not perfectly intent on getting me out of this. If I were mindless perhaps there would be no difficulty whatsoever. I would simply go on aware of nothing but my step by step success in getting over the ground. The thing to do is to keep alert, keep my mind fixed in alertness, recognise these treacherous paralysing, yes, lethal thoughts the second they enter, catch them before they can make that burrowing plunge down the spinal cord.

Then gently and without any other acknowledgment push them back—out into the snow where they belong. And that *is* where they belong. They are the infiltrations of the snow, encroachments of this immensity of lifelessness. But they enter so slyly! We are true, they say, or at least very probably true, and on that account you must entertain us and even give us the run of your life, since above all things you are dedicated to the truth. That is the air they have, that's how they come in. What do I know about the truth? As if simpleminded dedication to truth were the final law of existence! I only know more and more clearly what is good for me. It's my mind that has this contemptible awe for the probably true, and my mind, I know, I prove it every minute, is not me and is by no means sworn to help me. Am I a lie? I must survive—that's a truth sacred as any, and as the hungry truths devour the sleepy truths I shall digest every other possible truth to the substance and health and energy of my own, and the ones I can't digest I shall spit out, since in this situation my intention to survive is the one mouth, the one digestive tract, so to speak, by which I live. But those others! I relax for a moment, I leave my mind to itself for a moment—and they are in complete possession. They plunge into me, exultantly, mercilessly. There is no question of their intention or their power. Five seconds of carelessness, and they have struck. The strength melts from me, my bowels turn to water, my consciousness darkens and shrinks, I have to stop.

What are my facts? I do have some definite facts.

Taking six steps every five seconds, I calculate—allowing for my brief regular sleeps—that I have been walking through this blizzard for five months and during that time have covered something equal to the breadth of the Atlantic between Southampton and New York. Two facts. And a third: throughout those five months this twilight of snow has not grown either darker or brighter.

So.

There seems no reason to doubt that I am somewhere within either the Arctic or the Antarctic Circle. That's a comfort. It means my chances of survival are not uniquely bad. Men have walked the length of Asia simply to amuse themselves.

Obviously I am not travelling in a straight line. But that needn't give me any anxiety. Perhaps I made a mistake when I first started walking, setting my face against the wind instead of downwind. Coming aganst the wind I waste precious energy and there is always this wearisome snow blocking my eyes and mouth. But I had to trust the wind. This resignation to the wind's guidance is the very foundation of my firmness of mind. The wind is not simply my compass. In fact,

I must not think of it as a compass at all. The wind is my law. As a compass nothing could be more useless. No need to dwell on that. It's extremely probable indeed and something I need not hide from myself that this wind is leading me to and fro in quite a tight little maze —always shifting too stealthily for me to notice the change. Or, if the sun is circling the horizon, it seems likely that the wind is swinging with it through the three hundred and sixty degrees once in every twenty-four hours, turning me as I keep my face against it in a perfect circle not more than seven miles across. This would explain the otherwise strange fact that in spite of the vast distance I have covered the terrain is still dead level, exactly as when I started. A frozen lake, no doubt. This is a strong possibility and I must get used to it without letting it overwhelm me, and without losing sight of its real advantages.

The temptation to trust to luck and instinct and cut out across wind is to be restricted. The effect on my system of confidence would be disastrous. My own judgment would naturally lead me in a circle. I would have to make deliberate changes of direction to break out of that circle—only to go in a larger circle or a circle in the opposite direction. So more changes. Wilder and more sudden changes, changes of my changes—all to evade an enemy that showed so little sign of itself it might as well not have existed. It's clear where all that would end. Shouting and running and so on. Staggering round like a man beset by a mob. Falling, grovelling. So on. The snow.

No. All I have to do is endure: that is, keep my face to the wind. My face to the wind, a firm grip on my mind, and everything else follows naturally. There is not the slightest need to be anxious. Any time now the Polar night will arrive, bringing a drastic change of climate—inevitable. Clearing the sky and revealing the faultless compass of the stars.

The facts are overwhelmingly on my side. I could almost believe in Providence. After all, if one single circumstance were slightly —only slightly—other than it is! If, for instance, instead of waking in a blizzard on a firm level place I had come to consciousness falling endlessly through snow-cloud. Then I might have wondered very seriously whether I were in the gulf or not. Or if the atmosphere happened to consist of, say, ammonia. I could not have existed. And in the moment before death by asphyxiation I would certainly have been convinced I was out on some lifeless planet. Or if I had no body but simply arms and legs growing out of a head, my whole system of confidence would have been disoriented from the start. My dreams, for instance, would have been meaningless to me, or rather an argument of my own meaninglessness. I would have died almost immediately, out of sheer bewilderment. It wouldn't need nearly such extreme differences either. If I had been without these excellent pigskin boots, trousers, jacket, gloves and hood, the cold would have extinguished me at once.

And even if I had double the clothing that I have, where would I be without my chair? My chair is quite as important as one of my lungs. As both my lungs, indeed, for without it I should be dead. Where would I have slept? Lying in the snow. But lying flat, as I have discovered, I am buried by the snow in just under a minute, and the cold begins to take over my hands and my feet and my face. Sleep would be impossible. In other words, I would very soon collapse of exhaustion and be buried. As it is, I unsnap my chair harness, plant the chair in the snow, sit on it, set my feet on the rung between the front legs, my arms folded over my knees and my head resting on my arms, and am able in this way to take a sleep of fully ten minutes before the snow piles over me.

The chain of providential coincidences is endless. Or rather, like a chain mail, it is complete without one missing link to betray and annul the rest. Even my dreams are part of it. They are as tough and essential a link as any, since there can no longer be any doubt that they are an accurate reproduction of my whole previous life, of the world as it is and as I knew it—all without one contradictory detail. Yet if my amnesia had been only a little bit stronger!—it needed only that. Because without this evidence of the world and my identity I could have known no purpose in continuing the ordeal. I could only have looked, breathed and died, like a nestling fallen from the nest.

Everything fits together. And the result—my survival, and my determination to survive. I should rejoice.

The chair is of conventional type: nothing in the least mystifying about it. A farmhouse sort of chair: perfectly of a piece with my dreams, as indeed are my clothes, my body and all the inclinations of my mind. It is of wood, painted black, though in places showing a coat of brown beneath the black. One of the nine struts in the back is missing and some child—I suppose it was a child—has stuck a dab of chewing-gum into the empty socket. Obviously the chair has been well used, and not too carefully. The right foreleg has been badly chewed, evidently by a puppy, and on the seat both black and brown paints are wearing through showing the dark grain of the pale wood. If all this is not final evidence of a reality beyond my own, of the reality of the world it comes from, the world I re-dream in my sleeps—I might as well lie down in the snow and be done with.

The curious harness needn't worry me. The world, so far as I've dreamed it at this point, contains no such harness, true. But since I've not yet dreamed anything from after my twenty-sixth birthday, the harness might well have been invented between that time and the time of my disaster. Probably it's now in general use. Or it may be the paraphernalia of some fashionable game that came in during my twenty-seventh or later year, and to which I got addicted. Sitting on snow peaks in nineteenth-century chairs. Or perhaps I developed a passion for painting polar scenery and along with that a passion for this particular chair as my painting seat, and had the harness designed specially. A lucky eccentricity! It is perfectly adapted to my present need. But all that's in the dark still. There's a lot I haven't dreamed yet. From my twenty-third and twenty-fourth years I have almost nothing—a few insignificant episodes. Nothing at all after my twenty-sixth birthday. The rest, though, is about complete, which suggests that any time now I ought to be getting my twenty-third and twenty-fourth years in full and, more important, my twenty-seventh year, or as much of it as there is, along with the accurate account of my disaster and the origin of my chair.

There seems little doubt of my age. Had I been dreaming my life chronologically there would have been real cause for worry. I could have had no idea how much was still to come. Of course, if I were suddenly to dream something from the middle of my sixtieth year I would have to reorganise all my ideas. What really convinces me of my youth is my energy. The appearance of my body tells me nothing. Indeed, from my hands and feet—which are all I have dared to uncover—one could believe I was several hundred years old, or even dead, they are so black and shrunken on the bone. But the emaciation is understandable, considering that for five months I have been living exclusively on will-power, without the slightest desire for food.

I have my job to get back to, and my mother and father will be in despair. And God knows what will have happened to Helen. Did I marry her? I have no wedding ring. But we were engaged. And it is another confirmation of my youth that my feelings for her are as they were then—stronger, in fact, yes a good deal stronger, though speaking impartially these feelings that seem to be for her might easily be nothing but my desperate longing to get back to the world in general—a longing that is using my one-time affection for Helen as a sort of form or model. It's possible, very possible, that I have in reality forgotten her, even that I am sixty years old, that she has been dead for thirty-four years. Certain things may be very different from what I imagine. If I were to take this drift of thoughts to the logical extreme there is no absolute proof that my job, my parents, Helen and the whole world are not simply my own invention, fantasies my imagination has improvised on the simple themes of my own form, of clothes, my chair, and the properties of my present environment. I am in no position to be sure about anything.

But there is more to existence, fortunately, than consideration of possibilities. There is conviction, faith. If there were not, where would I be? The moment I allow one of these "possibilities" the slightest intimacy—a huge futility grips me, as it were physically, by the heart, as if the organ itself were despairing of this life and ready to give up.

Courageous and calm. That should be my prayer. I should repeat that, repeat it like the Buddhists with their "O jewel of the lotus". Repeat it till it repeats itself in my very heart, till every heartbeat drives it through my whole body. Courageous and calm. This is the world, think no more about it.

My chair will keep me sane. My chair, my chair, my chair—I might almost repeat that. I know every mark on it, every grain. So near and true! It alone predicates a Universe, the entire Universe, with its tough carpentering, its sprightly, shapely design—so delicate, so strong. And while I have the game I need be afraid of nothing. Though it is dangerous. Tempting, dangerous, but—it is enough to know that the joy is mine. I set the chair down in the snow, letting myself think I am going to sleep, but instead of sitting I step back a few paces into the snow. How did I think of that? The first time, I did not dare look away from it. I had never before let it out of my hand, never let it go for a fraction between unbuckling it and sitting down on it. But then I let it go and stepped back into the snow. I had never heard my voice before. I was astonished at the sound that struggled up out of me. Well, I need the compensations. And this game does rouse my energies, so it is, in a sense, quite practical. After the game, I could run. That's the moment of danger, though, the moment of overpowering impatience when I could easily lose control and break out, follow my instinct, throw myself on luck, run out across the wind.

But there is a worse danger. If I ran out across the wind I would pretty soon come to my senses, turn my face back into the wind. It is the game itself, the stage of development it has reached, that is dangerous now. I no longer simply step back. I set the chair down, turn my face away and walk off into the blizzard, counting my steps carefully. At fourteen paces I stop. Fifteen is the limit of vision in this dense flow of snow, so at fourteen I stop, and turn. Let those be the rules. Let me fix the game at that. Because at first I see nothing. That should be enough for me. Everywhere, pouring silent grey, a silence like a pressure, like the slow coming to bear of some incalculable pressure, too gradual to detect. If I were simply to stand there my mind would crack in a few moments. But I concentrate, I withdraw my awe from the emptiness and look pointedly into it. At first, everything is as usual—as I have seen it for five months. Then my heart begins to thump unnaturally, because I seem to make out a dimness, a shadow that wavers deep in the grey turmoil, vanishes and darkens, rises and falls. I step one pace forward and using all my will-power stop again. The shadow is as it was. Another step. The shadow seems to be a little darker. Then it vanishes and I lunge two steps forward but immediately stop because there it is, quite definite, no longer moving. Slowly I walk towards it. The rules are that I keep myself under control, that I restrain all sobs or shouts though of course it is impossible to keep the breathing regular—at this stage at least, and right up to the point where the shadow resolves into a chair. In that vast grey dissolution—my chair! The snowflakes are drifting against the legs and gliding between the struts, bumping against them, clinging and crawling over the seat. To control myself then is not within human power. Indeed I seem to more or less lose consciousness at that point. I'm certainly not responsible for the weeping, shouting thing that falls on my chair, embracing it, kissing it, bruising his cheeks against it. As the snowflakes tap and run over my gloves and over the chair I begin to call them names. I peer into each one as if it were a living face, full of speechless recognition, and I call to them—Willy, Joanna, Peter, Jesus, Ferdinand, anything that comes into my head, and shout to them and nod and laugh. Well, it's harmless enough madness.

The temptation to go beyond the fourteen paces is now becoming painful. To go deep into the blizzard. Forty paces. Then come back, peering. Fifteen paces, twenty paces. Stop. A shadow.

That would not be harmless madness. If I were to leave my chair like that the chances are I would never find it again. My footprints do not exist in this undertow of snow. Weeks later, I would still be searching, casting in great circles, straining at every moment to pry a shadow out of the grey sameness. My chair meanwhile a hundred miles away in the blizzard, motionless—neat legs and elegant back, sometimes buried, sometimes uncovering again. And for centuries, long after I'm finished, still sitting there, intact with its toothmarks and missing strut, waiting for a darkening shape to come up out of the nothingness and shout to it and fall on it and possess it.

But my chair is here, on my back, here. There's no danger of my ever losing it. Never so long as I keep control, keep my mind firm. All the facts are on my side. I have nothing to do but endure.

ROBERT CREELEY

(1926-   )

Robert Creeley was born in Massachusetts and lived in New England in his youth. The Second World War carried him to India and Burma; afterward he travelled across the United States and abroad, especially in France and Spain. His fiction reflects his belief that writing is not simply a controlled response to experience. It is, instead, a demonstration of the fact of co-existence: while the writer is using experience for his own purposes, he in turn is being used, so that a story is always more than he intended it to be. There is, one might say, a kind of reciprocity agreement at work. One of the best introductions to the work of Robert Creeley is his own Preface to THE GOLD DIGGERS:

Had I lived some years ago, I think I would have been a moralist, i.e., one who lays down, so to speak, rules of behavior with no small amount of self-satisfaction. But the writer isn't allowed that function anymore, or no man can take the job on very happily, being aware (as he must be) of what precisely that will make him.

So there is left this other area, still the short story or really the tale, and all that can be made of it. Whereas the novel is a continuum, of necessity, chapter to chapter, the story can escape some of that obligation, and function exactly in terms of whatever emotion best can serve it.

The story has no time finally. Or it hasn't here. Its shape, if form can be so thought of, is a sphere, an egg of obdurate kind. The only possible reason for its existence is that it has, in itself, the fact of reality and the pressure. There, in short, is its form—no matter how random and broken that will seem. The old assumptions of beginning and end—those very neat assertions—have fallen way completely in a place where the only actuality is life, the only end (never realised) death, and the only value, what love one can manage.

It is impossible to think otherwise, or at least I have found it so. I begin where I can, and end when I see the whole thing returning. Perhaps that is an obsession. These people, and what happens to them here, have never been completely my decision—because if you once say something, it will lead you to say more than you had meant to.

As the man responsible, I wanted to say what I thought was true, and make that the fact. It has led me to impossible things at times. I was not obliged, certainly, to say anything, but that argument never made sense to me.

R. C.

The Boat

No one was moving but for William, and they paid him little attention. He came, now, down through the trees, and behind them, very carefully, to a huge rock that overlooked the water. The boat was too far out to see who was in it, but the sails looked beautiful, tight out and driving the boat through the water in a series of chopped lunges. He climbed up on the rock, took a stick he found there, and leaning out, dabbled it in the water. He wrote his own name three times, then his wife's, then those of their three children.

Way off up the field Mrs. Peter had talked of the weather, and she repeated herself, endlessly. The heat came, the sun rising very high and white in the sky, and beyond the field the trees in the orchard looked wilted and dull. She cried. Her face grew very tiny and alone, and with a sense of relief the other man, her friend, bent over quietly with a white handkerchief and dabbed at her eyes. He implored her to have reason, the conversation had been so tiring, and if they were to be together, ultimately, they must have the necessary courage. But she cried again, until her face was wet, and he held the handkerchief on her cheeks, rubbing them, hopelessly involved to be sure, but some small part of him seemed heroic and manly, and that was the part she looked to.

William, on the rock, knew nothing much more than the heat,

and if the sun got any higher, he said, he would lose his mind entirely. The trees rustled slightly, the wind went past them with a murmur, but it was a hot wind, and William crawled down lower on the
rock to wet his face in the water. And feeling it cool, he quickly took
off his clothes and left them there, and jumped in.

All this the children were aware of, and in the boat they prepared to attack him, not sullenly, but as quickly as he had thought
to go into the water like that, they as well saw him and wanted to
surprise him by bearing down on him with the boat. They tacked,
and the boat shuddered. For a minute the smallest boy's legs were
covered with the foam, and he shouted to them all to look. But coming off, the boat righted itself, and again they watched William who
swam beyond them.

Hence, in a vague way, it was all, Mrs. Peter said, a question
of the heat. William could not hear her, he would not have heard
her in any circumstances, but to her friend, recovered, the comment
was apt and sensible. Weather as an inexhaustible subject, or he answered her, that this as well they would have to consider, and above
all its effects on William's nerves. The right time would be precisely
the time when, at an impasse with everything, and with, particularly,
the heat, he should no longer give much of a damn about anything,
and if he did treasure her, or anything, even so would give it all up
quietly enough.

Supposition, she said, was not accurate. The wind blew. But to
be in love was to be something, and if heat were elemental, they
were likewise of nature's force.

It was a ridiculous time for anything. She couldn't really say
that she loved him, and had to think quickly, which one. Her friend
looked at her, her eyes were a little red but the face was not for him.
He took her hand, because he wanted something, and she let the
pressure come, then relax, and squeezed back a little and smiling,
wondered again what would become of them.

William was not the question, she knew, or at least she thought
it, and then kissed the other man, in almost trite fashion, saying it
is very like it always is. And, do I now think what I think because I
think other people have thought it. For this there was no reply, the
kiss being remote, and very near insult. The speech anyhow a question, which the friend wanted to answer, but could not. He dressed
in a loose shirt, worn outside of his pants, and with a check-like design. The pants were brown, something like khaki. He had black

hair, and a small clipped beard on the end of his chin. To be romantic was to be insular in one's concern for others, and in love he acted as though he were looking in a mirror.

Against all that, viciously, the boat went on and in it the children hung one to the rudder, and one to the jib lines, while the third kept hold of the rope for the boom, and sighted William for the one sitting behind him. They were almost there. William's head showed itself a little off to the right, and with a sudden push, the rudder went over, and they were on top of him.

At that moment he saw them, and why he hadn't before, or heard them, he had no time to think of, but dove, the boat's bottom hitting his head. He went down and down, and in spite of it, thought of them all up there, on the surface. The boat had gone over, the water again grew light, and from his mouth a very thin line of little bubbles. Time passed, the weeds shone blue and green in the depth, the mud felt cool and close on his body. Then he gave a push with his feet and felt them sink in, then lift, and then he swam, up, and broke the water with a kind of gasped cry.

They were on the shore, and called out to him, and he answered by a wave of his hand and swam to them, slowly, feeling his head ache but had no resentment. The three children were there, the boat was now anchored and the sails rolled up, and tied. The rudder had been taken off, and lay across the back of the boat, drying. At the top of the mast a small red flag flapped in the breeze and the boat lifted and dropped in the ground-swell.

It was very lovely, he thought, but even more, this immediate solicitation, and pulling himself out of the water, he let himself fall into their hands, and be carried all the long distance to the house, as the friend took the bulk of the load by holding him under the armpits, gently, and lifting him very carefully so as not to joggle his head. He swore at the children, and they came behind him, somewhat afraid. He made no conditions, the sound of his own voice was ugly, or seemed ugly, to him. When he had been lowered to the sofa, he wanted to cry, and let them see it. But their faces were too far away, and he found himself asleep.

He dreamt of three tigers, in a forest. Their bodies were striped as he had expected. Their faces were long, with, on each one, a red tongue lolling out over white teeth. He gave a banana to each one of them. They ate the bananas, and put the skins to one side, whereupon he grew frightened, shifted his position, and began to snore.

Mrs. Peter continued with the business in hand, and she had no doubt that it was, despite the difficulties, an act that could be transacted as elaborately and as completely as the buying of potatoes. In the garden, she drew up a chair, close to the friend whom the matter of the boat had frightened. He felt himself now an outsider, or, more simply, unable to recover his own place with quite the same manipulation. To quiet him, she took off her sun-hat and began to fan herself, then fanned him, so that the moving air lifted the collar of his shirt, which he had left unbuttoned to the middle of his chest, and blew it against his beard.

Now, she said, that there is quiet, now we can settle all of this. He raised himself to listen, and to say what he himself would have to. She said, do you love me. To that, certainly, he replied, yes. They kissed.

But, she said, being married and all, does it matter to you that another man has had my love. And that was not a fair question. The woman who loves is beyond it, she does not see anything more than what she does have, just there and then, in front of her nose. He said, if it does not matter to you, it does not matter to me.

It was enough, and might have been for anyone else, but not for her. She wanted to go away, a long voyage, or anything to get away from him, and from both of them. Well, she said, I love you, but you don't love me. For my own part I think we are not so much in love as I had thought, but, seeing that we have no reason to hurry, take a walk to the beach, and in an hour I will come and join you.

Once he was gone, she went back into the house to look at William. He lay with an arm down over the edge of the sofa, and she could see the place where the boat had hit him. The bruise began at the edge of his hair, back of his ear, then went into the hair itself. It all looked swollen and painful. But she was not sure that she loved him.

If she whistled, or cried out, one of the two might come. Otherwise, she then thought, I have three children. Who would have killed their father this morning, and not even meant to do it.

So it was impossible not to think about life, or the sense of the kind of life she herself might find possible. The room came in, a picture of her own father, or someone, hung at an odd angle over the cold fireplace. There was no fire and yet she screamed. But did not scream. In the emptiness she saw William coming toward her, carrying an oar. He was about to found a city.

As an alternative she left the room, and went out again into the garden. The remains of their lunch were still there, and, over the plates, she saw a swarm of flies. Looking past them, she saw a brief-case, on the seat of a chair, with gold initials just over the lock. She went over and picked it up, and tried to open it, but could not, and threw it back in the chair in anger. It was the life of a dead man, not to have kindness, and openness, in each person met or dealt with. To have secrets was finally to have desires, and if she could not sat-isfy them, to keep them like that was dishonest. She picked up the briefcase again and threw it into a bed of yellow flowers. What she gave was open, and all air, she thought. But for them it was the careful locking up of each particular, because they thought they were men.

The children used another way of things, and taking in the friend, now they played with him, and soon he was exhausted, pant-ing after them, foolishly, up and down the beach. He had taken off his shirt, but they ran too fast, and if he caught one, another sud-denly pelted him with a handful of sand, and, in trying to see which had done it, he lost hold of the one he had had, and found his eyes full of sand and tears.

He wanted her to come very badly, he saw their future life to-gether floating over his head, and, as the wind might take it, blown away from him. He indulged in this metaphor, and was like a man lost in himself completely. If he wanted her, then, he thought, it must be that they leave together right away. To have the children, he said, and a stone hit him, and a small spot of blood appeared on the inner side of his ankle.

Mrs. Peter watched all this, and again was powerless. But, com-ing down, she told the children to stop, and from their own audacity, which they felt they had perhaps taken too far, they stopped, and ran down the beach and out of sight. Then she said, love me, very simply. And, as she asked it, he brushed off his pants, and came to her, and then led her back to the field, where they lay down. I want you to be for me, she said, but she hated him. As his hands touched her, she felt cold finally, and thanked him for that.

QUESTIONS

1. In the section entitled "Theme," we mentioned the critical view that sees all drama, fiction, and narrative verse structure in terms of a beginning-middle-end. Robert Creeley, on the other hand, sees the short story as a form so dominated by "single effect" that it has no "beginning" and no "end." It is, so to speak, all "middle." To what extent does his story, "The Boat," conform to this concept of total unity? Is it possible to break his narrative down into these three parts? Perhaps Creeley means that beginning-middle-end is a mechanical organization of narrative, and that the short story's single effect should predominate over it. Try to state what that effect is in "The Boat." To do that, you will have to analyze such individual elements as character, action, setting, atmosphere, and theme. Obviously, single effect is a complex matter. Nevertheless, an effort to define it here may lead us to a better understanding of the story, as well as to a surer grasp of what Creeley means when he says that such an effect is more important than traditional three-part structure.

2. One of the unusual aspects of "The Boat" is the apparent incompleteness of the characters. They have physical outlines, but their personalities are suggested rather than fully developed. This is especially true of the husband, William, and the nameless lover, whom we seem to view from a distance. The wife, Mrs. Peter, is more carefully drawn, and her thoughts and emotions dominate the story. But even she seems uncertain about the nature of her relationships and desires. Nor is there a clear resolution of the action, just as there was no clear beginning to it. We seem to have rounded unexpectedly upon a scene already under way, and we are forced to leave before anything decisive happens. In effect, we are left hanging in mid-air, at least in terms of plot. Without a plot that ties everything up into a neat bundle, and with figures that are little more than outlines, the story is likely to leave us feeling frustrated and bemused. It may be that the narrative's uncertainty is intended to be an important part of its effect. Approach the story from the standpoint of theme to see if that clarifies matters. The story's theme, in turn, should perhaps be approached through point of view. Where does the narrative focus of the story lie? After you have worked with each of these problems separately, try to put them together to arrive at some statement of the story's total effect.

DOUGLAS WOOLF

(1922-   )

*Born in Manhattan, Woolf grew up there and in New England. He
served in the Second World War as ambulance driver and navigator.
Since his return to the United States he has led an itinerant existence,
seldom settling down for more than a year at any one place. In the
process he picked up a degree at the University of New Mexico and
wrote "five novels, two now too true, John-Juan and Ya! That's better than eulogized slavery." These novels, and his short stories, were
the product of what he called "twenty part-time years of picking berries, etc., and peddling ice cream, etc." while searching for that
will-o'-the-wisp, personal freedom, in an age of over-population, in-
dustrialization, and technology. "The Flyman" confronts us directly
with the ennui characteristic of life in the Twentieth Century. Modern times have perverted the concept of work, so that it is no longer
an expression of the individual, no longer an art: "The art of working, whether with the hands or with language, is a true one. At least
I have found it so in my own life and writing." The result is George
Nader, who looks forward eagerly to nine long months of winter in
St. Paul.*

The Flyman

When the moving men had shoved and strapped the last piece, the
last slippery convenience, inside the moving van, George Nader
looked about him with very little sense of loss, for everything that
remained, the flypaper, the swatters, and he believed the turtle bowl,

was his. Had Zoe been divorcing him and taking along her legal property as dowry to another man, the division of goods would have been exactly this, except of course that she would then have been leaving George himself behind to enjoy the pure, seeming inconvenience of the house. He would never know what time it was: only sit at the back-door and watch the cactus shadows on the sand outside, perhaps noting whether the sun or the moon was moving them. With the hours thus confused there would be no prompt, rude guests to demand his silent presence in the livingroom; their polished mahogany cage would be gone, not to mention their electricity. He would look without commitment at the mirrorless walls, for the loathsome electric razor would be buzzing the fuzz on some other cheek or the stubble underneath Zoe's arms. He would sleep, night or day, in the built-in bathtub, and survive on grapefruit and oranges and the neighbors' eggs. Delighted with such pictures, smiling upon Zoe's swollen rear, he took up a handy swatter and brandished it enchantingly until the men returned.

What he liked about the moving men was their pride in being watched. They spoke in low rough voices, cursing only humorously when his flypaper caught them up, pausing occasionally in their work to compliment Zoe upon this piece or that but once outside tossing her furniture quite insultingly among them as though it were simply so much stuff which they alone knew the real value of. At the very first, when they had stood in the livingroom wondering where to begin, he had said, "Take everything with faces, or legs," and had settled in a chair to watch how nicely it worked out that way, with the exception of a few planters of ivy and the pasteboard boxes of odds and ends, until they had taken the chair itself from under him. "Easy now," he had standing said, and when they smiled expectantly as though hoping he had found some failure in their work: "Everything but me, that is." And now he stood grinning as they shoved respectfully past Zoe at the door, where she hoped her presence would urge them to use a little more care, less skill, in their wild slippery sprint to the van, but as the van door cracked shut he sobered his face for her turn to him.

"Looks different, doesn't it?" he quickly said, not in sympathy or even sincerity but only wanting to take the words from her pursing mouth. "Bleak?"

"It does, it does," she agreed, forced to it, but hastily regained herself: "We filled two-thirds of a van, you know."

"Big baby too," he shot.

"It was," said Zoe.

He looked fiercely away from her fuzzy head, to the grey, permanent shadow of the departed television-radio. What had she expected of him once, that he had not given her? He supposed that at first it had been children, although as a struggling, wild-eyed veteran his reasons had been entirely economic, plausible, and she had agreed with him. Only in time, as he progressed, had the question become less economic than eugenic, and she had agreed again. How could she not. For it had grown increasingly clear that no child of his could have the common view, or chance. Today the question was no longer asked, yet he felt that secretly, in whatever depths she had, Zoe would have welcomed the pleasures of an abortion, the living proof that in fact she could create. Few men would help her prove it now, he and time had taken care of that. So they had settled on an easier enmity, as less harrowing, more mentionable, her loss of the housewife's sweet dependence which he had so easily usurped for himself. Deprived of her empty days, Zoe had filled her nights with appliances. Looked at in this way the unwieldy procession which he had just witnessed could not be said to betoken Zoe's unfathered children so much as a bitter, accurate accounting of Zoe's paychecks, and this cynical view of it made him able to turn to her again. "Wait until we get up north," Zoe said.

"Oh, wait." He followed her zigzag course toward the kitchen, even he finding it oddly difficult to avoid the flypaper strips with the furniture no longer there to inhibit him, and he fancied he heard soft curses among Zoe's fat breaths. Watching her unwind from a gummy strip, he felt himself struck by a change in her appearance, the first he could recall in years. It was as though the moving men had carted off not only her movables but her very makeup itself, that pink, almost livid glaze with which she regularly hid from him and all the world the face he had loved twelve, maybe fifteen years before. And seeing in this abrupt way how dry and sucked of life she was, finally justifying her endeavor to look like anyone else but Zoe, he felt a sudden terror of time and reached his hand to her. "Zoe."

Zoe took his hand.

"I'm sorry, Zoe."

She patted it, and now he watched her puffy fingers drape gummed paper along the soft, freckled flesh of his outstretched arm

until it clung to the hairs there securely enough for her to draw free
of it. Looking up from dead and drying flies, he saw her bright black
eyes twinkle with something between defiance and disgust. "Why
this?"

"Because," she said. "It's yours, isn't it?"

"Ah." His hand shot sidewise for a buzzing fly, caught it effortlessly in mid-flight and tossed it stunned to the floor for his ready
foot to quash. There had been a time when Zoe would have watched
this exhibition with genuine admiration, but today she turned
sharply off as though he had belched or gassed the place. Well, as
the doctor said, some men hate Mexicans and Republicans, some
beat their wives.

"George, promise you'll have it all cleared out when I get back?"

"Back?"

"From the market, George."

He suddenly smiled, at the picture of them following that two-
thirds van of conveniences through eighteen hundred miles of ice
and snow and stopping from time to time to eat cold canned goods
beside the road. Certainly he would not build a fire, and he could not
imagine heat from a fire of Zoe's. This was not a new thought, but
he added to it now the one that Zoe would surely have packed the
can opener away in the kitchen appliance box, and he spoke hurriedly lest she too might think of it. "You hurry right along," he said.
"I'll take care of everything."

"Well . . ." He followed once more as she zagged through the
kitchen, the front room, the hall, somehow this time escaping en-
tanglement but turning finally at the front door to seek her purse.
With all the furniture gone, there was nowhere for Zoe to hunt. Even
at best, things had been, as he thought, fuzzy around their home.
For Zoe's talents were almost purely operative, or rather her affini-
ties: she was a superlative driver of automobiles, unhampered by
any comprehension of what made them run; she could twirl painful
clarity from television sets, just so long as their extension cords and
socket plugs were good; and of course over both their lives loomed
that cryptically initialed machine, monstrously dialed, with which
she made airplane parts whose names and places she did not know.
Otherwise there was that fuzziness, that flapping, searching, be-
seeching, wasted fuss which made him grind his teeth and wince.
But we do not hate people, he recalled, not even for enduring us, and

grinned a wistful grin at Zoe before turning his attention to his papered arm. "Look on the mantel piece," he said, and imagining Zoe's bleak glare of thanks waved his swatter graciously.

He felt her departure in much the same way that he felt the fly-paper tear free of his hair and flesh, as a paradox of pain, relief. He tensed to the chattering porch, to the car's whamming doors, to the pitiable whine of a young motor overtaxed and finally to the smoth-ering cloud of dust that seeped through the fine-meshed screens, yet he was glad. When he turned it was almost as though Zoe had really left, scattering her own ashes behind her over the neighborhood; in twenty minutes, he knew, she would be back to stir them up again.

Meanwhile he did not mind too much what he had to do. It was the thought alone that had almost paralyzed him, when the furniture and Zoe had still been there, the thought of tearing down all his ingenious, tactically flawless stations without the possibility or ne-cessity of ever replacing them. But now in the empty house his de-fenses hung like so much random paper, forlornly grouped, disor-ganized. What he did, quickly, was start at the front door and work his way in as nearly a straight line as possible along the south wall, yanking flypapers as he came to them and draping them in careless yet attractive disarray over the handle of the swatter which he still held. Then quickly back along the other wall and crisscross here and there about the room. When he had filled his swatter he reached for another, presently a third, but half a fourth finished the living-room. The bedroom and kitchen yielded two swattersful apiece, one each for the bathroom, pantry, hall. Back in the livingroom he stuck his entire collection upended in the empty turtle bowl. Gathering the remaining, unused swatters, he added them one by one with flourishes to his bouquet, stood back to pass on it.

He was glad to have found some use for the turtle bowl. It had not worked at all. Despite weeks of enthusiastic experimentation, under the most favorable conditions he could devise, George had never known a turtle to catch a fly. Place twelve flies within two hun-gry turtles overnight in a covered bowl, and in the morning twelve unmolested flies emerge. Put syrup on a turtle's nose, a fly may eat his sweets in peace. It did not work! Only if you dropped a fly into a turtle's water would it partake, and George refused to offer such sacrifices, dead or alive, simply that a turtle might stuff himself. He donated his turtles to the neighborhood and turned his attention to new pursuits. Chronologically the gyrotraps had come next after the turtle failure, and it was these he would attend to as soon as he had disposed of the mess in the turtle bowl.

Most weekends he did not go outside, except very briefly at lizard rotation times, for these were George Ingersoll's days at home. Not that he disliked the other George, he simply did not like the sense of driving him indoors. There had been a time when their weekends had been quite otherwise, they had become almost more than neighbors, finding several dependable interests in common such as their handicaps (mostly physical for the other George), their memories of beautiful, terrible northern winters which in past years they had somehow both survived, and more particularly their memory of North Africa and its big, blood-sucking flies which a man could look down upon, whether feeding on his own sores or on a corpse of whatever nationality, and say this is Evil, it isn't the Jerries after all. They had of course also had their common dismay at finding themselves banished by doctors to another Africa, a New World Sahara, their sense of loneliness and exile in this wasted land and their exasperated fascination with its flora, fauna and insect life. Weekends they had fought the desert together side by side in their backyards, tearing up its cactus and tumbleweed, coupling their two hoses to lay its dust, attacking its blackwidows, scorpions, flies with lethal insecticides, all the while offering bitter, gasping encouragement to one another across the fence. But soon it had become clear that their intensities were not the same, that one could be satisfied with a mere surface tidiness that the other fiercely disdained. George Ingersoll spent more and more time resting on his canvas chairs, now looking contentedly at his swept backyard, now at George, his occasional shouted encouragement grown amused, polite. A certain restraint had grown between them as nowadays it so easily did (people no longer visited the Naders, they came in small explorative groups instead) and it ended with their reverting to a neighborly distrustfulness. George understood. The other still had the so-called job, was employable, while George himself had long ago lost the benign effects of the six-day purge. He understood, yet it surely hurt him that his neighbor no longer showed sympathy for what he was trying to do, neither took time to enquire about his experiments nor looked at them. Thus he was surprised, or a little angry, to find George on this last day lingering outside, hanging on the fence above the rubbish cans which they had found it easiest to continue sharing stealthily. "Morning George . . . Ah morning George." They performed this ceremony solemnly, each glancing sidewise to see if the other still smiled at it. Neither did, though with George Ingersoll it was hard to say, for pain and the desert sun had long ago combined to draw back the brittle skin around his mouth into a permanent grimace. Whenever George looked up at him he was unpleasantly aware of his own soft juiciness. "Hello, George," he said again, and falsely coughed. "How have you been?"

"Oh fine, fine," George Ingersoll said, and now he did appear to smile at a ghastly joke. "And you?"

George also smiled. "Haven't seen you around much, George," he said, at the last minute muffling the "for a year or two."

"Yes, been busy inside," was said. There was a pause, while George tugged at the stubborn garbage lid. "Well, Zoe's transfer came through at last?"

"Yes, it came through," George said, banging the lid with his free fist.

"Give it one on the other side," George Ingersoll advised, and George gave it a brutal one. "No, one on the side of the *top*," and George belabored it everywhere. He put down the turtle bowl, grasped the lid handle with both big hands and lifted the entire barrel off the ground, shaking it furiously from side to side. But we do not take out our anger on inanimate objects, and cursing he let the whole thing drop. The lid bounced off. "Ah," he said, swatters clattering in.

"I wouldn't mind having that bowl, if you're done with it."

George passed the bowl over his shoulder, over the fence. "It's no good," he said, wiping his hands of it.

"Looks like just the thing for Miriam's fish."

"'Oh fish—I never did try fish."

George Ingersoll patted the bowl. "I don't suppose you'll need any of this, up north?"

"No, none of it."

Still patting, George Ingersoll glanced at his neighbor's yard, then shamefully away again. "What about your lizards, George?"

George, who had stooped for the garbage lid, straightened quickly to the sidewise face. "You'd like them, George?"

"No no no, just curious."

"Ah." George came down hard, jamming the lid back on for George.

"I don't suppose they'd live through the winter there, even if you needed them?"

George shook his head, and it was almost as though he were shivering.

George Ingersoll too looked cold. "George, what does the doctor say?"

"The doctor? Not much—it might be good for me." Probably what the doctor had said to Zoe was that anything, even painful death, could be considered a benefice. But the doctor was no medical man, George had long ago passed them. "They say there's work up there, you know."

"I certainly hope so, George." When they looked briefly at one another now, it was almost in their old way, with common memories. George Ingersoll put out his hand. "I certainly hope the change of climate is good for you."

"Well, thanks, George," he said, taking the knotty hand reluctantly in his own soft freckled one. What he would like to have known before he took it was whether his eyes blurred at the sympathy of a friend or at the certain euphemisms of a hypocrite.

"We'll certainly miss you, George."

"Oh, well now," George said, and it almost blinded him, his dubious sentiment. He yanked free his hand to wheel away. "*Well* now, George."

"I certainly . . ." Fortunately some of the Ingersoll children were fighting now, and hugging the turtle bowl George moved to disentangle them. "I'll see you, George."

Oh oh oh, will you now, George thought, stalking quickly along the fence to the garage, the shop. He emptied the wheelbarrow of rusty tools and dragged it wickedly to the shop's locked door. He had the key, had it at all times on a string looped around his belt. Quickly inside, he swung the door on howling Ingersolls. Two years ago he had papered the ceiling and walls with flypaper (no paste, no waste, the flies make their own design) but now in the broken light of the one narrow window he noted how the ceiling curled and peeled, the walls writhed disgustingly, their glue had dried. The place smelled greyly of dust and wings, nor did the 200-watt ceiling lamp do much to clear the atmosphere. As it turned out, he would not have to redecorate.

His inventions lay everywhere, on the benches and shelves, and on the floor. These were mostly the gyrotraps, tiny razor-blade fans which he had connected in series to a motor salvaged from a Lionel train. Each fan was designed to fit snugly into a No. 2 can liberally coated with marmalade. (These had worked, although their blades required daily honing and from time to time their shafts would gum.) Then too there was the syrup door: a delicate device which the weight of three inverted flies could trip, slamming them against a red brick wall. (There were only three of these, for he had been unable to make them react to the weight of a single fly, and it had tormented him to think how many strays escaped.) There were several examples of the Infallible Fly Bath, simply a solution of molasses and hydrochloric acid (which he made himself by combining sulphuric acid with common table salt) in small glass tubes. These had worked very satisfactorily indeed, until neighbors began to understand what was happening to the noses of their cats. So it did not bother him very much to dump everything in a box and wheel it out for the garbage man. He did at the last minute leave one example of each behind, on the slim chance that some future scientist might find them a starting point, a useful groundwork for further exploration in the field. Not that this possibility greatly moved him either, for in his heart he knew that with the lizards he had come as close to a final answer to the problem as any man could, or would.

Here at last was what did hurt, having to gather his beer bottles now at the very time when he had finally perfected a formula for their rotation, a formula based on the observed frequency of flies at a given location at a given hour of a given day, as modified by such known variables as temperature, cloud covering, wind, humidity, and taking into account too such intangibles as the probable traumatic effects upon flies of his increasingly devastating war against their kind. Yet if the rotation formula was a marvel of deviousness, the trap itself was almost casual in its simplicity. Squeeze a small, vaselined lizard into an empty beer bottle, feed him just enough flies to prevent his escape; now coat the bottle mouth with almost anything at all, and wait. (No electricity, no mechanical parts, after a few days at large a lizard may be used again.) He gathered the bottles quickly but gently, arranging them in neat tiers in the wheelbarrow, and he wheeled them smoothly out over the desert to a rock he knew. There he cracked each of the forty-eight bottles with deft little taps, being careful that the lizards were not cut by the broken glass. Even at that, and despite his practice of selecting his lizards for healthiness, one lizard had succumbed. Impossible to say how many flies he had taken first, although in death he did look well-satisfied. George buried him. Now he stood for a while watching the others stagger over the desert, their bloated bodies unwieldy on their stiff short legs. Facing his wheelbarrow toward the house, he steered with care among his glutted friends. Ahead Zoe's dust was in the air, and Zoe herself waited at the kitchen door for him. "You did a nice job," she said.

"Thanks, Zoe."

"All ready now?"

Silently he looked about his experimental yard, a desert once again. He raised his eyes to an evilly buzzing fly, too high for him, and he did not move or speak until it came back again. He did not snare it at once but watched it cautiously circle his head, allowing it this last time the appearance of teasing him. When it finally settled on a freckled arm, he picked it off and held it out to view. "When you are, Zoe."

"Oh, why don't you get in the car," she said, and she followed him.

"You've remembered everything?"

"Yes."

It almost seemed she had. The canned goods lay boxed in the front seat, a shiny new opener visible. He knew their bags had been in the trunk for several days, and climbing into the car, into the back, he could smell the sweet insecticide. Despite the noonday temperature, all windows were tightly shut. He smiled at how narrowly Zoe opened the driver's door, how nearly flat she squeezed, how quickly she slammed once she was in.

"Mind if I open a window, Zoe?"

"Please, let's not."

"It's hot in here."

"It's hot everywhere."

"It smells."

"Let's wait until we're underway, at least," as the motor howled.

"Ah." Outside, George Ingersoll was leading his wife forward to see them off, and Zoe stopped the car to point the friendly neighbors out to George. All arms were raised; with the windows up the pantomimic mouths could have said anything, oh-oh-oh perhaps. Now the saving children must have yelled, for the Ingersolls turned their wagging heads and ran. Releasing brakes, Zoe gaily blotted out the farewell scene.

"Now?"

"Wait until we're on the highway, George."

So he sat waiting, his eyes closed to the dusty light, his breath almost closed off too, until he felt the car spring free of sand and heard the tires take up their gleeful howl on a highway paved with kitten fur. "Now, Zoe?"

"Oh, *wait*."

But he leaned forward anyway, not toward the window but toward the driver's seat, his hand going up. He might have slapped down on her then and there, had Zoe not caught the movement in her overhead looking glass. He hung there rigidly.

"Did you see one, George?"

"No."

"Well, please remember our frontseat rule."

"Sorry, Zoe." Leaning back again, tilting his head to rest, he continued to look at Zoe. But from the lower edges of his sight he could see his great short-sleeved spotty arms, folded across his chest, and from the fuzzy edges of his consciousness could hear his big hands slapping quietly.

"What now?" Zoe wanted to know.

"Don't worry, Zoe." He watched her shaking head. "You're happy, Zoe."

"Well?"

"No, I'm glad for you," he said. His hands were working harder now, moving rhythmically and conscientiously from freckle to freckle over his juicy arms, as Zoe turned round to him. Slap slap slap, he answered her. "I'm really glad for you."

"The temperature in St. Paul last night was two below."

"Oh, it was? Below?"

"Snow is probably falling now."

"It *is?*"

In her looking glass she smiled at him. "They say the winters are nine months long."

"That's all right," he said, and also smiled, for he would have lots to do.

MICHAEL RUMAKER

(1932-)

Michael Rumaker was born in Philadelphia and grew up in New Jersey, one of a large family of Irish-Polish Catholics. He was graduated from Black Mountain College in 1955, where his short stories appeared in the BLACK MOUNTAIN REVIEW. In 1959 several of his stories were published as a group in SHORT STORY 2; in 1962 he published a novel, THE BUTTERFLY. His most recent book is a collection of the best of his short stories, GRINGOS AND OTHER STORIES. Like Douglas Woolf, he spent some time wandering across the United States, and his stories reflect these peregrinations. His focus is on small groups of characters, among whom there is often one who has a sense of the poetic about him: the Hamlet-like William in "The Desert," for example, or Marrie in "The Bar." Rarely do these figures have any kind of permanent abode. They are drifters, fugitives, wanderers without a home, characters whom Rumaker catches in a moment of particular intensity. One of the dominant qualities of his narratives is concreteness. This quality is deceptive, however, for Rumaker intends the concrete world to appeal to the subconscious as well as to the conscious mind, to elicit responses from the deeper layers of thought and feeling. This effort seems peculiarly successful in "The Pipe."

The Pipe

Five men stood around the mouth of the big corrugated pipe. The length of the pipe, propped on wooden planks and bolted crosswise, stretched in a wavering line over the flat, sun-baked mud of the land, dipped about a hundred yards on over the edge of the bluff and could be seen, from where the men stood, trailing in a thin, black line across the beach far below and running on stilts out over the water to the dredgeboat anchored in mid-river. The sky was light green from the intense heat of a sun that beat down unmercifully on the broad level land. Flat acres of bleached clay, hardened and cracked in huge irregular slabs curled at the edges, billowed up heavy waves of shimmering, colorless heat. A flock of chicken hawks, wings taut and motionless, wheeled slowly high overhead. There was not a tree or a cloud in sight. The men were silent. Their rubber boots sank ankle deep into the mud and when a man shifted from one foot to the other, his boots made sucking noises. The mud spread in a wide pool around the mouth of the pipe.

One of the men, Alex, his face dark brown under the brim of his hat, pulled out a pocket watch. He glanced at the dial, then snapped the lid shut and thrust the watch back in his pocket. Shading his eyes with one hand, he looked out over the river to where the dredge-boat lay anchored.

"What time is it?" Carp said.

"The blow's just about due."

"I wish to hell they'd hurry it up. I'm sweating my balls off. Not a breeze. No nothing."

Carp's face and hands were burned red from the sun. The skin was peeling from his cheeks and around his neck. He kept picking off pieces of the loose flesh and rolled them into little balls between his thumb and forefinger. He dropped these pellets in the mud between his boots.

"Just be patient," Alex said. "You'll work yourself into a lather over it. Get yourself a sunstroke to boot. Why can't you be patient, like Billy there."

Billy glanced up. He was tall and thin and hatless.

"Billy's simpleminded," Carp said. "He don't feel anything. What do you feel, Billy? What're you feeling now?" he called.

"Don't torment the boy," said Alex.

"I'm a chicken hawk," Billy said, rolling his eyes to the sky.

The men chuckled.

"You see? He's a chicken hawk," Carp said. "It don't make sense."

"Billy's a queer bird all right, all right," laughed Ruby. He was short and fat and had a red bandana knotted around his throat. He wore a wide leather kidney belt with a big silver buckle and studded with brass rivets. There was a big floppy felt hat on his head that covered half his face.

"I'm a chicken hawk," Billy repeated.

"Hey, Billy, like this?" Ruby started flapping his arms like a bird.

"Never you mind."

Ruby laughed, fluttering his arms, his belly shaking. He winked at Billy. Billy looked away.

"Me and you, Billy," he chuckled. "Birds of a kidney."

His face went scarlet with laughing and he had a fit of coughing and turned away, doubled up and still laughing, and fanned his face with his hat.

The men grew silent, watching the dredge-boat out on the river. Carp tore a long layer of skin off the back of his neck and began rolling it between his fingers. Bunk and Sam were standing off a little from the others. Bunk had his thumbs hitched in the loops of his belt and was sliding the sole of his boot back and forth over the mud. On his upper lip was a sore that a couple of flies buzzed around. He kept reaching up with his hand, brushing them away. Sam was big, with broad shoulders and thick arms and legs. His face was red and sweating and his dull eyes gazed listlessly out over the water.

Billy walked away from the group, beyond the pipe to where an old mud-spattered chevvy stood, its back seat torn out and that place jammed with rusty pieces of odd-shaped metal, piled almost to the ceiling and jutting out the windows. On either side of the chevvy was a handcart and a wagon made of orange crates, each filled with a couple of pieces of mud-caked metal. There were two burlap bags lying near the cart and wagon, and they were yellow with dust and bulging slightly. Billy sat down in the shade on the runningboard of the car. His cheeks were flushed and he was breathing heavily. He ran his fingers through his sweaty hair, then propped an elbow on one knee and cupped his chin in his hand.

"Penny by penny," he gasped. "Bye and bye."

"Them hawks make me nervous," snapped Carp. "Wisht to hell they'd go away."

He picked up a stone and flung it at the sky.

"You'd have to have a damned good arm to hit one of them

birds," said Alex. He pushed back his hat and wiped the sweat from his brow with a piece of flannel.

"They get on my nerves, swimming around and around up there, like they could wait forever for something dead. I wisht they'd go away."

"I'll tell them to go away, Carp," Billy said, grinning and looking up open-mouthed at the hawks. "If you want me to, Carp."

"Whatta you going to do, fly up?"

"Sure, Carp. I can talk to them."

"You're loco, Billy."

"The heat's got him," Sam said.

"No I'm not, Carp. I can fly up there and talk to them and tell them to go away if they're bothering you. Honest I can, Carp."

"Well, you go on, Billy."

"Sprout wings," snorted Ruby.

"Not today, Carp."

"Why not?"

"It's too hot."

"Smart bird."

"I'll do it tomorrow, Carp."

"Okay. That's a promise."

"I learned when I was a baby."

"Sure, Billy."

"Billy, you oughta get yourself some kind of cap," said Alex. "The sun'll affect you coming out here bareheaded."

"It's affecting him already," Ruby said. "You hear how he thinks he can fly."

"I got a cap of silver and diamonds," Billy said. "But it's too good to wear out here."

"Listen to it, will you?" sneered Carp. "Billy, you're a grown man. You oughta have more sense'n to talk like that."

"Well, I do. I bought that cap in New York City. You can't say I didn't."

"You're just making it up. When was you ever in New York City?"

"Never you mind. I'm gonna get a cap of gold next. When I get enough junk out of that pipe, that's what I'm going to do. I'm not kidding."

"Okay, Billy," Carp guffawed. "You show me."

"Well, I will."

"Whatta you do for a woman, Billy?" Ruby shouted.

"Let the boy alone," said Alex.

Carp yelled, "Oh, I bet he has wild nights with hisself, don't you, Billy?"

Billy giggled and pulled his hand over his eyes.

"The world's topsy-tursy, ain't it, Billy?" Ruby was shaking with laughter, the brim of his hat flopping up and down.

Billy snatched the hand away from his eyes.

"Why, no, sir."

"But you see things different from most people."

Billy hugged his knees with his arms, then said, "The world's round. Everybody knows that. But here," he said, his eyes moving slowly over the land, "it's flat as a checkerboard. God's lying."

"Now you be careful, Billy."

"Of what?"

"The Judgement Day. Talking about God like that, calling God a liar ain't healthy."

"It don't scare me none."

"Listen to him talk!" howled Carp. "Talking awful high and mighty, ain't you? You still a chicken hawk?"

Billy stared down at the mud.

"Don't tease me, Carp."

"I'm not teasing. I just want to know if you're still a chicken hawk, that's all."

"Well, I am if you want to know," Billy said angrily. "And tomorrow I'll fly up and tell them they annoy you."

The men burst out laughing. Bunk rubbed his hands agitatedly up and down his thighs, beating clouds of dust from his dungarees.

"Billy, you do take the cake!" he shouted.

"And I eat it, too. I like cake."

The men roared. Alex bent down at the mouth of the pipe and stuck his head in sideways, listening.

"What're they saying?" Sam asked, inching up close to Alex.

"One guy says, 'Lay off the chains'— That means the blow's about due. One guy's calling another one a bastard."

"He should if it's his fault the blow's late," Carp said.

"Something must be holding them up," Ruby said. "I sure wisht they'd hop to it. I feel like I'm being fried in deep fat."

"Well, if you feel that way, it's your own you're sizzling in," said Carp.

"Look here, Mr. Dry Bones, you're so thin I can smell the—"

"Shut up," Sam snapped. "Alex, what else they saying?"

"Nothing but racket. Nobody saying anything." Alex ducked out from the pipe and straightened up, squaring his hat straight on his head.

"Oh, come on, you last blow of the day!" Carp shouted, shaking his fist at the dredge-boat. "I want to get to Tarkie's, ditch my junk, and have me a cold bottle of beer."

"Go on and take a swim," Alex said. "Cool off."

"Not in that stinking water."

Ruby held his fingers to his nose and said, "Go on, Carp, go take a bath and give us a break."

"Be like a chemical bath," Bunk said. "Besides, the river's black with polio."

"That's Nigger Buddy's blood," Billy said, from the running-board of the car. "Nigger Buddy made the river black."

"Who's Nigger Buddy?"

"You never heard of Nigger Buddy?"

"No, I never did. Another one of your stories I guess."

"Tell them, Carp. Tell them about Nigger Buddy Carson the day he went swimming off Blower Rocks. He made the river black."

"He did no such thing," Carp said. "He never made the river black."

"What happened? Come on, Carp, tell us."

"It ain't nothing much. Hardly worth telling."

"Come on. I bet it's something good. You're being selfish keeping it to yourself."

"Oh, it's good all right," Billy said, leaning forward and rubbing his hands together. "It's the reason the river's why it is."

"Talk about the river black, Mr. Bill Big-Lie," Carp said, turning on him, "I'd like to get a squint at that soul of yours. There can't be a shade difference'n you and the river the lies you jaw."

"Well, tell them, Carp. Let them judge for themselves."

"He never *got* to the water, I tell you. He took a low dive on the rocks and smashed his head open. They had to scrape his brains off with a piece of cardboard."

"Was his brains black?" Billy said. "I never seen a nigger bare. What's it look like, Carp?"

"Carp can't tell you," Sam said, grinning and showing his long yellow teeth. "He dreamt the whole thing up."

"It's true. I was there. Seen it with my own two eyes!"

"Tall tales, tall tales," Sam sneered. "What was you doing, hiding in the grass and peeking at a naked nigger? I don't know what to think of that."

"I was fishing a little way off, you fool. You think I'm hot to see a boogie's dingle, the way Billy is?"

"What color is it, Carp?"

"Honest to God, Billy—"

"He'll tell you it's zebra-striped," laughed Sam. "Go on, tell him, he's so hot to know—zebra-striped with purple polka-dots."

"I'm telling you, Sam, I saw it all. You calling me a liar?"

"Answer my question, Carp."

"Tall tales," howled Sam, slapping his thigh. "Just more of your plain long-legged lies!"

"I'm warning you, Sam."

"Sam, you zipper your trap," Ruby said. "Let Carp go on and tell the story."

"Was it really black, Carp?"

"Let Carp tell us how many drinks he had beforehand," Sam chuckled. "Go on, Carp, tell us."

"Nary a one. I tell you, his brains was splattered all over them rocks. They had to pick off the pieces with a fork."

"Now it's forks. Oyster forks I guess, huh?"

"What's an oyster fork?"

"An oyster fork!" Carp snarled, turning on Ruby with such violence that Ruby backed away. "You mean you never heard of an oyster fork?"

"No, I haven't. I'm ashamed to say I never knew an oyster had one."

"Why, oysters don't grow them, you fool," Carp spluttered, his face reddening. "That's a fork for spearing oysters at high-falooting dinners. I seen plenty when I used to waiter in Atlantic City."

"What's Atlantic City like, Carp?"

"You mean there's more than one kind of fork outside of a pitchfork?" Ruby said, squinting at Carp and spitting a wad of tobacco juice plop in the mud.

"Why sure. Everybody knows that. First off, there're forks for olives. Now, you see, the rich got it all pretty complicated. I say *forks* for olives, 'cause there's forks for black olives, and forks for plain green olives (them with the pits still in), and then there's forks for olives stuffed with red gut. And, you see, you gotta know these things, else when you sit down to table and look baffled a minute at that long line of forks, people'll know you're dumb and not the ritz at all. They laugh at you behind their hands. I seen it happen."

"You know the difference between all these forks, huh?" Sam said. "You could put your knees under any fancy table and stick the right olive with the right fork, huh? You could do that?"

"Why sure. Didn't I used to waiter in a lush hotel? I watched and learned them things."

" 'Case you get rich someday, huh?"

"In case. Now you take oyster forks," Carp said, turning to Ruby. "Same thing there."

"Oh God, here it comes!"

"No, you listen," Carp said over his shoulder to Sam. Then to Ruby, "There's a fork for Blue Point oysters and a fork for Pawtucket oysters and another for Queen of Sheba oysters and then one for Jersey oysters— A fork for all the kinds of oysters in the world."

"Aw, come on. How they have room on the table for all them forks?"

"Oh, they have room," Carp said, not looking at Sam. "Big, grand table. 'Course, they don't serve *all* the oysters in the world at one sitting."

" 'A course not. Nor all the olives, I bet."

Carp turned and eyed Sam haughtily, folding his arms across his chest.

"Well, there's more kinds of oysters than olives," he said. "You got more forks to remember with oysters. Olives is easy. But the most pretty fork of all the oyster forks is a eensy-beensy silver one, all kinds of loops and curls carved on it, and the handle studded with diamonds. They usually have a couple of them on every table. Just in case."

He paused, smiling mysteriously through Sam. Sam watched him, waiting, but Carp kept on smiling and didn't say anything. Finally Sam said, "In case of what?"

Carp stopped smiling and stared at him blankly, as though he hadn't seen him before.

"I beg your pardon?"

"Don't give yourself airs," Sam grumbled. "I say, in case of what?"

"Was you referring to them special eensy-beensy silver oyster forks I was mentioning a couple of minutes ago?"

Carp drew himself up grandly.

"You know damn well I am."

"Well," Carp drawled slowly, flicking a speck of imaginary dust off the tip of his nose. "They have a couple of them forks on each table just in case some lady or gent pokes into their oyster and strikes a pearl. Then right off, there's a lot of excitement and laughing, and the lady—I seen it happen to a lady once, barebacked she was with the prettiest little freckles on her shoulders—I seen it happen to her."

He paused, carefully inspecting his fingernails.

"What?" Sam said in a cracked voice.

Carp glanced up at him. "Why, just what I been talking about. She comes up with a pearl in her oyster. And, right off, she lays down her fork—blue pointers was served that night so it was a blue point fork—she lays that fork down and reaches over for the little fork studded with diamonds and scoops in under that oyster and brings up the prettiest pearl you ever seen—all soft silver and kind of glowing in the light of the chandeliers, and pure round as a marble. She held the pearl up on that special fork and showed everybody. And what a commotion was raised about how beautiful it was. The ladies started hollering to see it so they passed it around the table for everybody to take a good squint at. I tell you, it was stunning."

"Me, something like that was passed my way," Sam said gruffly, "I'd pocket both pearl *and* fork and go on nonch'lant with my soup."

"You, you would. You don't know nothing about breeding and manners."

"But you do?"

"I ain't bragging. I can hold my own. But, you listen, didn't I have a chance to learn it with my own two eyes?"

"Lot of good it'll do you."

"You never can tell. I might cash in one of these days on this here dredge."

"Don't hold your breath. Better you go spearing oysters at fancy dinners."

"Don't you think I couldn't."

"Ha-ha."

"I may not know anything about manners," Ruby said. "But I can sure show you something about breeding."

"What's that?"

"You just match me with any woman, I'll show you the grandest blue-ribbon breeding you ever saw."

The men laughed.

"That ain't the kind of breeding I mean."

"There ain't no other kind, Carp. Not in my books."

"That just shows how dumb you are."

"Ruby laid the baby in the pipe."

"What're you talking about, Billy?"

"I know. I saw him do it. Alex, tell us how you found that baby in the pipe."

"Billy, I've told you that story a dozen times. I'd think you'd be sick of it by now. Besides, it's not a nice story to tell. It wasn't Ruby's baby anyway."

"It wasn't my baby," Ruby said.

"I'm not tired of it, Alex. I like it. Tell it again."

"Billy, you know that story as well as I do. Why don't you tell it?"

"I'm not very good."

"Get out," Carp said. "You know you're busting to tell it."

"Well, maybe I am. Shall I tell it, Alex?"

"I told you, Billy. I'd like to hear it. How 'bout you boys?"

"Go on, Billy. Do your stuff," Ruby said. "You can't be any worse than Alex."

"You be careful. I'll tell whose baby that was."

"I ain't done any cavorting. You can't blame that on me. That's a terrible thing to say, Alex."

"Well, just you mind how you criticize my storytelling."

"I was only funning."

"Shut up, you two," Sam said. "Spin it out, Billy."

"All right. But you mustn't laugh."

"I'll bust your nose you blame that baby on me."

"Shut your flap, Ruby. We know you ain't capable," Carp said. "Hey, Billy— Can we listen?"

"Why sure. How else? But you mustn't laugh."

"Can we look?"

"At me?"

"Who else?"

"Well, all right. But you mustn't laugh. If you laugh I can't tell it."

"I'll be a juke box feather plucked nigger of an angel," snapped Bunk. "Get on with it, Billy, for Jesus sake."

Billy walked over to the mouth of the pipe and stood very erect. He set his lips firmly and stared straight ahead of him.

"I'm ready," he said solemnly.

"Shall we draw the curtain, Billy?"

Billy looked around, flustered, then glanced uncertainly at Carp.

"Well, okay," he said finally. "You can do it now."

Billy watched as Carp took a gigantic stride forward, made a sweeping bow to the tips of his boots. He swung out his arm and, grazing Billy's nose with his hand, grandly pulled back an imaginary curtain. Turning, he bowed from the waist to the men, one hand clapped smartly on his hip. The men applauded and stamped their boots in the mud. Billy squirmed and wriggled, still at attention, and glanced impatiently at Carp, who continued bowing up and down and tipping his cap to the men. The men went on shouting and clapping.

"Now you got them laughing!" Billy shouted, red in the face and clenching and unclenching his fists. Carp paid no attention to him and as he bent down for another bow, Billy gave him a shove in the buttocks with his foot. Carp reeled around, dead pan, and slapping the heels of his boots together, gave Billy a smart salute.

"Sorry, Cap'n," he said, rubbing his backside.

"Scoot!" snapped Billy, shooing a hand at him.

Carp made another snappy salute, then marched stiff-legged over to the men, grinning, his face flushed. The others hooted and slapped him on the back.

"That was some show, Carp! That was all right!"

"Real fine acting, Carp! Real fine!"

"You want to hear this story or not!" Billy shouted, glaring at them.

"Oops, there's the curtain up and us ignoring the main actor," chuckled Ruby. He genuflected on one knee and blew a kiss to Billy. "Proceed. Proceed."

Billy took a step forward and shook his fist at Carp. "Damn you, Showoff, you spoiled everything!"

"I'm awful sorry, Cap'n," Carp said, pulling off his cap and hanging his head sheepishly. He twisted his cap around and around in his hands.

"Well, you spoiled it, Mr. Movie Star. I'm about ready to close this curtain and forget the whole thing."

"Aw, don't do that," Bunk pleaded.

"Men, here's the way," Carp said, turning briskly to the group and spreading his arms. His face relaxed in a serious and solemn expression. Ruby stifled a giggle behind his hand and settled down and grew quiet. They each put on a quiet, listening face.

"I'll do it now," Billy said.

He walked over to the pipe and leaned one elbow on it, crossing one foot in front of the other.

"Well, to begin—Alex was leaning on the pipe one day. Just like this. Huh, Alex?"

"That's right, Billy."

"It was terrific hot. The old sun burned a trillion billion watts a second."—He wiped his hand over his brow—"Just like now."—He glanced up at the sun— "Well, the old pipe here . . ."—He gave it a terrific thump with his fist—"started chuckling and gurgling for the last blow. Alex steps back and waits."—He moved backward, folding his arms over his chest and glared steadily at the pipe—"Then the whole pipe begins jerking and dancing off its pins as the blow gushes close."—He started to leap in the air and flailed his arms about—"Then out she wooshes!" he shouted, and dove at the men who leapt back in alarm—"And there's a great explosion of water and mud and rock and junk a thousand feet high!" he screamed, the muscles in his throat red and swelling.

"Make it fifteen feet, Billy."

"Anyway," Billy gasped, licking his lips and stalking around, "the blow peters off—begins to sicken and fall."—He staggered back, his lids half drooping, one hand pressed to his forehead, lips quivering and teeth chattering—"And dies!"—He keeled over in the mud and lay still.

"Billy, you'll get your clothes all—"

"Then! Quick as a flash! Up he bounds!"—He scrambled to his knees—"And starts clawing through rock and mud for junk!" —He rooted savagely in the earth with his fingers, flinging stones and mud over his shoulder, his hair flying in his face—"He finds a good hunk—pitches it aside—and another."—He heaved a stone in the direction of the men—"Finds another—pitches it aside—and another—it's a real good day—coming in copper—a good blow—another good hunk!" The last stone struck Ruby's boot and Ruby let out a howl and began hopping around on one foot while holding the other in both hands.

"Hey, careful, Billy—"

"Then all of a sudden!"—Billy knelt back on his heels and lifted his arms in amazement. His eyes bulged from his head as he stared down terrified at a particular spot in the mud. His mouth hung open. The men crowded forward, craning their necks to see what he was looking at. He let out a long low cry and slowly pressed his fingers into his cheeks. Then, gently reaching down, he pulled an imaginary object from the mud. He held it aloft, shrinking from it and glancing sideways at it, his eyes rolling with terror.

"It was the baby," he whispered.

The men stared uncomfortably at Billy's outstretched hand.

"It's all mangled and black," he said, rising slowly from his knees. "You can hardly tell it is a baby. Black like a nigger. Black and bloated from the river." He pinched his nostrils with his fingers. "It stinks like fish in the sun. Nigger, it don't have no legs. Legs ripped up in the dredge or in the pipe. But maybe—" He clutched the baby under one arm and frantically searched the ground at his feet. "Maybe them two legs come out with the blow. Maybe they're buried here under all this mud and rock." He carried the baby over to dry ground and laid it down carefully. Then he raced back to the mouth of the pipe and going down on his hands and knees began scratching and digging through the mud. "Them legs might be here. They just might be."

Ruby hurried forward.

"Look there, Billy!" he said excitedly, pointing. "There."

"Where? Here?" Billy swung around. "Ah, here, huh?" He started tearing away in that place, searching. Finally he stopped and wiped the sweat off his face with the sleeve of his shirt. He stood up and peered at the earth, then over to the dry ground where he had laid the baby. "Not here. Nowhere. Not anywhere. No legs. Baby ain't got no legs. Baby gets buried without no legs." His shoulders were shaking and he started to cry. "No legs. Not anywhere." He swung around and ran over to the pipe. Bending down, his hands gripping his knees, he stared grinning into the mouth of the pipe.

"Next gush!" he cried, his voice echoing inside the pipe. "Another blow— Maybe them legs'll turn up. I'll keep an eye out. I'll scratch the mud. I'll find them legs. Last thing I do, I'll find them baby's legs. I'll glue 'em back on.''

He spun around, laughing, and dancing a jig from foot to foot, clapping his hands over his head. "Next blow!" Abruptly he stopped and stood stiff and straight, his arms pressed tightly at his sides.

"Police come and take the baby." He fell to the earth and hopped around on his knees. "No legs. Baby ain't got no legs. Got wings, no legs." He scraped around in the mud. "Day after day— another—next blow—they don't turn up—mud, rock, junk—no legs—baby gone—no legs—oh, where could they be?" He jumped up and stood once more at attention, his heels close together, staring straight ahead of him. "Lord, I don't look anymore. I forget about it."

He looked down at his toes, wriggling them.

"Well, that's the way it went, wasn't it, Alex?"

"You done it a thousand times better, Billy." Alex blew his nose hard on the piece of flannel. "That was a very fine performance."

"There, that just closes it up," Bunk said, stepping over and drawing the curtain shut.

"You oughta go on Broadway," Ruby said.

"You think so?"

"You got talent. That was something to see, Billy, I'm telling you."

"Next time I go into New York City, I'll look into that. Where do you go?"

"I was at the Ziegfield Follies once," Ruby said. "Let's see—" He rubbed his heavy cheeks. "That must of been 20-22 years ago. Mighty fine theater. Good show. You just go there. They'll fit you in."

"You think so?"

"I'm certain. You just do the act you did here for us."

"I'd have to practice."

"Well, practice."

"No, Ruby, I think I'd rather go to Hollywood. I like movies better."

"Do what you like. You're wasting your time in this desert. Whatta you want being a junkie?"

"I don't know, Ruby."

Billy was silent a moment.

"You suppose somebody didn't want that baby?" he said, turning to Alex.

"What do you mean?"

"Well, say a fella gets a girl fixed good and them not being married or anything, they get rid of it tossing it in the river. Say maybe the girl has the baby off in the woods somewhere by herself and when it's born puts it in a paper bag, like what you get at the A&P, and carries it to the river and goodbye, trouble. Say maybe the boyfriend helps her."

"I don't know, Billy. Might be. I don't know where that baby come from."

"Well, if the boyfriend was to help her," Ruby said, "I think that it'd take plenty of nerve to dive into her again. I can't imagine wanting anything more to do with her. It's bad enough being in the same house when one of your kids is born. You listen to her howling like that and it makes you feel bad."

"But you forget," Sam said.

"Hell yeah."

"That's why I hustle my old lady to the hospital every time. On account of the noise she makes. And the names she calls me when she's in the throes of it—'Alex, you bastard, you touch me again I'll kill you— So help me I'll cut it off— You nogood sonuvabitch, you got me like this— You touch me again I'll kill you.' Stuff like that. Hospitals, they take care of the scream and the mess. It's worth the money."

"It's hell to have to listen to. They're out of their heads."

"But they forget."

"Oh, sure."

"Thank God for that. That'd really be hell, eh, boys? I mean if they never forgot and would never let you touch them again after that."

"It ain't natural. Earth'd empty in no time. So you needn't worry."

"God provides," Billy said.

They laughed.

"I guess it's toughest on the woman. What's that in the Bible—?"

"Now don't go spouting that stuff."

"No, but I mean there's something in there about woman. Goes —first the pleasure and then the pain. Then the whole thing all over again, never stopping. Us men are lucky—pleasure and more pleasure and never worry about a day of reckoning."

" 'Cepting in case you get a dose of something."

"Well, I always say you should pick a wife clean when you pick her."

They all laughed.

"I didn't mean that. I mean when you're off on a toot and ain't careful. A man's gotta watch out he don't catch something."

"No, that's one thing can knock up a man."

"Put him out of commission—but good."

"Something a woman don't have to worry about. I read somewhere she can carry it and dose a man up proper, but it don't mean she's gonna bust out in sores and go blind."

"No, that's tough on a man."

They stared at Bunk's upper lip.

He grinned and pointing to his mouth said, "That ain't nothing. Just a cold sore."

"You can't be too sure," Sam said. "It looks funny to me, Bunk. Now I don't mean to say you're diseased or anything, but that scab of yours sure does look peculiar."

"It's nothing, I tell you."

"You've had that *cold* sore as long as I've known you, Bunk. That's been ten years."

Bunk shrugged his shoulders and jammed his hands into his back pockets. He turned away, shading his eyes with one hand, and looked out over the river.

"Wonder when that blow's coming?" he said.

There was a silence. Then Alex said, "But a man's lucky, I will say that. He don't have to put up with the monthly bleed or be afraid of getting pumped full of baby every so often."

"You said the truth there," Sam said. "Let's have a drink on that. Whatta you say, boys?"

"I wouldn't throw *my* glove in the glass," chuckled Ruby, rubbing his hands together.

Sam took a whiskey flask out of his hippocket and unscrewed the lid.

"Sam, can I have some?"

"A mouthful, Billy. Just enough to fill a cavity in a tooth. You know how rammy you get on a little whiskey."

"All right, Sam. I'll hunt the biggest cavity I can find."

"I don't mean your belly," Sam said, tilting the bottle to his lips. He took a long drink and rinsed it around in his mouth before swallowing it. He wiped his mouth on his sleeve and passed the bottle to the others.

"Pass Bunk by," he said, pulling out his penknife and scraping the dirt between his nails. "I don't want a man with a scab sore on his mouth sucking on my bottle."

Bunk ground his heel in the mud, then looked up at the sky, watching the chicken hawks drift in big circles overhead. He glanced secretly at the others out of the corner of his eye. Carp had the bottle now and as he lifted it to his lips, Bunk saw muddy thumbprints smeared around the neck of it. His fingers moved up to his mouth and brushed away the flies buzzing there.

Suddenly the pipe began to vibrate and the men straightened up, tense and waiting. Ruby passed the bottle to Billy. Billy looked around at the men and they were staring at the pipe, so he took a long pull on the bottle, choking a little, then walked over and gave the bottle back to Sam. Sam held the bottle up in the sunlight, squinting one eye and making a peeved clucking noise in his throat as he measured the whiskey.

In the pipe was the sound of rock clanking against metal, the noise of it coming at a fast clip and growing steadily louder. Sam stepped forward, screwing the lid on the bottle, then thrust it in his pocket. He put his hands on his hips, watching the pipe and running the tip of his tongue over his lips.

"It's coming," Alex said.

" 'Bout time," said Carp, striding over and standing directly in front of the pipe, legs spread.

A faint roar came out of the mouth of the pipe, along with a steady gust of stagnant air. The men were silent, bearded jaws hanging slack on sun-burned faces, and intense narrowed eyes hypnotised by the dark mouth of the pipe. The roar increased and the entire length of the pipe hummed and shook as though trying to free itself from the earth. There was the slosh and suck of water, and the blast of air pushing from the opening increased in pressure, flattening Carp's clothes against his body. His hat blew off but he didn't move and stood rooted there, his arms folded tightly over his chest.

"It's cool!" he shouted. "Damned cool! But what a stink! Whew!"

"Get back, Carp! It's coming! It's coming!" Billy cried, hopping up and down behind the men. "It'll cut you to pieces! Drown you, Carp!"

Carp leapt aside. The men scattered. Billy started to run, but tripped and fell, sprawling face flat on the ground. Sam and Bunk ran back and each grabbed one of his arms and pulled him away from the pipe.

The black water pounded out like an explosion, shooting straight out, slapping the earth hard and driving up a wall of mud and rock before it, flattening the earth and pocketing it deeper with ton after ton of water.

The men stood at a distance watching. Billy had his back turned on the flood and was rubbing at a skinned elbow. Above the roar of the water they could hear the shrill whistle of the dredge-boat and looking, saw a cloud of black smoke billowing from the boat's stack. After a few minutes the whistle stopped blowing and gradually the column of water slackened, growing shorter until only a narrow steady gush spilled from the lip of the pipe.

The men dove forward, splashing kneehigh in the muck. Each bent down low, his bare arms slopping and stirring through the mud. As a man found a piece of pigiron or junk, he tossed it to dry ground, shouting, "Mine!" and went on dipping for more. Sam and Alex worked close together, several times bumping into each other. They each grabbed onto a piece at the same time. They glared at each other for an instant, then the mud rippled between their struggling arms at each tried to pull the object away from the other.

"It's mine! I found it first!" Sam shouted in his face, clenching his teeth and gripping the object tightly beneath the surface.

"No, mine! My hand touched first!"

"Liar! You're poking in my territory!"

"Your territory! Mine, you mean!"

"Let go!"

"I won't! I grabbed first. It's mine!"

"The hell you say. You drop that end. This piece belongs to me."

"Fight for it, boys!" Ruby yelled, quickly glancing over his shoulder, then bending down and slurping through the mud again.

"Drop yours. It's my prize. I touched first!" Sam bellowed.

"Touched first, hell!"

"Let go!"

"You let go!"

They began to tug hard on the object, pulling it half way out of the mud. Sam gave a strong jerk and the object slipped from their hands, sliding back into the mud with a silent plop. Their arms splashed down in the mire as each fought to get hold of it again, their arms in deep to the elbows and their hands feeling and thrashing blindly. Sam plunged down to his shoulders and found an edge of the object.

"Damn you, Alex, I am warning you. I got it for certain this time."

Alex crouched in the mud.

"I got my end too, goddamn you. I ain't letting you cheat me."

"Nobody's cheating. You're the goddamn cheater. You always was a cheat, Alex. Everybody knows that."

Alex let his end of the object drop. Sam pitched forward under the weight and he dropped his end, the object disappearing under the surface. He made a grab for it and Alex reached out and gave him a shove on the shoulder. He slowly placed his hands on his hips, scowling at Sam.

"You say that again," he said quietly.

Sam glared at him, breathless, his mouth hanging open, his face blood red and sweating.

"You're a cheat!" he shouted, straining forward. "Everybody knows it."

Bunk and Ruby and Carp swung around and stared at the two men. Billy went on splashing around in the mud, beating his arms through it and snatching up hunks of slimey pigiron.

"Once more," Alex said, wading closer. "Just tell me that once more."

"Once is enough," Sam said, inching backward and looking awkwardly away. He stumbled and caught his balance, then lifted his head and stared straight at Alex. "I don't have to call you a cheat three times to let you know it."

Alex stopped, gritting his teeth, and eyed Sam up and down. Then, swinging his arm back as far as it would go, he shot it forward, slamming Sam's jaw with all his strength. Sam groaned and his eyes rolled up in his head as he toppled backward in the pool of muck. Alex snatched him around the throat before he went under and dragged him to dry ground. Sam struggled to get free as Alex swung back his fist again. Sam's lips were quivering and he peeled at the mud on his cheeks as he stared into Alex's face. Alex held him by the shirt buttons, like a limp thing, his lower lip jutting and snarling, holding his arm back, when Sam suddenly wrenched loose and bounded away, falling and dragging himself through the dust. He stopped a few yards away and looking back at Alex, dug a rock out of the ground and held it clenched in his hand.

"Come one step more, Alex, I'm warning you," he choked.

"You wanta throw rocks?" jeered Alex. He glanced quickly around, spotted Billy's mound of pigiron and snatched a crude metal flange, still wet and muddy, from the heap. He came at Sam with the flange held tight in his fist, the jagged end out.

"I'm warning you," Sam gasped, dragging himself away from Alex. "I'm warning you."

Alex stood over him.

"Get up."

Sam struggled to his feet, slowly raising the rock in one hand as he lifted himself. He had pulled himself up into a stooped position, the rock held high over his head, when Alex shouted, "Me, cheat! You nogood bastard!" and walloped Sam's head with the metal flange, ripping a chunk of the skull away. Sam crumpled in a heap and lay still. The rock had flown from his hand and landed a few feet away, raising a cloud of dust where it struck the earth. The men stood in the mudhole staring, their arms hanging loose at their sides. Billy gaped, one arm pressed across his belly and the fingers of his other hand stuffed in his mouth. Alex turned his back on them and still holding the bloody flange in one hand, stared down sullenly at his muddy boots.

"Me, cheat!" he gasped.

Billy floundered out of the mud, kicking his legs high. He started to run toward Alex but stopped a few feet from him and began rubbing his hands up and down his thighs. He bit his lip and jerked his head back, to where the men were standing. He tried to call to them but could not raise his voice. The three men glanced uneasily at each other, then waded slowly out of the water. When they got on dry ground, each stamped his boots vigorously, knocking off the mud. Bunk stamped the longest and finally he stopped and the three stood, hands in pockets, uncomfortably looking at Alex and then at the dead man and back at Alex.

"What're you going to do, Alex?" Billy whispered.

Alex did not answer but remained standing with his back to them.

"'You didn't have to do that, Alex," Carp said. "You didn't have to go that far."

"Sam didn't mean it," Bunk said. "He was out of his head."

"He was afraid of you, Alex."

There was silence. Billy lurched forward, his body loose and stooped, his mouth open. He was staring wide-eyed across the land.

"What's the matter, Billy?"

Alex swung around.

"He's in a temper," he said. "Billy, come out of it. Don't do that. I'll take you home in my car."

Billy's throat worked rapidly, his adam's apple bobbing up and down. His tongue fluttered noiselessly over his dry lips. He lifted a hand and pointed in the distance.

"More of your tricks?" Carp snapped. "More of your tricks? Whatta you see?"

Billy's arm was trembling, his body shook from head to foot.

"Them men in black!" he sputtered. "They're coming this way with leather belts in their hands."

The men shielded their eyes and stared off hard in the distance. There was the broad expanse of land running unbroken the length of the horizon, ash-white in the heat, and empty.

"There's nothing out there but mud—"

Alex turned away, passing a hand over his face. He pulled his hat low over his eyes.

"Give him some water, Christ, somebody—"

"They're passing against the sky," Billy said thickly, his eyes dull and listless. A dribble of saliva ran down his chin. "They dropped the straps. The casket's gray."

"Shut up, Billy!" snapped Carp angrily. "This ain't no time for that kind of nonsense."

"But where're they going? Where're they gonna bury the casket here? The mud's too hard for digging. I'd better go tell them. They'd better go take that casket some place else."

He took a few steps forward and stopped, pressing his knuckles into his eyes. "Where're they going?" he said softly.

Carp sprang to him and spun him around, grabbing him tight by the shoulders.

"Softhead! Softhead!" he screamed in his face.

"Don't hurt me, for godsake, don't—"

Carp shook him violently.

"Shut up! Shut up!"

"Let him alone," Alex said. "He's sick. Let him alone."

"Carrying on with your tricks after what's happened," Carp sneered.

He gave Billy a shove, pushing him away, and turning on his heel, strode angrily back to the others. Billy tottered a moment, lifted his hand to his face, his eyes rolling wildly in his head, then suddenly pitched forward, diving flat on the ground close to Alex and lay there kicking his legs and muttering and growling, his knuckles digging frantically into the earth. Alex leapt back as Billy's arm shot out, his hand clamping tightly around Alex's ankle. He continued to squirm and writhe on his belly and beat the other fist in the dust.

"It's a clamp of steel!" Alex cried. "Bust his fingers loose! He's stopping the blood in my foot! He'll snap the bone!"

None of the men made a move. Beads of sweat stood out on Alex's brow, his eyes darted from one silent face to the other, then down at the hand squeezing his ankle in a death grip.

"Are you going to stand there like dummies?" he cried. "He's breaking my leg!"

The men were silent, staring with fascination at the thin figure rolling in the dust.

Alex glanced at the metal flange that he still held in one hand. He looked at the men then quickly bent down and whacked Billy's fist again and again with the bloody end of the flange. Billy held on tight. Alex beat harder until the white, tense knuckles were slashed and raw. He kicked his leg back and the hand fell away, striking the earth, the fingers uncoiling in a pool of blood and dust. Billy lay still, on his side, the arm flung over his head.

"Damn fool!" Alex gasped. "Damn fool, you!"

He tossed the flange as far as he could throw it.

"You oughtn't to done that," Ruby said. "That's evidence."

"Evidence?"

Alex stared at him.

"You know what I mean."

Alex glanced quickly at the dead man, then turned hastily away, breathing heavily. He pulled out the piece of flannel and mopped his face.

"I guess I'll go in my car now," he said, stuffing the rag back in his pocket. "I guess I'll drop Billy off at his house first."

He watched the faces of the men, then stared at the ground, putting his hands awkwardly in his pockets.

"You'll know where to find me."

He lifted Billy in his arms and carried him over to the chevvy. Reaching under with one hand, he opened the door and set Billy on the seat. He slammed the door and crossed around to the other side, got in and started the motor. Billy sat unconscious, his head bumping and rolling from side to side on the dirty green felt of the backrest. Alex sat stiff and erect at the wheel, his eyes unblinking and staring straight out the windshield. As he turned the car north, Billy's head swerved off the seat and banged against the window sash. It rested there, one cheek bumping against the metal, his eyes closed and his mouth open and twisted to one side of his face.

The men watched as the car jolted slowly away, moving off in a straight line over the land and raising a slow steady cloud of dust behind it. They watched until the cloud of dust hid the chevvy, then turned and each looked for an instant at the dead body sprawled in front of the mouth of the pipe. The blood was drying and hardening in a brown crust where the piece of skull was ripped away. Flies crawled black in the wound.

Bunk clapped his hand over his mouth, then vomited in the mud. He looked up, embarrassed, wiping the puke from his mouth with the back of his hand.

The others moved over to where the sacks and the carts were.

"We can't let him lie here like this," Bunk said.

"You can't touch the body," Carp said, shoving the metal around and arranging it in the wagon. "They always tell you that."

"We got to go into town and tell the police," Ruby said. "That's all we can do."

"Well, oughtn't we to cover him?" Bunk said, glancing over his shoulder at the dead man. He shuddered and stared down at the earth. "It gags me. I mean, God, look at him."

Ruby and Carp were silent. They looked uneasily at each other.

"What can we do?" Ruby said.

"Dump the junk out of one of the sacks," Bunk said. "That's the least we can do. Keep the flies and sun off his head."

"Whose sack?"

"It don't matter. You or Ruby empty your sack. I'll carry your load in my wagon."

Ruby and Carp gazed silently at each other, then looked away, each scuffing a foot in the dust.

"I'll keep the junk separate. I won't mix it with mine or try to cheat you," Bunk said. "My God."

"Well, I'll do it," Ruby said. He pulled up the mouth of his burlap bag and dragged it over to Bunk's pushcart.

"Give a hand here, Carp."

Carp came over and together they emptied the bag of junk into the cart.

"Now bring the sack here," Bunk said.

"I'll pitch it to you."

"Well, all right. Pitch it."

Ruby wadded the bag into a ball and tossed it to Bunk. It fell a few feet from Bunk and Bunk walked over and picked it up and carried it to the mouth of the pipe. He unwadded it and turning his back on the dead man, gave the bag a couple of smart snaps, shaking it out. He moved his head to one side, not looking, as he prepared to spread the bag over the dead man, but he stopped and first leaned down to shoo the flies from the wound. The flies scattered, buzzing furiously. As soon as he lifted his hand away the flies once more infested the bloody cavity. He swiped at them again and again with his hand, but only a few flew off.

"Hustle it up, Bunk. You want to look at the thing all day?" Carp called.

"Come on, Bunk. Else we'll leave without you."

Bunk did not answer. Suddenly he darted his fingers into the wound and worked it around and around in it, scraping away the wall of flies. The flies flew off in an angry swarm. He pulled the finger away and wiped it on the seat of his dungarees. Quickly he spread the burlap over the upper part of the body. He stared at a ragged hole showing a bit of the dead man's throat through the cloth. His hands moved swiftly over the ground, scooping in four small stones. He laid a stone on each of the four corners of the bag, then stood up and hurried over to where the men were waiting.

"What do you want to be so neat for?" Carp said. "He's dead ain't he?"

Bunk did not answer. Suddenly he darted his finger into the hand on each handle and tried to lift it, but the cart was too heavy.

"Carp, give a hand here. Ruby, you pull Billy's wagon."

Carp took hold of one of the handles and Bunk took the other. Together they lifted the cart and pushed it along. Ruby trudged behind, pulling the wagon of orange crates. They moved off in the direction of town, Bunk and Carp struggling with the cart over the ruts. Their footsteps sent up little balls of dust.

As they moved off over the land, the chicken hawks swooped in lower and smaller circles until they were flapping in tight rings just over the spot where the dead man lay, his long legs sticking out from the bottom of the burlap covering. The birds flew around and around, descending still lower in fluttering narrow loops until their wings brushed the burlap cloth. The air was filled with their harsh, agitated cries. When the men disappeared over the horizon, one of the hawks hurtled down and with a noisy flapping of its wings, alighted on the mouth of the pipe. One by one the hawks darted from the flock and dropped to the earth where they strutted in small circles, several bristling their feathers and crying sharply to one another, as they reeled and turned, hopping closer to the body of the dead man.

QUESTIONS

1. As in "On Official Business," setting plays an important role in this narrative. Examine the details of setting. Notice particularly that the setting is not, strictly speaking, limited to the immediate area where the six men stand, waiting. In fact, the very first point made about setting concerns a large pipe which stretches off into the distance, becoming "a thin, black line across the beach far below and running on stilts out over the water to the dredge-boat anchored in mid-river." What does this element of distance add to the general impression that setting makes?

2. We soon discover that this large, corrugated pipe plays a central role in the narrative. Its obvious purpose is to channel out of the river the mud and debris brought up by the dredge-boat. The men's view of its function is quite different, however. Discuss their view. How does the pipe affect their lives? The relationship between the men and the pipe is actually rather complex. Billy uses it as a prop in performing his act, Alex relays to the others the voices that come out of it, and the pipe is the source of the grisly tale which Billy acts out. To what extent does the term "naturalism" apply to the situation?

3. Examine the story's atmosphere. There are several things which contribute to establishing that atmosphere, in addition to setting. *Imagery* is one of them. Discuss the story's imagery and the ways in which it helps to establish the atmosphere. Trace the intensification of atmosphere.

4. Although the six characters—Alex, Carp, Billy, Ruby, Bunk, and Sam—have distinct personalities, the narrative focuses on one of them more than on the others. Which? Analyze the ways in which this figure's statements and actions comment indirectly on the world in which the men live (and die).

5. What kinds of stories fascinate all of these characters? Discuss the function of these stories in terms of atmosphere, characterization, and theme.

6. In some ways, this story resembles Gorki's "Twenty-Six Men and a Girl." Compare and contrast such elements as characterization, setting, atmosphere, and theme.

ALAIN ROBBE-GRILLET

(1922-   )

Alain Robbe-Grillet is one of the leaders and spokesmen for the French New Novelists (see FOR A NEW NOVEL). To Robbe-Grillet, fiction is an end in itself, not a tool by which one makes moral judgments or offers social comment, nor even a means by which one communicates a view of man and his world. The attitudes reflected in his fiction are fragmentary, even contradictory. His style often reflects the movies in its cinematographic fluidity, and attention is frequently focused on objects rather than action. The result is that his work sometimes has a static quality, or a sense of uneven movement, as in "The Secret Room." There may also be an appearance of objectivity which permits him to ignore the conventions of his time and cultural milieu. His novels include THE ERASERS, THE VOYEUR, JEALOUSY, and IN THE LABYRINTH. He also wrote the screen play for the film, LAST YEAR AT MARIENBAD. A collection of his shorter works is soon to be published in the United States.

The Secret Room

To Gustave Moreau.

The first thing to be seen is a red stain, of a deep, dark, shiny red, with almost black shadows. It is in the form of an irregular rosette, sharply outlined, extending in several directions in wide outflows of unequal length, dividing and dwindling afterward into single sinuous streaks. The whole stands out against a smooth, pale surface, round in shape, at once dull and pearly, a hemisphere joined by gentle curves to an expanse of the same pale color—white darkened by the shadowy quality of the place: a dungeon, a sunken room, or a cathedral—glowing with a diffused brilliance in the semi-darkness.

Further back, the space is filled with the cylindrical trunks of columns, repeated with progressive vagueness in their retreat toward the beginning of a vast stone stairway, turning slightly as it rises, growing narrower and narrower as it approaches the high vaults where it disappears.

The whole setting is empty, stairway and colonnades. Alone, in the foreground, the stretched-out body gleams feebly, marked with the red stain—a white body whose full, supple flesh can be sensed, fragile, no doubt, and vulnerable. Alongside the bloody hemisphere another identical round form, this one intact, is seen at almost the same angle of view; but the haloed point at its summit, of darker tint, is in this case quite recognizable, whereas the other one is entirely destroyed, or at least covered by the wound.

In the background, near the top of the stairway, a black silhouette is seen fleeing, a man wrapped in a long floating cape, ascending the last steps without turning around, his deed accomplished. A thin smoke rises in twisting scrolls from a sort of incense burner placed on a high stand of ironwork with a silvery glint. Nearby lies the milk-white body, with wide streaks of blood running from the left breast, along the flank and on the hip.

It is a fully rounded woman's body, but not heavy, completely nude, lying on the back, the bust raised up somewhat by thick cushions thrown down on the floor, which is covered with oriental rugs. The waist is very narrow, the neck long and thin, curved to one side, the head thrown back into a darker area where even so, may be discerned the facial features, the partly opened mouth, the wide-staring eyes, shining with a fixed brilliance, and the mass of long, black hair spread out in a complicated wavy disorder over a heavily folded cloth, of velvet perhaps, on which also rest the arm and shoulder.

It is a uniformly colored velvet of dark purple, or which seems so in this lighting. But purple, brown, blue also seem to dominate in the colors of the cushions—only a small portion of which is hidden beneath the velvet cloth, and which protrude noticeably, lower

down, beneath the bust and waist—as well as in the oriental patterns of the rugs on the floor. Further on, these same colors are picked
up again in the stone of the paving and the columns, the vaulted
archways, the stairs, and the less discernible surfaces that disappear
into the farthest reaches of the room.

The dimensions of this room are difficult to determine exactly;
the body of the young sacrificial victim seems at first glance to occupy a substantial portion of it, but the vast size of the stairway leading down to it would imply rather that this is not the whole room,
whose considerable space must in reality extend all around, right
and left, as it does toward the far-away browns and blues among the
columns standing in line, in every direction, perhaps toward other
sofas, thick carpets, piles of cushions and fabrics, other tortured
bodies, other incense burners.

It is also difficult to say where the light comes from. No clue, on
the columns or on the floor, suggests the direction of the rays. Nor is
any window or torch visible. The milkwhite body itself seems to
light the scene, with its full breasts, the curve of its thighs, the
rounded belly, the full buttocks, the stretched-out legs, widely
spread, and the black tuft of the exposed sex, provocative, proffered,
useless now.

The man has already moved several steps back. He is now on
the first steps of the stairs, ready to go up. The bottom steps are wide
and deep, like the steps leading up to some great building, a temple
or theatre; they grow smaller as they ascend, and at the same time
describe a wide helical curve, so gradually that the stairway has not
yet made a half-turn by the time that it disappears near the top of
the vaults, reduced then to a steep, narrow flight of steps without
handrail, vaguely outlined, moreover, in the thickening darkness
beyond.

But the man does not look in this direction, where his movement none the less carries him; his left foot on the second step and
his right foot already touching the third, with his knee bent, he has
turned around to look at the spectacle for one last time. The long,
floating cape thrown hastily over his shoulders, clasped in one hand
at his waist, has been whirled around by the rapid circular motion
that has just caused his head and chest to turn in the opposite direction, and a corner of the cloth remains suspended in the air as if
blown by a gust of wind; this corner, twisting around upon itself in

the form of a loose S, reveals the red silk lining with its gold embroidery.

The man's features are impassive, but tense, as if in expectation—or perhaps fear—of some sudden event, or surveying with one last glance the total immobility of the scene. Though he is looking backward, his whole body is turned slightly forward, as if he were continuing up the stairs. His right arm—not the one holding the edge of the cape—is bent sharply toward the left, toward a point in space where the balustrade should be, if this stairway had one, an interrupted gesture, almost incomprehensible, unless it arose from an instinctive movement to grasp the absent support.

As to the direction of his glance, it is certainly aimed at the body of the victim lying on the cushions, its extended members stretched out in the form of a cross, its bust raised up, its head thrown back. But the face is perhaps hidden from the man's eyes by one of the columns, standing at the foot of the stairs. The young woman's right hand touches the floor just at the foot of this column. The fragile wrist is encircled by an iron bracelet. The arm is almost in darkness, only the hand receiving enough light to make the thin, outspread fingers clearly visible against the circular protrusion at the base of the stone column. A black metal chain running around the column passes through a ring affixed to the bracelet, binding the wrist tightly to the column.

At the top of the arm a rounded shoulder, raised up by the cushions, also stands out well lighted, as well as the neck, the throat, and the other shoulder, the armpit with its soft hair, the left arm likewise pulled back with its wrist bound in the same manner to the base of another column, in the extreme foreground; here the iron bracelet and the chain are fully displayed, represented with perfect clarity down to the slightest details.

The same is true, still in the foreground but at the other side, for a similar chain, but not quite as thick, wound directly around the ankle, running twice around the column and terminating in a heavy iron ring embedded in the floor. About a yard further back, or perhaps slightly further, the right foot is identically chained. But it is the left foot, and its chain, that are the most minutely depicted.

The foot is small, delicate, finely modeled. In several places the chain has broken the skin, causing noticeable if not extensive depressions in the flesh. The chain links are oval, thick, the size of an eye. The ring in the floor resembles those used to attach horses; it lies almost touching the stone pavement to which it is riveted by a massive iron peg. A few inches away is the edge of a rug; it is grossly wrinkled at this point, doubtless as a result of the convulsive, but necessarily very restricted, movements of the victim attempting to struggle.

The man is still standing about a yard away, half leaning over her. He looks at her face, seen upside down, her dark eyes made larger by their surrounding eyeshadow, her mouth wide open as if screaming. The man's posture allows his face to be seen only in a vague profile, but one senses in it a violent exaltation, despite the rigid attitude, the silence, the immobility. His back is slightly arched. His left hand, the only one visible, holds up at some distance from the body a piece of cloth, some dark colored piece of clothing, which drags on the carpet, and which must be the long cape with its gold embroidered lining.

This immense silhouette hides most of the bare flesh over which the red stain, spreading from the globe of the breast, runs in long rivulets that branch out, growing narrower, upon the pale background of the bust and the flank. One thread has reached the armpit and runs in an almost straight, thin line along the arm; others have run down toward the waist and traced out, along one side of the belly, the hip, the top of the thigh, a more random network already starting to congeal. Three or four tiny veins have reached the hollow between the legs, meeting in a sinuous line, touching the point of the V formed by the outspread legs, and disappearing into the black tuft.

Look, now the flesh is still intact: the black tuft and the white belly, the soft curve of the hips, the narrow waist, and, higher up, the pearly breasts rising and falling in time with the rapid breathing, whose rhythm grows more accelerated. The man, close to her, one knee on the floor, leans further over. The head, with its long, curly hair, and which is alone free to move somewhat, turns from side to side, struggling; finally the woman's mouth twists open, while the flesh is torn open, the blood spurts out over the tender skin, stretched tight, the carefully shadowed eyes grow abnormally larger, the mouth opens wider, the head twists violently, one last time, from right to left, then more gently, to fall back finally and become still, amid the mass of black hair spread out on the velvet.

At the very top of the stone stairway, the little door has opened, allowing a yellowish but sustained shaft of light to enter, against which stands out the dark silhouette of the man wrapped in his long cloak. He has but to climb a few more steps to reach the threshold.

Afterward, the whole setting is empty, the enormous room with its purple shadows and its stone columns proliferating in all directions, the monumental staircase with no handrail that twists upward, growing narrower and vaguer as it rises into the darkness, toward the top of the vaults where it disappears.

Near the body, whose wound has stiffened, whose brilliance is already growing dim, the thin smoke from the incense burner traces complicated scrolls in the still air: first a coil turned horizontally to the left, which then straightens out and rises slightly, then returns to the axis of its point of origin, which it crosses as it moves to the right, then turns back in the first direction, only to wind back again, thus forming an irregular sinusoidal curve, more and more flattened out, and rising, vertically, toward the top of the canvas.

QUESTIONS

1. Robbe-Grillet, in "The Secret Room" and elsewhere, has applied the technique of the camera to the writing of fiction. In what ways is this technique in evidence here?

2. The scene is rather obviously melodramatic. What elements contribute to the melodrama? Why do you think he chose a melodramatic scene, given the limitations and weaknesses of melodrama? (See the questions and comments on Frank Rooney's "Cyclists' Raid" [p. 452], for a brief discussion of melodrama.)

3. Some of the most interesting characteristics of this work are its strong appeal to the senses, its static quality, and the treatment of point of view. How do these characteristics affect such matters as atmosphere, action, and reader response? Among other things, we should take into consideration the word "canvas" which appears at the end of the story. Do you think Robbe-Grillet intends the reader to take this word literally or metaphorically? Clearly part of its purpose is to heighten the *scenic,* as opposed to the *narrative,* quality of the story. One of the results is that we become more conscious of the act of perceiving, recognizing that the senses, reason, memory, and imagination all play a part in that act. Why

should Robbe-Grillet try to make us more aware that we are examining a work of art? Why, that is, should he work toward increasing the aesthetic distance?

4. It is possible to argue that "The Secret Room" is not a short story at all. Discuss the characteristics of the short story and the specific ways in which this story varies from those characteristics. (You may wish to refer to the essay, "The Short Story as a Literary Type," in the introductory section of this anthology.)

APPENDIX

APPENDIX

Action and Character

In good fiction, the relationship between (1) what happens in a story, and (2) the people in that story, is a close one. It becomes virtually impossible to talk about one without talking about the other. The significance of *what* happens is practically inseparable from the characters *to whom* it happens, just as the meaning of *what is done* is closely tied to *who does it*. We can go on to say, therefore, that a primary consideration in understanding fiction is that of the characters, since it is they who act and are acted upon.

To show how action and character interplay, let us examine a story that reflects the author's feeling for the union of the two: Hemingway's "The Short Happy Life of Francis Macomber." This narrative focuses on three figures—Macomber, his wife Margot, and the white hunter, Robert Wilson—who are on safari. We quickly become aware that it is what happens to Macomber that involves us in the action. His wife and the white hunter are important figures too, of course, but Macomber is clearly the central figure.

What happens to Macomber? we ask. The answer is, simply stated, that he changes. How does he change? That is, what was he to begin with, and what does he then become? To answer our questions about this central character, we turn immediately to the pattern of incidents, since it is through these incidents that the personality of Macomber is revealed to us. At the beginning of the story, we learn that Macomber has run from a lion: he is a coward. But Hemingway is not content with giving us information at second hand. To make us realize fully the enormity of this act, he gives us a *flashback*. Now the scene itself is before us. Macomber and the lion come face to face, and the "next thing he knew he was running; running wildly, in panic in the open, running toward the stream." We *see* his cowardice, and what we see is so realistically presented, the focus so intense, that we even *feel* the fear that races through Macomber's whole being, overpowering him. We are given the "ocular proof" that Shakespeare's Othello, in another context, so terrifyingly demands.

When characters are revealed to us in this fashion, they take on a fullness of dimension that mere statements *about* them cannot provide. Hemingway knows this, and so he reveals Macomber through a whole series of acts ending with Macomber facing a charging water buffalo. This time, however, he kneels unflinching and fires "with the buffalo's huge bulk almost on him and his rifle almost level with the on-coming head, nose out, and he could see the little wicked eyes and the head started to lower." The basic point about action and character should now be clear. Action depends primarily upon character if that action is to have significance for the reader. And character, although it may be revealed to us in a number of ways, is most persuasively communicated through action. We can now separate the two elements and examine them in greater detail.

Action

In our introduction to action and character, we used the term "action" rather loosely to mean "anything that happens in a narrative." If we examine action carefully, however, we will see that it actually occurs on two different levels: first, on the level of individual incidents, which are separate and rather easily distinguishable; and second, on the level of *plot,* which links incidents together on the basis of their cause-and-effect relationship. On the first level, we ask the question, "What happens to Macomber?" and we get such replies as "He runs from a lion," or "His wife shoots him." These incidents, and others, do indeed occur, but they tell us "what happens" only in a very limited sense. More important is our recognition that something has happened to Macomber that no single incident can account for. Macomber, we discover, has undergone a significant change in his attitude toward both himself and the world around him: " 'You know something did happen to me,' he said. 'I feel absolutely different.' " Such a change is a broadly encompassing incident that might be said to begin with Macomber running wildly from the lion, and to culminate in his stand before the charging buffalo. Or the change can be seen in the relationship between Macomber and his wife. Before Macomber changes, we are told that "Margot was too beautiful for Macomber to divorce her and Macomber had too much money for Margot ever to leave him." But after Margot shoots Macomber, Wilson tells her, " 'He *would* have left you too.' " These incidents, and all others between, are necessary to an understanding of action in the broad sense. We may distinguish between the two levels, then, by saying that action on the level of plot involves a *major development or change* to which the individual incidents and scenes contribute.

We've all read stories that simply try to entertain us. These stories are usually all surface; that is, what happens on the physical level is the whole story, and the change that occurs there is, more or less, a physical change: someone wins an exciting race, or inherits a large sum of money, or solves a crime. When these incidents are ends in themselves—when they convey no additional meaning—then we may say that the plot *is* the action, and we read such stories to escape from reality, not to probe into it.

But what happens on this external, physical level often *does* convey additional meaning. In Gorki's "Twenty-Six Men and a Girl," for example, there is a change in the relationship between the men and the girl Tanya, a change that is effectively dramatized by Gorki in a near-assault which the men make upon her. The physical nature of the conflict is certainly exciting, but we should not let that excitement mask the scene's real function. Through it we are forcibly made aware of the kind of life the men lead. They are creatures without joy or hope who idolize and idealize the one person who deigns to recognize their existence: Tanya. Her failure to live up to their expectations takes from them the one ray of sunshine that filtered into their damp and gloomy dungeon. When she walks through them at the end, she pretends not to see them. For the moment, they do not even exist. Gorki uses this physical scene to heighten the pathos of the men's lives.

Stories which emphasize action on the physical level can easily mislead us into thinking there is nothing more to the narrative or that the meaning is to be found entirely in what happens in the physical sense. Often, however, these incidents are intended to reflect action—change or development—that is *internal*. Hemingway's story uses incident in this way. The real change is *inside* Macomber, and the incidents that comprise the plot reflect what is taking place there. The conclusion we arrive at is an important one, the second of our two basic statements about action: *the central action of a story may be internal.*

We have yet to deal with another type of story, one that lies at the far end of the scale from those which give us action on the physical level. In a good many stories, little or nothing seems to "happen." Chekhov's "On Official Business" is a good example of this type, for in it the characters wander aimlessly about the countryside, and the conclusion appears to conclude nothing. Yet another story like Chekhov's is Katherine Mansfield's "The Fly." The incidents here consist of a brief visit to the boss by old Woodifield, followed by an equally brief glimpse into the boss's thoughts and emotions after Woodifield leaves. Apparently, nothing has changed: the boss seems the same at the end as he does at the start. These stories tend to puzzle us because they lack "handles"—significant incidents—that we easily recognize and seize upon. There are few clear-cut *acts* to function as landmarks by which the reader can orient himself.

Here, the problem is that we are looking for change where there is none—*outside* the characters—or we are insisting that there be reflections on the physical level of an internal change. What we should realize is that, in some stories, virtually everything that happens, happens internally. With this realization, we soon discover that "On Official Business" involves a change in the examining magistrate Lyzhin's attitude toward life. The real incidents of the story all take place within his mind. Similarly, in "The Fly," we see a man who seems to remain in control of the world around him, who continues to take pleasure in his material goods, and who orders his employees about in the same fashion as before. At the same time, however, he has sensations that are new to him: a "grinding feeling of wretchedness" and an inability to remember "what it was he had been thinking about before." What do these statements mean in terms of a change that has taken place *inside* the boss? We cannot understand either of these two stories until we have succeeded in orienting ourselves toward *internal action*.

Character

A "character" is a person who appears in a story. Characters are important because what a writer says and how he says it are matters closely related to the people he creates for his narrative. We have already discussed at some length the interdependence of action and character. But to understand fully the important matter of character, we need to look at the kinds of characters the writer creates, the functions he assigns them, and the ways in which he goes about creating them.

There are two basic character types that we encounter in fiction; it will help us to visualize the difference between these two types if we refer to them as *flat* and *round*. Briefly, a *flat* character is one that is not fully developed, lacks individualizing qualities, and is often a common, easily recognizable figure. Such a character represents a serious weakness in the story if his role calls for a fully realized and carefully individualized— *round*—figure. The stock figures of melodrama generally fall into the category of flat characters. They are stereotypes, cardboard cut-outs whose two-dimensional nature conflicts with our knowledge of the complexity of human personality. Thus we have the "Dirty Work at the Crossroads" kind of story, in which the Villain twirls his black mustache and cries, "Aha, I've got you now, me beauty" to the Innocent Girl, a symbol of purity whose loveliness has captured the heart of the Valiant Young Man. The latter is a strong, handsome, and pure (but not terribly bright) fellow who somehow manages to defeat the villain and save the girl, whom he then marries.

But flat characters are not necessarily evidence of artistic failure. Some roles do not demand in-depth characterization, and in fact the compact nature of the short story rarely permits the full development of every character. Just as in real life, there are always characters whose involvement in any given action is relatively slight; our interest in them is limited to their role in the story, not to their activities and personality generally. To develop such characters fully would extend them beyond their function in the story, distract the reader from both the central figures and the central action, and burden us with extraneous detail.

Regardless of whether he makes his characters flat or round, the writer is concerned with presenting people whose characteristics are consistent with their actions. If he makes his figures act in an arbitrary fashion, he runs the risk of being accused of *plot manipulation*. In effect, the hand of the author becomes visible, forcing things to happen rather than making them seem the logical product of character. In addition to this consistency of characterization, he must make his figures credible. Usually this credibility refers to realistic portrayal, but characters do not have to be persons whom we easily recognize, or whom we can easily imagine existing around us. By themselves, they may be quite unbelievable, even fantastic. But characters do not exist in a vacuum; they exist in a story, and it is possible to make an incredible figure perfectly believable through the *narrative context* in which he appears. This is why we accept the Bound Man in Ilse Aichinger's story, or the figure of Melville's Bartleby, even though we may find it difficult to imagine their existing in real life. Such characters also serve to remind us that art is not life in the sense of photographic fidelity to truth. Art is never required to reproduce reality with a mechanical accuracy in order to convey an emotion or to mirror some aspect of life's meaning.

Finally, a character may be either static or changing, depending on what the author is trying to communicate in terms of theme, and what the demands of plot and action are. Macomber clearly undergoes an internal change. In Galsworthy's "The Japanese Quince," neither Nilson nor Tandrum changes, and their failure to change gives dramatic impact to the story's theme. Again, the character may be revealed to us gradually, so that our own attitude toward that character is likely to change as we learn more about him. In Carson McCullers' "Madame Zilensky and the King of Finland," we arrive by stages at an understanding of why Madame Zilensky acts the way she does. Mr. Brook, another character in the same story, mirrors the change in attitude which we undergo. His—and our—willingness to believe in a King of Finland is neatly and comically summed up when, after watching an Airedale run backwards down the street, Mr. Brook calmly turns back to his work.

A major function of character, of course, is to reveal theme. A character may do this by acting as the *narrative point of view,* providing us with a particular focus by which we observe what happens (see "Point of View," pp. 623-626). He may function as a *foil,* a character whose purpose is to contrast with and thus set off another character. As *protagonist,* he acts as the central figure of the narrative. This is a better word than "hero," because characters in fiction are rarely heroic in either actions, appearance, or personal qualities. An *antagonist* is in conflict with the central figure and directly opposes him. The antagonist and the foil manipulate the reader's responses in particular ways—through opposition and contrast—maneuvering him into the kinds of reactions and attitudes that the writer wishes the reader to have. Thus we see that a broad and very important function of character is to control the reader's responses. Characters may also give us a concrete, dramatic representation of an idea or an emotion. When this is their main role, we call such characters *symbols*. For John Cashmore of "A Blue Blonde in the Sky over Pennsylvania," the beautiful blonde he meets on the train becomes a symbol of the freedom and individuality that his way of life denies him. To some extent, then, characters may literally embody the meaning of a story.

There are three basic ways in which a writer may convey a character to us: (1) through what the character does, (2) through what he and others think and say, and (3) through exposition. Often, what a character does reflects the *conflicts* in which he is involved. A character may find himself in conflict with any of a multitude of things: other characters, physical forces (such as a storm at sea, or the wild beasts which Macomber has to face), conditions around him (as in John Cashmore's revolt against his job and everything it stands for), even with himself (the character Nanni in Verga's "The She-Wolf," or the first person narrator of Svevo's "Generous Wine"). Characters are also revealed through dialogue, monologue, interior monologue, stream of consciousness, and other devices which utilize talk or thought rather than action. With exposition, we are simply handed information directly by the narrator or author who says, in effect, "Here is something you need to know." Verga uses exposition at the start of "The She-Wolf" to explain how Pina got her name: "In the village they called her the She-wolf, because she never had enough— of anything." There are many things we need to know about a story's characters which we need not see acted out. Indeed, it might be awkward if a writer were forced to render absolutely everything in terms of action. But the problem with exposition is that it does not involve the reader in the narrative directly. In fact, it tends to make him aware of the artificial nature of fiction and thus to increase, rather than decrease, the distance between reader and story (aesthetic distance). Usually the writer tries to achieve a balance among the three methods, using exposition for purposes of compression and to maintain the focus on the principal action, and dialogue and action to involve the reader by *showing* him what happens rather than simply telling him.

Both character and action are crucial to our understanding of fiction. If we can grasp the way in which the writer uses both of these elements to convey his meaning, we are well on our way to grasping in its entirety the experience which the story creates for us. But a writer builds his narrative out of more than just character and action. Let us go on to examine a particular device, point of view, and then look at such things as setting, atmosphere, structure, and theme.

Point of View

The writer of fiction has always been faced with a difficult problem: how is he to deal with his own presence as the actual narrator of the story? Should he call attention to his role as creator by addressing his audience directly, or should he try to remain out of sight? At first, a good many writers used the "Dear Reader" approach, a technique which is still found from time to time and one which can be made very complex, especially in the novel. (See Thackeray's *Vanity Fair,* for example.) But more and more writers chose to place themselves in the background of their stories; rarely do we find an author today who "speaks" directly to the reader. More often, he creates a figure who tells the story for him, or through whom we view the action. This "mask" has the initial effect of removing the author from the scene, an advantage in terms of the writer's need to create and maintain an illusion of reality. The reader is put into a direct relationship with the story itself from the opening lines, through a figure who operates within the narrative but who is not its author. But the *point of view* which the author sets up in this fashion has another—and perhaps more important—function. It gives the writer a lens he can focus to clarify details, to discover new facts, to examine relationships—in short, to suggest the meaning of the things we see, by the way in which we see them.

Point of view is extremely important, therefore, since it is one of the devices by which a story's meaning is communicated to us. What we have to do, then, is to try to discover precisely how that meaning has been affected, or even distorted, in passing through this lens. Sometimes the picture we get will represent an objective report. Often, however, the attitudes and limitations we find in our viewer will color that report, so that he acts as a subjective—and possibly less reliable—source of information. Our first task becomes one of determining what those attitudes and limitations are. These factors vary, of course, with every story. But we can guide our analysis of point of view by asking two essential questions, and by looking at some of the basic patterns that writers have developed in their own dealings with this problem of perspective.

The first question forces us to examine the relationship between point of view and action: "Is the narrator of the story inside or outside the action?" If he is a participant in the story he narrates for us, the nature of his involvement may influence or *slant* his report of what happens. The narrator of Gorki's "Twenty-Six Men and a Girl" is such a participant. What the events of this story mean to him is very largely what they mean to us. It is he who describes the setting as a "dungeon"; who points out the contrast between the horror of the men's conditions and the beauty of the girl, Tanya; and who recognizes the tragic nature of their loss. Part of the narrative's power stems from the fact that the narrator is a part of that tragedy. The meaning of what he tells us reflects his involvement.

In Gorki's story, the point of view is that of a first person narrator who is a part of the events he describes. But a first person narrator is not always a participant. His involvement may be very slight, or he may stand completely outside the action. Despite this disengaged position, he may still exhibit a bias which colors his interpretation and selection of events. We have to ask, "What is the nature of that bias and how does it affect the meaning of what we are told?" The narrator of Conrad's "Il Conde," for example, is clearly sympathetic towards the aged Count because they are friends. As a result, his focus is on the Count, and the pathos and irony we find in the story are largely the products of that sympathy. The meaning of what he tells us has been influenced by the narrator's bias, which is his friendship with the central figure of the narrative.

There is a third position from which a story may be narrated. So far we have talked about point of view in terms of three-dimensional characters standing on *terra firma,* either taking an active part in the events of the narrative or looking on from the periphery of those events. But the narrator need not be such a three-dimensional figure at all. We are, after all, primarily interested in the story that is told, not the character who tells it or through whom the narrative is channeled. The report might be rendered just as effectively by a roving eye or intelligence, a disembodied voice that operates from a position completely outside the action. Such a point of view is often used. One obvious advantage lies in its flexibility. Since it is not bound by the physical limitations of a body, this "eye" may be permitted to appear wherever and whenever needed to focus on events. It may also be allowed to penetrate at will into the minds of the characters, revealing to us their innermost thoughts and emotions. This kind of roving intelligence operates in Hemingway's "The Short Happy Life of Francis Macomber." While we listen to Macomber and his wife argue, for instance, we also have access to Wilson's silent commentary: "When she left, Wilson was thinking, when she went off to cry, she seemed a hell of a fine woman. She seemed to understand, to realize, to be hurt for him and for herself and to know how things really stood. She is away for twenty minutes and now she is back, simply enamelled in that American female cruelty. They are the damnedest women. Really the damnedest." The observation is important to the story's meaning, and only through the narrator's unlimited access into Wilson's thoughts are we admitted to the observation.

Not every disembodied intelligence, however, is permitted such freedom of movement. In Robbe-Grillet's "The Secret Room," for example, the eye is only a camera, not an X-ray machine: "The man's posture allows his face to be seen only in a vague profile, but one senses in it a violent exaltation, despite the rigid attitude, the silence, the immobility." Note the key word, "senses." The narrator's liberty to see into the minds of the characters, so important to the understanding of Hemingway's story, has been eliminated entirely from Robbe-Grillet's. We see much, but we see *into* nothing. The narrator's mobility has been sharply limited, and so has ours.

This story also makes us aware of the need to question the narrator's conclusions. He consistently offers interpretations of those points that are most ambiguous: the emotion behind a facial expression, the meaning of a gesture, even the size of the room. Despite his admission that the light is poor—"white darkened by the shadowy quality of the place: a dungeon, a sunken room, or a cathedral—glowing with a diffused brilliance in the semi-darkness"—he gives us a detailed description of the scene, including color, line, form, and movement. It is quite possible that his interpretations are the result of what he wants to see, rather than what he actually does see. He may, therefore, be a very unreliable source of information.

Another limitation which may characterize this point of view pertains to the number of characters on whom the roving intelligence reports. Often what we discover is that there has been a narrowing of the focus, a process of exclusion by which we concentrate on a small number of figures inside the action. When this happens, point of view is in effect *transferred* to these figures. We now see the story primarily through them, and we must ask of them the same questions concerning involvement and bias. The disembodied voice may still comment on the action, or he may simply vanish into the wings. In Rooney's "Cyclists' Raid," the principal focus is on a single character, the hotel owner, Joel Bleeker. The actual narrator is invisible. He offers no comments or interpretations of his own. The meaning of the story is suggested through Bleeker's responses and observations, not the narrator's. Point of view has moved from a position outside the action to one inside, through a narrowing of the narrator's focus.

And so we come full circle: point of view is back inside the action just as it was in Gorki's "Twenty-Six Men and a Girl." The perspective is different, however, because the story is told in the third person, not the first; narrator and narrative focus are no longer one and the same. But the mechanical identification of point of view is not what we are after. Point of view, remember, is essentially a device by which the *meaning* of the story is communicated to us. It is like a window opening onto a courtyard scene: the scene should hold our attention, not the window.

Regardless of where point of view lies, we must ask the two basic questions that keep us oriented toward meaning rather than mechanics: "To what extent is the narrator involved in the action?" and "How is the narrative meaning affected by the limitations imposed upon that point of view?" We may discover that point of view has little significance in a story. It may, on the other hand, provide the key to the narrative's real meaning. Point of view can heighten the drama of events, but not because we have succeeded in categorizing it. While it may communicate the "you are there" sensation, you are there as a result of art, not pronouns. We have to look beyond technique at what poet-critic Ezra Pound called simply "the thing ITSELF": the whole work. That is what the experience of literature is all about.

Setting

In one very specific way, every story is like life: it has to happen *somewhere*. A story, in other words, needs a specific locale; it must provide a sense of location, or *setting*. We can hardly expect a narrative to take place in a vacuum. We need to know where to put the characters as they act and are acted upon, how they are affected by the place in which we find them, what the location tells us about them and about the situation generally. We might, then, think of setting as a story's physical background, except that the setting is not always physical; it might be within a character's mind. And setting often refuses to stay in the background: setting certainly occupies the foreground in Bowles' "The Scorpion." So let us understand the term "setting" as the *element of place*, regardless of where that place is, or what it is intended to do.

Simply identifying where a story occurs is a fairly rudimentary step. What the reader has to consider with a great deal of care is the *function* or *purpose* of setting. More important than the question, "Where does the story take place?" is the question, "What effect does setting have on character, on action, on meaning?" This second question is important because it does not treat setting as something isolated; it forces us to put the matter of place into the context of the whole story, where it belongs. One element of a story rarely contains all of that story's meaning. In this sense, setting is no different from action, character, symbol, or any other element. But setting *can* do some things that are very important, and we will understand the significance of setting much better if we look at some of those things rather closely.

One of the principal functions of setting is to lend concreteness to a narrative. Concreteness is important because it helps us bring people and events down out of some vague Never-Never Land where the reader's imagination functions only with great difficulty, like an astronaut who has ventured outside his spacecraft. To put it another way, concreteness gives the reader a common ground of experience with the characters in the story. We live, after all, in a world of sense as well as idea; it seems reasonable to expect a narrative to reflect both thought *and* feeling, if it is to seize all of our attention and hold it. The old woman of Bowles' story is not just any old woman whose son has come to take her away. She lives in a cave, the walls of that cave are of red clay, water runs down across the mouth of the cave, and from inside she can see the bare earth and grey sky and sometimes large dry leaves driven by the wind. When she finally leaves the cave, we feel what that departure means, and how her life has been affected by living there, because we have been in that cave with her, we have seen her smash the scorpions that crept across the walls, we have watched her huddle motionless and soundless as people walked by, not knowing she was there.

Through concreteness we are able to share in the experience that the story communicates, even though that sharing is vicarious. But even more important is the simple fact that concreteness in general, and setting in particular, increases a narrative's credibility. We are more likely to believe in what we *experience* than in what we are merely *told*. Few of us are complete rationalists. Rather, we depend more or less heavily on what our senses tell us in arriving at our conclusions about what life is like, and what it means. Good fiction recognizes the degree to which man relies upon his senses, and it appeals to those senses directly through concreteness.

The significance of setting can be seen in Giovanni Verga's "The She-Wolf." There the country background seems merely to provide a realistic environment for the peasant drama that unfolds. Its role is to *reinforce* the action—at least at first. The She-wolf, Pina, falls in love with a young man "mowing hay with her in the fields." Her love is so strong that "she suffered the thirst one has in the hot hours of June, deep in the plain." The images that project emotions and relationships coincide with the story's setting, and we accept their drama the more readily for this unity of action, character, and setting. Indeed, the relationship between setting on the one hand, and action and character on the other, is so close that Verga never permits us a view of the countryside devoid of human involvement. At first, the setting never obtrudes; it hovers around the figures, giving to their tragedy of passion a local habitation and a name. But gradually we begin to see that the characters and what happens to them are so much a part of their surroundings that we cannot separate them. The tragedy involves a whole way of life, not just a few people who happen to be peasants. Characters, setting, and action merge so entirely by the end of the story that the climactic moment depends equally on the three elements:

As he saw her from the distance, in the green wheat fields, Nanni stopped hoeing the vineyard, and went to pull the ax from the elm. The She-wolf saw him come, pale and wild-eyed, with the ax glistening in the sun, but she did not fall back a single step, did not lower her eyes; she continued toward him, her hands laden with red poppies, her black eyes devouring him.

"Ah! damn your soul!" stammered Nanni.

The entire scene is like a painting by Van Gogh, the red poppies as violently a part of the incident as the ax itself, or the black eyes of the She-wolf. The green wheat fields, the hoe, the vineyard, the elm, all contribute to the emotional force of the confrontation between the two.

The general *mood* which pervades a story we call atmosphere. It can be produced by many things: the kinds of figures peopling the narrative, the things they say, the nature of the action. The mood that characterizes Flannery O'Connor's "A Good Man is Hard to Find" is produced by what happens to the family, certainly, but also by the character of The Misfit and his chilling philosophy of nihilism, a kind of epicureanism in reverse: " 'No pleasure but meanness,' he said and his voice had become almost a snarl." *Setting is a major source of atmosphere,* and O'Connor uses the story's setting to help establish mood. As the first shots ring out from the woods, the grandmother "could hear the wind move through the tree tops like a long satisfied insuck of breath." The woods themselves are "tall and dark and deep," and there was "not a cloud in the sky nor any sun. There was nothing around her but woods." Atmosphere is here all the more effective because it is unexpected; the story opens in a different mood entirely, as the family prepares to go on vacation. As they drive along, the trees are "full of silver-white sunlights and the meanest of them sparkled." Individual scenes, then, can have their own mood, but these should ultimately be subordinated to the atmosphere that characterizes the story as a whole. In "A Good Man is Hard to Find," that atmosphere is one of terror. Vacations, games, family quarrels, all these commonplace realities become meaningless in the hard light of The Misfit's view of man's Christian heritage:

"Jesus was the only One that ever raised the dead," The Misfit continued, "and He shouldn't have done it. He thrown everything off balance. If He did what He said, then it's nothing for you to do but throw away everything and follow Him, and if He didn't then it's nothing for you to do but enjoy the few minutes you got left the best way you can—by killing somebody or burning down his house or doing some other meanness to him."

Atmosphere, when developed carefully, can heighten the impact of action and character on the reader, and it can provide a clue to theme. It can also make setting a pervasive influence in the story through the close association between setting and atmosphere. Atmosphere is like the fog that rolls in from the ocean to settle upon man and city: suddenly it is as though part of the sea had reached out to surround us. In much the same way, setting can project itself into the action through the atmosphere it creates.

Setting can also be used effectively to delineate character. The African setting of Hemingway's story thrusts a harsh light upon Macomber's cowardice. Macomber has had his skill, his intelligence, his strength, his money, and his social position tested by the playboy life he has led, but never his courage. Africa, he quickly learns, is not Manhattan. A safari is the Dark Continent's symbol of the savage and violent conflict between man and beast, and between man and man, that characterizes life there. Values on the African veldt are not the same as those in the ballroom of a Hilton Hotel. Macomber learns this fact the hard way, and setting is largely responsible for the high drama of the lesson. But it is not just the whole of Africa *versus* Francis Macomber. Setting is built up out of concrete, limited scenes. When Macomber runs from the lion, for example, he runs into a clearing, and this clearing serves to isolate him physically just as his act has isolated him ethically from the others. Moving across the clearing to return to the others, Macomber's tallness seemed "a naked reproach," and Wilson and the two gunbearers "looked back at him in contempt." The clearing thus focuses attention on his cowardice; there is no place for him to hide, either literally or figuratively. Character can be revealed in a variety of ways, of course, as we have pointed out in the section on "Action and Character." But setting should not be overlooked simply because it is often a less obvious means than, say, action or dialogue. Hemingway's use of setting is a dramatic example of another way to reveal character.

In the work of many writers, setting represents a peculiarly individual *region* out of which characters and action spring. The South of Faulkner and Flannery O'Connor is this kind of region, and it is characterized by a sense of permanence, of unchanging solidity. The characters are, to some extent, what they are because of *where* they are. They seem to evolve out of their geographical locale. Setting not only reflects a way of life, but in some way seems responsible for it. We feel this deterministic force in as minor an incident as a Faulkner character working his bare feet into the dirt of a country road, or a scene focusing on a road sign (see the "RED SAMMY" passage in "A Good Man Is Hard to Find," for example). When used in this way, setting has a timelessness that underscores the time-driven quality of the characters and what happens to them. It can evoke a heightened awareness of man's evanescence; as an individual, man seems to be, as much as anything else, a *temporary* creature, whereas the locale of his drama is fixed, unchanging, eternal.

Theme

Fiction, as we have said, is a means of creating or re-creating an experience for the reader; and, as we have discovered, there are several elements with which the writer is concerned when he goes about the business of putting that experience together as a short story: action, character, plot, setting, atmosphere, point of view, and so forth. There is one very important aspect of fiction, however, which we have not taken up, and that is the aspect of *theme:* the element that gives a short story its significance, or its meaning. Without theme, a story says nothing beyond the immediate narrative level. A simple plot summary will tell us everything we need to know about such a narrative. Like a shaggy dog story, it leaves us wondering, "So what?" When we introduce the matter of theme, we are talking about what gives events their "punch," what makes those events reach inside us and *do* something to us: making us aware of the need for compassion, for instance, or that man often feels intensely isolated from the rest of the world.

Perhaps we can make this business of theme clearer by contrasting it with a story's *subject*. The subject of a narrative is what that narrative deals with in terms of its characters, its setting, its action, or the situation in which the characters are placed. Sometimes the story's title will tell us what that subject is. Gorki's story, for example, has as its subject twenty-six men and a girl. (Remember that titles can be misleading: a fly is hardly the main subject of Mansfield's "The Fly.") Theme, on the other hand, involves the author's *comment on* that subject. It is relatively easy to identify a story's subject; it is sometimes much more difficult to determine precisely what a writer is saying *about* that subject.

There are several reasons why we may not immediately seize upon the theme of a story. The first and most obvious reason is that good writers don't come forward with a theme and hand it to us like an olive on a toothpick, saying, "Here, have a theme. It's delicious." Stories are written to be stories, not to be vehicles for themes, or settings for themes, or anything of the sort. A theme is something that grows out of the total effect of a story, that we become aware of as sensitive, appreciative readers—willing, at least for the moment, to let the writer have his way with us. Nor is it something that we beat the brush for, as though we were hunting quail. Meaning emerges gradually out of what happens in a

story, out of the kinds of characters we find there, what they say, the kind
of setting and atmosphere, the imagery and symbols we encounter, in
short, out of all the aspects of the story.

All of which leads us to a second reason why theme is often a demanding matter: with so many elements involved, a theme may be so
complex that it cannot be stated easily or simply. Themes aren't always
terribly complicated matters, but we have to be prepared to handle the
problem of complexity in a theme if it arises. And finally, a story's meaning may be ambiguous; that is, a story may have several different levels of
meaning, and no single statement is likely to account for all of those
levels. There is certainly no federal statute which says stories must mean
only one thing. There may be several themes at work, and we will understand better what a story is attempting to communicate if we don't try to
force it into a neat pigeonhole.

We should also insist on calling a story's meaning its "theme" rather
than its "message" or "moral." Since the writer of short stories is usually
concerned with communicating *experience,* he is less concerned with convincing us that we should accept his opinion about human nature, human relations, the cosmos, or whatever. A theme reflects a particular attitude toward war, or love, or hate, or man's isolation, without trying to
persuade the reader to accept finally and absolutely the truth of that
attitude. Instead, the writer tries through his theme to broaden our awareness of what is going on around us, and to demonstrate that it is quite
possible to take any one of dozens of attitudes toward life's experiences.
Fiction tries to make sophisticates of us, if by that term we mean individuals who are "finely experienced and aware" of life's complexity, rather
than people who are lacquered with a thin veneer of "manners." To a
large extent, life is the art of communication. If we shut out everyone
whose attitude is unlike our own, we may very well receive a lesson in the
art of isolation, instead. Perhaps few of us would agree that life is as
harsh or forbidding as Paul Bowles or William Faulkner makes it appear,
simply because we have not observed the same things, or seen them in
the same light. But the deficiency is at least partly in *our* experience, not
just in theirs. Fiction tries to alter our *perspective,* not necessarily our
opinions, by broadening our experience.

There is one other reason why it is important to think of the short
story's meaning in terms of theme rather than message. That reason is
related to the function of meaning in a story. In a didactic work (a work
with a message), every element is subordinated to the supreme importance
of the message. That message has to get across at all costs. The story acts
as a vehicle whose sole purpose is to transport that message, like an elephant carrying a potentate. When the potentate has completed his journey, the elephant goes back to the barn (or wherever elephants go); and

once we have a story's message, the story has done its duty and can go back on the shelf. But the relationship between a narrative and its theme is a different matter entirely. Granted, it is the theme which makes the narrative spring to life; but that theme remains an integral part of the story as a whole. Meaning can, of course, be discussed in a broad sense: we talk about the theme of isolation, for instance, or of self-discovery. But theme leaves the world of abstract idea and becomes a part of the reality of experience only when we see it in its narrative context.

What kinds of things should we be alert to, then, in order to understand what a story means? As a matter of fact, we have already looked at one very important element of theme: *change*. In Hemingway's story about Francis Macomber, we saw that there was a change inside Macomber which was reflected in the story's sequence of incidents. Our first step is to determine exactly what kind of change took place. Next, what does that change imply about the nature of reality and the way in which man faces that reality? The same questions apply to Chekhov's "On Official Business," except that the change is not so clearly reflected in physical events. In order to determine how these characters change, we have to examine the characters themselves. What do they look like, what are their motives, how are they strong or weak, what are they interested in, what is the nature of their involvement in the action? If it is a situation that changes, we must determine how action directs that change and how the characters are affected. Gorki's "Twenty-six Men and a Girl" involves a change in situation, and the way in which the characters are affected underscores the kind of lives they lead. In addition, both setting and atmosphere can guide us to a story's meaning, as we saw in O'Connor's "A Good Man is Hard to Find." And let us not overlook the obvious: what do the characters say, either in conversation or thought? In Pirandello's "In the Abyss," Gabriella Vanzi comes very close to stating the theme outright when she concludes her remarks to Donna Bicetta Daddi by saying, " 'Who knows? Who can *ever* know?' " Symbols frequently give us concrete representations of theme; Pirandello's "abyss" is a symbol directly related to the meaning of the story. Paul Bowles' scorpion and Hawthorne's butterfly function in the same way.

One very important way in which a writer communicates his meaning is through *narrative structure*. When a writer patterns incidents in order to emphasize their cause-and-effect relationship, he is setting up the story's plot. But he can also arrange those incidents in such a way as to clarify the meaning of what happens, and when he does this, he is ordering those incidents on a broader level that we call structure. In effect, he puts the incidents together into blocks or groups which permit us to see more clearly the *stages* in the theme's development. The structure of Galsworthy's "The Japanese Quince" is fairly simple, and it follows the traditional beginning-middle-end sequence that we are all familiar with. First, Nilson becomes aware of a strange sensation within him as he prepares to go to work. Then, he crosses to the little park in front of his house, where he meets Tandram and examines the quince. Finally, he and Tandram return to their homes, where each furtively gazes back at the tree. Each group of incidents makes a single point, and those points link together to form the story's theme.

There are other patterns we may notice in addition to the pattern of incidents. A story's imagery, for example, may indicate various stages in a theme's development. The imagery of Aichinger's "The Bound Man" reflects changes in the seasons. We begin in early summer, with the sun warm and bright upon the man as he awakens, and then we move steadily through summer into autumn frost, and thence into winter, where darkness and cold predominate. What does this pattern of imagery suggest in terms of the story's meaning? Shifts in setting as well as in action and imagery may be related to a story's structure. But regardless of the kinds of patterns that emerge, the main thing to keep in mind is that structure is intended to clarify the meaning of a particular work, not to obscure that meaning.

It should now be evident that the short story is a complex form indeed. There are many things that we must be aware of while we read, so many, in fact, that our heads may swim. Nevertheless, a good story is never *just* symbols, or character, or setting. We have to try not only to understand these individual elements but to bring them together into a unified whole, and to understand the story as a whole. If we succeed in doing this, the rewards will be great, in both enjoyment and learning. And in case these discussions have stressed the learning part too heavily, let us redress the balance now. There should always be a sense of joy associated with the reading of fiction: because we are being delightfully entertained, because we sense ourselves growing through the experience that fiction offers, or because we recognize the artistry that went into the making of the story. The best stories, of course, give us all three.

Glossary of Literary Terms

ACTION   On one level, "action" refers to what happens in terms of individual incident. On this level, the action is often physical, and it frequently involves many incidents. But on a much broader level, "action" refers to the single most significant *change* which occurs in the narrative, a change that is the result of all the incidents working together (see PLOT). Here, the action may be internal (psychological) as well as external (physical).

AESTHETIC DISTANCE   Briefly, the reader's awareness that he is experiencing art, not life. Too much distance may alienate the reader from the experience which the work attempts to communicate; the separation between the two then becomes a break. Too little distance may result in total involvement or identification with the characters and what happens to them, so that the reader has difficulty in understanding the meaning of the experience. He may also be less able to appreciate the art which went into the story's making.

ALLEGORY   A narrative which states a doctrine or thesis, and whose characters, setting, and events represent abstractions. Perhaps the best known allegory is Bunyan's PILGRIM'S PROGRESS, in which Christian symbolizes the idea of Christian perfection. All such symbols are organized into a rather rigid pattern, in which the meaning of each symbol is determined by its position in the pattern (i.e., its relationship to the other symbols). Meaning in an allegory thus tends to be restricted to (1) the literal level of narrative action, and (2) the one symbolic level which carries the work's thesis. (See also SYMBOL and THEME.)

AMBIGUITY   Multiple levels of meaning; not to be confused with "obscurity."

ATMOSPHERE   A *mood* which may characterize either an individual scene or the narrative as a whole. It may be produced by a variety of elements, such as character, action, setting, and symbol. Atmosphere is often used to intensify the impact of theme and is an important part of the total effect which a work has on a reader. It conditions the reader to expect events to develop in a direction consistent with that atmosphere, an expectation not always fulfilled. The mood at the start of O'Connor's "A Good Man is Hard to Find," for example, hardly prepares us for the events which follow, a deception intended to increase the element of shock. (See EFFECT and TONE.)

BALANCE   The juxtaposition of various elements within a narrative—such as characters, incidents, minor themes, or patterns of imagery—for any of several reasons: to achieve emphasis and increase clarity through what is essentially a kind of repetition; to increase dramatic tension through parallels and contrasts; to create patterns by which the sense of narrative unity is heightened. Such balance often has a direct relationship to the main theme. In Hawthorne's "The Artist of the Beautiful," for example, we first see that the characters are balanced against each other. The sensitive young artist (Owen Warland) is juxtaposed against the pragmatic and materialistic old man (Peter Hovenden). The other characters may be made to fit into this basic pattern. But there is also a balance within each character. Hovenden's pragmatism and materialism are not completely evil, nor is Warland's sensitive nature without its failings. Hawthorne's view of the conflict between the artist and reality is not a simplistic one, and the story's theme must be stated in the light of this careful balance which Hawthorne sets up.

CHARACTER   A figure in a narrative, whose psychological and ethical makeup, as well as physical appearance, may be revealed.

CLIMAX   The crisis or turning point in a story; the dramatic high point.

CONVENTION   (1) An artificial device, often unrealistic, which is understood and accepted as such by the reader. The telescoping of time is a "conventional" method of reducing a narrative to readable length without sacrificing its realism. (2) A traditional character type, theme, or scene. The hard-boiled detective, the journey of self-discovery, and love at first sight are literary "conventions" of this kind. (See also STEREO-TYPE and the discussion of melodrama in the comments and questions on Rooney's "Cyclists' Raid.")

DENOUEMENT   The literal meaning of this French word is "to untie." As a literary term, it refers to the unravelling of plot. More specifically, it is that part of a narrative in which the principal conflicts are resolved.

EFFECT   The impact upon the reader of a specific scene or incident; or, the total impression which a work as a unified whole makes upon him. In the latter case, the "effect" involves reader response on a scale much broader than can be encompassed by any statement of the narrative's theme. Theme is thus a part of a narrative's total effect, not vice versa. (See THEME, ATMOSPHERE, and TONE.)

EXPOSITION   Presentation of information essential to the reader's understanding of the narrative. This information often concerns matters which have taken place before the story actually begins. The acting out (*dramatic* presentation) of such a prior episode is called a "flashback."

FORM   Although the word "form" is often used to refer to a work's "structure" (see below for discussion of STRUCTURE), it is helpful to think of "form" as a type or genre with distinguishing characteristics. The short story is one literary type or "form," the novel another. The short story "form" is characterized by the use of prose, rather than poetry, to tell a fictional narrative containing the elements of conflict and of change, a high degree of compression, and total unity of effect. For a full discussion of these matters, see the introductory essay, "The Short Story as a Literary Type."

IMAGERY   Refers to that which appeals to any of the reader's senses. Sometimes the imagery is a part of what is called "figurative speech," as when the protagonist of Aichinger's "The Bound Man" "rid himself of the rope like a snake discarding its skin." This particular figure of speech is called a "simile"; there are many ways of saying one thing in terms of another, among them "metaphor," "metonymy," "personification," and "synecdoche." But simple concrete description is also part of a work's imagery. Hemingway in particular leans heavily on such descriptive passages in "The Short Happy Life of Francis Macomber."

INTERIOR MONOLOGUE   A character's thoughts are often communicated directly to us. When his thoughts take the form of a carefully ordered and coherent "conversation with himself," so to speak, we call these thoughts an "interior monologue." Interior monologue is a convention in literature because it frequently orders thought in a more coherent, organized fashion than is usually the case in reality. (See also STREAM OF CONSCIOUSNESS.)

IRONY   Involves a discrepancy (but not necessarily a contradiction) between the literal meaning of a statement and its intended meaning (verbal irony), between the expected conclusion to a series of events and the actual conclusion, or between the characters' understanding of the meaning of a situation and the audience's understanding. In the latter case, the characters have a tragic misconception of what the situation means, whereas the audience is aware of the true significance. Irony of this sort is called dramatic, Sophoclean, or tragic irony. Irony is central to O'Connor's "A Good Man is Hard to Find."

METAPHOR   A figure of speech which equates one thing with another for the purpose of emphasizing certain qualities or characteristics in both, but without using "like" or "as."

MOTIF   A recurrent idea, character, incident, situation, object, or image whose repetition adds to the meaning of a work and helps pattern that meaning. The word "blue" in Crane's "The Blue Hotel," for example, is part of a pattern of images out of which the motif of isolation develops.

NARRATIVE   Story. A general term applicable to any literary form which tells a story, including, for example, the novel and the epic poem as well as the short story.

NATURALISM   In literature, naturalism was a movement that began fairly late in the nineteenth century and carried into the first few decades of the twentieth. It cannot be defined absolutely, since both techniques and content of naturalist works varied from author to author, and in fact sometimes shifted significantly from one work to another by a single author. In general, though, naturalism was characterized by a realistic portrayal of ordinary life from an apparently dispassionate viewpoint, but with materials actually selected with great care to suggest that man is a creature whose character and destiny are determined by the natural forces of heredity and environment. Associated with the naturalist movement, in addition to Stephen Crane (see "The Blue Hotel"), are such writers as Hamlin Garland, Frank Norris, and Theodore Dreiser. The philosophical basis of naturalism may be found in the writings of Thomas Malthus, Charles Darwin, Thomas Huxley, and others. (See also REALISM.)

PLOT   The sequence of narrative events as the author arranges them, with emphasis upon their cause-and-effect relationship rather than upon their chronological order.

POINT OF VIEW   The eye or mind through which the narrative is communicated to the reader; also, the narrative focus of a story.

PROTAGONIST   The central figure in a narrative. "Protagonist" is a better word than "hero" because the main character in modern fiction, as in modern drama, is rarely heroic.

REALISM   A nineteenth century literary movement which attempted to convey the details of ordinary life as those details could actually be observed in society. Naturalism (see above) might be called "selective realism," since it chose its details to support a particular view of the human condition, a view which was largely deterministic.

SETTING   The element of place in a narrative; often, a story's physical background or geographical location.

STEREOTYPE   A character, plot, situation, or response which conforms so completely to a well-established and familiar pattern as to lose any trace of originality.

STREAM OF CONSCIOUSNESS   The representation of pre-speech levels of consciousness; that is, of all purely mental activity as it reflects the total spectrum of thought, from the highly conscious level, characterized by order and awareness of the thought processes, to the fringes of the unconscious level, where mental activity is impulsive, fragmentary, unpatterned, and tends to relate to emotions and instincts rather than to ideas. Although interior monologue (p. 636) is usually considered a part of the stream of consciousness technique, it might be well to separate the two, since interior monologue is essentially unrealistic, a literary convention of a clearly definable sort. Beyond this ultra-conscious level, stream of consciousness attempts to represent accurately and realistically the fluid and often chaotic nature of the mind's workings. One of the difficulties with stream of consciousness as a technique involves the necessity for rendering all mental activity in verbal terms, whereas the closer one gets to the unconscious, the more likely is that activity to be expressed non-verbally through images which utilize the body's senses.

STRUCTURE   The arrangement of incidents and scenes into a meaningful pattern supporting both the narrative's theme and its total effect. (See also FORM.)

SYMBOL   Any concrete element which stands for both the material world and the world of the abstract or ineffable. Symbols, except in allegory, tend to have multiple meanings and are often responsible for much of the ambiguity of a narrative's meaning.

THEME   The meaning of a narrative. It is important to distinguish between "theme" and "message" or "moral." A work which has a message has a didactic purpose: it teaches a lesson, and the lesson is always more important than the story by which it is conveyed. Theme, on the other hand, is not dominated by a suasive purpose. Instead, it attempts to broaden the reader's awareness of the nature of man and of the world in which he lives by involving him in an experience first, and then offering its meaning without insisting upon its correctness.

TONE   The author's attitude toward events and characters which is implied in the narrative. The tone of O'Connor's "A Good Man is Hard to Find" is largely ironic, while in Jackson's "The Witch" it is satirical. (See also ATMOSPHERE.)